CARBONIUM IONS
AN INTRODUCTION

CARBONIUM IONS
AN INTRODUCTION

by

D. BETHELL
Department of Organic Chemistry
University of Liverpool
Liverpool, England

and

V. GOLD
Department of Chemistry
King's College
London, England

1967
ACADEMIC PRESS
LONDON AND NEW YORK

ACADEMIC PRESS INC. (LONDON) LTD.
BERKELEY SQUARE HOUSE
BERKELEY SQUARE
LONDON, W.1

U.S. Edition published by
ACADEMIC PRESS INC.
111 FIFTH AVENUE
NEW YORK, NEW YORK 10003

PRINTED IN GREAT BRITAIN BY
SPOTTISWOODE, BALLANTYNE AND CO. LTD.
LONDON AND COLCHESTER

PREFACE

Since their discovery shortly after 1900, carbonium ions have played a key role in shaping the course of organic chemistry. The very concept of valency was shaken by the realization that trivalent carbon species, i.e. carbonium ions and free radicals, existed. Since then few branches of organic chemistry have not been affected in some way by developments in the carbonium-ion field. Among the diverse advances brought about or stimulated by investigations of carbonium ions are the development of physical techniques of detection and identification of species in solution, rational approaches to the understanding of molecular rearrangements and steric hindrance, the use of reaction kinetics as a tool for probing subtleties of reaction mechanism, the application of quantum-mechanical methods to organic species, the discovery of new reactions and compounds, and the formulation of basic concepts concerning ionic interactions, especially in non-aqueous solvents.

No serious student of chemistry can today afford to remain ignorant of carbonium-ion chemistry. The literature of the field is vast and, while most text-books on physical organic chemistry give brief discussions of carbonium-ion formation and reactions and though some fine reviews of particular aspects of the subject exist, we have for some time recognized the need for a general text in which carbonium-ion chemistry is treated as a whole and which interconnects the various strands of development. The present volume is an attempt to fill this gap. We have tried to write a book that is elementary in the sense of requiring little previous acquaintance with carbonium ions. It should be intelligible to advanced undergraduate students or to graduate students at the beginning of their studies. Knowledge of physical and organic chemistry appropriate to this stage of study is assumed. However, our coverage was

v

dictated not by the limitations set by particular courses but by the shape of the subject as we find it today.

Naturally, with a topic of this size, we have had to restrict the scope of our treatment. We have limited the subject by a strict though fairly inclusive definition of carbonium ions: this is explained in Section 1.1. Even so, a comprehensive treatment or even comprehensive literature citations were clearly out of the question. In presenting the material it proved impossible to do justice to the many distinguished workers in the field: the inclusion of particular examples had to be based on personal judgement of their importance or elegance and regrettably not always on priority. In order to offset some of our omissions and direct the reader to more detailed accounts of particular areas of carbonium-ion chemistry, we have added a bibliography of the subject in the Appendix.

Many battles have been and are still being fought over carbonium ions. Some of these are no longer of other than historical interest and we have not discussed them. Of current controversies the most noteworthy is that concerning the nature of so-called "non-classical" carbonium ions. Because of the current interest and because we feel that previous discussions have sometimes suffered from the tendency of authors to over-generalize, we have devoted Chapter 7 to a fairly detailed and comprehensive examination of this topic. Future writers of books on carbonium-ion chemistry may perhaps see no necessity for treating such species separately.

Many of our colleagues have contributed directly or indirectly to the development of ideas which we have sought to express in this book. In acknowledging this debt, it would be invidious to name particular persons. However, we wish to thank Drs. A. Ledwith and D. Whittaker, who read and commented on parts of the manuscript, and Messrs. K. C. Brown, D. B. Frankham, A. R. Newall, P. J. Powers and R. J. E. Talbot, who checked most of the references.

D. BETHELL

July 1967   V. GOLD

CONTENTS

Preface v

1. Introduction 1
  1.1. Definitions 1
  1.2. The analogy between carbonium carbon and boron . . 4
  1.3. Nomenclature of carbonium ions 5
  1.4. Historical: early evidence for carbonium ions (1901-1946) . 6

2. Experimental Techniques for the Detection and Study of Carbonium Ions 12
  2.1. General considerations 12
  2.2. Crystallography and infra-red spectroscopy of solid salts . . 13
  2.3. Spectroscopy of solutions 15
    2.3.1. Nuclear magnetic resonance spectra 16
    2.3.2. Infrared spectra 24
    2.3.3. Electronic spectra 25
  2.4. Colligative properties 28
  2.5. Electrolyte behaviour 28
    2.5.1. Conductivity measurements 28
    2.5.2. Electrolysis 29
    2.5.3. EMF measurements 30
    2.5.4. Polarography 30
  2.6. Reaction kinetics 31

2.6.1. Mechanistic classification 32

2.6.2. Rate laws 32

2.6.3. Effects of added salts 36

2.6.4. Trapping of carbonium ions 37

2.6.5. Activation parameters 39

2.7. Chemical methods 39

2.7.1. Racemization 40

2.7.2. Rearrangement 40

2.7.3. Elimination 42

3. Sources of Carbonium Ions

3. Sources of Carbonium Ions 44

3.1. General considerations 44

3.2. Heterolytic fission of a larger molecular entity . . . 46

3.3. Addition of cations to neutral molecules 53

3.4. Electron removal from neutral species 57

4. Formation of Carbonium Ions: Quantitative Aspects

4. Formation of Carbonium Ions: Quantitative Aspects . 59

4.1. Energetics of carbonium-ion formation 59

4.1.1. General consideration 59

4.1.2. The quantitative definition of carbonium-ion stability . 60

4.1.3. Ionization potentials and appearance potentials . . 62

4.1.4. Electrical conductance 68

4.1.5. Spectrophotometry 71

Ionization of triazylmethyl halides 72

Ionization of alcohols in acidic media . . . 73

Proton addition to unsaturated systems . . . 81

4.1.6. Distribution and vapour pressure measurements . . 85

4.1.7. EMF measurements 87

4.2. Rates of carbonium-ion formation 88

4.2.1. The status of rate measurements in relation to carbonium-ion stability 88

4.2.2. S_N1 reactions 90

4.2.3. Substituent effects: σ^+ and σ^* values 95

4.2.4. Heterolytic reactions in the gas phase 101

4.2.5. Aromatic hydrogen isotope exchange 105

4.2.6. Olefin hydration 108
4.2.7. Isotope effects 109
4.3. Survey of stable carbonium ions 110

5. Factors Governing the Stability of Carbonium Ions . 117

5.1. General considerations 117
5.2. Internal factors 118
5.2.1. Electrostatic arguments 118
5.2.2. General aims of quantum-mechanical calculations on carbonium ions 119
5.2.3. The HMO method for conjugated carbonium ions . . 121
5.2.4. The extent of planarity of conjugated carbonium ions . 128
5.2.5. Substituent effects and modifications of the HMO method
for conjugated carbonium ions 129
5.2.6. Aliphatic carbonium ions 133
5.3. External factors 136
5.3.1. Introduction: some electrostatic considerations . . 136
5.3.2. Solvation of carbonium ions 139
The nature of the interaction between carbonium ions
and the solvent 139
Energetics of solvation. Definitions 140
Effect of the structure of the carbonium ion . . 142
Effect of the solvent 144
Measures of solvent polarity 147
5.3.3. Interaction of carbonium ions with other ions . . . 148
Non-specific interaction 148
Ion association. Electrostatic theory 150
Evidence for ion-pair formation in carbonium-ion
reactions 152
5.3.4. Charge transfer 159

6. Reactions of Carbonium Ions 160

6.1. Introduction 160
6.1.1. Carbonium ions as electrophiles 160
6.1.2. The reaction products 161

6.1.3. Chemical consequences of charge delocalization . . 164

6.1.4. Influence of the source of the ion on carbonium-ion reactions 166

6.2. Attack of carbonium centres on non-bonded electron pairs . 168

6.2.1. Introduction 168

6.2.2. The influence of the nucleophile 169

6.2.3. Effect of carbonium-ion structure on reactivity . . . 171

6.2.4. Stereochemistry 174

    Reaction at an asymmetric carbon atom . . . 174

    Reactions of allyl cations 177

6.3. Attack of carbonium centres on π-bond electrons . . . 179

6.3.1. Introduction 179

6.3.2. Aromatic alkylation 179

    Nature of the reaction 179

    The reactivity of aromatic compounds . . . 182

    The influence of carbonium-ion structure on reactivity 185

6.3.3. Reaction of carbonium ions with olefins 186

    Scope and nature of the reaction 186

    Cationic vinyl polymerization 188

    Olefin structure and reactivity 190

6.3.4. Attack of carbonium centres on C–X multiple bonds . 192

6.4. Attack of carbonium centres on σ-bond electrons . . . 194

6.4.1. Introduction 194

6.4.2. Olefin formation and related reactions 195

    E1 Elimination. Mechanism 195

    The effect of carbonium-ion structure . . . 197

    Fragmentation of carbonium ions 200

6.4.3. Carbonium-ion rearrangements 204

    The scope and nature of the reaction . . . 204

    The mechanism and stereochemical course of rearrangement 207

    Structural effects on carbonium ion rearrangements. The direction of rearrangement 211

    Migratory aptitude 212

6.4.4. Intermolecular hydride transfer 218

    Introduction 218

    Scope of the reaction 219

    Structural effects 220

7. Bridged Carbonium Ions 222

7.1. Terminology 222

7.2. History 225

7.2.1. Neighbouring-group participation 225
Neighbouring acetoxyl 226
Neighbouring bromine 227

7.2.2. Bridged carbonium ions 229

7.3. Experimental criteria of bridged-ion formation . . . 231

7.3.1. Physical methods 231
7.3.2. Kinetic data 231
7.3.3. The reaction products 235
7.3.4. Stereochemistry 236

7.4. Electron-sufficient bridged carbonium ions . . . 239

7.4.1. Aryl-bridged ions 239
The 3-phenyl-2-butyl system 239
Other β-phenylethyl systems 243
Substituents in the phenyl bridge . . . 246
Bridging of non-adjacent carbon atoms . . 248
Aryl bridging in cyclic systems . . . 249

7.4.2. Alkenyl-bridged ions: homoallylic cations . . 250
Open-chain systems 250
Cyclic systems 253
Cycloalkenylmethyl systems 254
Cycloalkenyl systems 255
Bicyclo[2,2,1]heptyl and related systems . . 256
Cholesteryl and related systems . . . 261

7.5. Electron-deficient bridged carbonium ions . . . 263

7.5.1. Alkyl- and hydrogen-bridging in acyclic systems . 263
7.5.2. The cyclopropylmethyl-cyclobutyl and related problems . 266
7.5.3. Bicyclo[2,2,1]heptyl and related systems . . . 271
Norbornyl compounds 271
Substituted norbornyl compounds . . . 277
7.5.4. Other saturated bicyclic systems 279

7.6. Bridged carbonium ions in the gas phase . . . 280

7.7. Conclusion 282

8. Related Species 283
  8.1. Acylium ions 283
    8.1.1. Nomenclature 283
    8.1.2. Stable acylium ions: physical evidence 283
        Conductivity 283
        Cryoscopy in sulphuric acid 284
        Absorption spectroscopy 285
    8.1.3. Acylium ions as reaction intermediates 287
        Substitution by nucleophiles having non-bonded electrons 288
        Aromatic acylation: substitution of acyl derivatives by aromatic nucleophiles 290
        Other reactions 292
  8.2. Other species with reactive centres on carbon . . . 294
    8.2.1. Carbenes 294
        Formation of carbenes 295
        Reactions of singlet carbenes 295
    8.2.2. Radical cations 299
  8.3. Hetero-atom analogues 302
    8.3.1. Introduction 302
    8.3.2. Siliconium ions 303
    8.3.3. Others 304

Appendix: A Bibliography of Carbonium-ion Chemistry . . 306
References 312
Author Index 349
Subject Index 367

1 | INTRODUCTION

1.1 Definitions

Carbonium ions are derivatives of the trivalent positively charged species CH_3^+ in which the hydrogen atoms may be replaced by other organic residues. CH_3^+ can be regarded as the parent "type" of this class of compounds in the same way that Kekulé considered methane as the parent "type" of ordinary, electrically neutral organic molecules. We know that the conceptual chain connecting methane with a structure such as benzene contains some subtly forged links and, in a similar way, the structures of some carbonium ions, e.g. the cycloheptatrienyl[1] cation (**1.1**) are not at all closely related to their notional progenitor CH_3^+.

According to our definition, the simple carbonium ions are singly charged organic cations containing even numbers of electrons. Organic cations containing odd numbers of electrons, such as $C_6H_6^+$—which is formed from benzene by loss of a single electron—can still be regarded as being derived from CH_3^+, as formula **1.2** (one of a set of possible valency bond representations) indicates. However, their chemistry is largely influenced by their free-radical

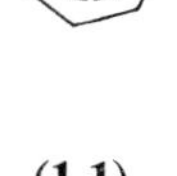

(**1.1**) 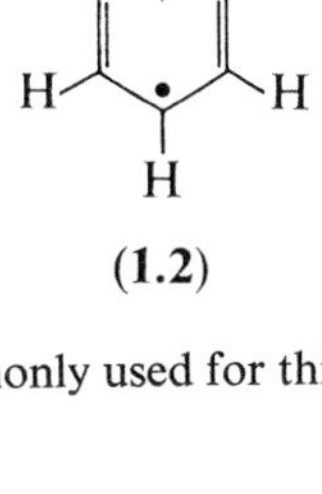   (**1.2**)

---

[1] The following trivial names are also commonly used for this species: tropylium, tropenium and tropyl ion.

character; such species do not represent typical carbonium ions and their discussion is deferred to one of the later sections of this book (Paragraph 8.2.2).

It is essential to this definition of carbonium ions as derivatives of CH_3^+ that the ions cannot be represented by any conceivable valency bond formula in which the "normal" valency rules (i.e. quadrivalency of carbon, univalency of hydrogen, etc.) are preserved. It should, however, always be possible to write at least one representation in which all atoms but one are "normal" in this respect, the one different atom being a positively charged trivalent carbon atom. Examples of such valency bond formulae are **1.3**, **1.4** and **1.5**. Of course it

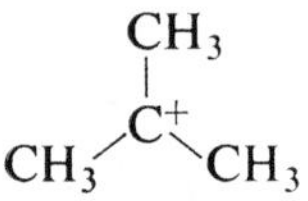

         (1.3) 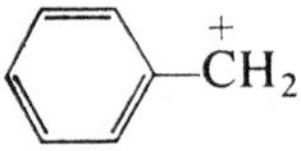   **(1.4)**   **(1.5)**

does not follow that a single valency bond formula is a good representation of the actual structure. In each of these three examples it is possible to write other bond formulae e.g. **1.6**, **1.7** and **1.8** and the actual mesomeric structure of

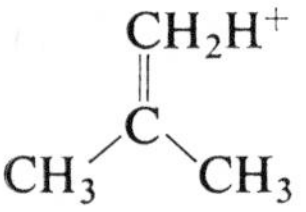

         (1.6) 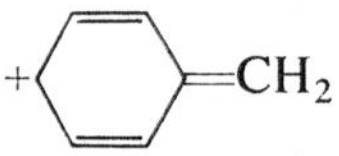   **(1.7)**   **(1.8)**

the carbonium ion will be a hybrid of all such representations. Some valency bond representations clearly look more credible than others and will contribute to a larger extent to the hybrid structure. For instance, **1.3** and **1.4** are nearer the truth than **1.6** and **1.7**, respectively, whereas structures **1.5** and **1.8** will have an equivalent status in this respect. Seven atoms share the charge in the cycloheptatrienyl cation (**1.1**). However, in many cases it will be correct to regard the positive charge (and trivalency) of the ion as being largely concentrated on one particular carbon atom. For example, formulae **1.3** and **1.4** fairly indicate the most important site of the abnormal valency situation of these two ions. One may then refer to a particular carbon atom as the *carbonium centre* and it will be found that the reactions of such carbonium ions are, to a good approximation, reactions of the carbonium centre. In other cases it may be impossible to single out a particular atom as the carbonium centre: such a case is exemplified by the cycloheptatrienyl cation (**1.1**). It is sometimes helpful to regard such ions as having several carbonium centres.

In the same way that it may be impossible to designate a single carbon atom as the carbonium centre of the ion because the charge is distributed between two or more positions, ambiguity may sometimes arise whether to designate an ion as a carbonium ion when part of the charge is located on an atom other than carbon. Formulae **1.9**, **1.10** and **1.11** represent the same species in the guise of a carbonium, oxonium, or imonium ion.[1] Only in those cases where the

$$(CH_3)_2N\overset{+}{-}CH-OEt \qquad (CH_3)_2N-CH\overset{+}{=}OEt \qquad (CH_3)_2\overset{+}{N}=CH-OEt$$

(1.9)   **(1.10)**   **(1.11)**

limiting structure having the positive charge located on carbon (e.g. **1.9**) is the most important one[2] shall we discuss such species as carbonium ions.

Not all organic cations are carbonium ions. The methylammonium ion, $CH_3\overset{+}{N}H_3$, for example, is a derivative of the ammonium ion. It is impossible to represent the methylammonium ion as a carbonium ion.

The term "*carbonium*" suggests that these ions are analogues of the other 'onium ions (ammonium, phosphonium, oxonium, sulphonium, iodonium, and others) and was coined by Baeyer[3] with such an analogy in mind. However the parallelism does not extend beyond the cationic charge of the species. Ammonium ions are formed by combination of an amine (which is an electron pair donor) with an electron pair acceptor (e.g. a proton). In this way the nitrogen atom acquires a positive charge and increases its covalency by one unit from three to four. Phosphorus(III), oxygen, sulphur, and iodine similarly possess lone pairs of electrons which can be donated with resultant formation of 'onium complexes. The carbon atom in compounds of its ordinary valency state does not possess a lone pair of electrons, and a carbonium centre exhibits a covalency of three, i.e. one unit *less* than the normal quadrivalency. This objection to the term "carbonium" was immediately pointed out by Gomberg[4] who proposed to call the salts of these ions "carbyl salts", but this suggestion did not gain acceptance. The derivatives of CH_3^+ which we call carbonium ions can be formally related to carbene, $:CH_2$, by electron pair donation from a carbene to an acceptor (e.g. $:CH_2 + H^+ \rightarrow CH_3^+$). It has accordingly been suggested that the term "carbenium ion" is more correctly applied to these structures[5]. The proposal has some force of logic and is occasionally followed in the German literature but the longer-established term carbonium ion is now used almost without exception.

[1] Meerwein, Hederich *et al.*, 1960.
[2] For examples of the use of spectroscopic methods in deciding such a question, see Ramsey and Taft, 1966.
[3] Baeyer and Villiger, 1902.
[4] Gomberg, 1902b.
[5] Dilthey and Dinklage, 1929; Arndt and Lorenz, 1930; Jennen, 1966.

1.2 The Analogy between Carbonium Carbon and Boron

The ion CH_3^+ formed by loss of H^- from methane contains the same number of electrons as the grouping BH_3 formed by hydride loss from BH_4^-, and the carbonium centre is isoelectronic with boron, having a sextet of electrons. It is the presence of the electronic sextet, i.e. an incomplete shell, which confers special reactivity on both boranes and carbonium ions. It is also expected that the geometry of bonding about a carbonium centre should be the same as that about a boron atom. Trimethylboron and the boron trihalides are known to have the boron atom at the centre of three coplanar bonds directed towards the corners of an equilateral triangle.[1] The electronic ground state of the boron atom is s^2p. Some excitation is required to produce the valency state sp^2 for which three trigonal bonds are expected. The same theoretical reasons and the analogy with boron require the trigonal bond arrangement about a carbonium centre. The resulting stereochemical consequences are important and will be central to some of the later and more detailed discussion. There is also very direct experimental support for the planar structure of stable carbonium ions derived from crystallographic and spectroscopic studies of stable carbonium salts (Section 2.2).

By contrast, saturated carbanions—derivatives of the "type" CH_3^-, being isoelectric with ammonia—are expected to be non-planar.[2]

The analogy between carbonium ions and boron compounds must, however, not be carried too far. In the first place, the positive charge on a carbonium centre would cause strong electrostatic repulsion in a species such as **1.12**, the isoelectronic analogue of diborane (**1.13**).

$$\left[\begin{array}{c} H \\ H \end{array}\!\!>\!\!C\!\!<\!\!\begin{array}{c} H \\ H \end{array}\!\!>\!\!C\!\!<\!\!\begin{array}{c} H \\ H \end{array}\right]^{2+}$$

(1.12)

$$\begin{array}{c} H \\ H \end{array}\!\!>\!\!B\!\!<\!\!\begin{array}{c} H \\ H \end{array}\!\!>\!\!B\!\!<\!\!\begin{array}{c} H \\ H \end{array}$$

(1.13)

In no case has tendency to dimerization of carbonium ions or the formation of other polynuclear structures bearing analogies to the boron hydrides been observed. Three-centre bonds, as in formula **1.13**, relieve the electron-deficiency at the boron atom whose complement of electrons is a sextet only. The energy gain achieved by the corresponding type of bonding between two carbonium centres is clearly insufficient to balance the concomitant electrostatic repulsion. An additional factor, again arising out of the electrostatic charge of carbonium ions, concerns the radial distribution of the electron cloud. The change in electron density with distance from the nucleus depends on the magnitude of the coulombic field in which the electrons are moving. As a result

[1] H. A. Lévy and Brockway, 1937.
[2] Cram, 1965.

the electrons around a positively charged carbonium carbon atom will be more closely and tightly held than those around boron (or, indeed, ordinary carbon) and, consequently, the bonds between the carbonium centre and attached groups are expected to be shorter than those between boron and the same groups.

These considerations have a bearing on the possible existence of bridged species half-way between boranes and carbonium ions, of which the ion **1.14** would be the simplest example. Such species would not be subject to the

$$\left[\begin{array}{c} H \\ H \end{array} \!\!\!>\! B \!<\!\!\! \begin{array}{c} H \\ H \end{array} \!\!>\! C \!<\!\!\! \begin{array}{c} H \\ H \end{array} \right]^{+}$$

(1.14)

disruptive influence of charge repulsion, which applies to **1.12**, and may therefore be stable provided the sizes of the orbitals involved allow for sufficient overlap.

Analogues of carbonium ions with central atoms other than boron are briefly discussed in Chapter 8.

1.3 Nomenclature of Carbonium Ions

A systematic nomenclature of carbonium ions can be based on an adaptation of the carbinol convention for naming alcohols. On this basis, the ion **1.3** would be called the trimethylcarbonium ion, by analogy with the name trimethylcarbinol for the alcohol $Me_3C.OH$. Names derived from this system are very generally used to describe the triphenylcarbonium ion (Ph_3C^+) and its analogues. However, not all authors name simpler carbonium ions in a manner consistent with this convention. For example, the ion $CH_3.CH_2^+$, on the adapted carbinol system, should be called the methylcarbonium ion. Yet a number of writers would refer to it as an "ethyl carbonium" ion, presumably on the ground that it has the skeleton of the ethyl group and is a carbonium ion.

In order to avoid the real ambiguities resulting from the simultaneous use of these two conflicting practices, we have, in the following, consistently avoided the inclusion of the term "carbonium" in the naming of the ions. This course is desirable also because the carbinol convention for alcohols is no longer accepted usage. A self-explanatory system which has commended itself to a number of workers in this field is followed in this book. Carbonium ions are named in the same way as the corresponding radicals, with addition of the word "cation". Thus the ions represented by **1.3**, **1.4** and **1.5** are referred to as the t-butyl cation, benzyl cation and allyl cation. The system can obviously be extended to carbanions: the species $Ph.CH_2^-$ is called the benzyl anion. Furthermore, the names are not restricted to hydrocarbon residues. The ion

$CH_3.CO^+$ is called the acetyl cation and specially-coined names such as acetylium, acetylonium, oxocarbonium can be avoided. The fact that the t-butyl cation is a carbonium ion does not appear in the name, but it is obvious from the context.

In the attempt to make the names of all organic cations end in "ium" or "onium" several other *ad hoc* names of certain ions have been coined and are found in the literature (e.g. "benzenonium", "benzenium", "phenonium"). The introduction of a new trivial name is to be deprecated unless it replaces a very complicated systematic name for a frequently-named species. Whether trivial names of particular carbonium ions fall into this category is a matter of taste. As a general rule it seems sensible to avoid them except where systematic names are excessively cumbersome.

As in the nomenclature of stable electrically neutral molecules, the name of a carbonium ion may not accurately convey the precise structure of the species. The term "1,3-butadiene" indicates that double bonds are found between the 1- and 2- and between the 3- and 4-carbon atoms of a four-membered aliphatic chain; it does not tell us that the link between the 2- and 3-carbon atoms also has partial double-bond character. The nomenclature of carbonium ions is similarly deficient, and the name "benzyl cation" does not reflect the contribution of structure **1.7** to the mesomeric state of the benzyl cation. In other cases the systematic name may be even more misleading in failing to indicate the factors stabilizing the ion. In our view it is more important that a chemically useful system of terminology should not hide the genetic relationship between the carbonium ion and its potential precursors; e.g. benzyl alcohol and benzyl chloride may give rise to benzyl cations. The present nomenclature is to be interpreted in this manner.

The convention adopted in this Book is one of those approved by the International Union of Pure and Applied Chemistry.[1]

1.4 Historical: Early Evidence for Carbonium Ions (1901–1946)

The idea of organic cations of this type emerged at the beginning of the present century as a result of work on triphenylmethane derivatives.[2] Ionic behaviour—in the strict sense of the word—was discovered by conductivity measurements on triphenylmethyl halides in liquid sulphur dioxide[3,4] and the salt-like character of the conducting solutes was pointed out by Gomberg.[4,5] Electrical

[1] I.U.P.A.C. 1965 Rules, *Pure Appl. Chem.*, **11**, 1 (Rule C83). As alternatives the I.U.P.A.C. 1965 Rules also admit names ending in "enium" and "ylium", for example 2-methylpropenium or 2-methylpropylium for the t-butyl cation (**1.3**).

[2] See Schmidlin, 1914.

[3] Walden, 1902, 1903.

[4] Gomberg, 1902b.

[5] Gomberg, 1902a.

conductivity of triphenylmethyl halides could also be detected in other solvents, for example, benzonitrile,[1] pyridine[2] or hydrogen cyanide.[3] These conducting solutions are yellow, whereas the pure substances are colourless. Similar colours, it had been noted, are produced when triphenylmethanol[4] or triphenylmethyl chloride[4,5] dissolve in sulphuric acid, or when triphenylmethyl chloride reacts with metal halides such as aluminium chloride or similar Friedel-Crafts catalysts.[5,6] Baeyer and his co-workers, early in their investigation of the nature of these coloured ("halochromic") solutions, had advanced the idea that the colour could be explained by salt formation. For the particular case of triphenylmethanol in sulphuric acid, a carbonium hydrogen sulphate with an abnormal "carbonium valency" between the triphenylmethyl group and the hydrogen sulphate group was postulated;[7] this was at first expressed by the formula **1.15**. (Quite incidentally, this was one of the earliest

$$(C_6H_5)_3C\text{\raisebox{0pt}{$\sim\!\sim\!\sim$}}HSO_4 \qquad\qquad (1.15)$$

attempts at drawing a distinction between covalency and electrovalency.)

The connexion between colour formation and ionic character was later placed on a firmer foundation by Hantzsch's demonstration[8] that the conducting power of solutions of the coloured perchlorate $Ph_3C . ClO_4$ in nitromethane was of the same order as that of other saline electrolytes. Hantzsch also studied the cryoscopic behaviour of triphenylmethanol in sulphuric acid and concluded that the freezing point depression corresponded to the formation of triphenylmethyl cations from dissolved triphenylmethanol,[9] a conclusion fully confirmed by subsequent and more refined work.[10] Later, Hantzsch connected this rather direct evidence for the chemical formula of the organic solute particle with the conductivity results by showing that the absorption spectrum of a solution of triphenylmethanol in sulphuric acid was identical with that of the conducting solutions of triphenylmethyl chloride in sulphur dioxide and other non-aqueous solvents.[8]

From these studies, particularly the incisive contributions made by Hantzsch, the reality of stable carbonium ions of the triarylmethyl cation type has not been in doubt for many years. Modern developments in the study of stable carbonium ions follow on from this stage and are concerned more with the

[1] Gomberg, 1902b.
[2] Hantzsch and Meyer, 1910.
[3] Gomberg and Sullivan, 1922.
[4] Kehrmann and Wentzel, 1901.
[5] Norris and Sanders, 1901.
[6] Gomberg, 1902a.
[7] Baeyer, 1905.
[8] Hantzsch, 1921.
[9] Hantzsch, 1907.
[10] Oddo and Scandola, 1909; Hammett and Deyrup, 1933; Newman and Deno, 1951a.

properties and structure of the ions rather than with the fact that stable carbonium ions exist (see Chapter 2).

Soon after these events came suggestions that carbonium ions could be involved, as fleeting intermediates, in a much wider range of reactions of organic compounds in solution.

Meerwein and van Emster, on the basis of rate measurements of terpene rearrangements, suggested the intermediacy of carbonium ions **1.17**, **1.18** in the conversion of camphene hydrochloride (**1.16**) into isobornyl chloride (**1.19**) and similar rearrangements.[1] The ionization hypothesis explains the

    (1.16)   **(1.17)**   **(1.18)**   **(1.19)**

increase of the reaction velocity with the ionizing power of the solvent used. The rearrangements are fastest in sulphur dioxide and nitromethane, which are also particularly good media for the detection of carbonium ions by conductivity measurements. Solvents such as benzene—in which triphenyl-methyl chloride gives a colourless non-conducting solution—are associated with low rearrangement velocities. It was also noted[1] that the rearrangement was catalysed by metal halides of the Friedel-Crafts catalyst type, precisely the same halides which gave rise to colour formation with triphenylmethyl chloride. The above rearrangement also takes place when chloride is replaced by other potential anionic leaving groups, and it was noted that the reaction velocity increased with the stability as an anion of the leaving group.[2] These studies by Meerwein not only provided some useful kinetic criteria for the detection of carbonium intermediates but, by their selection of the bicyclo-[2,2,1]heptyl system, focused attention on a class of carbonium-ion reactions of uncommon interest.

The ionization hypothesis has remained the pivotal part of the arguments concerning this and similar rearrangements, but our detailed views have undergone some changes. These changes were in some senses implied[3] as early as 1939 but their development falls mainly in the period since 1946 (see Chapter 7).

In the years following Meerwein and van Emster's work analogous re-arrangements on acyclic systems were extensively studied by Whitmore and his school.[4] This work provided a unified theory[5] of a variety of seemingly

[1] Meerwein and van Emster, 1922.
[2] Meerwein, Hammell *et al.*, 1927.
[3] Nevell, de Salas and Wilson, 1939.
[4] Reviewed by Whitmore, 1948.
[5] Whitmore, 1932.

unrelated rearrangements. Their common feature, on this theory, was the initial formation of an unstable intermediate containing, as Whitmore preferred to call it, an atom with an "open sextet" of electrons. In many cases this intermediate is a carbonium ion. The theory convinces by the variety of cases that are covered by it rather than by the completeness of the argument as applied to any individual example. The work led to the general acceptance of simple aliphatic carbonium ions as reaction intermediates and also provided an experimental criterion for assessing the relative stability of different ions. To take as an example the rearrangement of neopentyl iodide (**1.20**) to t-pentyl acetate (**1.23**) in the presence of silver acetate:

$$(CH_3)_3C.CH_2I \qquad\qquad\qquad (CH_3)_2C(OAc).CH_2.CH_3$$

(1.20) $\searrow$ $\qquad\qquad\qquad\qquad$ $\nearrow$ $\qquad$ **(1.23)**

$$(CH_3)_3C.CH_2^+ \longrightarrow (CH_3)_2\overset{+}{C}.CH_2.CH_3$$

$$\textbf{(1.21)} \qquad\qquad\qquad \textbf{(1.22)}$$

The conversion of the primary halide into the tertiary acetate is held to imply the spontaneous conversion of the primary carbonium ion **1.21** into the tertiary ion **1.22** and hence the greater thermodynamic stability of the latter. The general rule emerging from such rearrangements is that progressive alkyl substitution at a carbonium centre stabilizes the ion, but the ramifications of this type of experiment are considerably wider (Section 6.4).

More direct evidence for the formation of aliphatic carbonium ions as reaction intermediates came from the observation of unimolecular nucleophilic substitution reactions. A significant example was the hydrolysis of t-butyl halides in aqueous alcohol or aqueous acetone. The velocity of this reaction is not increased even by moderately large concentrations of alkali,[1] whereas the hydrolysis of methyl and ethyl halides in aqueous alcohol[2] is kinetically of first order with respect to alkali. The hydrolysis of the t-butyl halides was therefore represented as the generation of the t-butyl cation

$$\text{t-BuX} \underset{\text{rate limiting}}{\overset{\text{}}{\rightleftharpoons}} \text{t-Bu}^+ + X^- \xrightarrow[+H_2O]{\text{rapid}} \text{t-BuOH} + H^+ + X^-$$

in a rate-limiting unimolecular step, which was followed by a rapid destruction of the cation by solvent attack. The symbol S_N1 (*S*ubstitution, *n*ucleophilic, unimolecular) was devised[3] to describe this mechanism, as a distinction from the bimolecular S_N2 mechanism. The implied duality of mechanism in substitution reactions of alkyl halides was also supported by the rate sequence Me > Et > i-Pr ≪ t-Bu of the above hydrolyses under comparable conditions in

[1] Hughes, 1935a; Cooper and Hughes, 1937.
[2] Grant and Hinshelwood, 1933.
[3] Gleave, Hughes and Ingold, 1935.

aqueous alcohol media. Here again the implication is that the cation is stabilized by alkyl substitution at the carbonium centre and also that the transition
state leading to formation of the ion is stabilized in the same sense.

The extensive studies on alkyl halides by Hughes, Ingold and their school
during the early thirties can be regarded as the real starting point of the almost
countless later investigations pertaining to carbonium ions through the
kinetics of solvolytic and other nucleophilic substitution reactions. Chronolo-
gically, matters did not start there. The ionization mechanism for an organic
halide (benzyl chloride) had been proposed by Ingold some years earlier,[1] as
had been the notion of a duality of mechanisms.[2] Also, Hughes's work on
alkyl halides had been preceded by consideration of the fission of alkyl-
ammonium and -sulphonium salts in terms of unimolecular and bimolecular
mechanisms.[3] The first clear cases of unimolecular kinetics in the hydrolysis of
organic halides had, however, already been demonstrated by Ward, who
interpreted his results by what was later termed the S_N1 mechanism.[4] The
particular substrates used, α-phenylethyl chloride[4] and diphenylmethyl
chloride,[5] are structurally half-way between triphenylmethyl chloride, for
which the formation of ions in sulphur dioxide had been demonstrated by
conductivity measurements, and t-butyl chloride which, at the time, seemed a
most unlikely structure to ionize. Further links between the studies in sulphur
dioxide and the solvolysis kinetics were provided by kinetic studies in sulphur
dioxide. It was observed that the racemization of α-phenylethyl chloride in
sulphur dioxide is independent of the concentration of added alkali halide.[6]
A later study showed that the rate of isotope exchange between t-butyl iodide
and radioactive alkali iodide is similarly independent of the concentration of
iodide ions.[7]

The demonstration that the occurrence of the ionization mechanism is
relevant to the steric course of substitution (i.e. the occurrence of racemization,
inversion or retention of configuration) was one of the most important early
successes of the ionization theory.[8] The connexion is provided by the planar
structure of the separated carbonium ion which, on recombination with any
nucleophile, should give a racemic product mixture. The detailed explanation
of the phenomena is considerably more complicated (for example, by ion
association).

A further important development was the establishment of a connexion
between Whitmore's hypothesis of the role of intermediates in saturated

[1] Ingold and Rothstein, 1928.
[2] Hanhart and Ingold, 1927.
[3] Hughes and Ingold, 1933a,b; Hughes, Ingold and Patel, 1933.
[4] Ward, 1927b.
[5] Ward, 1927a.
[6] Bergmann and Polanyi, 1933; Bergmann, Polanyi and Szabo, 1936.
[7] Tuck, 1938.
[8] For a review, see Hughes, 1938.

rearrangements and the kinetic evidence for S_N1 ionization mechanisms.[1] It was found that, depending on experimental conditions, neopentyl halides could solvolyse by either unimolecular or bimolecular mechanisms. The latter is a very slow reaction and was shown to give unrearranged products, whereas rearranged (t-pentyl) derivatives resulted from the unimolecular path.

The foregoing brief summary of the main developments which led to the acceptance of carbonium ions as very common reaction intermediates has omitted to mention the many objections that were raised on the way but which are no longer relevant today. It is conversely true that some phenomena which seemed simple when they were first discovered are now recognized to be less straightforward, as will appear from the more detailed consideration of these topics in the subsequent chapters.

[1] Dostrovsky and Hughes, 1946; Dostrovsky, Hughes and Ingold, 1946.

2 | EXPERIMENTAL TECHNIQUES FOR THE DETECTION AND STUDY OF CARBONIUM IONS

2.1 General Considerations

The detection of carbonium ions presents a different problem according to whether the ions are obtainable in high concentration or not. In the former case, the methods differ only in detail from common procedures of analytical, physical or organic chemistry. In the latter case, the direct physical detection, especially when one is dealing with a minute stationary concentration of a labile species, may be quite impossible.

Carbonium ions, except the radical ions discussed in Paragraph 8.2.2, do not possess any property which, at the present time, allows their easy detection in very low concentration. They differ in this respect from free radicals, the electron spin of which is often observable even at extremely low concentrations by electron spin resonance spectroscopy.

Indirect criteria have therefore to be used. These facts have already been illustrated in the preceding historical account. We shall now summarize the useful or promising methods more fully.

Carbonium-ion chemistry is largely, though not entirely, concerned with liquid solutions. The electrochemical problems concerning ion association and the nature of solvation are ever present in all considerations of the chemistry of ionic solutions, and electrolytes containing a carbonium ion as the cation are no exceptions in this respect. In fact, the particularly detailed studies of carbonium ions have greatly sharpened the discussion of interionic forces and solvation, especially in solvents of low dielectric constant. The ways in which these interactions are thought to modify the properties of carbonium ions are discussed in Section 5.3. It is, however, useful to be aware of these possible complications already when considering the methods of studying and detecting carbonium ions in solution for, as in the case of other electrolytes, the distinction between ion pairs and unionized molecules is more difficult to establish than the distinction between dissociated ions and unionized molecules. Some of the subtle problems that have had to be considered in carbonium ion chemistry are a direct consequence of the use of solvent systems with a low dielectric constant and low capacity for solvating ions and in which ion association is consequently an important feature.

The following parts of this Chapter consider first the physical methods applicable to stable ions (Sections 2.2–2.5) and then the kinetic methods employed for unstable ions (Section 2.6), together with some illustrative results. The consideration of quantitative results is in general deferred till later sections.

One of the most sensitive methods for the detection of carbonium ions (and related cations) is by use of the mass spectrometer. In this instrument the ions, generated in the gas phase usually by electron impact, are separated magnetically according to their mass/charge ratio and detected electronically. In suitable cases, the ion formed initially decomposes by fragmentation which may be accompanied by rearrangements, both parent ions and product ions being analysed and detected. Thus mass spectrometry has provided much information about the behaviour and energetics (Paragraph 4.1.4) of carbonium ions in the gas phase. However, this technique does not contribute to the detection of carbonium ions in solutions or salts.

Analogies between carbonium-ion reactions in solution and reactions of gaseous carbonium ions generated and detected by the mass spectrometer have often been pointed out. This branch of mass spectrometry is in fact undergoing very intensive study at the present time. The extent to which one may apply such results to reactions in solution (and vice versa) is an open question, in particular because the mass spectrometer measures only the ratio of mass to charge. Thus it does not provide direct information about the structure of gaseous carbonium ions, and there is ample evidence to suggest that it is frequently not safe to assume that carbonium ions are generated from their precursors in accordance with the rule of least structural change.[1]

2.2 Crystallography and Infrared Spectroscopy of Solid Salts

Though many elucidations of complex organic structures have been made and many crystalline salts containing triarylmethyl and related cations are known, some of them (chiefly perchlorates and complex halides) for a long time,[2] X-ray crystallography has only recently begun to contribute to the knowledge of their structure.

[1] McLafferty, 1963.

[2] Extensive lists of carbonium salts are already to be found in the reviews by Schmidlin, 1914, and Pfeiffer, 1927. A recent summary is contained in a review by Olah and Meyer, 1963.

2*

The detailed structural information that is obtainable from this source is illustrated by the study of triphenylcyclopropenyl perchlorate[1] which reveals that the three phenyl groups are twisted out of the plane of the central three-membered ring (see Paragraph 5.2.4) and that the bonds in this ring are unusually short (1.37Å). In the case of the triphenylmethyl salts the bonds linking the phenyl groups to the carbonium centre are coplanar. The propeller shape is now more pronounced but the crystallography is complicated and precise bond lengths and angles have proved more difficult to obtain.[2] The position is more securely established for tri(p-aminophenyl)methyl perchlorate where the rings show bond lengths corresponding to a quinonoid structure and are twisted through 29°, 34° and 34°.[3] In another study[4] X-ray crystallography disproved the accepted formula of a carbonium ion and established the correct one. The technique also provided supporting evidence for charge-transfer interaction (Paragraph 5.3.4) between the cycloheptatrienyl cation and iodide ion.[5]

The propeller shape of the triphenylmethyl cation with a coplanar arrangement of the three bonds about the carbonium centre is also deduced from the molecular symmetry (D_3), as indicated by the splitting of well-defined infrared bands of single rings of several stable triphenylmethyl salts.[6]

Perkampus and his collaborators have studied the infrared spectra at low temperatures of sublimed films of salts of the stoichiometry ArH-HX-MX$_3$ (where ArH is benzene or a methylbenzene, and MX$_3$ is one of AlCl$_3$, AlBr$_3$, GaCl$_3$ or GaBr$_3$).[7] The nature of MX$_3$ has no significant effect on the spectrum of the complex, and this spectrum differs markedly from that of the aromatic hydrocarbon ArH. The observed spectra of the complexes are therefore ascribed to the carbonium salts ArH$_2^+$ MX$_4^-$. The addition of a proton to ArH changes the symmetry of the aromatic species—this is most pronounced in the case of benzene itself—and, as a result, some bands which are forbidden in the parent compound appear in the proton adduct. On the basis of these considerations and with the help of deuterium isotope effects on the spectra, a far-reaching vibration-frequency assignment of the C$_6$H$_7^+$ ions (**2.1**) has been

(**2.1**)

[1] Sundaralingam and Jensen, 1966.
[2] Gomes de Mesquita, MacGillavry and Eriks, 1965.
[3] Eriks and Koh, 1963.
[4] Bryan, 1964.
[5] Kitaigorodskii, Struchkov et al., 1960.
[6] Sharp and Sheppard, 1957.
[7] For a review, see Perkampus, 1966.

proposed.[1] Corresponding assignments have also been discussed for the methylbenzenes.[2]

An analysis of the infrared spectra of two salts of trihalocyclopropenyl cations, $C_3Cl_3^+AlCl_4^-$ and $C_3Br_3^+AlBr_4^-$, has also been reported.[3]

With the obvious limitation that the structures of solid salts at low temperatures may not always correspond to the structures in solution, the measurements on solids promise to become an important source of information about the detailed structure of carbonium ions, in the same way that these techniques have proved successful with other compounds.

2.3 Spectroscopy of Solutions

Solutions have been examined by NMR, ultraviolet, and infrared spectroscopy. The use of Raman spectroscopy is also possible but does not seem, so far, to have made a substantial contribution to the study of carbonium ions. Of the above three techniques, NMR spectroscopy is most informative in establishing the structure of an organic species, and ultraviolet absorption spectroscopy is the most accurate method for determining the concentration of carbonium ions in solutions, and has therefore been frequently used in equilibrium studies. Infrared spectroscopy (in the NaCl region) is less helpful in either of these respects, but, as for the infrared spectra of the solid salts and provided it is possible to analyse the spectra and assign frequencies, yields information about the intramolecular motions.

In interpreting the results of spectroscopic measurements, especially in solvents of low dielectric constant, it must be borne in mind that ion association (in the sense of the term used by Bjerrum or Kraus and Fuoss; see Paragraph 5.3.3) has but a minor effect on spectra, in contrast to its profound influence on electrical conductivity. It is therefore difficult to draw reliable conclusions concerning dissociation and association from spectra. The optical detection of ions need not imply high electrical conductivity of the solution. Similarly, it is not certain that covalent attachment of solvent molecules to carbonium ions (as in the formation of oxonium ions)

$$R^+ + R'OH \longrightarrow R-\overset{+}{O}\overset{R'}{\underset{H}{\diagdown}}$$

can always be distinguished from carbonium ions that are less specifically solvated (see Paragraph 5.3.2). These possible ambiguities should be borne in mind also in relation to the following examples, and especially where the spectroscopic results point to the formation of primary or secondary carbonium ions.

[1] Perkampus and Baumgarten, 1963.
[2] Perkampus and Baumgarten, 1964a.
[3] West, Sadô and Tobey, 1966.

However, the optimum conditions for the formation of carbonium and oxonium ions are not the same, and in some cases the very different NMR spectra of both protonated alcohols and the corresponding carbonium ions are known.[1]

2.3.1 NUCLEAR MAGNETIC RESONANCE SPECTRA

The proton magnetic resonance spectra of a variety of carbonium ions have been recorded in solutions where these species are stable. Early measurements include the familiar triphenylmethyl cation,[2] the 1,1-diphenylethyl cation[3] and carbonium ions produced by protonation of aromatic hydrocarbons[4] and azulenes.[5] The spin-coupling pattern of proton resonance spectra usually proves diagnostic in structure elucidations, and the analysis of the spectra proceeds as for any other organic compound. The method has more recently served to establish the formation and identity of less stable carbonium ions. These include alkyl cations, such as s-propyl and t-butyl cations,[6] formed by the solution of alkyl fluorides in antimony pentafluoride, and the proton adducts of benzene, toluene and similar hydrocarbons in acidic solvents at low temperatures.[7]

A typical structural problem that can be solved by NMR spectroscopy is exemplified by carbonium ions with cyclopropyl groups attached to the carbonium centre. The spectrum of the ion **2.2** in SO_2-$SOClF$-SbF_5 as

$$\begin{array}{c} CH_2 \\ | \quad \diagdown \\ \quad \quad CH-\overset{+}{C} \diagup \overset{CH_3}{\diagdown} \\ | \quad \diagup \quad \quad \quad CH_3 \\ CH_2 \end{array}$$

(2.2)

solvent at $-75°C$ shows that the two methyl groups are chemically non-equivalent:[8] the two signals are separated by 0·54 p.p.m. The result implies that the CH_2—CH_2 bond cannot be parallel to the line joining the centres of the two methyl groups and that rotation about the bond linking the cyclopropyl group to the carbonium centre is slow on the NMR time-scale. To satisfy these requirements, the ion has been represented by a structure in which the plane of the cyclopropyl ring is at right angles to the carbonium ion plane. Such an orientation ("bisected" structure) of cyclopropyl rings in cyclopropylmethyl cations had speculatively been proposed on entirely different

[1] Olah and Namanworth, 1966.

[2] Moodie, Connor and Stewart, 1959; Dehl, Vaughan and Berry, 1959; Berry Dehl and Vaughan, 1961.

[3] O'Reilly and Leftin, 1960.

[4] MacLean, van der Waals and Mackor, 1958.

[5] Danyluk and Schneider, 1960; Schaefer and Schneider, 1963.

[6] Olah, Baker et al., 1964.

[7] MacLean and Mackor, 1961, 1962; Birchall and Gillespie, 1964; Olah, 1965b.

[8] Pittman and Olah, 1965a,b.

grounds.[1] The spectroscopic evidence does not strictly allow us to go as far as this: in fact, there is only a single orientation of the cyclopropyl group which makes the methyl groups equivalent. In principle, more could be learned from the pattern of the resonances of the hydrogen nuclei of the cyclopropyl ring, but they are poorly resolved at 100 MHz. The structure of the tricyclo-propylmethyl cation is slightly puzzling, for the very opposite reason. Its NMR spectrum consists of a single sharp line,[2,3] although even the sym-metrical "paddle wheel" structure (2.3) contains three non-equivalent

$$(\beta_1)H \diagdown \quad \diagup H(\beta_2)$$
$$H(\alpha)$$
$$(\alpha)H \diagup \quad \diagdown H(\beta_1) \qquad \textbf{(2.3)}$$
$$(\beta_2)\dot{H} \diagdown \quad H(\beta_2)$$
$$H(\alpha)$$
$$H(\beta_1)$$

((2.3) viewed from above the plane of the carbonium valencies)

groups of hydrogen atoms, designated α, β_1 and β_2 in the formula. No chemical explanation of the spectroscopic equivalence of all the hydrogen atoms in this ion has come to light; for example, there is no exchange with solvent or scrambling of the α and β hydrogen atoms in isotopically labelled ions.[2] The simplicity of the spectrum is therefore interpreted as accidental identity of the chemical shifts of hydrogen atoms in non-equivalent positions. The explana-tion gains some credibility from the fact that the α- and β-hydrogen atoms in tricyclopropylmethyl alcohol in SO_2 at $-60°$ are only poorly resolved in the NMR spectrum.[4]

In a similar fashion the ^{19}F resonance from fluorine-substituted triphenyl-methyl cations has been used to confirm the propeller structure[5] and to derive information about the ease of rotation of phenyl groups about the bond linking them to the carbonium centre.[6]

Special features of interest arise if several isomeric carbonium ions are in equilibrium.[7] In such cases line-broadening and signal-collapse may be observable by varying the temperature of the specimen. Provided the reciprocal life times of the species in equilibrium are comparable to the

[1] Deno, 1964a; for other evidence, see Sharpe and Martin, 1966; H. C. Brown and Cleveland, 1966.

[2] Deno, Richey et al., 1962b.

[3] Hart and Law, 1962; Pittman and Olah, 1965b.

[4] Pittman and Olah, 1965b.

[5] Colter, Schuster and Kurland, 1965.

[6] Kurland, Schuster and Colter, 1965.

[7] MacLean and Mackor, 1962; Brouwer and Mackor, 1964; Brouwer, MacLean and Mackor, 1965.

frequency separation of the signals due to the individual species, it is then possible to evaluate the rate constants and activation energies of such processes. In some cases the two "isomers" may be chemically identical (in the absence of isotope labelling), as for the rearrangement

$$(CH_3)_2\overset{+}{C}.CH_2.CH_3 \rightleftharpoons CH_3.CH_2.\overset{+}{C}(CH_3)_2$$

$$(2.4a) \qquad\qquad (2.4b)$$

At low temperatures the spectrum of **2.4** contains two separate resonances which are due to the two non-equivalent kinds of methyl groups. Each of these is split into a triplet by spin-coupling with the two protons of the methylene group, but above $-20°$ the triplets broaden since the above reaction places each of the methyl groups alternately in α- and β-positions relative to the carbonium centre. From this effect the rate constant of the rearrangement has been found to be $k = 5 \times 10^{12} \exp(-14, 300/RT)$.[1] Even higher rearrangement rates should lead also to merging of the two methyl resonances. A wide range of rates of rearrangement is found even within a family of closely related carbonium ions, a result which requires more detailed study.[2]

The technique has also been applied to measurements of the rate of rearrangement (by intramolecular hydrogen migration) of the cation **2.5**, the proton adduct of hexamethylbenzene, and of the corresponding deuteron

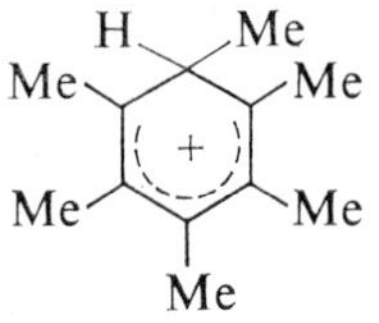

$$(2.5)$$

adduct of hexamethylbenzene to give the kinetic hydrogen isotope effect of the reaction.[3]

Similar effects of line-broadening and signal-collapse occur when a carbonium ion is in rapid proton-transfer equilibrium with the solvent, as in the reaction

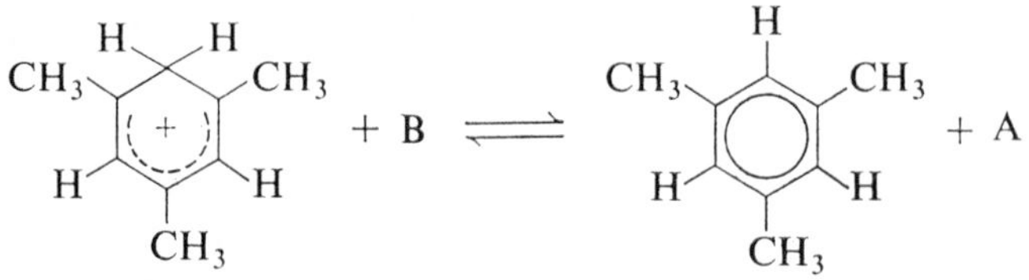

1 Brouwer and Mackor, 1964.
2 M. Saunders, Schleyer and Olah, 1964; Brouwer, MacLean and Mackor, 1965.
3 Mackor and MacLean, 1964.

where B is a basic species of the solvent and A is an acidic one.[1] Likewise, chloride exchange between triarylmethyl chloride and triarylmethyl cation can lead to line-broadening at low temperatures in methylene chloride solution.[2]

The NMR technique is suitable for following the progress of slow reactions of carbonium ions (such as rearrangements or deuterium uptake) by the observation of spectral changes over a period of time.[3] NMR measurements can also be used after the fashion of conductimetric titrations to establish the stoichiometry of rapidly reversible chemical reactions. For example, if acid is gradually added to a strong base, there is a systematic displacement of the position of the resonances which stops when one equivalent of acid has been added. This behaviour indicates (a) that the base is strong, so that its conversion to the conjugate acid is analytically complete when acid is added, (b) that the interconversion of the base and its conjugate acid is rapid, so that a single set of signals is obtained from a mixture of the two species in solution, their positions being given by the weighted means of the positions of the resonances of the separate forms, and (c) that the reaction involves one equivalent of acid per molecule of organic compound.[4] In many carbonium ion-forming reactions these conditions may not be met.

The fast interconversion of isomeric carbonium ions (as that between **2.4a** and **2.4b**) is easily confused with the formation of an ion of intermediate structure. The difficulty is resolved if lowering of the temperature reduces the rate of isomerization sufficiently for the observation of the spectra of the separate, isomeric ions. To the examples already cited we can add work on the dianisylnorbornyl cation formed by solution of **2.6** ($R = p$-MeO.C_6H_4) in strong acid. Alternative structures discussed for this ion included the symmetrical bridged structure **2.7** as well as the pair of unsymmetrical equilibrating ions **2.8**. At ordinary temperatures the NMR spectrum indicates equivalence of the two anisyl groups, but at $-70°C$ the spectrum accords with either of the unsymmetrical structures implied by the two chemically equivalent formulae **2.8a** and **2.8b**.[5]

Close relatives of the ions formed by protonation of aromatic hydrocarbons (**2.1**) are represented by the anthracene derivatives **2.9** and **2.10**.[6] The ion **2.9** is formed by protonation of the corresponding carbonyl compound **2.11** in sulphuric acid; **2.10** is produced by loss of the OD group from **2.12** in SO_2-SbF_5 mixture at $-55°C$. The evidence rests on the detailed analysis of NMR spectra. A notable feature of these is the chemical shift of the protons of the

[1] MacLean and Mackor, 1961, 1962; Birchall and Gillespie, 1964.
[2] Freedman, Young and Sandel, 1964.
[3] Deno, Friedman *et al.*, 1963.
[4] Meuche and Heilbronner, 1962.
[5] Schleyer, Kleinfelter and Richey, 1963.
[6] Eberson and Winstein, 1965.

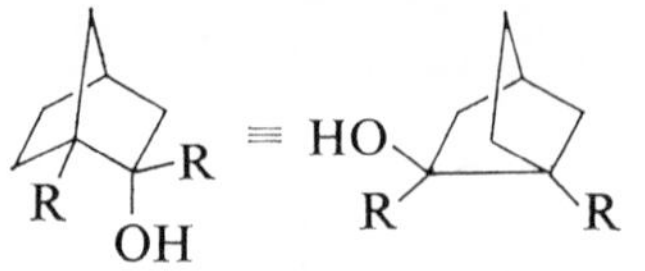

(2.6) 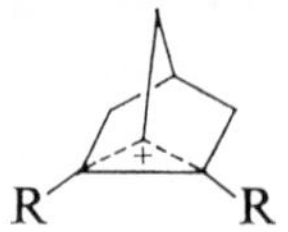   (2.7)

(2.8a)   (2.8b)

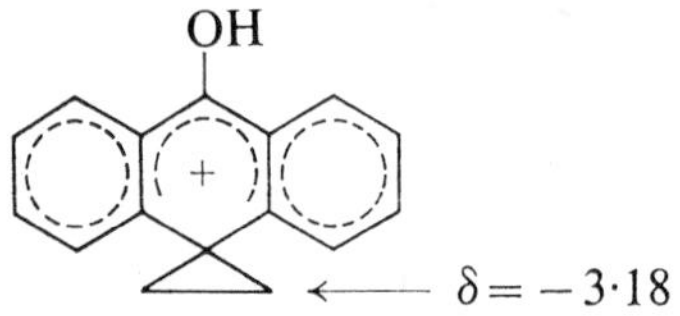

$\delta = -3\cdot18$ $\delta = -3\cdot44$

(2.9) 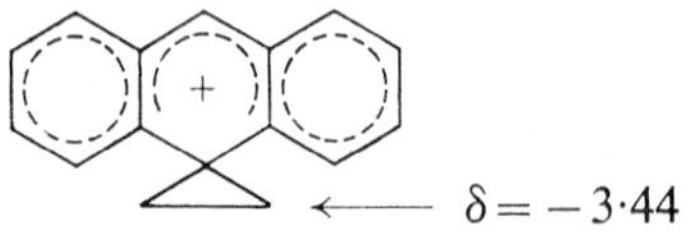   (2.10)

$\delta = -1\cdot84$ $\delta = -1\cdot20$

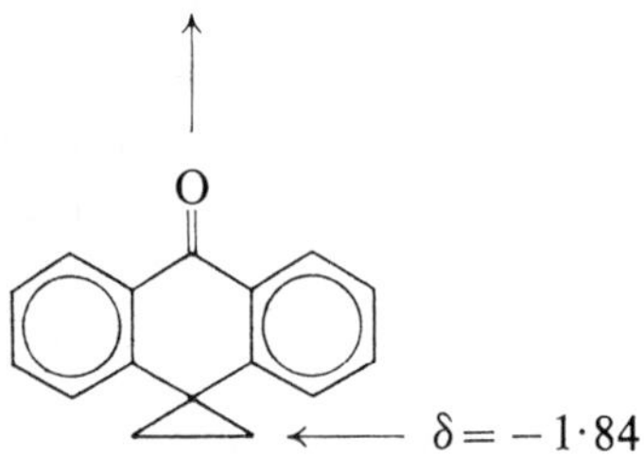

(2.11) 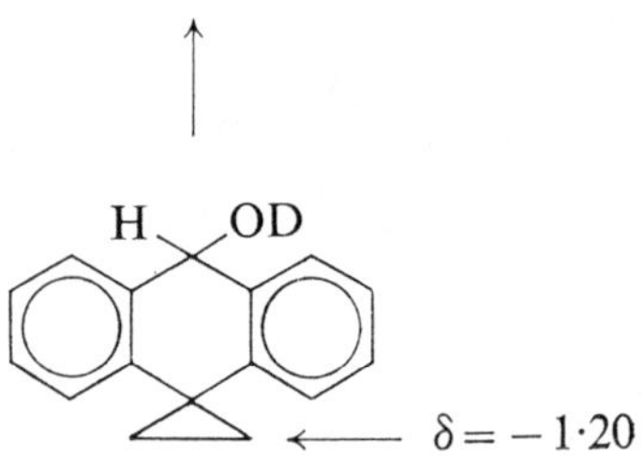   (2.12)

cyclopropane ring which undergoes a large and apparently characteristic change on formation of the cation. The NMR spectra also support the bridged

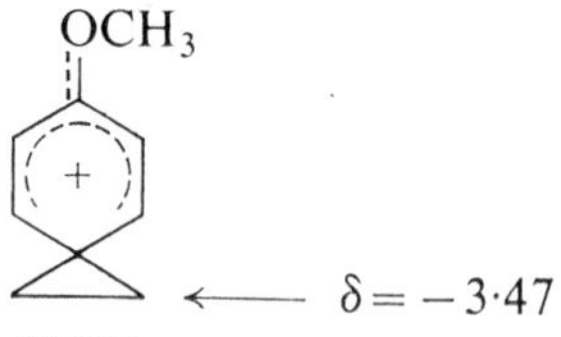

$\delta = -3\cdot47$

(2.13)

structure 2.13 for the ion formed from p-methoxyphenylethyl chloride in SbF_5-SO_2 at $-70°$, and the analogous structure for the corresponding mesityl compound.[1] (However, contrary to an earlier report,[2] similar bridged ions

[1] Olah, Namanworth et al., 1967.
[2] Olah and Pittman, 1965b.

have not so far been detected by NMR in systems where an unsubstituted phenyl group would occupy the bridging position. Both the chemical evidence and the NMR spectrum suggest that the species formed by reaction of 3-phenyl-2-butanol in SO_2-SbF_5-FSO_3H mixture at low temperatures is doubly charged and contains a protonated OH-group.[1])

An even more complex structure analysis by NMR spectroscopy is that of the 7-norbornadienyl cation[2] (see Chapter 7).

The chemical shift values of protons and other nuclei in carbonium ions are of interest not only because of their application to the elucidation of structures but also because they measure the screening of the nuclei. In the absence of special factors the proton chemical shift (δ) can be approximately represented as a linear function of the charge density (ρ) at the neighbouring carbon atom, i.e. $\Delta\delta = k\Delta\rho$ where $\Delta\delta$ is the difference between the chemical shift in the ion and in a related neutral species.[3] The proportionality constant k is found to have a value in the region of -10 p.p.m. per electronic charge. An analogous expression has been proposed for the chemical shifts of the protons of methyl groups attached to the seat of the cationic charge, with a k-value of about -3 to -5 p.p.m. per electronic charge.[4] These relations have been applied to discussions of the distribution of the cationic charge in carbonium ions (see Chapter 5).

The correlation of chemical shifts with charge densities cannot be applied blindly and several reservations have been voiced regarding this use of NMR data. The theory of chemical shifts is too complex as yet to be applied rigorously to large molecules and, for this reason, it is at present important to restrict comparison to protons in chemically similar surroundings. Under such conditions the differences in chemical shift are more likely to reflect a change in electron density than when there are changes in chemical environment close to the proton concerned. Such changes do, of course, occur for protons near the carbonium centre as a result of conformational adjustments during the ionization of an alkyl fluoride, say. On similar grounds one would suspect detailed comparison of proton chemical shifts in triphenylmethyl and diphenylmethyl cations unless there is explicit consideration of the effect of the neighbouring phenyl group and its angle of tilt.[5] In this particular case the resonances of protons in *p*-positions are probably more easily linked with charge densities than those in *o*- or *m*-positions.[6] Support for this view also comes from the study of ^{19}F-resonances in triphenylmethyl cations of the

[1] Olah, Pittman *et al.*, 1966a; Brookhart, Anet and Winstein, 1966; Brookhart, Anet *et al.*, 1966.

[2] Story, Snyder *et al.*, 1963.

[3] Fraenkel, Carter *et al.*, 1960; Musher, 1962; Schaefer and Schneider, 1963; see also Schug and Deck, 1962; Seiffert, Zimmermann and Scheibe, 1962.

[4] MacLean and Mackor, 1961; Katz and Gold, 1964.

[5] See also Breslow, Höver and Chang, 1962.

[6] Farnum, 1964.

general formula **2.14**[1] where again the nucleus probed is well removed from

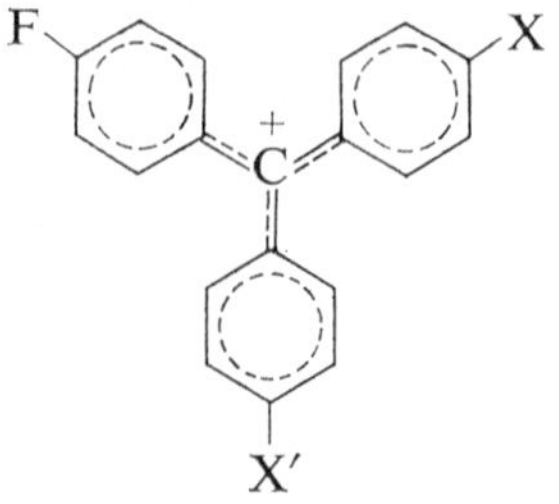

(2.14)

the direct screening effect of the groups X and X′. The chemical shift of the ^{19}F resonance is related to the effect of the groups X and X′ on the stability (as determined by EMF measurements, see Paragraph 2.5.3) of the corresponding carbonium ions without the fluorine substituent. If the expected connexion between charge dispersal and stability applies (see Section 5.1), these results then provide justification of the use of ^{19}F screening constants as a measure of charge density. It is also reassuring that the fluorine shifts are in this case independent of the nature of the solvent used. In general, this possibility presents a problem, though it does not appear to be a serious one for triarylmethyl cations. A related question concerns the possible magnetic anisotropy resulting from ion pairing (Section 5.3).[2]

Some illustrative values of proton chemical shifts are listed in Tables 2.1 and 2.2.

Proton resonance spectra of carbonium ions show relatively large coupling constants (J_{HH}) between methylene and methyl groups separated by the carbonium centre: J_{HH} amounts to *ca.* 7 Hz for the grouping $(CH_3)_2\overset{+}{C}.CH_2—$.[3] This finding can perhaps be rationalized in terms of what is known about the dependence of coupling constants on dihedral angles,[4] since the carbonium grouping is planar. Another contributory cause could be the raised bond order between the C—C bonds as a result of hyperconjugation (see Paragraphs 2.3.2 and 5.2.6).

The formation of carbonium ions can also be detected by NMR signals from the counter-ion. A good example is provided by the ^{19}F resonance from solutions of antimony pentafluoride complexes of acyl or alkyl fluorides in sulphur dioxide solution. The (single) fluorine resonance is shifted to a position characteristic of SbF_6^-: it follows that the organic portion of the solute

[1] Taft and McKeever, 1965; see also Taft, 1960a.
[2] Ng and Adam, 1964.
[3] Olah, Baker *et al.*, 1964.
[4] Karplus, 1959.

must carry the balancing cationic charge. Systems studied in this way include $Ph_3C^+SbF_6^-$ and analogous salts of alkyl cations.[1] Further support of this conclusion comes from the disappearance of H–F coupling which can be observed in alkyl fluorides of appropriate structure.

Table 2.1. *Proton chemical shifts (p.p.m. from TMS[a]) in aliphatic carbonium ions and related uncharged species in SbF$_5$ solution at ca. 1°C[b]*

Species	$\overset{+}{C}$—H or CF—H	C^+—CH_2 or CF—CH_2	C^+—CH_3 or CF—CH_3	C^+—C—CH_3 or CF—C—CH_3
$(CH_3)_3C^+$	—	—	−4·35	—
$(CH_3)_3CF$	—	—	−1·30	—
$(CH_3)_2\overset{+}{C}H$	−13·5	—	−5·06	—
$(CH_3)_2CHF$	−4·64	—	−1·23	—
$(CH_3)_2C^+ . CH_2 . CH_3$	—	−4·93	−4·50	−2·27
$(CH_3)_2CF . CH_2 . CH_3$	—	−1·85	−1·55	−1·25

[a] TMS = tetramethylsilane.
[b] Olah, Baker *et al.*, 1964.

Table 2.2 *Proton chemical shifts (p.p.m. from TMS) of phenylalkyl cations in SO$_2$-SbF$_5$ solution at −30°C[a]*

| Ion | C^+—CH_3 or C^+—H | Aromatic CH | | |
		ortho	*meta*	*para*
$C_6H_5C^+(CH_3)_2$	−3·60	−7·95	−8·87	−8·56
$(C_6H_5)_2C^+CH_3$	−3·70	−7·53	−7·96	−8·12
$(C_6H_5)_3C^{+b}$	—	−7·01	−7·51	−7·76
$(C_6H_5)_2C^+H$	−9·8	−7·92	−8·49	−8·37

[a] Olah, 1964.
[b] $Ph_3C^+SbF_6^-$ in SO_2.

The ^{11}B resonance from the BI_4^- ion has been similarly used to infer the formation of carbonium ions as tetraiodoborate salts.[2]

Observation of ^{13}C resonance promises to become a good method for investigating the position of the positive charge in a carbonium ion. Whereas in proton resonance spectroscopy one is observing a nucleus attached to the carbonium centre, ^{13}C resonance can probe the centre itself. The method at

[1] Olah, Baker *et al.*, 1964; Olah, Tolgyesi *et al.*, 1963.
[2] Harmon and Cummings, 1962.

present entails heavy enrichment of the compound with ^{13}C and a double resonance technique to allow the signal to be detected for a dilute solution.[1] The value of the proton-^{13}C spin coupling-constant is thought to be proportional to the percentage s-character of the carbon atom and this has been used to demonstrate the sp^2 hybridization of the carbonium centre in the ions $(CH_3)_2{}^{13}CH^+$ and $(C_6H_5)_2{}^{13}CH^+$.[2]

2.3.2 INFRARED SPECTRA

The infrared spectra of several solutions thought to contain simple aliphatic cations have been recorded.[3] To test their significance, normal co-ordinate calculations have been carried out for the t-butyl, isopropyl and t-pentyl cations on the basis of assumed molecular models and force constants. Comparison of observed and calculated spectra shows that, even at this early stage of the investigation, the main observed features of the spectra can be explained in terms of the model calculations. The frequency assignment arrived at on the basis of the calculations implies that C—H stretching fundamentals are exceptionally low in frequency (2730–2830 cm^{-1}) and that the asymmetrical C—C—C stretching mode is exceptionally high in frequency (1260–1295 cm^{-1}). This is not unreasonable on the view that the ions are stabilized by hyperconjugation (see Paragraph 5.2.6) which, in the case of the t-butyl cation, would imply contributions from nine equivalent

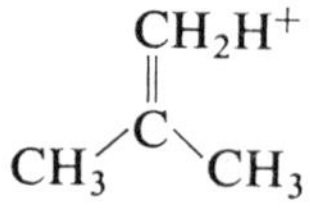

$$CH_2H^+$$
$$\|$$
$$CH_3 \diagup C \diagdown CH_3$$

(2.15)

structures (2.15) and which would evidently result in weakened C—H and strengthened C—C bonding. However, a note of caution must be sounded since part of the C—C—C frequency increase is due to the planarity of the ions.[3]

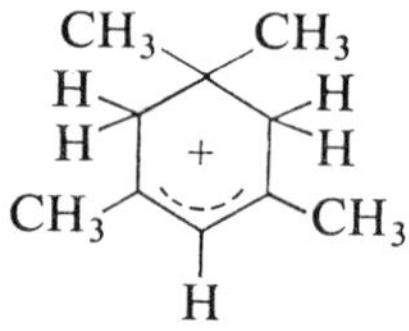

$$
\begin{array}{c}
CH_3 \diagdown \diagup CH_3 \\
H \diagdown \diagup H \\
H \diagdown + \diagup H \\
CH_3 \diagup \diagdown CH_3 \\
H
\end{array}
$$

(2.16)

[1] Olah, Tolgyesi *et al.*, 1963; Olah, Baker and Comisarow, 1964.
[2] Olah and Comisarow, 1966a.
[3] Olah, Baker *et al.*, 1964.

Spectra of more complicated ions, e.g. the cyclohexenyl cation **2.16**,[1] can also be observed in the infrared.

2.3.3 ELECTRONIC SPECTRA

Since their colour is the most striking property of a large number of carbonium ions, it is not surprising that very many electronic (ultraviolet and visible) spectra of carbonium ions have been recorded. For structure elucidation these spectra have so far proved considerably less helpful than, in particular, NMR spectra, since the exact prediction of electronic spectra of complex species in solution is not yet possible.

An exception to this rather negative statement is provided by cases in which absorption measurements are supplemented by polarization measurements on fluorescence spectra, when information about molecular symmetry can be obtained. Such a study provided definite evidence concerning the symmetry of the triphenylmethyl and the trixenylmethyl[2] cation.[3]

In other cases of conjugated cations it is possible to make an approximate prediction of the position of electronic transitions by calculations of π-electron energy levels. Such calculations have been used to support chemical inferences concerning the identity of ions but rarely in a more diagnostic fashion. There has been much interest in the calculation of electronic spectra of protonated azulene and related cations.[4]

An extreme example of the difficulties one may meet is provided by the intense absorption band at 293 ± 2 mμ ($\epsilon \sim 6400$) reported for solutions of t-butyl alcohol and isobutene in concentrated sulphuric acid solution.[5] This was originally attributed to the t-butyl cation, and later work[6] (on $Me_3C^+SbF_6^-$) suggested (but did not prove) that this ion does indeed have an absorption band centred at that wavelength but with a much lower extinction coefficient (~ 500). However, it is now known that, in FSO_3H-SbF_5 solution at $-65°$, there is no absorption at all above 210 mμ.[7] Alternative proposals for the source of the intense absorption in sulphuric acid solution (or at least part of that absorption) included the isobutenyl cation[5,8] $CH_2\!=\!C(CH_3)\!-\!CH_2^+$, and the butenyl cation,[8] $CH_3\!-\!CH\!=\!CH\!-\!CH_2^+$, produced by oxidation, the cyclohexyl cation[8] (derived from the cyclohexane solvent used in the experiments), a mixture of alkenyl cations[9] and a mixture of methylated cyclo-

---

[1] Deno, Richey *et al.*, 1962a.
[2] Xenyl = *p*-biphenylyl.
[3] Chu and Weissman, 1954; see also Ng and Adam, 1964.
[4] See, e.g., Meier, Meuche and Heilbronner, 1962.
[5] Rosenbaum and Symons, 1960.
[6] Olah, Baker *et al.*, 1964.
[7] Olah and Pittman, 1966; Olah, Pittman *et al.*, 1966a.
[8] Leftin, 1962.
[9] Deno, 1964a.

pentenyl and cyclohexenyl cations.[1] A condensation product with acetic acid is considered to be responsible for the absorption of t-butyl alcohol or iso-butene in acetic acid-sulphuric acid mixture.[2] It is impossible to reject any of these suggestions from the appearance of the spectra though, for chemical reasons, some seem less probable than others. Similar difficulties arise in connection with benzyl cations.[3]

Occasionally, the similarity between spectra of different solutes may be so striking as to suggest far-reaching similarity in structure. One such case is presented by the species formed on dissolution of 1,1-diphenylethylene and anthracene in concentrated sulphuric acid.[4] These spectra are very similar despite the profound difference between the spectra of the parent compounds in inert solvents. This suggests that the two species in sulphuric acid are carbonium ions produced by protonation of the parent molecule and possessing structures **2.17** and **2.18**, both of which have the conjugated system of the diphenylmethyl cation indicated. Predictably, the correspondence of the spectra is even closer between 1,1-diphenylethylene and 9-methylanthracene[5] (which is expected to produce the ion **2.19**).

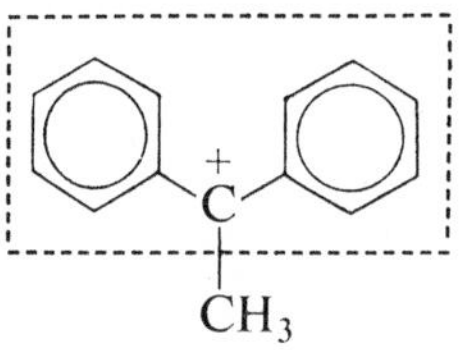

(2.17) 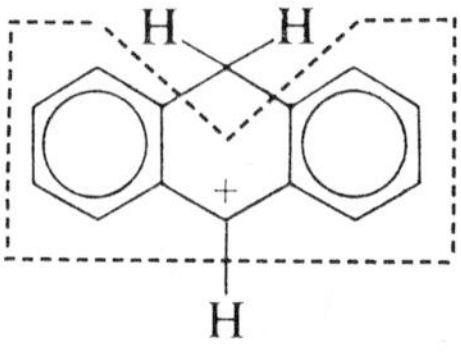   (2.18) 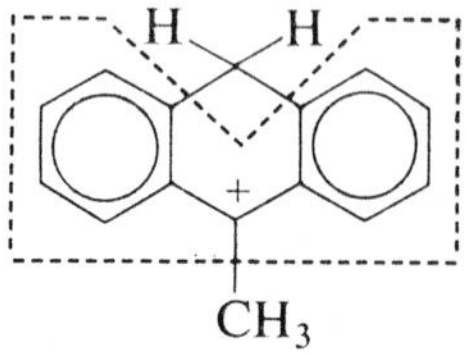   (2.19)

It is obvious that the observation of both NMR and electronic spectra of the same solutions has made the attribution of ultraviolet bands to certain species much more reliable.[6] Some ultraviolet-spectral data which have been confirmed by NMR in this manner are given in Table 2.3.

Because of the intense light absorption by organic chromophores in the visible and ultraviolet regions of the spectrum, the intensity of light absorption can be accurately determined for quite dilute solutions. This fact, coupled with the knowledge that the spectral position of the absorption is characteristic of the solute, lies at the basis of all uses of indicators in homogeneous solution. It has also been extensively applied to the study of indicator equilibria involving carbonium ions, such as

$$Ph_3C\!-\!OH + H^+ \rightleftharpoons Ph_3C^+ + H_2O$$

[1] Deno, Richey et al., 1962b.
[2] Finch and Symons, 1965.
[3] Olah and Pittman, 1966.
[4] Gold and Tye, 1952a.
[5] Grace and Symons, 1959.
[6] Olah, Baker et al., 1964.

and $\qquad$ $Ph_2C{=}CH_2 + H^+ \rightleftharpoons Ph_2\overset{+}{C}.CH_3$

and hence to the quantitative study of solvent acidity (usually expressed as "acidity functions").[1] As far as the chemistry of carbonium ions is concerned, the importance of the measurements lies in the fact that ionization ratios (in

Table 2.3. *Ultraviolet absorption maxima of representative simple carbonium ions $RR'R''C^+$ in FSO_3H-SbF_5 solution*[a]

R	R'	R''	$\lambda_{max}(m\mu)$	$10^{-3}\epsilon$
Ph	Ph	Ph	429	38·7
			403	38·7
Ph	Ph	Ph—C⫶C—	504	36·9
			449	26·6
Ph	Ph	cyclo-C_6H_{11}	427	36·1
			338	17·1
Ph	Ph	cyclo-C_4H_7	388	6·75
			335	22·9
Ph	Ph	cyclo-Pr	435	30·1
			358	8·36
			319	10·35
Ph	Ph	iso-Pr	422	29·5
			322	18·8
Ph	Ph	Et	427	27·6
			316	11·8
Ph	Ph	Me	422	37·0
			312	11·05
Ph	Ph	CF_3	485	21·5
			331	4·3
Ph	Ph	H	440	38·0
			292	2·9
Ph	Me	cyclo-C_6H_{11}	394	0·99
			347·5	22·3
Ph	Me	cyclo-C_4H_7	382	6·0
			334	22·0
Ph	Me	cyclo-Pr	404	2·14
			316	15·2
Ph	Me	Et	397	1·32
			321	10·2
Ph	Me	Me	390	1·4
			326	11·0
Ph	Me	CF_3	347	3·4
Ph	H	cyclo-Pr	343	18·0
Me	Me	cyclo-Pr	289	10·8
cyclo-Pr	cyclo-Pr	H	273	12·2
cyclo-Pr	cyclo-Pr	cyclo-Pr	270	22·6

[a] Olah, Pittman *et al.*, 1966a.

[1] For reviews see Paul and Long, 1957; Deno, 1964c.

particular those of the general type $[Ar_3C^+]/[Ar_3C.OH]$), for different indicators of the same family in the same medium, lead to equilibrium constants, such as those for the reactions

$$Ar_3C.OH + Ar_3'C^+ \rightleftharpoons Ar_3'C.OH + Ar_3C^+$$

2.4 Colligative Properties

The freezing-point depression of organic solutes in sulphuric acid has been the most useful of these properties (see the review by Gillespie and Leisten[1]). Solutions of triarylmethanols in sulphuric acid were found in this way to contain four solute particles per molecule of alcohol dissolved ($\nu=4$).[2] Similarly, tricyclopropylmethanol gives initially a four-fold depression.[3] The technique allows this mode of reaction, which gives rise to a carbonium ion,

$$ROH + 2H_2SO_4 \rightarrow R^+ + H_3O^+ + 2HSO_4^- \qquad \nu = 4$$

to be distinguished from alternative processes, such as

$$ROH + H_2SO_4 \rightarrow ROH_2^+ + HSO_4^- \qquad \nu = 2$$

$$ROH + 2H_2SO_4 \rightarrow RHSO_4 + H_3O^+ + HSO_4^- \qquad \nu = 3$$

A two-fold freezing point depression is obtained with tertiary aliphatic alcohols; the three-fold depression is characteristic of freshly prepared solutions of other aliphatic alcohols.[4] Other complications, such as sulphonation of an aromatic ring of the solute, or polymerization, may likewise be detected by the value or stability of the freezing-point depression. In cases where sulphonation is troublesome, methanesulphonic acid may be a better solvent for cryoscopy.[5] The formation of a carbonium ion by protonation of $Ph_2C{=}CH_2$ ($\nu = 2$) was also first inferred from cryoscopic measurements in sulphuric acid.[6]

2.5 Electrolyte Behaviour

2.5.1 CONDUCTIVITY MEASUREMENTS

Because of their electrolyte nature it is possible to measure the conductivity of carbonium salts and to obtain information about dissociation equilibria in this way. Liquid sulphur dioxide has been the solvent most extensively used for this purpose (see Section 1.4. The more recent work is reviewed in detail by

[1] Gillespie and Leisten, 1954.
[2] Hantzsch, 1922 and earlier papers; Hammett and Deyrup, 1933; Newman, Craig and Garrett, 1949; Newman and Deno, 1951a.
[3] Deno, Richey et al., 1962b.
[4] Hantzsch, 1907, 1908; Oddo and Scandola, 1909; Newman, Craig and Garrett, 1949; Gillespie, 1959.
[5] Craig, Garrett and Newman, 1950.
[6] A. G. Evans, 1951; Gold, Hawes and Tye, 1952.

Lichtin[1]). Sulphur dioxide is eminently suitable because of its good ionizing power despite a comparatively low dielectric constant ($D = 15$) and because it does not undergo irreversible reactions with carbonium ions. In its ionizing power it is far superior to nitrobenzene ($D = 35$),[2] one of the other solvents that have been used, although $Ph_3C^+BF_4^-$ is said to be a strong electrolyte in nitrobenzene.[3] However, even electrolytes which are ionic in the crystalline state are partially associated into ion pairs in sulphur dioxide solution, and one must therefore admit the same possibility to electrolytes which can exist in covalent form, such as triarylmethyl halides. The repercussions of this effect on the quantitative interpretation of conductivity data were first pointed out by Ziegler and Wollschitt.[4] They are discussed in Paragraph 4.1.4.

It should also be possible to determine transport numbers of carbonium salts and hence ionic mobilities of carbonium ions in various solvents, but no such measurements have so far been reported. However, it is known that in sulphuric acid as solvent the mobility of the hydrogen sulphate ion greatly exceeds that of all cations that have been examined,[5] and therefore the conductivities of solutions in sulphuric acid can be used to establish the concentration of hydrogen sulphate ions. Such measurements thus throw light on the nature of the reaction that occurs when a substance is dissolved in sulphuric acid and, in this respect, resemble cryoscopy in sulphuric acid. Alternatively, if the chemical change involved in the solution process is not in doubt, the conductivity measurements can be used to obtain its equilibrium constant.[6] This technique does not seem as yet to have been applied to solutes that give rise to carbonium ions in solution.

Similarly, in formic acid solution most of the current is transported by the formate ion,[7] and conductance values of solutions of bases in this solvent can again be used to establish the nature of the ionization. Because formic acid is much weaker than sulphuric acid, measurements in this solvent are chiefly of interest for carbon bases of exceptionally high basicity. The method has been used to show that azulene dissolves in formic acid with formation of a univalent cation.[8]

2.5.2 ELECTROLYSIS

The view (first expressed by Gomberg in 1902) of the ionic nature of the conducting solutions of triarylmethyl halides in sulphur dioxide suggested that

[1] Lichtin, 1963.
[2] E. Price and Lichtin, 1960.
[3] Aléonard, 1958.
[4] Ziegler and Wollschitt, 1930.
[5] Hammett and Lowenheim, 1934; Gillespie and Wasif, 1953a.
[6] Gillespie and Wasif, 1953b.
[7] Schlesinger and Bunting, 1919.
[8] Plattner, Heilbronner and Weber, 1952.

it might be possible to electrolyse such solutions to obtain the radicals corresponding to the carbonium ions. Successful experiments along these lines were reported in detail many years ago.[1] The radicals formed may dimerize to give hexa-arylethanes. The value of the equilibrium constant of the dissociation of the corresponding hexa-arylethane into triarylmethyl radicals determines the extent of dimerization.

2.5.3 EMF MEASUREMENTS

Galvanic cells can be devised which involve the process

$$R^+ + e^- \rightleftharpoons \tfrac{1}{2}R_2$$

as a half-cell reaction. Early EMF measurements were carried out with chloranil reference electrodes in acetic acid as solvent, with the aim of obtaining quantitative information about the related processes[2]

$$Ph_3C^+ + e^- \rightarrow Ph_3C\cdot$$

and

$$Ph_3C\text{—}OH + e^- \rightarrow Ph_3C\cdot + OH^-$$

The measurements included potentiometric redox titrations of carbonium ions with chromous and vanadous salts.

Basic organic substances with a strong tendency towards carbonium ion formation reduce the acidity of a medium and can therefore be titrated potentiometrically with acid by use of an indicator electrode which responds to the acidity. The glass electrode is suitable for such titrations of basic alcohols with perchloric acid in glacial acetic acid.[3] Similar potentiometric titrations have also been peformed in other solvents[4] (see Paragraph 4.1.5).

The most promising experimental arrangement uses the cell

$$Pt|R_2, R^+BF_4^-, CH_3CN(solvent) \vdots AgNO_3, CH_3CN(solvent)|Ag$$

in which the liquid junction is made through an asbestos fibre.[5] Results obtained by this technique are given in Table 4.14 (Paragraph 4.1.7).

2.5.4 POLAROGRAPHY

Several workers have recorded polarographic observations of the reduction of carbonium ions, but the nature of the reduction process appears sometimes to be complex and the interpretation of the corresponding half-wave potentials

[1] Schlenk, Weickel and Herzenstein, 1910.
[2] Conant, Small and Taylor, 1925; Conant and Chow, 1933.
[3] Rennhard, Di Modica et al., 1957.
[4] Breslow, Höver and Chang, 1962.
[5] Jenson and Taft, 1964.

is correspondingly complicated. The two waves observed in the polarographic reduction of triphenylmethanol in methanesulphonic acid in the presence of some water have been attributed to the one-electron and two-electron processes[1]

$$Ph_3C^+ + e^- \rightarrow Ph_3C\cdot \rightarrow \tfrac{1}{2}Ph_3C\text{---}CPh_3$$

and

$$Ph_3C^+ + 2e^- \rightarrow Ph_3C^- \xrightarrow{H^+} Ph_3C\text{---}H$$

respectively. In the absence of water, only the two-electron process takes place, but at high concentrations of water the first wave is split into two or three steps. The chemical explanation of this behaviour is not altogether clear.

The preparation of cycloheptatrienyl cations prompted polarographic investigations of their stability in relation to other carbonium ions.[2] For similar reasons, the polarographic reduction of substituted cyclopropenyl cations was studied and the results confirmed the high thermodynamic stability of these carbonium ions.[3] This investigation employed the same solvent (acetonitrile) and reference electrode (silver/silver nitrate) that were later successfully used in EMF studies of carbonium ions[4] (Paragraph 2.5.3).

Whilst these investigations have established the practicability of the technique, as well as its difficulties, the method has not as yet produced a substantial body of coherent data.

2.6 Reaction Kinetics

The formation of an unstable intermediate can be inferred from a detailed analysis of reaction kinetics. The degree of conviction which this method carries generally depends on the range of kinetic phenomena and compounds for which a consistent mechanistic picture emerges. In this respect the method may properly be compared to the classical methods of structure determination of organic compounds by degradation and synthesis, where it was long recognized that a structure could not properly be assigned on the evidence of a single reaction. However, kinetic evidence is rarely allowed to stand entirely on its own. The postulation of an unstable intermediate is frequently made more plausible by experiments that show that small changes of structure or of experimental conditions allow the intermediate to be stabilized sufficiently for its presence to be detected by one of the methods described in Sections 2.3 and 2.4. The following discussion of this section is exclusively directed towards one single aspect of the kinetic method, the detection of carbonium ions.

[1] Wawzonek, Berkey and Thomson, 1956.
[2] Vol'pin, Zhdanov and Kursanov, 1957; Zhdanov and Frumkin, 1958; Zhdanov, 1958; Zuman, Chodkowski et al., 1958.
[3] Breslow, Bahary and Reinmuth, 1961.
[4] Jenson and Taft, 1964.

2.6.1 MECHANISTIC CLASSIFICATION

The methodology of the purely kinetic approach to organic ionization reactions in the liquid phase was systematized by Hughes and Ingold with reference to the reactions of alkyl halides.[1] In this case the tests are largely concerned with the distinction between the bimolecular, associative mechanism (S_N2) in which co-ordination of the entering substituent is synchronous with the detachment of the leaving group, as in

$$\overset{-}{Y} + R—X \rightarrow [Y\ldots\overset{-}{R}\ldots X]^{\ddagger} \rightarrow X^- + R—Y \qquad (2.1)$$
$$\text{transition state}$$

and the unimolecular, dissociative mechanism (S_N1) in which detachment precedes attachment so that a carbonium ion intermediate is involved, as in

$$R—X \rightleftarrows R^+ + X^- \xrightarrow[+Y^-]{} X^- + R—Y \qquad (2.2)$$

There is evidence in some bimolecular substitutions that the attachment may even precede the severance of the R—X bond but this mechanistic detail of S_N2 reactions is not germane to the present discussion.

The mechanistic criteria that have been applied to this problem on the basis of kinetic studies can roughly be divided into two categories: (a) evidence derived from the examination of the kinetic rate laws of reactions, and (b) the effects of structural or other variations in the systems studied upon reaction velocities. There is some overlap between these two categories since structural and other variations may also affect the kinetic reaction orders. The detailed study of rate laws of substitution reactions affords more certainty and insight regarding the generation of carbonium ions as reaction intermediates. On the other hand, it is true that the measurement of reaction velocities without the close study of kinetic details is a much easier task and more information is therefore available under heading (b). However, such studies would not today be performed with the object of establishing the formation of carbonium ions and, for this reason, we defer their consideration to Section 4.3.

Strictly speaking, the rate of formation of a carbonium ion—important though it is to the subject-matter of this book—is not a property of the carbonium ion, but a property of the parent molecule and of the transition state leading from it to the carbonium ion (see, however, Paragraph 4.2.1).

2.6.2 RATE LAWS

The rate-limiting step of a chemical reaction involving carbonium ions as reactive intermediates is usually that in which the carbonium ion is formed. In certain circumstances, however, detailed examination of such reactions can yield information about the carbonium ion-consuming steps. Consider a

[1] Hughes, 1941; Ingold, 1953.

reaction in which a free carbonium ion is formed by a process which is at least in principle reversible, viz.:

$$RX_1 \underset{k_1}{\overset{k_d}{\rightleftarrows}} R^+ + X_1 \tag{2.3a}$$

$$R^+ + X_2 \overset{k_2}{\longrightarrow} P_2; \quad R^+ + X_i \overset{k_i}{\longrightarrow} P_i, \text{ etc.} \tag{2.3b}$$

This formulation is more general than Equation (2.2) by allowing for more than a single path for the further reaction of the carbonium ion (other than by recombination with X_1). The parallel routes for the destruction of the carbonium ion are written as involving a series of competing nucleophilic entities $X_1, X_2 \ldots X_i$, with respective rate constants $k_1, k_2 \ldots k_i$. The first of these, X_1, is the anion of the group initially combined with the carbonium ion in the species RX_1. Assuming that the concentration of R^+ is always small compared with the concentrations of other species and applying the steady-state hypothesis, we have

$$-\frac{d[RX_1]}{dt} = \frac{d\sum[P_i]}{dt} = \frac{k_d[RX_1] \sum_{i=2}^{i} k_i[X_i]}{k_1[X_1] + \sum_{i=2}^{i} k_i[X_i]} \tag{2.4}$$

This may be rewritten

$$-\frac{d[RX_1]}{dt} = \frac{k_d[RX_1]}{(k_1[X_1]/\sum_{i=2}^{i} k_i[X_i]) + 1} \tag{2.5}$$

Three experimentally distinguishable situations may arise, depending on the relative magnitude of the two terms in the denominator. For convenience, we shall refer to the dimensionless quantity

$$k_1[X_1]/\sum_{i=2}^{i} k_i[X_i]$$

as the selectivity, S, of the carbonium ion.

(i) $S \ll 1$ throughout the reaction:

$$-\frac{d[RX_1]}{dt} = k_d[RX_1] \tag{2.6}$$

Carbonium-ion formation [step (2.3a)] alone is rate-limiting, a simple first order kinetic law is obeyed, and kinetic studies provide no information about the reactivity of the intermediate.

(ii) $S \gg 1$ throughout the reaction:

$$-\frac{d[RX_1]}{dt} = \frac{k_d[RX_1]}{k_1[X_1]} \sum_{i=2}^{i} k_i[X_i] \tag{2.7}$$

Carbonium-ion destruction as well as formation is now kinetically important.

This situation is usually designated S_N2C^+, since the concentration of the nucleophiles involved now enters the kinetic equation, and the rate-limiting step is bimolecular reaction between the carbonium ion and nucleophiles [step (2.3b)].

(iii) S varies during the course of the reaction. If the value of k_1 is sufficiently large and the reaction medium contains little or no X_1 initially, then the magnitude of $k_1[X_1]$ and hence S may vary appreciably during the course of the disappearance of RX_1. Should S become comparable with or much greater than unity, then the simple first-order kinetic law [Equation (2.6)]— as in case (i)—will no longer be obeyed: the reaction rate will decrease more rapidly than expected on the basis of (i).

Both cases (ii) and (iii) are governed by kinetic equations explicitly containing rate constants for stages in which the carbonium ion is consumed. In favourable cases, kinetic studies can, therefore, provide these constants, generally as ratios.

Equation (2.3) assumes that a single nucleophilic reagent X_i will produce a single product P_i by reaction with the carbonium ion. This need not be the case: the attack of X_i on R^+ may result in several products (e.g. d- and l-isomers by attachment to a carbonium ion $RR'R''C^+$). These cases are included in the general scheme by allowing for the composite nature of k_i and X, i.e.

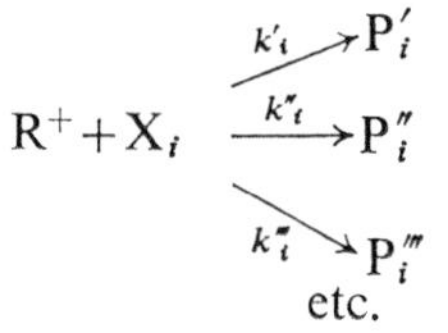

$$R^+ + X_i \quad \overset{k'_i}{\underset{k''_i}{\nearrow}} \begin{array}{l} P'_i \\ \xrightarrow{\;\;} P''_i \\ \searrow P'''_i \end{array}$$
$$\text{etc.}$$

so that

$$k_i = k'_i + k''_i + k'''_i \;\ldots$$

and

$$[P_i] = [P'_i] + [P''_i] + [P'''_i] \;\ldots$$

A further generalization would allow for different stoichiometries of product formation, e.g. steps of the type $R^+ + X_i \rightarrow 2P_i$; but, as we are not aware that any such reaction is actually known, this elaboration is unnecessary.

Some of the Equations [(2.4), (2.5) and (2.7)] will, of course, be simpler if only two nucleophilic entities need be considered, viz. the original X_1 and the nucleophile X_2 which gives rise to a product RX_2. In this case the sums

$$\sum_{i=2}^{i} k_i[X_i]$$

are replaced by the single term $k_2[X_2]$. The simpler equations are then

$$-\frac{d[RX_1]}{dt} = \frac{k_d k_2 [RX_1][X_2]}{k_1[X_1] + k_2[X_2]} \tag{2.4'}$$

and
$$-\frac{d[RX_1]}{dt} = \frac{k_d[RX_1]}{\dfrac{k_1[X_1]}{k_2[X_2]}+1} \tag{2.5'}$$

If X_2 is the solvent, its concentration is constant, and the ratio $k_1/k_2[X_2]$ can be treated as a constant parameter, frequently referred to as the "mass-law constant" and by the symbol α, i.e.

$$\frac{d[RX_1]}{dt} = \frac{k_d[RX_1]}{1+\alpha[X_1]}$$

The corresponding form of Equation (2.7) is then obtained by assuming $\alpha[X_1] \gg 1$, so that

$$\frac{d[RX_1]}{dt} = \frac{k_d[RX_1]}{\alpha[X_1]} \tag{2.7'}$$

Equations (2.4'), (2.5') and (2.7') are more familiar in appearance[1] but the rate constants of the steps of the mechanism have been labelled differently by different groups of workers.

The observable consequences of the various rate laws will now be considered.

The rate law (2.6) implies that the reaction velocity is the same as the rate of heterolysis of RX_1. The rate of disappearance of RX_1 should be the same irrespective of the number of reagents $X_2 \ldots X_i$ involved or their concentrations. In principle, this constitutes a clear test for the formation of an intermediate without participation of the entering group. In practice, this test and the inference to be drawn from it are frequently less straightforward. With substrates susceptible to attack by nucleophilic reagents, reaction often involves—intentionally or unintentionally, entirely or in part—the solvent as the substituting reagent. Examples of such reactions (known as solvolytic reactions or solvolyses) are the formation of alcohols or ethers from alkyl halides in aqueous or alcoholic solution. Since the reaction order with respect to a major component of the medium cannot be ascertained by the examination of the reaction order with respect to that component, the kinetic role of the entering group cannot be established and the rate law [Equation (2.6)] becomes indistinguishable from the rate law for a bimolecular process involving RX_1 and the solvent. To apply this test, it is therefore necessary for the substituting reagent to be present in low concentration, so that the kinetic order with respect to it can be established by changing its concentration. If a dependence on the concentration of X_2 is then not found the result may still not prove the applicability of Equation (2.6) to the reaction. It may happen that the low-concentration X_2 is less effective in the reaction than the solvent which is present in much higher concentration. To establish the S_N1 mechanism in these circumstances it is essential to prove that the product of the reaction is indeed RX_2 and not

[1] See, e.g., Hughes, 1941; Ingold, 1953; Streitwieser, 1956b; Bunton, 1963.

the solvolysis product.[1] Unhappily this test is not available where hydroxide ions in water are the nucleophilic reagent in question (or likewise for alkoxide ions in ethanol), since solute and solvent lead in these cases to the same substitution product.[2]

These particular difficulties can be avoided by working in a solvent that is unreactive towards the substrate RX_1. However, this course of action may bring its own problems if the solvent differs very markedly in other properties, such as dielectric constant, from the reagent added in low concentration. For example, the addition of water or of an alcohol to an inert solvent may affect a reaction velocity not only if it enters into a bimolecular transition state with the substrate in the capacity of substituting reagent, but also by virtue of the change in solvent properties brought about. The exact analysis of reactions of this type may therefore not be simple.

2.6.3 EFFECTS OF ADDED SALTS

A similar type of problem applies more generally to the addition of an electrolyte solute. The large electrostatic forces exerted by ionic charges may affect reaction velocities in several ways. A resulting rate increase may therefore give the appearance that the anion of the electrolyte solute is involved as the nucleophile in a bimolecular transition state. Several factors have been considered to make contributions to these "salt effects". There is, first of all, the non-specific ionic-atmosphere effect which, at low concentrations of electrolyte, tends to stabilize more polar solutes more effectively than less polar ones. If the transition state of the reaction is more polar than the reactants (i.e. a more highly charged ion, or a smaller ion, or a molecule possessing a larger dipole moment) then this larger stabilization of the transition state by electrolyte will lower the potential energy barrier along the reaction path, i.e. there will be a positive (accelerating) salt effect on the reaction which might be mistaken for an S_N2 contribution to an S_N1 reaction. This first effect is a purely electrostatic charge–charge or charge–dipole interaction and formal electrostatic treatments of this effect have been given. Secondly, the influence of electrolytes on non-polar solutes is by no means insignificant. It arises through the effect of ions on the structure of water and other hydrogen-bonded liquids. The theory of these phenomena is still at a somewhat qualitative stage and its quantitative application to a situation as complex as the nucleophilic substitution reactions of organic substrates still appears to be some way off. A third factor to which attention has been called applies only to reactions in solvent mixtures which have frequently been used as media for such reactions. If the polar characteristics of the components of the solvent mixture are very different, then one may expect an ionic solute to

[1] Streitwieser, 1956b, p. 610.
[2] For an exception, involving a carbonium ion in which skeletal rearrangement can occur, see Diaz, Brookhart and Winstein, 1966.

cause a partial salting out, through concentrating the more polar component in the immediate vicinity of the ions, and thereby to affect the reaction rate.

The kinetic demonstration of the intermediacy of carbonium ions can be more definite if the first term in the denominator of Equation (2.4) is not negligible compared with the second one. In the limiting case (ii) Equation (2.7) applies. Case (ii) behaviour has usually been observed for very stable carbonium ions (e.g. triphenylmethyl cation) or very weak nucleophiles (e.g. aromatic hydrocarbons). Under such conditions the reaction velocity is sensitive to the presence of the anions of the displaced group, X_1 (i.e. "common" ions). This common-ion effect on the rate can be detected in two ways, either by the gradual deceleration of a reaction velocity as, during the course of the reaction, the concentration of the product ion X_1 builds up [case (iii)], or by the decreased initial rate constant when a reaction is performed in the presence of an initially added salt with the anion X_1 as a constituent. Such effects are sometimes clearly distinguishable from the frequently much smaller general electrolyte effects of added ions as, for example, in the hydrolysis of triphenylmethyl chloride in 85% aqueous acetone.[1] Alternatively, the common-ion effect can be studied by comparing the rates of solvolysis and liberation of $^{36}Cl^-$ ions from $R^{36}Cl$.[2]

Although the addition of the common ion has been singled out in this discussion, it should be borne in mind that other anions which can combine with the carbonium ion may likewise affect the velocity and character of the reaction. The result achieved by the addition of a non-common anion, say X_2, should depend on the relative rates of the two competing recombination reactions

$$R^+ + X_1 \rightarrow RX_1$$
$$R^+ + X_2 \rightarrow RX_2$$

and that of the expected product-forming reaction

$$R^+ + X_3 \rightarrow RX_3$$

as well as on the reactivity of the diversion product RX_2 relative to RX_1. If RX_2 is very unreactive as, for example, when it is RN_3, formed by the diversion of a reaction by addition of azide ions, then the formation of the ordinary product RX_3 will be much reduced. On the other hand, such an effect by added azide ions will not be observed if the reaction rate is being followed either by the disappearance of RX_1 or the formation of X_1 in the solution.

2.6.4 TRAPPING OF CARBONIUM IONS

If the amount of RX_2 (in the above example, RN_3) in the product is the observed quantity, then we can regard this type of experiment as the "trapping"

[1] Swain, Scott and Lohmann, 1953.
[2] Bailey, Fox et al., 1966.

of a reactive intermediate in a stable form. Azide ions are particularly effective in this way and experiments with them provide some of the clearest evidence for unstable carbonium ions.[1] In the reaction of diarylmethyl halides in aqueous acetone the addition of low concentrations of sodium azide diverts most of the reaction from solvolysis to the production of the diarylmethyl azide. However, the increase in rate produced by the salt is comparatively small, which argues against direct attachment of azide ions to the organic halide as the cause of formation of the organic azide by an S_N2 process.[2] The slight rate increase observed has been attributed to a salt effect. Another example of this method is the comparison of the azide intervention in the hydrolysis of diphenylmethyl chloride and bromide. These compounds hydrolyse at very different velocities in 90% aqueous acetone in the presence of 0·1M sodium azide: the rate constants differ by a factor of over 33. The percentage of product diverted to azide is, however, practically the same (34·0% for diphenylmethyl chloride and 33·5% for the bromide) which strongly argues that, in both cases, the product-forming step involves reaction of azide ions with the same species, most plausibly a carbonium ion.[3]

The relative effectiveness of reagents in trapping carbonium ions can be used to establish a scale of reactivity of nucleophiles towards a carbonium ion (see Paragraph 6.2.2).

The effects of ions in tests of mechanism by Equations (2.6) or (2.7) or by trapping experiments are again subject to some complications arising from electrostatic interactions of a more general type, and these can even over-shadow the mass-law effects. As a general rule, the mass-law effect is more important and easily discernible the larger the ratio k_1/k_2 is, and this condition generally coincides with the stability of the carbonium ions and their ease of detection by other methods. The consequences of charge interaction become progressively more serious as the dielectric constant of the medium decreases. In solvents of low dielectric constant, oppositely charged ions attract each other so that the predominant species in solution are not free ions but ion pairs or even larger clusters. It also follows that reactions in which ions are involved do not obey the simple kinetic laws, such as Equation (2.6), derived on the assumption that the ions are kinetically free. Ion-pairing effects on kinetics are discussed in Section 5.3.

Equation (2.7) implies the presence of a low equilibrium (or rather pseudo-equilibrium) concentration of carbonium ions in solution, a consequence which again emphasizes that this case is most likely to be met with comparatively stable and therefore unreactive carbonium ions. In favourable cases

[1] Bateman, Church et al., 1940; for a recent application of the same principle to a system in which the intermediate carbonium ion is thought to be present as an ion pair, see Sneen and Larsen, 1966.

[2] Bateman, Hughes and Ingold, 1940.

[3] Church, Hughes and Ingold, 1940.

this concentration may be sufficiently high for the direct spectroscopic detection of the intermediate carbonium ion.[1]

2.6.5 ACTIVATION PARAMETERS

Rate constants are formally related to Gibbs free energies of activation and from their dependence on temperature and pressure it is therefore possible to derive the corresponding enthalpies $(\Delta H^{\ddagger})$, entropies $(\Delta S^{\ddagger})$, heat capacities $(\Delta C_{p}^{\ddagger})$ and volumes $(\Delta V^{\ddagger})$ of activation. All of these activation parameters have been determined for reactions in solution in an attempt to provide additional mechanistic information such as might afford a distinction between S_N1 and S_N2 reactions. The ideal would be to be able to calculate values of one of the parameters on the basis of alternative models of the transition state and then to assign the mechanism by comparing the measured value with the calculated ones. Current knowledge and practice fall short of this ideal. What has been done in some cases is to measure the entropy of activation, say, for a reaction series in which a change in mechanism is suspected from other evidence in order to see whether the entropy likewise shows a change at the point of mechanistic change. In several instances such behaviour has been found. Furthermore, the change in $\Delta S^{\ddagger}$, $\Delta V^{\ddagger}$ or $\Delta C_{p}^{\ddagger}$ associated with the mechanistic change can sometimes be shown to be in the direction and of the order of magnitude expected for reasonable models of the transition states corresponding to the two mechanisms. In such circumstances it should be possible to invert the argument and assign mechanisms on the basis of measured activation parameters. The degree of success that has been achieved by this procedure, especially in the distinction between S_N1 and S_N2 mechanisms, has been the subject of recent review articles.[2]

2.7 Chemical Methods

As a result of studies from which the formation of carbonium ions was inferred by one of the more direct methods listed in the earlier parts of this Chapter, it was recognized that carbonium ions underwent certain characteristic reactions not found with other structures. It has thus become possible to reason from the formation of certain products to the probable involvement of carbonium ions in a reaction. In a sense, the intervention of azide ions through reaction with carbonium ions is an example of the formation of such a product. However, in that case the consideration of the effect required not only the fact of the nature of the product but also the effect of the diverting reagent on the rate of reaction. Like the azide reaction, the reactions now to be considered concern the fate of the carbonium ion *after* its formation, whereas the unimolecular rate law [Equation (2.6)] and the effects of

[1] Swain, Kaiser and Knee, 1955.
[2] Schaleger and Long, 1963; Whalley, 1964; Kohnstam, 1967.

substituents on S_N1 reactions constitute evidence about carbonium ions derived from the carbonium ion-forming step. As for most attempts to create sharp divisions in the field of reaction mechanisms, we shall find later that certain reservations have to be made regarding this classification.

2.7.1 RACEMIZATION

It is an attribute of S_N2 reactions that every act of substitution is accompanied by stereochemical inversion about the centre of substitution. Optical activity (of inverted sign) persists. The valencies emanating from a carbonium centre tend to be coplanar, and free carbonium ions are therefore expected to combine with nucleophiles to give a mixture of enantiomers, i.e. an optically active substrate (asymmetric about the centre of substitution) would lead to a racemic product. However, whereas no exceptions to the stereochemical rule for S_N2 reactions are known, the steric course of known reactions involving carbonium ion intermediates ranges from the "ideal" result of complete racemization to complete inversion. Accordingly we can state as a general rule that racemization is strong evidence for carbonium ions, but that inversion is not evidence against them. Complete racemization is the result obtained in the solvolysis of substrates giving rise to relatively stable carbonium ions (for example substituted diphenylmethyl cations), whereas a significant proportion of inversion is associated with unstable carbonium ions. In the usual phraseology, the carbonium ion is said to be shielded on one side by the receding displaced anion (or other displaced group) so that nucleophilic attack on the carbonium centre must come from the opposite side of the plane containing the bonds from the carbonium centre. The factors which govern the importance of such shielding are more fully discussed in Paragraph 6.2.4.

This picture of racemization as a concomitant of carbonium-ion formation can conceivably be obscured if there are more substitution events than events forming the final product. Examination of the final product in such a case may then indicate complete racemization. Such a path can be envisaged in the reaction of an alkyl halide if for every product-forming act of substitution there are several substitution steps by halide ions (either bimolecular or within ion pairs) which lead to the same chemical, but optically inverted, species. This situation can be experimentally detected by examination of the optical activity of the starting material.

2.7.2 REARRANGEMENT

The occurrence of carbonium-ion rearrangements is generally due to the existence of isomeric structures with comparable or greater stability than that of the ion derived from the reactant by the principle of least structural change. In some rearrangements different isomeric ions are thought to be capable of separate existence and to interconvert: in others, only a single structure of the ion, which already contains a partly or completely rearranged skeleton, may be capable of existence. The subject of rearrangement is more fully treated in Section 6.4, but we shall mention here some of these changes that have been considered to be diagnostic of carbonium-ion reactions.

A frequently quoted case of rearrangement in an acyclic system is the neopentyl → t-pentyl change mentioned in Chapter 1 (**1.20** → **1.23**). The change is thought to occur in the sense indicated because the tertiary carbonium ion **1.22** is more stable than the primary ion **1.21**. In other cases the rearrangement involves only a hydride shift.

Reactions in which substantial rearrangement has occurred in the carbonium ion, formed by ionization of a chloride, for instance, are common in the terpene series. For example, the previously quoted (Section 1.4) Wagner-Meerwein rearrangement of camphene hydrochloride (**2.20**) to isobornyl chloride (**2.22**) may involve a bridged structure (**2.21**) with a partially rearranged skeleton of intermediate structure (cf. **1.16**–**1.19**; see also Chapter 7).

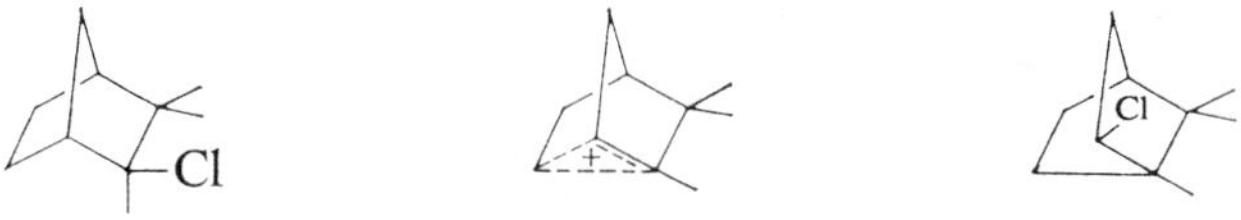

(2.20)   (2.21)   (2.22)

These ions are somewhat complicated examples of mesomeric carbonium ions in which no single carbon atom can properly be designated as the carbonium centre, and which can therefore in principle give rise to both rearranged and unrearranged products. Conceptually simpler examples are

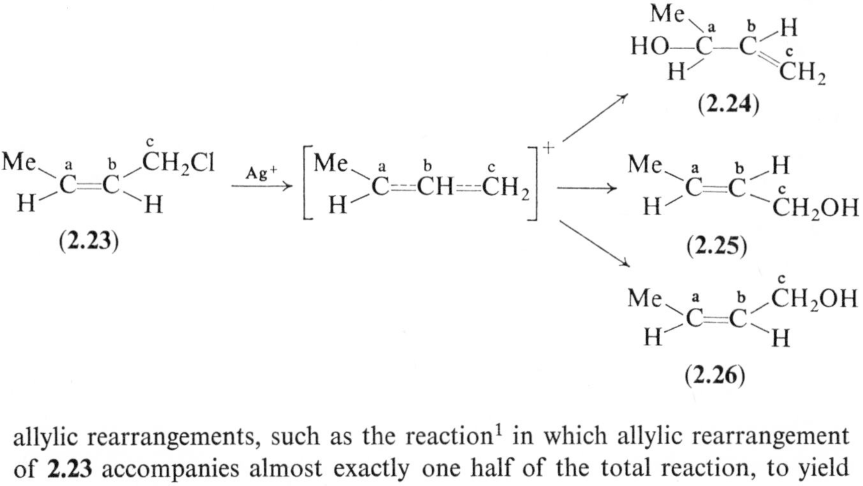

allylic rearrangements, such as the reaction[1] in which allylic rearrangement of **2.23** accompanies almost exactly one half of the total reaction, to yield

[1] W. G. Young, Sharman and Winstein, 1960.

2.24. The cationic charge in the carbonium ion is largely concentrated in the positions a and c of the allyl system. This particular system can also be used for the study of another type of rearrangement in which the product (**2.25**) is formed without allylic rearrangement but with the opposite geometrical configuration from the starting material (Paragraph 6.2.4). The product without either type of rearrangement is **2.26**.

Rearrangements closely related to the allylic ones just mentioned undoubtedly occur in the cycloheptatrienyl system (**2.27**) and other systems in which ions with a distributed charge are found.

(**2.27**)

However, the occurrence of allylic rearrangements is not unequivocal evidence for carbonium ions: other pathways, both heterolytic and homolytic, may have to be considered in any specific instance.

2.7.3 ELIMINATION

We have so far mentioned reactions of unstable carbonium ions in which the cationic charge is lost by combination with an anion. An alternative process by which a neutral molecule can be formed is the ejection of a cationic atom or group. In carbonium ions that contain a hydrogen atom on a carbon atom adjacent to the carbonium centre, the ejection of a proton by transfer to a suitable base—which may be the solvent—thus leads to an olefin. Elimination reactions of this type via a carbonium ion are not the only mechanisms by which an olefin can be formed from an alkyl halide or similar reactant, RX. The characteristic feature of the carbonium ion mechanism is that substitution (S_N1) and elimination (E1) occur at a stage when the group X has become detached from the residue R. It then follows that the nature of X should be without influence on the parallel substitution and elimination reactions of the carbonium ion.[1]

$$RX \longrightarrow \underset{(+X^-)}{R^+} \overset{Y^-}{\underset{Base}{<}} \begin{array}{l} RY \\ Olefin \end{array}$$

This result is observed for a number of groups R in good ionizing solvents (Table 2.4). The remarkable feature is that a wide range of reaction velocities, attending the change in the group X, has virtually no effect on the proportion

[1] Hughes, Ingold and Shapiro, 1937.

of olefin formed. The small effect that is found is generally attributed to a residual influence of X owing to its ion-pairing with or shielding of the carbonium ion. On the other hand, very divergent proportions of olefins are produced if the same systems are solvolysed in less ionizing media or if alkyl groups less disposed towards the formation of carbonium ions are employed (see Paragraph 6.4.2).

Table 2.4. *Proportion of olefin in unimolecular solvolysis of alkyl derivatives RX^a*

Solvent	Temp. °C	R	X	$10^5 k_1$ (sec^{-1}) (total rate)	% elimination
60:40 EtOH-water (v/v)	100	2-n-octyl	Cl	0·805	13
			Br	26·8	14
80:20 EtOH-water (v/v)	25	t-butyl	Cl	0·854	16·8
			Br	37·2	12·6
			I	90·1	12·9
80:20 EtOH-water (v/v)	65·3	t-butyl	Cl	89·7	36·3
			+ SMe$_2$	11·8	35·7
80:20 EtOH-water (v/v)	25·2	t-pentyl	Cl	1·50	33·3
			Br	58·3	26·2
			I	174	26·0
80:20 EtOH-water (v/v)	50	t-pentyl	Cl	28·5	40·3
			+ SMe$_2$	6·66	47·8

[a] From the summary by Cooper, Hughes *et al.*, 1948.

3 | SOURCES OF CARBONIUM IONS

3.1 General Considerations

Carbonium ions have been generated by a large number of reactions which may roughly be systematized as follows:

(a) by heterolytic fission of a larger molecular entity,
(b) by addition of a cation to an unsaturated system,
(c) by electron removal from an electrically neutral species.

Some illustrative examples of these reactions will now be given. A fourth type of reaction is, of course, the isomerization of one carbonium ion to give a different one. Examples of these reactions are found in Chapter 6.

The formation of a carbonium ion from a stable precursor may require somewhat vigorous reagents, for example the use of a strongly acidic medium. Apart from leading to carbonium ions, these are liable to induce other reactions in the substrate which may be misinterpreted as carbonium ion formation. Oxidation reactions are common complications, and of these the formation of radical cations from a neutral substrate by electron transfer to an oxidizing agent can be particularly intrusive. Its occurrence can be established by the paramagnetism of radical cations, and consequently, their electron spin resonance spectra.

Whether a particular ion will react further in a given solution, so that its formation will only be transient, will depend on the reactivity of the species present. To obtain stable solutions of carbonium ions it is therefore also necessary to use a solvent that is chemically inert towards carbonium ions. The largest extent of ionic dissociation will additionally be favoured by a medium of high dielectric constant which will decrease the electrostatic attraction between the carbonium ion and its balancing counter-ion. The three desirable solvent properties, capacity for stabilizing the anion, chemical inertness, and high dielectric constant, are rarely found together and some compromise must usually be accepted. Sulphuric acid and sulphur dioxide were for a long time the preferred media for the study of stable carbonium ions, although neither is ideal according to the above criteria. More recently, antimony pentafluoride has been found to be useful.

The considerations are slightly different when carbonium-ion reaction mechanisms, rather than the ions themselves, are to be studied. In such cases the chemical inertness of the solvent towards carbonium ions may be relatively unimportant: it may be that the reaction with the solvent is actually under investigation or that the addition of a second reagent with even greater reactivity towards carbonium ions is part of the procedure.

It is well known that organic residues have vastly different tendencies to be formed as carbonium ions. For example, in the formation of the carbonium ion R^+ by heterolysis of the halide RX the precise nature of the group R has an important influence on the energetics of the ionization process. This factor, which is mainly electronic in origin, will be considered in Section 5.2. At this stage our concern will be with other factors by which the tendency of the ion R^+ to be formed can be enhanced. It should, however, be borne in mind that an *exact* division of factors influencing ionization into those concerned with the group R and those concerned with the group X is not possible, as the following consideration of steric effects will illustrate.

Suppose that the parent compound CY_3X [where X can be any group attached to the radical CY_3 ($\equiv R$) corresponding to the carbonium ion CY_3^+] has a crowded molecule in which there is compressional steric strain between different parts of the molecule, e.g. mutually between the groups Y (which need not all be chemically identical) and between the groups Y and X. This strain will be lessened during the ionization process, with resultant stabilization both of the transition state of the reaction and of the product ions relative to CY_3X. The mutual compression of the groups Y will be eased because the inter-bond angles open out on going from tetrahedral to planar trigonal co-ordination around the carbonium centre. This is an effect exclusively concerned with the nature of R. The compression between Y and X will generally diminish as the C—X distance lengthens during formation of the transition state, and will disappear entirely when the two ions are fully formed. The magnitude of this effect is jointly controlled by both the nature of R and the nature of X. If the Y groups are small, increase in size of X need not introduce any steric strain into the molecule CY_3X; conversely if a small group X is involved, even a large group Y will not suffer compression by it. Only when both Y and X are beyond a certain size will their mutal compression be important, and it is then impossible to apportion this part of the steric enhancement of ionization between R and X.

However, the importance of these steric effects is usually not easily assessed.

3*

3.2 Heterolytic Fission of a Larger Molecular Entity

The heterolysis of a carbon-X valency so that the carbon atom loses both bonding electrons

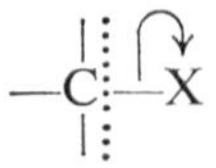

$$-\overset{|}{\underset{|}{C}}\!\!:\!\!X$$

is the most commonly studied mode of formation of carbonium ions. The parent molecule may be either electrically neutral or positively charged, although the possibility of forming carbonium ions even from anions by heterolysis with accompanying formation of a more highly charged anion is also conceivable.

In these reactions the problem of obtaining stable solutions of a particular carbonium ion appears to be not so much concerned with stabilizing interactions between the carbonium ion and particles of the medium as with the stabilization of the residue. In fact, the main driving force is provided by high stability of the residue formed along with the carbonium ion, since the latter is usually a species of inherently low thermodynamic stability. In the formation of a carbonium ion from a larger cation, as in the cleavage of 'onium ions [Equation (3.1)],

$$
\begin{aligned}
R_2{}^+S \!\!:\!\! R &\longrightarrow R_2S + R^+ \\
R_3\overset{+}{N} \!\!:\!\! R &\longrightarrow R_3N + R^+
\end{aligned}
\tag{3.1}
$$

the decrease in size of the charge-carrying particle will reduce its electrostatic stability, and this must be at least partially compensated in some manner if the carbonium ion is to possess some stability relative to its precursor. The groups attached to the central atom of an 'onium ion need not all be the same, in which case we may have to consider competing modes of decomposition, such as Equation (3.2).

$$
R_3\overset{+}{N}R' \Big\langle
\begin{array}{l}
\longrightarrow R'^+ + R_3N \\
\longrightarrow R^+ + R_2NR'
\end{array}
\tag{3.2}
$$

Because of the high stability of hydrogen ions in solution a carbonium ion is not a favoured product in the case of ammonium ions formed by protonation of amines: the most likely decomposition is instead by loss of the added proton. The molecules R_2S and R_3N are species of high stability, and so are the N_2

molecule and metallic mercury which accompany the formation of carbonium ions by the reactions (3.3) and (3.4).[1]

and

$$R \mathbin{\vdots} N^+ \equiv N \longrightarrow N_2 + R^+ \tag{3.3}$$

$$R \mathbin{\vdots} Hg^+ \longrightarrow Hg + R^+ \tag{3.4}^1$$

The formation of carbonium ions by breakdown of diazonium ions [Equation (3.3)] is usually considered as the last step in the deamination of aliphatic amines by nitrous acid (although this may not be the only mechanism for this reaction).[2] The deamination reaction has received a great deal of attention as a source of carbonium ions, particularly the question whether carbonium ions generated in this way are chemically identical with those from other sources (see Paragraph 6.1.4).

A somewhat special reaction in this group is the gas-phase heterolysis of the methylhelium cation, formed by the β-decay of tritiomethane.[3]

$$\left. \begin{array}{l} CH_3T \rightarrow CH_3{}^3He^+ + e^- \\ CH_3{}^3He^+ \rightarrow CH_3^+ + He \end{array} \right\} \tag{3.5}$$

The reaction is of great potential interest as a source of carbonium ions in the gas phase. If the ions are generated in the presence of other gaseous substances it is possible to study chemical reactions of such carbonium ions.[4]

In the decomposition of oxonium ions formed by protonation of an alcohol or ester the loss of a carbonium ion may be the preferred reaction. This ion may be a stable and distinctly recognizable product, as in the reaction (3.6).

$$Ph_3C-OH \xrightarrow{+H^+} \underset{\text{unstable}}{(Ph_3C-\overset{+}{O}H_2)} \longrightarrow Ph_3C^+ + H_2O \xrightarrow{+H^+} Ph_3C^+ + H_3O^+ \tag{3.6}$$

High acidity and hygroscopicity of the medium will favour such processes.[5] In other cases it may be possible to infer the transient formation of a less stable carbonium ion from the nature of the reaction products, as in the ester hydrolysis shown in Equation (3.7).

In most cases there is no direct evidence concerning the mechanism of the acid-induced C—O rupture in an alcohol or ester, but the formation of intermediate oxonium ions is a reasonable postulate, since such ions are known to be present in acid solutions of alcohols or esters under conditions when they do not break down into carbonium ions.[6]

[1] Jensen and Ouellette, 1961, 1963; Winstein, Vogelfanger et al., 1962.
[2] Maskill, Southam and Whiting, 1965.
[3] Snell and Pleasanton, 1958.
[4] Cacace, Ciranni and Guarino, 1966.
[5] Conant and Werner, 1930; Gold and Hawes, 1951.
[6] Arnett, 1963; Olah and Namanworth, 1966.

$$CH_3.CO.OC(CH_3)_3 \qquad\qquad (CH_3)_3C.OH$$

$$\searrow H^+ \qquad\qquad\qquad \nearrow \text{ stable} \qquad (3.7)$$

$$CH_3.CO.O\!\!<^{\overset{+}{C(CH_3)_3}}_{H} \longrightarrow (CH_3)_3C^+ + CH_3.CO.OH$$

unstable   unstable

The sequence of reactions [Equation (3.7)] which result in the hydrolysis of t-butyl acetate under acidic conditions is only one of a number of mechanisms by which an ester can be cleaved into alcohol and acid. This particular mechanism ("$A_{AL}1$" in Ingold's terminology) is distinguished in that it involves rupture of the bond between oxygen and the alkyl group rather than the more commonly observed mechanisms involving rupture between oxygen and the acyl group. This position of bond rupture is demonstrated by the isotopic composition of the alcohol when the reaction is performed in an ^{18}O-containing medium.[1] The formation of t-butyl methyl ether in the acid-catalysed methanolysis of t-butyl benzoate provided analogous evidence by a non-isotopic method.[2] Because other mechanisms, not involving carbonium-ion formation, can compete with the $A_{AL}1$ mechanism, this mechanism is of importance in the hydrolysis of esters of carboxylic acids mainly when comparatively stable carbonium ions (e.g. t-butyl or triphenylmethyl cations) are involved. By the principle of microscopic reversibility a carbonium ion mechanism would similarly apply to the reverse reaction, acid-catalysed esterification, under the same conditions.

The formation of the triphenylmethyl cation from the corresponding alcohol [Equation (3.6)] can also be taken as the pattern for the formation of carbonium ions from other neutral molecules. Leaving aside the question whether or not an oxonium ion is an intermediate in this reaction, the main feature of the ionization is the stabilization by the medium of the OH^- group split off. For the alcohol ionization (3.6) this stabilization is achieved by double protonation. Stabilization of the leaving group is also illustrated by the formation of carbonium ions from ethers and boron trifluoride when the formation of boron–oxygen bonds favours the occurrence of the reaction (3.8).[3]

$$3Ph_3C.OEt + 4BF_3 \rightarrow 3Ph_3C^+ + 3BF_4^- + B(OEt)_3 \qquad (3.8)$$

In the case of halides or arenesulphonate esters the anion formed is very stable and non-specific interaction with the solvent often appears to supply sufficient stabilization for ionization mechanisms to predominate. This is exemplified by the unimolecular solvolysis of tertiary alkyl halides and toluene-p-sulphonates in water–alcohol mixtures. However, much greater

[1] Bunton, Comyns and Wood, 1951.
[2] Cohen and Schneider, 1941.
[3] Meerwein, Hederich et al., 1960.

stabilization can be expected by specific combination of halide with a component of the medium. A spectacular example of the application of this principle is the use of antimony pentafluoride as solvent for alkyl fluorides,[1] for which the ionization reaction can be written as in Equation (3.9).

$$t\text{-BuF} + SbF_5 \rightarrow t\text{-Bu}^+ + SbF_6^- \tag{3.9}$$

The great stability of the hexafluoroantimonate ion allows the quantitative conversion of t-butyl fluoride into t-butyl cations. A similar explanation applies to the use of aluminium chloride and other Friedel-Crafts catalysts as one of the components of the medium to promote ionization or to encourage reactions by mechanisms involving carbonium ions. Indeed, this was one of the first principles concerning the formation of carbonium ions to be recognized following the discovery of triphenylmethyl radicals and cations.[2]

Estimates of the efficiency of different metal halides in promoting the formation of carbonium ions from organic chlorides come from measurements of the ionization of triarylmethyl chlorides in acetic acid solution[3] ($SbCl_5 \geqslant FeCl_3 \gg SnCl_4 \gg BiCl_3 > HgCl_2 > SbCl_3$) and, less directly, from rates of reactions, such as the rearrangement of camphene hydrochloride[4] ($SbCl_5 > SnCl_4 > FeCl_3 > HgCl_2 > SbCl_3$; PCl_3 and $SiCl_4$ being too weak), the racemization of 1-phenylethyl chloride where the relative effectiveness of metal halide catalysts was found to depend on their concentrations,[5] and the acetylation of toluene by acetyl chloride.[6] All halides of boron form complex halides BX_4^-, of which carbonium salts are known.[7] On the basis of their interactions with pyridine bases[8] or with xanthone[9] the Lewis acidity of these halides is $BI_3 > BBr_3 > BCl_3 > BF_3$. Various other estimates have been cited in a review by Olah.[10]

Quantitative estimates of the extra stabilization through co-ordination of the anion to the solvent in boron trifluoride solution

$$X^- + BF_3 \rightarrow BF_3X^- \tag{3.10}$$

have been obtained from thermochemical (ΔH) measurements. (F^-, 75 kcal; OH^-, 79 kcal; Cl^-, 25 kcal; Br^-, 11 kcal.)[11]

A somewhat different but effective method of stabilizing the anion is

[1] Olah, Baker et al., 1964.

[2] Norris and Sanders, 1902.

[3] Cotter and Evans, 1959.

[4] Meerwein and van Emster, 1922.

[5] Bodendorf and Böhme, 1935.

[6] Dermer and Billmeier, 1942.

[7] Witschonke and Kraus, 1947; Harmon, Harmon and Cummings, 1961; Harmon and Harmon, 1961; Harmon and Cummings, 1962.

[8] Gillespie, 1963.

[9] Cook, 1963.

[10] Olah, 1963, Chapter 11.

[11] Skinner, 1953.

involved in the reaction of anhydrous silver tetrafluoroborate with an organic bromide, as in the metathesis (3.11).[1]

It has been suggested that even the ethyl cation can be generated as a transient species in this way.[2] The leaving bromide anion is here stabilized in the form of the insoluble silver salt, the lattice energy of which is large.

It seems likely that the peculiar effectiveness of sulphur dioxide as a solvent for carbonium halides is also due to some form of chemical interaction—perhaps charge transfer complex formation—between halide ions and the solvent[3] (see Paragraph 5.3.4).

In some cases the ionic stabilization normally supplied by solvation is available from the lattice energy of the R—X crystal, and this in part explains the existence of certain carbonium salts. The lattice energy is sufficient to stabilize triphenylmethyl perchlorate as the salt.[4] It is, however, not enough to stabilize ionic crystals of triphenylmethyl chloride or arenesulphonate esters: these are covalent in the solid state.

The principle of energy compensation illustrated in the preceding paragraphs can be applied in a more obvious and quantitative form to the ionization of hydrocarbons by hydride transfer. The reaction[5] (3.12) on the one hand

generates a carbonium ion and a C—H bond, and on the other destroys such an ion and bond for different species. The equilibrium position can be used for estimating the energetics of such reactions.[6] The carbonium ion-forming process is in this case an intermolecular hydride transfer. The occurrence of rearrangements by hydride migration to the carbonium centre is the intramolecular parallel of this reaction (see Section 6.4).

Hydride abstraction from neutral molecules can be effected by NO^+ ions[7] and more conventional oxidizing agents.[8] The evidence that such a process occurs

[1] Olah, Pavláth and Olah, 1958.
[2] Meerwein, Hederich et al., 1960.
[3] Lichtin, 1963.
[4] Gomberg and Cone, 1909.
[5] H. J. Dauben, Gadecki et al., 1957.
[6] Conrow, 1961.
[7] Olah and Friedman, 1966.
[8] Westheimer and Nicolaides, 1949; Sager and Bradley, 1956.

need not in every instance imply that a carbonium ion is set free: it is conceivable that the hydride transfer is part of a more complicated change. Carbonium ions are, however, produced from triphenylmethane and related molecules by treatment with bromine and acetic acid–phosphoric oxide mixture;[1] the *p*-methoxy analogues are oxidized, perhaps by air, when dissolved in sulphuric or phosphoric acid.[2] In the chromic acid oxidation of triphenylmethane and methylcyclohexane in acetic acid, the presence of carbonium ions as intermediates has been shown by trapping experiments.[3] The simplest representation of this result is a hydride cleavage [Equation (3.13)] but kinetic evidence[4] suggests that the carbonium ion may be formed by a less direct route.

$$Ph_3CH + Cr(VI) \rightarrow Ph_3C^+ + Cr(IV) \tag{3.13}$$

Hydride abstraction also appears to occur when triphenylmethane is adsorbed on a silica-alumina cracking catalyst. The ultraviolet spectrum of the adsorbate is that of the triphenylmethyl cation.[5]

On occasions the generation of a carbonium ion is accompanied by the formation of more than one further particle, and one then speaks of the "fragmentation" of the parent molecule.[6] The process may be important not only energetically: if one of the species split off is gaseous and is allowed to escape, as in the reaction (3.14),[7]

$$Me_3C.CO.Cl + AlCl_3 \rightarrow Me_3C^+ + CO + AlCl_4^- \tag{3.14}$$

the system is not subject to the usual equilibrium considerations. [The same is true for the decomposition of the diazonium ion, Equation (3.3).] Although the escape of gas prevents the re-formation of the starting material, the ion produced may, of course, combine with other nucleophiles present to yield a different uncharged species. However, the reaction is reversible if the liberated carbon monoxide remains confined in contact with the solution.[8]

Reaction (3.14) can also be regarded as the decomposition of the acyl cation [Equation (3.15)] which is a most probable precursor, i.e.

$$Me_3C.CO^+ \rightarrow Me_3C^+ + CO \tag{3.15}$$

so that the reaction conforms once again to the general pattern of heterolytic dissociation processes in which only two particles are formed.

[1] Deno, Friedman *et al.*, 1962.
[2] Deno, Saines and Spangler, 1962.
[3] Necsoiu and Nenitzescu, 1960.
[4] Wiberg, 1965.
[5] Leftin, 1960.
[6] Whitmore and Stahly, 1933, 1945; Grob, 1962.
[7] Rothstein and Saville, 1949.
[8] Koch and Haaf, 1958, 1960; Pincock, Grigat and Bartlett, 1959; Balaban and Nenitzescu, 1960; Stork and Bersohn, 1960.

An important general application of this process involves carboxylic acids. The decomposition of triphenylacetic acid in sulphuric acid[1] [Equation (3.16)]

$$Ph_3C.CO_2H + H^+ \rightarrow Ph_3C^+ + CO + H_2O \qquad (3.16)$$

or the formation of substituted cyclopropenyl cations[2] [Equation (3.17)] are

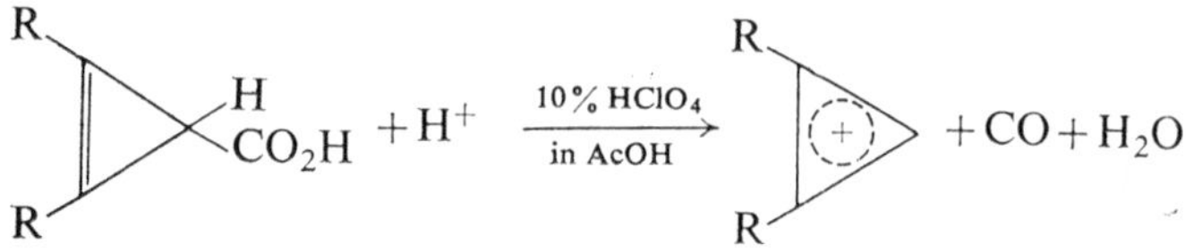

$$(3.17)$$

typical examples. The fact that the reverse reaction (of carbonium ions with carbon monoxide) has proved useful in the synthesis of carboxylic acids again argues strongly for the intermediate formation of acyl cations (see Section 8.1).

A somewhat more complex fragmentation reaction is the formation of cycloheptatrienyl cations by the routes (3.18) and (3.19)[3]

$$C_7H_7.CO.Cl \xrightarrow[\text{MeNO}_2]{\text{AgClO}_4 \text{ in}} C_7H_7^+ + ClO_4^- + AgCl + CO \qquad (3.18)$$

$$C_7H_7.CH_2.C(CH_3)_2.Cl \xrightarrow[\text{in MeCN}]{\text{AgClO}_4} C_7H_7^+ + ClO_4^- + AgCl + CH_2{=}C(CH_3)_2$$
$$(3.19)$$

and a fragmentation mechanism is also implied by Equation (3.20),

$$RO^- + \ddot{C}X_2 \rightarrow X^- + R{-}O{-}\ddot{C}{-}X \rightarrow R^+ + CO + 2X^- \qquad (3.20)$$

proposed to account for the interaction of alkoxide ions with dihalocarbenes to form predominantly olefins.[4]

Examples of fragmentation routes to carbonium ions in which other stable molecules are split off are given in Equations (3.21)–(3.23). The starting materials in these reactions are easily prepared from the corresponding amines.[5]

$$RNSO + NO^+SbF_6^- \rightarrow R^+SbF_6^- + N_2 + SO_2 \qquad (3.21)$$

$$RNCO + NO^+SbF_6^- \rightarrow R^+SbF_6^- + N_2 + CO_2 \qquad (3.22)$$

$$RNCS + NO^+SbF_6^- \rightarrow R^+SbF_6^- + N_2 + COS \qquad (3.23)$$

[1] Bistrzycki and Herbst, 1901; Bistrzycki and Reintke, 1905; Ropp, 1960.
[2] Breslow and Höver, 1960; Farnum and Burr, 1960.
[3] Dewar and Ganellin, 1959; Conrow, 1959.
[4] Skell and Starer, 1959.
[5] Olah, Friedman et al., 1966.

3.3 Addition of Cations to Neutral Molecules

The addition of a proton to an unsaturated molecule can sometimes lead to the same carbonium ion as the loss of an anionic group from a saturated species, as shown by the two routes (3.24) to the 1,1–diphenylethyl cation.[1]

$$
\begin{array}{ccc}
\text{Ph} & & \text{Ph} \\
\quad\diagdown\!\!C\!\!\diagup^{CH_3} & & \quad\diagdown C{=}CH_2 \qquad (3.24)\\
\text{Ph}\diagup \quad \diagdown\text{OH} & & \text{Ph}\diagup
\end{array}
$$

$$
\overset{+}{Ph_2C}\!\!-\!\!CH_3
$$

In a similar way the formation of transient carbonium ions is thought to be an intermediate step in electrophilic addition reactions, for example the hydration of certain olefins,[2] though this is not the only mechanism for such reactions.[3] Electrophilic addition is, of course, the reversal of heterolytic elimination, and the established multiplicity of mechanism in elimination implies (according to the principle of microscopic reversibility) the same potential multiplicity for addition.

Carbonium-ion formation by proton addition will clearly be favoured by the strength of the source of the protons as an acid, and this consideration will now be foremost in deciding the choice of reaction medium, in addition to the usual desiderata of power for anion stabilization, chemical inertness and high dielectric constant. Concentrated sulphuric acid and, to a smaller extent, other strong mineral acids were therefore the first media employed in such reactions. Sulphuric acid is in many respects a very suitable solvent[4] but presents problems connected with its high reactivity both as a sulphonating agent and as an oxidant. For this reason methanesulphonic acid,[5] chlorosulphuric acid,[6] fluorosulphuric acid[7] and liquid hydrogen halides, especially hydrogen fluoride, have been used.

The protonating power of a Brönsted acid can be increased by stabilizing the counter-ion formed alongside the carbonium ion. This brings us back to the considerations of Section 3.2 regarding the stabilization of anions. If the Brönsted acid used is a hydrogen halide, the proton-donating power of the medium can be increased by adding a substance with a strong specific affinity for chloride ions, e.g. aluminium chloride. Acid–halide combinations that

[1] Gold, Hawes and Tye, 1952.
[2] Schubert, Lamm and Keeffe, 1964; Schubert and Lamm, 1966; Gold and Kessick, 1965a; Deno, Kish and Peterson, 1965.
[3] Boyd, Taft et al., 1960; Gold and Satchell, 1963a; Dewar and Fahey, 1963a; Gandini and Plesch, 1965c.
[4] Gillespie and Robinson, 1965a.
[5] Craig, Garrett and Newman, 1950.
[6] Farnum, 1964.
[7] Birchall and Gillespie, 1964.

have found extensive use as media for the generation of stable carbonium ions include $HCl-AlCl_3$, $HCl-BCl_3$,[1] $HF-BF_3$,[2] $HF-SbF_5$,[3] and FSO_3H-SbF_5.[4] They are superior to sulphuric acid both in acidity and chemical inertness. Furthermore, they can be used at quite low temperatures, which are chosen in order to slow down reactions by which unstable carbonium ions are destroyed, whereas sulphuric acid freezes at the relatively high temperature of $+10.37°C$. The solutions can be diluted with sulphur dioxide[3] to increase their suitability for work at low temperatures.

The high acidity of hydrogen fluoride or hydrogen chloride by itself is due to hydrogen-bonding of the halide ions, to produce the anions HF_2^-(which has long been known to be important) and HCl_2^-.[5] This interaction to form HCl_2^- is evident in the fact that the triphenylmethylation of phenol by triphenylmethyl chloride in o-dichlorobenzene is catalysed (and autocatalysed) by hydrogen chloride.[6] More direct evidence relates to the isolation of HCl_2^- salts of triphenylmethyl[7] and cycloheptatrienyl cations.[8]

Several indirect estimates have been given[9] for the relative efficiency of fluorides in conjunction with hydrofluoric acid, of which the sequence[10]

$$SbF_5 > AsF_5 > PF_5$$

appears to be quite firmly established. Since the acid is kept the same throughout the series, the sequence reflects the stabilities of the corresponding complex fluorides.

Estimates based on the relative activity of metal halides in promoting the polymerization of olefins in conjunction with acids (as judged either by polymer yield or rate of polymerization) are less reliable.[11]

Two factors are thus mainly operative in determining the acidity of Brönsted acid (HX)-Lewis acid (MY_n) combinations, and the overall process for the protonation of a base (B) by such a system can be considered in terms of the hypothetical steps

$$HX + MY_n + B \overset{1}{\rightleftharpoons} BH^+ + MY_n + X^- \overset{2}{\rightleftharpoons} BH^+ + MY_nX^- \quad (3.25)$$

The first of these will depend on the Brönsted acidity of HX and the second one on the tendency of X^- to co-ordinate with MY_n. The effectiveness of acids HX

[1] Peach and Waddington, 1962.
[2] McCaulay, Shoemaker and Lien, 1950.
[3] Olah, 1965b.
[4] Olah, Comisarow et al., 1965.
[5] For a review of the evidence, see Peach and Waddington, 1965.
[6] Hart and Cassis, 1954.
[7] Sharp, 1958.
[8] Harmon and Davis, 1962.
[9] McCaulay, Higley and Lien, 1956; Muetterties, 1957; Muetterties and Phillips, 1957; Gillespie, 1963.
[10] Clifford, Beachell and Jack, 1957; cf. Olah, 1963, Chapter 11.
[11] Pepper, 1964.

in producing highly acidic media is therefore governed by two properties of X^- which will tend to oppose each other. This fact is illustrated by the thermo-chemical data quoted on p. 49. (The anion of the stronger acid HCl interacts less strongly with BF_3 than the OH^- ion derived from the weaker acid H_2O.) Further evidence comes from the study of a proton transfer reaction (aromatic hydrogen exchange) in the presence of stannic chloride and a group of carb-oxylic acids.[1]

In strongly acidic media protonation even of aromatic systems is possible, despite the disruption of aromatic conjugation thereby entailed. Protonated azulenes (**3.1**)[2] and anthracene (**3.2**)[3] were probably the first systems for which the generation of stable carbonium ions by this route was clearly demonstrated.

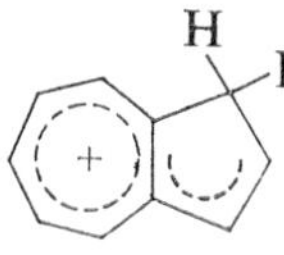

(3.1) 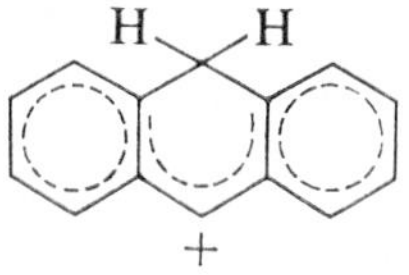   (3.2)

Distribution measurements of aromatic hydrocarbons between organic solvents and acidic media have also been interpreted in this fashion.[4] The existence of analogous structures as intermediates in hydrogen isotope exchange reactions of aromatic molecules had been postulated some years earlier.[5] The role of carbonium ions in such exchange reactions is now securely established (see Paragraph 4.2.5). Stable carbonium ions have more recently been obtained by proton addition to compounds even of quite low basicity (such as benzene, the xylenes and other polymethylbenzenes) by use of HF-SbF_5 and other highly acidic systems:[6] the same ions can be isolated by metathesis of the bromocyclohexa-1,4-dienes with $AgSbF_6$[7] [cf. Equation (3.11)].

Carbonium ion-forming proton transfer reactions which have no closely related counterpart in solution are thought to occur during gas-phase γ-radiolysis of organic compounds in the presence of nitric oxide, hydrogen and usually one of the rare gases. The highly acidic species H_3^+, ArH^+ (argon hydride cation), KrH^+, XeH^+, CH_5^+ can transfer a proton to various organic molecules. The following reactions have been deduced to occur with one or more of these gaseous acids: protonation of an olefin to give a carbonium ion

[1] Satchell, 1961.
[2] Plattner, 1950.
[3] Gold and Tye, 1952a.
[4] H. C. Brown and Brady, 1952.
[5] W. G. Brown, Widiger and Letang, 1939.
[6] Olah, Pavláth and Kuhn, 1956; Olah and Kuhn, 1958; Mackor, Hofstra and van der Waals, 1958a,b; MacLean and Mackor, 1961, 1962.
[7] Olah, 1965b.

(e.g. 2-propyl cation from propene), protonation of cyclopropane or cyclobutane to give 2-propyl and 2-butyl cations respectively, and protonation of n-pentane. The protonated n-pentane (an unconventional kind of species) decomposes into an alkane and a carbonium ion [Equation (3.26)].[1]

$$C_5H_{13}^+ \rightarrow C_nH_{2n+2} + C_{5-n}H_{11-2n}^+ \tag{3.26}$$

The addition of a carbonium ion to an olefin or aromatic molecule to produce a larger carbonium ion is the analogue of the above protonation reaction. The system $CH_3Cl\text{-}AlCl_3$ has been shown to be capable of transferring a cationic methyl group to hexamethylbenzene to produce the carbonium salt (3.3).[2]

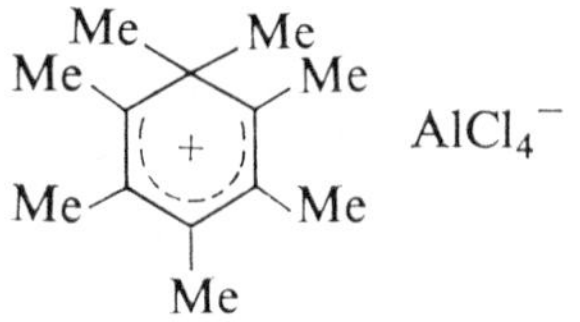

(3.3)

(The existence of free methyl cations in the solution is not implied by this process any more than the existence of free protons in $HF\text{-}SbF_5$ solutions.) Application of the principles described earlier in this section should lead to a variety of analogous salts by this general route. As for the protonation of aromatics, the intermediate formation of carbonium ions such as (3.4) has

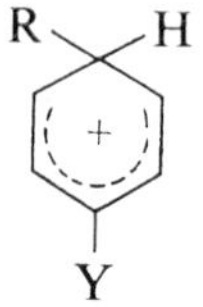

(3.4)

long been regarded as a possible step in the alkylation of the benzene derivative ArY by RHal in presence of a Friedel-Crafts catalyst.[3] This mechanism is a particular case of the generally accepted formulation of electrophilic aromatic substitution (see also Paragraph 6.3.2).

The addition of a carbonium ion to an olefin is thought to be the chain-propagating step [Equation (3.27)] in the cationic polymerization of olefins.[4]

$$RCH_2.\overset{+}{C}HR' + RCH{=}CHR' \rightarrow RCH_2.CHR'.CHR.\overset{+}{C}HR' \tag{3.27}$$

[1] Ausloos and Lias, 1965.
[2] Doering, Saunders et al., 1958.
[3] C. C. Price, 1941; H. C. Brown and Grayson, 1953.
[4] Whitmore, 1932; 1948; For a review, see Pepper, 1964.

In support of this interpretation it has been found that t-butyl perchlorate[1] and tetrafluoroborate,[2] for example, are capable of initiating the polymerization of certain olefins. The formation of polymeric materials explains why stable carbonium ions are not normally prepared by this reaction. The occurrence of polymerization need not imply the formation of free carbonium ions as chain carriers. Related "pseudocationic" mechanisms, not involving free carbonium ions, have also been proposed.[3]

Carbonium-ion addition to olefin is also reported to take place during the gas-phase γ-radiolyses mentioned above.[4] γ-Irradiation of liquid olefins leads to cationic polymerization.[5]

The simplest "unsaturated" species which can be considered in this class of reaction is methylene, CH_2, and carbenes derived from it. Equation (3.28) represents an as yet unrealized reaction of this type. (See also Paragraph 8.2.1.)

$$R^+ + R'\overset{..}{C}R'' \rightarrow RR'\overset{+}{C}R'' \qquad (3.28)$$

3.4 Electron Removal from Neutral Species

The loss of one electron from an ordinary closed-shell molecule leads to a radical cation. It has been explained (see Section 1.1) that, although such species *can* be looked upon as carbonium ions, their odd-electron complement sets them apart from the normal, diamagnetic carbonium ions. For this reason they will be referred to outside the main account of carbonium ions, in Chapter 8. It may, however, be mentioned at this stage that radical cations are normally formed by one-electron loss from a stable molecule, either by chemical oxidation or by collision with an energetic photon, electron, or particle of higher mass in radiolytic experiments. Correspondingly, the formation of an ordinary carbonium ion can be achieved by electron loss from an electrically neutral free radical. Electron impact can, for example, generate carbonium ions from free radicals in the mass spectrometer. This is not a reaction so far of interest as a practical preparation, but its study has led to information on the energetics of the formation of carbonium ions (see Paragraph 4.1.3).

Even in solution the oxidation of free radicals to carbonium ions is not a frequently exploited route to carbonium ions. In the first place, the preparation of free radicals generally presents greater difficulty than the generation of carbonium ions by alternative routes. Secondly, free radicals tend themselves to

[1] Longworth and Plesch, 1958.

[2] Olah, Quinn and Kuhn, 1960.

[3] Gandini and Plesch, 1964, 1965a,b; but see Bywater and Worsfold, 1966; Bertoli and Plesch, 1966.

[4] Ausloos and Lias, 1965.

[5] Bonin, Busler and Williams, 1965, and references quoted therein.

be very reactive species, so that the electron abstraction has to compete with other rapid reactions. Thirdly, the oxidation must be performed with electron acceptors showing little tendency to combine covalently with the radical. For this reason, oxygen and similar oxidizing agents are unsuitable, since they react with the radicals to form peroxidic products.

Anodic oxidation of intermediate triarylmethyl radicals seems to be the most likely mechanism for the forward reaction of the equilibrium (3.29)

$$\tfrac{1}{2}R_2 \rightleftharpoons (R\cdot) \rightleftharpoons R^+ + e^- \qquad (3.29)$$

which has been studied as a galvanic cell reaction (Paragraph 2.5.3). The fact that some Kolbe reactions of carboxylate ions lead to products apparently derived from carbonium ions suggests that anodic oxidation can effectively compete with other reactions of intermediately formed radicals, i.e.[1]

$$\left.\begin{aligned} RCO_2^- &\rightarrow RCO_2\cdot + e^- \\ RCO_2\cdot &\rightarrow R\cdot + CO_2 \\ R\cdot &\rightarrow R^+ + e^- \end{aligned}\right\} \qquad (3.30)$$

or[2]

$$\left.\begin{aligned} RCO_2\cdot &\rightarrow RCO_2^+ + e^- \\ RCO_2^+ &\rightarrow R^+ + CO_2 \end{aligned}\right\} \qquad (3.31)$$

Similar reasoning suggests that chemical oxidation of radicals to carbonium ions occurs in the reaction of carboxylate ions with lead tetra-acetate[3] and in the decomposition of peresters and alkyl hydroperoxides in the presence of free or complexed cupric ions.[4] Chemical oxidation of triphenylmethyl radicals to give triphenylmethanol or its derivatives can be achieved with chromic acid in glacial acetic acid or with potassium permanganate in acetone,[5] or by the reaction with nitrosobenzene in benzene in the absence of air. In each case electron transfer seems a likely process, e.g.[6]

$$Ph_3C\cdot + PhNO \rightarrow Ph_3\overset{+}{C} + PhNO^- \qquad (3.32)$$

In the reactions with metallic oxidizing agents the formation of co-ordination complexes almost certainly constitutes one facet of the mechanism.[7]

---

[1] Corey, Bauld et al., 1960.
[2] Koehl, 1964.
[3] Corey and Casanova, 1963.
[4] Kochi, 1962.
[5] Schlenk, 1912.
[6] Goldschmidt and Christmann, 1925.
[7] H. J. Dauben and Honnen, 1958; Fischer and Fischer, 1960; H. J. Dauben and Bertelli, 1961; Schrauzer, 1961; Mahler and Pettit, 1962.

4 | FORMATION OF CARBONIUM IONS: QUANTITATIVE ASPECTS

4.1 Energetics of Carbonium-ion Formation

4.1.1 GENERAL CONSIDERATIONS

Before discussing the role of structure in relation to carbonium ions, their formation and reactions, it is relevant to consider the main experimental sources from which quantitative information about the relative stability of different carbonium ions can be derived, and the significance of each type of measurement.

Of course, some insight into carbonium-ion stability can be gained from a purely qualitative consideration of the types of organic structures in connexion with which carbonium ions are mostly frequently encountered and also from the direction of molecular rearrangements. Neither of these criteria bears close scrutiny. The accidents of discovery and especially the tendency of most work to follow on from rather closely related antecedents has tended to concentrate much carbonium-ion research on a few groups of structures. For example, the cycloheptatrienyl (**4.1**) and substituted cyclopropenyl cations (**4.2**) remained unknown until quite recently not because of their low stability—both are very stable structures—but because their conception and synthesis required a departure from well-trodden paths.

The direction of carbonium ion rearrangements is also a fallible guide to the

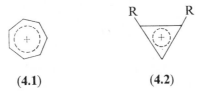

(**4.1**)   (**4.2**)

relative stability of ions, because the identified reaction products may not be found in the ratio of their precursor ions but according to the velocity of destruction of these ions, which is frequently in the opposite order. Figure 4.1 shows how a kinetically controlled product composition may favour the product derived from the less stable ion and also the less stable product itself. In other cases the formation of rearranged and unrearranged products does not require the existence of two distinct precursor carbonium ions (Paragraph 6.4.3), and an analysis of rearrangement data in terms of separate ions would be ill-conceived.

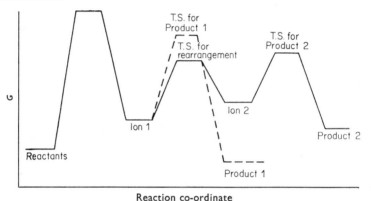

Reaction co-ordinate

FIG. 4.1. Schematic free energy profile for the rearrangement and destruction of carbonium ions.

4.1.2 THE QUANTITATIVE DEFINITION OF CARBONIUM-ION STABILITY

The more quantitative methods which will now be discussed are all directed towards the determination of stabilities of carbonium ions. Stability is, of course, a relative concept and, without specification of the chemical species relative to which the stability is expressed, the term is meaningless. It is equally true that in chemical systems carbonium ions are not present by themselves but rather with negatively charged particles which balance the charge in the system. We have already seen, in a qualitative way, the effect which some changes in the anion have on the stability of the carbonium ion with its counter-ion (Section 3.2). We have also made the point that, given a common anion for a series of carbonium ions, the equilibrium constants for ionization will be mainly governed by the attributes of the carbonium ion rather than those of the parent neutral molecule. The basis for this assertion is harder to quantify precisely but generally relies on the experience that equilibrium constants of notional reactions (4.1)

$$RX + R'^{+} \rightleftharpoons R'X + R^{+} \qquad (4.1)$$

are not sensitive to the nature of X, unless steric strain in either RX or R'X is important (Section 3.1). Nevertheless, chemical investigation in this field has the objective of making the understanding of carbonium ions more precise and the information more quantitative. Table 4.1 is therefore given to specify more closely the process to which the data resulting from each type of measurement, detailed in the following section, refer. Attention to this matter is probably most significant in relation to non-spectral data. The entry in the last column is

Table 4.1. *Reference systems for expressing carbonium ion* (R^+) *stabilities*

Experimental method	Typical reaction	Measured stability of ion relative to
Ionization potential of radical (p. 62)	$R \cdot \rightarrow R^+ + e^-$	$R \cdot ^a$
Appearance potential (p. 62)	$RX \rightarrow R^+ + X \cdot + e^-$	$RX - X \cdot ^a$
Conductivity (p. 68)	$RX \rightarrow R^+ + X^-$	$RX - X^{-b}$
Spectrophotometric determination of concentration of ions:		
Halides in SO_2 (p. 69)	$RX \rightarrow R^+ + X^- + R^+ X^-$ $RX \rightarrow R^+ X^-$	— —
Halides in presence of Friedel-Crafts catalysts (p. 72)	$RX + MX_n \rightarrow R^+ + MX_{n+1}^-$	$RX + MX_n - MX_{n+1}^{-c}$
Alcohol ionization (p. 73)	$ROH + H^+ \rightarrow R^+ + H_2O$	$ROH + H^+ - H_2O$
Protonation of hydrocarbons (p. 81)	$B + H^+ \rightarrow R^+$	$B + H^+$
Potentiometric titration (p. 30, 78)	$ROH + H^+ \rightarrow R^+ + H_2O$	$ROH + H^+ - H_2O$
EMF (p. 30, 87)	$\frac{1}{2}R_2 \rightarrow R^+ + e^-$	$\frac{1}{2}R_2^d$
Polarography (p. 30)	$R^+ + e^- \rightarrow R \cdot$	$R \cdot ^d$

^{a} Assuming products to be formed without excess energy.
^{b} Assuming $[RX] \gg [R^+X^-]$; $R^+X^- =$ ion pair.
^{c} Assuming absence of ion pairing.
^{d} Subject to assumptions regarding elimination of diffusion potential.

expressed in the form $P - Q$, where P denotes the progenitors of the carbonium ion and Q the chemical particle formed alongside the carbonium ion. The symbols are meant to indicate that a given value of the equilibrium constant (or of $\Delta G°$) of the carbonium ion-forming reaction $A + C \rightarrow R^+ + B$ will correspond to a more stable carbonium ion the greater the stability of A and C and the lower the stability of B. It is implicit that the stability of all species concerned should be considered in the phase appropriate to the particular reaction.

Of course the stability of a carbonium ion (*plus* its counter-ion) could in principle be expressed by the standard Gibbs free energy of formation (from the elements), as is customary for expressing thermodynamic stabilities of other substances, and no doubt this manner of representation will be more generally adopted as the necessary data become available in sufficient numbers.[1]

Because the "stability" of an ion depends on the standard of reference chosen, the following paragraphs of this section, dealing with quantitative results, have been arranged according to experimental methods used rather than according to classes of ions. In practice the arrangement is not as arbitrary from the chemical point of view as might at first be thought. The mass-spectrometric methods (Paragraph 4.1.3) contribute largely to our present knowledge of the stability of aliphatic carbonium ions, whereas all other methods, except the indirect ones based on rates of ionization reactions, are restricted to systems in which carbonium ions are very stable, and have to an overwhelming extent been concerned with triarylmethyl and closely related cations.

4.1.3 Ionization Potentials and Appearance Potentials

Carbonium-ion reactions in solution inevitably involve solvated ions; the carbonium ion and its counter-ion are stabilized by interaction with the solvent (Section 5.3). Since such stabilization is primarily associated with the presence of electric charges, it follows that the ionized form will be favoured relative to the unionized form by increased solvation. All solvents exert some stabilization, relative to the gas phase. The gas phase therefore represents a standard state for ionization processes in which intramolecular factors are not complicated by intermolecular ion-solvent forces.

In principle, the simplest reaction giving rise to carbonium ions which can be studied in the gas phase is the ionization process

$$R\cdot \rightarrow R^+ + e^-$$

which occurs on impact of an energetic particle on the radical. The minimum energy (A_1) which an electron is required to have in order to produce the cation R^+ by collision with the radical $R\cdot$ can be determined in a mass spectrometer. This "appearance potential" corresponds to the ionization energy or, to use the more established term, ionization potential (I). The determination of this threshold energy is, however, beset with difficulties, in part connected with the problem of obtaining a beam of electrons with a single, well-defined, and narrow range of energies. Nevertheless, many measurements of ionization potentials both of ordinary molecules and radicals—the procedure is essentially the same—by the "conventional" electron impact method have been reported and, although there is no agreement about their precise significance, these values are frequently used for comparisons. Because of the relatively poor reproducibility of measurements from different laboratories such comparisons should not combine data from different sources.

[1] Cf. Bernecker and Long, 1961.

There are other methods for obtaining ionization potentials to which these objections do not apply, at least not to the same extent. The best defined of these methods is the spectroscopic determination of the convergence limit of Rydberg series of electronic transitions, but it has been applied to only comparatively simple species, such as the methyl radical. In another method, the photoionization technique, the electron is removed from the radical by collision with an energetic photon. Because it is comparatively easy to obtain a beam of monochromatic light, the photon energy at which R^+ ions appear is much better defined than the electron energy in the conventional electron impact method. A refinement of the electron-impact method, known as the "retarding potential difference" (RPD) method, is an improvement in this respect, and results obtained by it are in better agreement with photoionization and spectroscopic values. However, until more measurements on radicals by photoionization and RPD methods become available, the extensive compilations of conventional electron impact values are the best available guide to structural effects on ionization potentials of radicals. As the general pattern of results appears quite self-consistent it seems reasonable to think that *relative* ionization potentials are reliable to within a few kilocalories. [Ionization potentials are usually expressed as multiples of the electron-volt as unit of energy but, since the results are to be compared with enthalpy and free energy data, they are tabulated (Tables 4.2 and 4.3) in units of kcal mole^{-1}.] The discrepancy between the electron-impact results and values obtained by other methods—where available—should serve to caution against confusing the apparent precision of the values with their absolute accuracy (Table 4.2).

An additional complication which arises in the interpretation of electron-impact values is that they are thought to be "vertical" ionization potentials, i.e. to correspond to ionization to an R^+ ion with the same internuclear distances and bond angles as the radical. According to the Franck-Condon principle this is the most probable ionization process, but it involves a somewhat larger energy than the "adiabatic" ionization, in which the nuclei are allowed to assume positions of minimum potential energy and which is the process to be related to thermochemical data. However, the comparison of photoionization and RPD measurements suggests that this effect is within the present limits of experimental error.

Ionization potentials can also be calculated from the appearance potentials, A_1, of a particular ion in mass spectra of various stable molecules. The energy necessary to produce the carbonium ion R^+ from a molecule RX exceeds the ionization potential of the radical, $I(R)$, since the formation of the ion by the process (4.2)

$$R\text{—}X + e^- \longrightarrow R^+ + X + 2e^- \tag{4.2}$$

also involves rupture of the R—X bond, i.e.

$A_1 \geqslant I(R) + D(R\text{—}X)$ (where D is the bond dissociation energy)

The inequality sign is written because of the difficulty of establishing in this case that the products of the reaction do not contain excess energy, i.e. that vertical and adiabatic potentials are the same. The problem is more serious in this case because a change from a tetrahedral arrangement in R—X to the trigonal bond arrangement in R is necessarily involved in the reaction. With these reservations, the combination of an appearance potential with the dissociation energy of the R—X bond yields information about the ionization potential of the radical and vice versa. There exist extensive critical compilations of such data,[1] and further results and discussions of methods are given in the volumes edited by McDowell[2] and McLafferty.[3]

Tables 4.2 and 4.3 contain collected values of some ionization potentials of special interest in relation to carbonium-ion chemistry.

The fact that an ion of a certain mass is formed in an ionization experiment is by itself no guide to the structure of the cation formed. Rearrangements of cations in the mass spectrometer are frequently suspected, but it may require detailed experiments on isotopically labelled parent species to establish the identity of a rearranged ion and the mode of its formation.[2] What the ionization potential measures is the energy required to produce ions of a certain mass. If the most stable of the various isomeric ions that may be possible is also the ion most directly related in structure to its precursor, it will presumably be the only species formed. However, if the most stable isomer can only be formed by skeletal rearrangement then the nature of the ion formed will depend on the activation energy required for the rearrangement. These considerations imply that the interpretation of ionization potentials of even seemingly simple systems may not be as straightforward as a superficial view suggests. They indicate why the difference between vertical and adiabatic ionization potential and the effect of the energy of the electron beam are matters of much concern in mass spectrometry, and that their progressing study can be expected to yield much detailed information of relevance to carbonium-ion chemistry.

The more refined methods for determining ionization potentials also allow further stages of ionization, involving the removal of successively more tightly held electrons, to be measured. Data of this kind should allow the complete energy-level diagram for the radical and carbonium ion to be established. The immediate chemical interest of the second ionization potential is that it is related to the chemical oxidation of free radicals to doubly charged radical cations.

The first ionization potentials of radicals are a measure of their ease of

[1] Field and Franklin, 1957; Bernecker and Long, 1961; Lossing, 1963; Harrison, 1963; Streitwieser, 1963; D. W. Turner, 1966.
[2] McDowell, 1963.
[3] McLafferty, 1963.
[4] Grubb and Meyerson, 1963; Meyer and Harrison, 1964.

Table 4.2. *Ionization potentials* ($kcal\ mole^{-1}$) *of simple alkyl radicals obtained by different methods*

	Spectroscopic[a]	Photoionization[b]	RPD[c]	Conventional electron impact[d]
$\dot{C}H_3$	226·9	226·4	226·0	229·4
$CH_3.\dot{C}H_2$	—	$\geqslant 194$	190·2	202·5
$CH_3.CH_2.\dot{C}H_2$	—	166 ± 5	187·9	200·4
$(CH_3)_2\dot{C}H$	—	< 173	173·4	182·2

[a] Herzberg and Shoosmith, 1956; Herzberg, 1961.
[b] Elder, Giese *et al.*, 1962; Murad and Inghram, 1964.
[c] Melton and Hamill, 1964.
[d] Lossing and co-workers, summarized by Harrison, 1963.

Table 4.3. *Ionization potentials* ($kcal\ mole^{-1}$) *of radicals derived from electron impact studies* (*due to Lossing and co-workers*)

Alkyl radicals		Olefinic and acetylenic radicals	
$\dot{C}H_3$	$229·4 \pm 0·7$	$CH_2={\dot{C}}H$	$217·9 \pm 1·2$
$\dot{C}D_3$	$229·4 \pm 0·7$	$CH_2=CH.\dot{C}H_2$	$188·2 \pm 0·7$
$CH_3.\dot{C}H_2$	$202·5 \pm 1·2$	$CH_2=C(CH_3)\dot{C}H_2$	$185·2 \pm 1·2$
$CH_3.CH_2.\dot{C}H_2$	$200·4 \pm 1·2$	$CH_3.CH=CH.\dot{C}H_2$	$177·8 \pm 1·2$
$(CH_3)_2\dot{C}H$	$182·2 \pm 1·2$	$HC\equiv C.\dot{C}H_2$	$190·2 \pm 1·8$
$CH_3.CH_2.CH_2.\dot{C}H_2$	$199·2 \pm 1·2$		
$(CH_3)_2CH.\dot{C}H_2$	$192·6 \pm 1·2$	Cycloalkylmethyl radicals	
$CH_3.CH_2.\dot{C}H.CH_3$	$182·9 \pm 1·2$		
$(CH_3)_3\dot{C}$	$171·8 \pm 1·2$	$\overline{CH_2CH_2CH}\ \dot{C}H_2$	$185·6 \pm 2·3$
$CH_3.\dot{C}H.CH_2.CH_2.CH_3$	$173·3 \pm 2·3$	$\overline{CH_2(CH_2)_2CH}.\dot{C}H_2$	$181·7 \pm 1·2$
$CH_3.CH_2.\dot{C}H.CH_2.CH_3$	$181·3 \pm 1·2$	$\overline{CH_2(CH_2)_3CH}.\dot{C}H_2$	$201·1 \pm 2·3$
$(CH_3)_2\dot{C}.CH_2.CH_3$	$164·2 \pm 2·3$	$\overline{CH_2(CH_2)_4CH}.\dot{C}H_2$	$176·6 \pm 0·7$
$(CH_3)_3C.\dot{C}H_2$	$192·1 \pm 2·3$	$\overline{CH_2(CH_2)_5CH}.\dot{C}H_2$	$152·2 \pm 2·3$

Arylalkyl radicals			
Benzyl	$178·9 \pm 1·8$	Benzyl,*o*-Me	$175·5 \pm 1·2$
Benzyl,$\alpha\alpha$-d_2	$177·8$	Benzyl,*m*-Me	$176·4 \pm 1·2$
Benzyl,*m*-F	$188·6 \pm 2·3$	Benzyl,*p*-Me	$172·0 \pm 1·2$
Benzyl,*p*-F	$179·4 \pm 2·3$	Benzyl,*p*-OMe	$157·7 \pm 2·3$
Benzyl,*p*-Cl	$183·3 \pm 2·3$	Benzyl,*p*-i-Pr	$171·1 \pm 2·3$
Benzyl,*m*-NO_2	$197·4 \pm 2·3$	α-Naphthylmethyl	$169·5 \pm 1·2$
Benzyl,*m*-CN	$197·9 \pm 2·3$	β-Naphthylmethyl	$174·3 \pm 1·2$
Benzyl,*p*-CN	$192·8 \pm 2·3$	Diphenylmethyl	$168·8 \pm 2·3$

oxidation to carbonium ions (or of the reduction of carbonium ions to radicals) and, with proper allowance for solvation effects, should be connected to such reactions in solution. Polarographic half-wave potentials for the reduction of carbonium ions should therefore show a dependence on these ionization potentials, but there are insufficient measurements for a thorough test of this prediction (cf. Paragraph 2.5.4).

Ionization potentials are not directly related to the common carbonium-ion forming reactions in solution, for example heterolysis of a larger species. The connexion between the thermochemical quantities involved is shown in the cycles given in Figure 4.2.

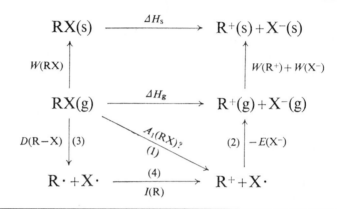

FIG. 4.2. Enthalpy cycles for heterolysis of RX. D=heat of dissociation; W=heat of solvation; I=ionization potential; E=electron affinity; A_1 (RX)=appearance potential of R^+ in mass spectrum of RX, for significance of query, see p. 63.

The combination of the terms involved, to give the enthalpies of gaseous ionization reactions for some simple carbonium ions, is illustrated in Table 4.4. The heterolysis of R—X is here taken along the hypothetical path 3–4–2 of Fig. 4.2, although it must be noted that dissociation energies (step 3) are sometimes obtained from a combination of steps 1 and 4. It follows that an accurate value of $I(R)$ does not necessarily lead to an equally accurate value of ΔH_g, since the less well defined appearance potentials $A_1(RX)$ may have been used in the calculation.

If it is fair to assume that bond dissociation energies of bromides differ from the corresponding dissociation energies of hydrides by an approximately constant value, then the relative values $\Delta \Delta H_g$ in Table 4.4 will express the enthalpy increments not only for hydride ionization but also for the ionization of the corresponding alkyl bromides and, with an analogous assumption, also for the ionization of alkyl chlorides and iodides.

In the case of the benzyl compounds (Table 4.5) there is some uncertainty whether the ionization potential of the radical corresponds to the formation of the benzyl cation or of a rearranged cation. This casts some doubt on the meaning of absolute values of ΔH_g but may not invalidate the $\Delta \Delta H_g$ values which are a measure of the substituent effects (see also Paragraph 4.2.3).

Table 4.4. *Enthalpies of gaseous ionization* $R—H \rightarrow R^+ + H^-$
("*heterolytic bond dissociation energies*")

R	$D(R—H)^a$	$I(R)^b$	$\Delta H_g{}^c$	$\Delta \Delta H_g{}^d$
Methyl	101	229	313	0
Ethyl	96	203	282	31
i-Propyl	94	182	259	54
t-Butyl	89	171	243	70
n-Propyl	100	200	283	30
n-Butyl	101	199	283	30
neo-Pentyl	95	192	270	43
Allyl	77	188	248	65

[a] Taken from the compilation by Cottrell, 1958, except for D(allyl—H) (Szwarc, 1950).

[b] Values from Table 4.3.

[c] Calc. as $\Delta H_g = D(R—H) + I(R) - E(H)$ with $E(H) = 17$ kcal (Pritchard, 1953).

[d] $\Delta \Delta H_g = \Delta H_g(\text{methyl}) - \Delta H_g$.

Table 4.5. *Enthalpies of gaseous ionization* $R—Br \rightarrow R^+ + Br^-$
("*heterolytic bond dissociation energies*")

R	$D(R—Br)^a$	$I(R)^b$	$\Delta H_g{}^c$	$\Delta \Delta H_g{}^d$
Methyl	~ 67	229·4	~ 214	—
Allyl	45·5	188·2	152	—
Benzyl	50·5	178·9	147	0
-p-Cl	50·1	183·3	151	-4
-o-Me	48·5	175·5	142	+5
-m-Me	50·5	176·4	145	+2
-p-Me	49·1	172·0	139	+8
-m-NO$_2$	48·4	197·4	164	-17
-m-CN	48·1	197·9	164	-17
-p-CN	49·7	192·8	161	-14

[a] Taken from the compilation by Cottrell, 1958, using, in the main, kinetic measurements by M. Szwarc and co-workers.

[b] Values from Table 4.3.

[c] Calc. as $\Delta H_g = D(R—Br) + I(R) - E(Br)$, with $E(Br) = 82$ kcal (Pritchard, 1953).

[d] $\Delta \Delta H_g = \Delta H_g$ (benzyl) $- \Delta H_g$.

4.1.4 ELECTRICAL CONDUCTANCE

Electrical conductance measurements in solution as a function of concentration lead to the fraction of solute present in the form of current-carrying charged particles (i.e. the degree of dissociation) and hence to an equilibrium constant for the dissociation. In simple applications of these principles, the only non-conducting form of the solute that is considered to have a significant concentration is the covalent molecule. This assumption is justified in conductimetric determinations of dissociation constants in aqueous solutions, especially those of proton-transfer equilibria (e.g. the measurement of the dissociation constant of acetic acid).

Table 4.6. *Equilibrium constants for protonation of methylbenzenes in HF*

Substituents in benzene	$K/K_{p\text{-xylene}}$		
	Conductance at $20°$	Vapour pressure and distribution measurements (HF-BF$_3$)	
	(K.L.)^a	(M.L.)^b	(M.H.W.)^c
—	0·09	—	0·0002
Me	0·63	0·01	0·26
p-Me$_2$	(1)	(1)	(1)
o-Me$_2$	1·1	2	1
m-Me$_2$	26	20	360
1,2,4-Me$_3$	63	40	—
1,2,3-Me$_3$	69	∼40	—
1,2,4,5-Me$_4$	140	120	—
1,2,3,4-Me$_4$	400	170	—
1,3,5-Me$_3$	13,000	2,800	200,000
1,2,3,5-Me$_4$	16,000	6,500	—
Me$_5$	29,000	8,700	—
Me$_6$	97,000	89,000	12,600,000

[a] Kilpatrick and Luborsky, 1953.
[b] McCaulay and Lien, 1951.
[c] Mackor, Hofstra and van der Waals, 1958b.

It appears also to apply to solutions in hydrogen fluoride as solvent (dielectric constant at $0°C = 84$).[1] Equilibrium constants for the formation of ions in this solvent have been determined for a series of methylbenzenes. These values are of interest in that they span an uncommonly large range for the same physical condition of the system. The conclusion that ion association is unimportant follows from the concentration-dependence of the conductance,[2]

[1] Fredenhagen and Dahmlos, 1929.
[2] Kilpatrick and Luborsky, 1953.

and can also be inferred from the fact that other techniques for the measurement of ionization in hydrogen fluoride solution[1] which would measure both free and associated ions (vapour pressure and distribution measurements) lead to very similar results (Table 4.6). The structure of the ions formed is, of course, not conveyed by either type of measurement.

In solvents of low dielectric constant, and especially when there is little tendency to covalency formation between the ionic portions, electrostatic attraction between the opposite charges results in clusters of ions which, in aggregate, are either uncharged or carry only the charge of a single excess positive or negative ion. The detailed conductivity-concentration curves of such solutions are complex and, even where their analysis is successful and the measurements of good precision, do not yield very accurate equilibrium constants. However, provided the solutions are dilute enough, the concentrations of ionic aggregates larger than ion pairs can be reduced below the level at which they make a significant contribution to the conductance, and a quantitative statement about the equilibria is then possible. These principles have been applied to the conductivity measurements on solutions of substituted triphenylmethyl halides in inert solvents, particularly sulphur dioxide, which appears to be more suitable than other inert solvents even of higher dielectric constant.[2]

By writing the formation of free carbonium ions as a stepwise process[3]

$$RX \underset{\longleftarrow}{\overset{K_1}{\longrightarrow}} R^+X^- \underset{\longleftarrow}{\overset{K_2}{\longrightarrow}} R^+ + X^- \tag{4.3}$$

via the ion pair R^+X^- [Equation (4.3)] we draw a distinction between the process of ionization characterized by the quotient

$$K_i = \frac{[R^+X^-] + [R^+]}{[RX]} = K_1(1 + K_2/[X^-]) \tag{4.4}$$

and the process of dissociation, characterized by the dissociation constant

$$K_d = \frac{[R^+][X^-]}{[RX] + [R^+X^-]} = K_1 K_2/(1 + K_1) \tag{4.5}$$

K_i can be determined by spectrophotometric measurements; K_d is obtained from conductivity measurements. ($K_d \sim K_1 K_2$ if $K_1 \ll 1$, as is generally the case for the data available.) Conductivity measurements by themselves do not permit the evaluation of K_1 and K_2 from K_d. Values of the chemically more interesting constant K_1 have been estimated by taking $K_2 = 0.01$, by analogy with the value of this constant in the dissociation of saline electrolytes in sulphur dioxide. This value is not an unreasonable one in the light of Bjerrum's

[1] McCaulay and Lien, 1951; H. C. Brown and Brady, 1952.
[2] For a review, see Lichtin, 1963.
[3] Ziegler and Wollschitt, 1930.

4

treatment.[1] The more precise dissection into K_1 and K_2 which would be possible by combination of conductivity and spectrophotometric results has not so far been systematically carried through.

The assumption that the value of K_2 is independent of the nature of the triarylmethyl cation is strongly supported by the fact that identical dissociation constants were observed by Ziegler and Wollschitt[2] for a series of triarylmethyl perchlorates. The lack of any dependence of the constant on structure must imply complete ionization of all the perchlorates, so that the observed dissociation constant is for these compounds a measure only of K_2.[3]

Table 4.7. *Relative values of K_d for triphenylmethyl chloride derivatives in liquid sulphur dioxide at $0°C$[a]*

Substituents in three rings			$K_d(Ar_3C.Cl)/K_d(Ph_3C.Cl)$
—	—	—	(1)
2-Cl	—	—	0·26
3-Cl	—	—	0·037
4-Cl	—	—	0·31
4-Cl	4-Cl	4-Cl	0·030
2-Methyl	—	—	15
3-Methyl	—	—	2·3
4-Methyl	—	—	16
3-t-Butyl	—	—	4·2
4-t-Butyl	—	—	18
4-t-Butyl	4-t-Butyl	—	81
4-neo-Pentyl	—	—	20
3-neo-Pentyl	3-neo-Pentyl	—	9·0
3-Phenyl	—	—	0·76
4-Phenyl	—	—	5·9
3-Phenyl	3-Phenyl	—	0·54
4-Phenyl	4-Phenyl	—	26
3-Phenyl	3-Phenyl	3-Phenyl	0·33
4-Phenyl	4-Phenyl	4-Phenyl	76

[a] Lichtin, 1963.

In the absence of precise information with which to go from K_d to K_1 and K_2, the values of K_d are mainly of comparative interest especially for related molecules for which, by reason of molecular geometry and general similarity, it is fair to assume that K_2 will have a constant value. *Ratios* of K_d values should then be a good approximation to *ratios* of K_1. A summary of such results, taken entirely from the work of Lichtin and collaborators, is given in Table 4.7.

[1] Lichtin, 1963.
[2] Ziegler and Wollschitt, 1930.
[3] Longworth and Mason, 1966.

By carefully maintaining identical experimental conditions in the measurements on the substances to be compared, isotope (^{2}H and ^{13}C) effects on K's have been studied.[1] These effects are small. The difference between Ph_3C—Cl and $Ph_3{}^{13}C$—Cl ($^{12}K_d/^{13}K_d = 0.9833 \pm 0.0032$), though small, is particularly informative by indicating that Ph—C bond in the carbonium ion is much stronger than that in triphenylmethyl chloride. The finding is consistent with the generally held view that the extension of conjugation endows the Ph—C bonds with partial double-bond character, as indicated by one of the valence bond structures (**4.3**) and with the observation that the C—Ph distance in the tris-*p*-dimethylamino analogue is greatly reduced below the normal single-bond C—C distance.[2] It has been suggested that the small carbon isotope effects on rates of carbonium-ion formation by S_N1 reactions[3] have an analogous explanation.[4]

(**4.3**)

4.1.5 SPECTROPHOTOMETRY

Quantitative studies on equilibria in which carbonium ions are involved are most frequently performed by measurements relying on the difference in electronic spectra between carbonium ions and other organic species, although differences in NMR spectra have also been employed.[5] Where these measurements relate to media of high dielectric constant, such as water or mixtures of strong mineral acids with water, it is fair to assume that all carbonium ions are present as free ions (rather than in pairs or higher aggregates). This assumption is not valid for solvents of low dielectric constant, but the possible repercussions of ion association on the results of equilibrium constant measurements by this technique have not been systematically examined. To a close degree of approximation it must be true that the electronic spectra of free triarylmethyl cations do not significantly differ from those of associated carbonium ions,[6] so that the spectrophotometric measurements can be taken to measure the sum of the concentrations of free and associated ions. This means that

[1] Kresge, Lichtin *et al.*, 1965; Lichtin, Lewis *et al.*, 1959; Kresge, Rao and Lichtin, 1961.

[2] Eriks and Koh, 1963; see also Section 2.2.

[3] Bender and Buist, 1958; Stothers and Bourns, 1960.

[4] Kresge, Lichtin *et al.*, 1965.

[5] A. E. Young, Sandel and Freedman, 1966.

[6] A. G. Evans, McEwan *et al.*, 1955; Bayles, Cotter and Evans, 1955.

spectrophotometrically determined equilibrium constants, for the ionization of halides, for example, correspond to K_i as defined on p. 69, but whether this assumption is always accurately valid and whether small differences in equilibrium constants for structurally somewhat dissimilar compounds can be relied on is not so certain.

With this assumption about the equality of extinction coefficients for free and associated ion pairs one can in principle obtain both K_1 and K_2 from a set of spectrophotometric measurements at varying concentrations of triphenyl-methyl chloride. From the definition of K_1 and K_2 we have, in the absence of solutes other than RCl,

$$[R^+Cl^-] = K_1[RCl]$$

$$[R^+]^2 = K_1K_2[RCl]$$

or
$$\frac{[R^+Cl^-]+[R^+]}{[RCl]} = K_1 + \left(\frac{K_1K_2}{[RCl]}\right)^{\frac{1}{2}} \tag{4.6}$$

A graph of $([R^+Cl^-]+[R^+])/[RCl]$, which is the ratio of ionized to unionized triphenylmethyl chloride, against $[RCl]^{-\frac{1}{2}}$ should accordingly be linear, with slope $(K_1K_2)^{\frac{1}{2}}$ and intercept K_1.[1]

A. G. Evans and his collaborators have in this way[1] collected extensive data on the *ionization of triarylmethyl chlorides;* these embrace not only the effect of substituent groups but also the influence of temperature and solvent.[2] Other evidence shows that hydrogen chloride stabilizes carbonium ions formed from organic chlorides in aprotic solvents by combining with the chloride ion to give rise to the HCl_2^- anion.[3] It has been suggested,[4] with some experimental support, that this assistance is significant under conditions where an unspecified reaction between triphenylmethyl chloride and nitromethane can generate some hydrogen chloride and that the detailed interpretation of some of Evans' results on the ionization of halides by themselves may have to be revised. Besides nitromethane, the solvents used in these studies include other nitro-alkanes, formic and acetic acid, 1,1-dichloro- and 1,1,2,2-tetrachloroethane, *m*-cresol, chlorobenzene and nitrobenzene.

To obtain a wide range of structural effects on equilibrium constants it is preferable to vary the ionizing power of the medium not by solvent change but by the addition of a metal halide capable of stabilizing the anion, and some of the most coherent sets of data of this kind were obtained by Evans *et al.* for the ionization of triarylmethyl chlorides in nitromethane with addition of mercuric

[1] A. G. Evans, Price and Thomas, 1955; Fairbrother and Wright, 1949.

[2] Bentley, Evans and Halpern, 1951; Bentley and Evans, 1952a,b; A. G. Evans, Jones and Osborne, 1954; Bayles, Evans and Jones, 1955, 1957; A. G. Evans, Price and Thomas, 1954, 1955, 1956; A. G. Evans, McEwan *et al.*, 1955; Bayles, Cotter and Evans, 1955.

[3] Sharp, 1958.

[4] Pocker, 1958.

chloride.[1] Since complexing of chloride by mercuric chloride is certainly a more important reaction than complexing by hydrogen chloride, these results are unlikely to be complicated by the latter reaction. The data summarized in Table 4.8 express the standard free energy changes at 17°C for the ionization and dissociation reactions (4.7).

$$RCl + HgCl_2 \overset{1}{\rightleftharpoons} R^+HgCl_3^- \overset{2}{\rightleftharpoons} R^+ + HgCl_3^- \qquad (4.7)$$

The wide limits of error quoted underline the difficulty of studying electrolyte equilibria in nitromethane. (An uncertainty of ± 0.4 kcal mole^{-1} implies an uncertainty of a factor of 2 in the corresponding equilibrium constant.) In benzene and chlorobenzene as solvents the situation is more complex and there is evidence of larger aggregates in solution even at quite low concentrations of mercuric chloride.

Addition of saline chloride to a solution of triphenylmethyl chloride in liquid sulphur dioxide (or in other solvents of low dielectric constant) should repress the dissociation

$$Ph_3C^+Cl^- \rightleftharpoons Ph_3C^+ + Cl^-$$

but should not influence the formation of ion-pairs

$$Ph_3CCl \rightleftharpoons Ph_3C^+Cl^-$$

except for a medium effect.

Table 4.8. *Free energy changes (kcal mole^{-1}) for ionization (ΔG_1°) and dissociation (ΔG_2°) of triarylmethyl chlorides (RCl) in nitromethane in presence of mercuric chloride at 17°[a]*

R	ΔG_1°	ΔG_2°	$\Delta \Delta G_1^\circ$	$\Delta \Delta G_2^\circ$
Ph$_3$C	-4.2 ± 0.2	7.8 ± 0.6	(0)	(0)
p-ClC$_6$H$_4$.CPh$_2$	-3.6 ± 0.2	7.8 ± 0.6	$+0.6 \pm 0.4$	0 ± 1.2
o-ClC$_6$H$_4$.CPh$_2$	-3.2 ± 0.2	9.3 ± 0.9	$+1.0 \pm 0.4$	1.5 ± 1.5
p-MeC$_6$H$_4$.CPh$_2$	-5.7 ± 0.3	7.4 ± 1.2	-1.5 ± 0.5	-0.4 ± 1.8
o-MeC$_6$H$_4$.CPh$_2$	-5.5 ± 0.5	7.4 ± 0.7	-1.3 ± 0.7	-0.4 ± 1.3
(p-ClC$_6$H$_4$)$_3$C	-1.9 ± 0.3	6.8 ± 0.3	$+2.3 \pm 0.5$	-1.0 ± 0.9

[a] Bayles, Evans and Jones, 1957.

It has been reported that this principle can be used to distinguish light absorption due to ion pairs from that of free carbonium ion and hence to determine the two separate equilibrium constants.[2]

Quantitative information on the *ionization of alcohols in acidic media* can

[1] Bayles, Evans and Jones, 1957.
[2] Pocker, 1959.

be obtained comparatively easily by spectrophotometric determination of the relative concentrations of the parent alcohol and the carbonium ion in solution. Again the spectra of the two forms are, as a rule, very different so that the substances behave as "indicators". The colour changes in fact frequently occur in the visible spectrum and some substituted triarylmethanols (e.g. dimethylamino-substituted ones) can be used as conventional acid-base indicators over the normal pH range. With these particular substituted triarylmethanols there is some ambiguity whether they are more correctly described as carbonium or ammonium ions (**4.4** and **4.5**) and for alcohols in which such ambiguity does not exist it is frequently necessary to employ highly acidic media to achieve a significant conversion of alcohol to carbonium ion. The level of acidity of the medium required for half-conversion of the indicator to the carbonium ion is then a measure of the ionizing tendency (in a thermodynamic sense) of the alcohol.

$$\left((CH_3)_2N-\!\!\left\langle\!\!\bigcirc\!\!\right\rangle\!\!-\right)_3 C^+ \qquad\qquad (CH_3)_2\overset{+}{N}\!\!=\!\!\left\langle\ \right\rangle\!\!=\!CAr_2$$

$$(\textbf{4.4}) \qquad\qquad\qquad\qquad (\textbf{4.5})$$

Although this may seem obvious it must be emphasized that spectrophotometrically measured equilibrium constants are relevant to our subject only if the spectral change is entirely due to formation of a carbonium ion rather than to protonation of the hydroxyl group of the alcohol. It is therefore a prerequisite of such studies that there should be adequate evidence on this point. Simple paraffinic alcohols generally do not ionize to form carbonium ions, which accounts for their absence from the tables of data in this section.

The formation of carbonium ions from alcohols can be symbolically written as in Equation (4.8),

$$R.OH + H^+ \rightleftharpoons R^+ + H_2O \qquad\qquad (4.8)$$

and R.OH can be designated a "secondary" base. Equation (4.8) specifies neither the source of the proton nor the fate of the water molecule involved in the equilibrium. A more specific version of this equation, applicable to concentrated sulphuric acid, would be Equation (4.9),

$$R.OH + 2H_2SO_4 \rightleftharpoons R^+ + H_3O^+ + 2HSO_4^- \qquad\qquad (4.9)$$

which correctly conveys the fact that virtually all the water formed according to Equation (4.8) would be protonated by a further molecule of acid. The difference between this indicator ionization and the reactions of Brönsted bases, symbolically written as Equation (4.10)

$$B + H^+ \rightleftharpoons BH^+ \qquad\qquad (4.10)$$

implies that different measures of acidity are appropriate to the two cases. The most obvious difference between Equations (4.8) and (4.10) is the appearance of water amongst the reaction products in the latter case.[1]

Ionization equilibria of weak Brönsted bases can be formally expressed and measured by the use of Hammett's acidity function[2] H_0, defined in Equation (4.11).

$$H_0 = pK_{BH^+} + \log \frac{[B]}{[BH^+]} \qquad (pK_{BH^+} \equiv -pK_B) \qquad (4.11)$$

The significance of H_0 can also be stated in terms of the proton activity and activity coefficients of the two forms of the indicator

$$H_0 = -\log \left\{ a_{H^+} \frac{f_B}{f_{BH^+}} \right\} \qquad (4.12)$$

The analogous operational definition for the ionization of secondary bases is Equation (4.13),

$$J_0 = pK_{R^+} + \log \frac{[ROH]}{[R^+]} \qquad (pK_{R^+} \equiv -pK_{ROH}) \qquad (4.13)$$

where J_0 (for which the alternative symbols H_R and C_0 are also in use) is the acidity function appropriate to this ionization. By analogy with Equation (4.12) we now have

$$J_0 = -\log \left\{ \frac{a_{H^+} f_{ROH}}{a_{H_2O} f_{R^+}} \right\} \qquad (4.14)$$

and the connexion between H_0, J_0 and the water activity[3] is, by combination of Equations (4.12) and (4.14),

$$J_0 = H_0 + \log a_{H_2O} - \log \frac{f_{BH^+} f_{ROH}}{f_B f_{R^+}} \qquad (4.15)$$

It also follows that $J_0 \to H_0 \to -\log [H_3O^+]$ as the composition of the solution tends to pure water.

Relative measurements of the J_0 function (and of pK_{R^+} values) were carried out even before the connexion between J_0, H_0 and $-\log[H_3O^+]$ was appreciated,[4] and more extensive data in several acidic media are now available.[5]

A basic problem affecting the use of acidity functions arises from the term involving the ratio of the activity coefficients of the two forms of the indicator. The generally adopted stepwise procedure for the determination of acidity functions with a series of overlapping indicators implies that this value of

[1] Conant and Werner, 1930; Gold and Hawes, 1951.
[2] For a review, see Paul and Long, 1957.
[3] Gold, 1955.
[4] Westheimer and Kharasch, 1946; Lowen, Murray and Williams, 1950; M. A. Murray and Williams, 1950.
[5] Deno, Jaruzelski and Schriesheim, 1955; Deno, Berkheimer et al., 1959; Arnett and Bushick, 1964.

f_B/f_{BH^+} (or of f_{ROH}/f_{R^+}) in a given medium is independent of the chemical nature of B or ROH. Undoubtedly this represents an approximation[1] but the best available measurements on secondary bases of the triarylmethanol type[2] show that it is valid within the limits of experimental accuracy (with the possible exception of poly-nitro-substituted compounds). For Brönsted bases the individual deviations for different indicators appear to be more marked. If the overlap principle and the constancy of activity coefficient ratios are correct, then the values of pK_{R^+} evaluated by this procedure do indeed measure thermodynamic constants applicable to the standard state of the dilute aqueous solution (to which the measurements on the most basic indicator of the group directly refer). For a number of these indicators the equilibria have been measured at several temperatures, and the heats and entropies of ionization, similarly relating to the dilute aqueous solution (at 25°C), have been evaluated. The results tabulated in Tables 4.9 and 4.10 refer almost entirely to di- and tri-arylmethanols. Measurements on most derivatives of benzyl alcohol previously reported are not now considered reliable and, with other values that

Table 4.9. *Equilibrium constants for formation of carbonium ions from arylmethanols in aqueous acids at 25° (pK_{R^+} values)*

(A) Triarylmethanols Substituents in three rings			$H_2SO_4{}^a$	$H_2SO_4{}^b$	$HClO_4{}^c$	$HNO_3{}^c$
4-OH	4-OH	4-OH	—	+1·97*	—	—
4-OMe	4-OMe	4-OMe	+0·82	+0·82	+0·82	+0·80
4-OMe	4-OMe	—^{e}	−0·89	−1·24	−1·14	−1·11
4-OMe	—	—	−3·20	−3·40	−3·59	−3·41
2-Me	2-Me	2-Me	—	−3·4	—	—
4-Me	4-Me	4-Me	—	−3·56	—	—
4-Me	4-Me	—^{e}	—	—	—	—
4-Me	—	—	−5·25	−5·41	−5·67	—
4-CD$_3$	—	—	—	−5·43	−5·67	—
3-Me	3-Me	3-Me	—	−6·35	−5·95	—
4-t-Bu	—	—	—	−6·1^d	—	—
4-t-Bu	4-t-Bu	—	—	−6·6^d	—	—
4-t-Bu	4-t-Bu	4-t-Bu	—	−6·5	—	—
4-i-Pr	4-i-Pr	4-i-Pr	—	−6·54	—	—
—	—	—	−6·44	−6·63	−6·89	−6·60
4-F	4-F	4-F	—	−6·05**	—	—
4-Cl	4-Cl	4-Cl	−7·73	−7·74	−8·01	—
4-NO$_2$	—	—	−9·44	−9·15	−9·76	—
3-Cl	3-Cl	3-Cl	—	−11·03	—	—
4-NO$_2$	4-NO$_2$	—	−13·45^d	−12·90	—	—
4-NO$_2$	4-NO$_2$	4-NO$_2$	−18·08	−16·27	—	—
F$_5$	F$_5$	F$_5$	—	−17·5**	—	—

[1] Boyd, 1963; Jorgenson and Hartter, 1963.
[2] Arnett and Bushick, 1964.

Table 4.9—*continued*

(B) Diarylmethanols Substituents in two rings		$H_2SO_4{}^a$	$H_2SO_4{}^b$	$HClO_4{}^c$	$HNO_3{}^c$
4-OMe	4-OMe	$-5·60$	$-5·71$	—	—
2,4,6-Me$_3$	2,4,6-Me$_3$	—	$-6·6$	—	—
4-OPh	4-OPh	—	$-9·85*$	—	—
4-Me	4-Me	—	*-10·4*	—	—
2-Me	2-Me	—	*-12·45*	—	—
4-F	4-F	—	$-13·03*$	—	—
4-t-Bu	4-t-Bu	—	*-13·2*	—	—
—	—	—	*-13·3*	—	—
4-Cl	4-Cl	—	*-13·96*	—	—
4-Br	4-Br	—	$-14·16*$	—	—
4-I	4-I	—	$-14·26*$	—	—
(C) Others					
Xanthydrol		$-0·17$	$-0·84*$	—	—
α,α,2,4,6-Pentamethylbenzyl alcohol		—	$-12·2†$	—	—
α,α,2,3,4,5,6-Heptamethyl-benzyl alcohol		—	$-12·4†$	—	—
9-Methylfluorenol		—	$-16·60$	—	—

[a] Taken from Arnett and Bushick, 1964. Enthalpies and entropies of ionization corresponding to the data in this column are given in Table 4.10.

[b] Asterisks in this column denote values from Deno and Evans, 1957; daggers, Deno, Groves *et al.*, 1960; double asterisks, Filler, Wang *et al.*, 1967; other values from Deno, Jaruzelski and Schriesheim, 1955. Italics indicate data of lower reliability than others given by the same authors.

[c] Taken from Deno, Berkheimer *et al.*, 1959, who additionally list results for amine and amide derivatives.

[d] Indicator added as triarylmethyl chloride (hydrolysed in solution).

[e] In aqueous HCl (Épple, Odintsova and Éntelis, 1962). pK_{R+} for 4,4′-dimethoxytriphenylmethanol $= -1·25$; for 4,4′-dimethyltriphenylmethanol $= -4·71$ (both interpolated to 25° from measurements at other temperatures).

are known to be incorrect or for which the mode of ionization is doubtful, have been excluded.

Apart from these systematic studies by which rather fine gradations in equilibrium constants can be evaluated, indicator measurements can also be used to determine isolated pK_{R+}-values by spectrophotometry in solutions of known J_0 acidity.

Occasionally it is possible or necessary to supplement the indicator method by other techniques dependent on the acid-base nature of the carbonium ion-forming reaction. This is particularly necessary for ionization reactions that are not accompanied by a change in absorption in a convenient part of the

4*

Table 4.10. *Apparent standard thermodynamic quantities for formation of carbonium ions from arylmethanols* $(ROH + H^+ \rightarrow R^+ + H_2O)^a$

	ΔG° kcal mole^{-1}	ΔH° kcal mole^{-1}	ΔS° cal mole^{-1} deg^{-1}
Triphenylmethanol	$+8\cdot78$	$+3\cdot41$	$-18\cdot0$
-4,4'4''-trimethoxy	$-1\cdot11$	$+2\cdot49$	$+12\cdot1$
-4,4'dimethoxy	$+1\cdot22(+1\cdot70)^b$	$+5\cdot68(+5\cdot72)^b$	$+15\cdot0(+13\cdot5)^b$
-4-methoxy	$+4\cdot37$	$+6\cdot48$	$+7\cdot1$
-4,4'-dimethyl	$(+2\cdot73)^b$	$(+4\cdot58)^b$	$(+6\cdot2)^b$
-4-methyl	$+7\cdot16$	$+3\cdot86$	$-11\cdot1$
-4,4',4''-trichloro	$+10\cdot13$	$+2\cdot49$	$-25\cdot6$
-4-nitro	$+12\cdot88$	$+0\cdot87$	$-46\cdot1$
-4,4'-dinitro	$+18\cdot35$	$-6\cdot06$	$-81\cdot9$
-4,4',4''-trinitro	$+24\cdot66$	$-16\cdot80$	$-139\cdot1$
Diphenylmethanol	—	—	—
-4,4'-dimethoxy	$+7\cdot64$	$+4\cdot10$	$-11\cdot9$
Xanthydrol	$+0\cdot23$	$+3\cdot86$	$+12\cdot2$

[a] Arnett and Bushick, 1964.
[b] Values in parentheses are based on work with HCl by Épple, Odintsova and Éntelis, 1962.

spectrum, as, for example, the formation of cyclopropenyl cations with alkyl substituents.[1]

Potentiometric titration curves for the neutralization of a strongly basic carbonium ion-forming alcohol with perchloric acid, for example, can be obtained with a glass electrode in various solvent systems (see Paragraph 2.5.3). The EMF value of the cell at half-neutralization (E) is then used to define a pK_{R^+}-value,

$$pK_{R^+} = \frac{E}{2\cdot303 \; RT/F} + \text{``constant''} \qquad (4.16)$$

For solvents other than water the "constant" in Equation (4.16) is not in general known or electrometrically determined for the purpose of such measurements. Instead, its value is found by including amongst the potentiometrically studied bases one or more whose pK_{R^+} values are known from spectrophotometric measurements. These potentiometric pK_{R^+}-values are thus related to spectrophotometric pK_{R^+}-values by a kind of interpolation procedure.

Somewhat specific solvent effects may complicate exact comparisons of results obtained in different solvents,[2] but do not appear to be large enough to detract from the general pattern of structural effects on pK_{R^+}-values thus obtained. The entries in Table 4.11, due to different workers and methods

[1] Breslow, Höver and Chang, 1962.
[2] Breslow, Lockhart and Chang, 1961.

Table 4.11. pK_{R^+} of various alcohols other than arylmethanols

Alcohol	pK_{R^+}	Solvent	Source
(A) Cycloheptatrienyl derivatives Cycloheptatrienol			
	+4·7	Water	Doering and Knox, 1954
-,benzo[a]	+1·7	Acetic acid	Naville, Strauss and Heilbronner, 1960
-,dibenzo[a,e]	−3·7 −5·8	Water	Berti, 1957 Rumpf and Reynaud, 1964
-,tribenzo[a,c,e]	~ −15	H_2SO_4	Stiles and Libbey, 1957
-,naphtho[1′,2′-a]	+2·2	Acetic acid	Naville, Strauss and Heilbronner, 1960
-,naphtho[2′,3′-c]	+0·3	Acetic acid	Naville, Strauss and Heilbronner, 1960
-,heptaphenyl	> +7	50% MeCN-MeOH	Battiste, 1961
(B) Cyclopropenyl derivatives[a] Cyclopropenol			
-di-n-propyl	+2·7	50% MeCN-H_2O	Breslow, Höver and Chang, 1962
-tri-n-propyl	+7·2	50% MeCN-H_2O	Breslow, Höver and Chang, 1962
-diphenyl	−0·67	23% EtOH-H_2O	Breslow, Höver and Chang, 1962
	+0·32	Water	Breslow, Höver and Chang, 1962
-n-propyldiphenyl	+3·8	23% EtOH-H_2O	Breslow, Höver and Chang, 1962
-triphenyl	+3·1	50% MeCN-H_2O	Breslow, Höver and Chang, 1962
	+2·8	23% EtOH-H_2O	Breslow, Höver and Chang, 1962
	+3·2	Water	Breslow, Lockhart and Chang, 1961
-p-anisyldiphenyl	+4·0	23% EtOH-H_2O	Breslow and Chang, 1961

[a] Results in MeCN-H_2O by potentiometric titration; others by spectrophotometry. Solvent compositions as % v/v.

Table 4.11—*continued*

Alcohol	pK_{R^+}	Solvent	Source
(B) Cyclopropenyl derivatives			
Cyclopropenol			
-di-*p*-anisylphenyl	+5·2	50% MeCN-H$_2$O	Breslow, Höver and Chang, 1962
	+5·2	23% EtOH-H$_2$O	Breslow, Höver and Chang, 1962
-tri-*p*-anisyl	+6·5	50% MeCN-H$_2$O	Breslow, Höver and Chang, 1962
	+6·4	23% EtOH-H$_2$O	Breslow, Höver and Chang, 1962
(C) Others			
9-Phenylfluorenol	−10·8	?	Breslow, 1965
1,2,3-Triphenylindenol	−12·6	?	Breslow, 1965
Tri-cyclopropyl-			
methanol	−2·3	Water	Deno, 1964b

for various solvent systems, are less certain than the coherent results given in Tables 4.9 and 4.10.

Several chemical complications must be guarded against in all such studies. The most obvious and most easily detected of these is the occurrence of irreversible reactions under conditions favouring the formation of carbonium ions. Oxidation, either to radicals or to more drastically altered species, and sulphonation may be met. Polymerization can be particularly troublesome at intermediate acidities where the cation and the parent neutral molecule, which it can attack, are both present in comparable concentration. Where the instability is due to a bimolecular reaction between cation and neutral molecule the velocity of the reaction responsible will pass through a maximum at the acidity for which the concentrations of the two forms are exactly equal. This fact can be turned to advantage, and the study of reaction velocity as a function of acid composition can in suitable cases lead to estimates of pK values.[1]

In addition, *reversible* processes may compete with the main equilibrium chosen for study and it may not always be easy to establish their importance. For example, an acidic reaction medium may partially (or virtually completely) esterify the alcohol. This is a strong possibility in acetic acid solutions, where the observed equilibrium may be[2]

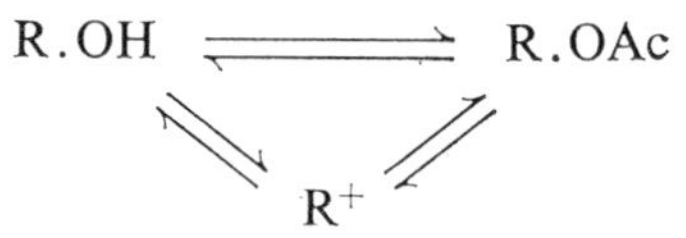

$$R.OH \rightleftharpoons R.OAc$$

$$R^+$$

(4.17)

[1] Myhre and Anderson, 1965.
[2] Bethell and Gold, 1958a.

Similar reactions are thought to occur with diarylmethyl chlorides.[1] Sometimes, a carbonium ion is in equilibrium with two isomeric alcohols, as in Equation (4.18),[2] and the experimentally obtained pK_{R^+}-value is not that

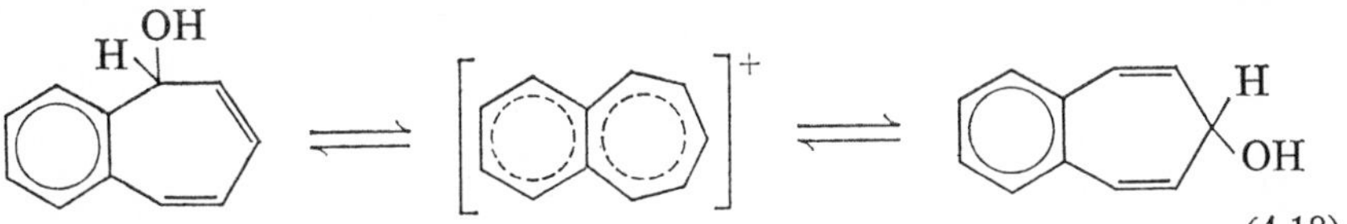

$$(4.18)$$

which applies to the alcohol taken: or there may be an alcohol–carbonium ion–olefin equilibrium[3] [Equation (4.19)].

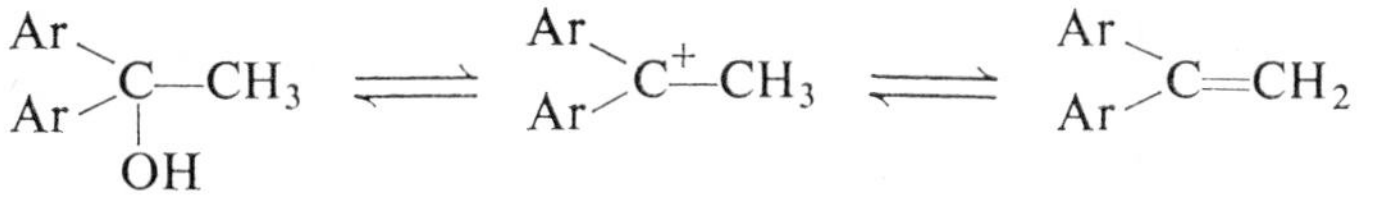

$$(4.19)$$

In all cases where more than two chemical forms of the indicator are involved, the exact analysis of experimental data is less straightforward, and requires knowledge of the equilibrium constants for the interconversion of isomers.

Indicator equilibria for *proton addition to unsaturated systems* can be studied in an analogous way to the alcohol–carbonium ion interconversions. These are Brönsted acid-base reactions and, as such, can be discussed in terms of Equation (4.11) in relation to Hammett's acidity function H_0.[4] These measurements are again subject to the general range of experimental complications mentioned in connexion with alcohols, but a more fundamental difficulty is the only recently recognized fact that the activity coefficient ratio f_B/f_{BH^+} is markedly dependent on the nature of the indicator base used.[5] In particular, the indicator behaviour of hydrocarbon bases does not at all conform to that of the nitroaniline derivatives on which the accepted values of the H_0 function depend. The differences between different types of indicator must be due to specific interactions. Since hydrogen-bonding is the most important of these in aqueous solutions, the discrepancies are plausibly attributed to hydrogen-bonding effects.[6]

The most obvious possibility of hydrogen bonding is that between solute and solvent, but it is also probable that specific effects on solvent–solvent hydrogen bonds, largely determined by the size of the solute particles, are significant.[7]

[1] Bethell and Gold, 1958b.
[2] Meuche, Strauss and Heilbronner, 1958.
[3] Deno, Groves and Saines, 1959; Deno, Groves et al., 1960; Kazanskii and Éntelis, 1962.
[4] For a recent general discussion of the problem of determining equilibrium constants for proton transfer to weak bases, see Arnett, 1963.
[5] Boyd, 1963; Jorgenson and Hartter, 1963.
[6] Taft, 1960b; but see Arnett and Burke, 1966.
[7] Long and Schulze, 1964.

Comparison of carbonium-ion stabilities by measurement of protonation equilibria in acidic solutions, to the same degree of reliability as for the alcohol ionizations, would therefore require the establishment of an acidity function appropriate to the particular substituted hydrocarbon bases to be used. Some

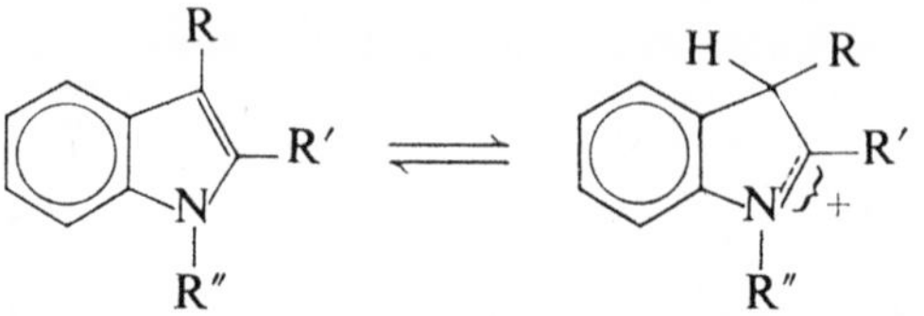

$$(4.6)$$

success along these lines has been achieved for substituted indoles as indicators,[1] the protonation being on carbon to form the carbonium-ammonium ion **4.6**,

Table 4.12. *Spectrophotometric measurements of the formation of carbonium ions by C-protonation of unsatured compounds in aqueous acid*

Base dissolved	Carbonium ion	pK	Acid conc. for half-ionization	Source
Azulene 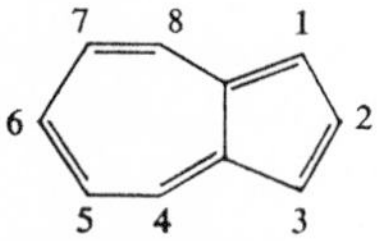	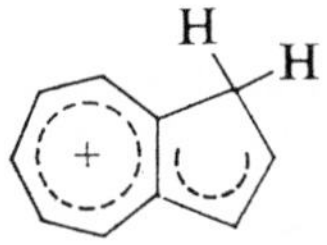	~ −1·7	2·30M HClO$_4$	Long and Schulze, 1964.
-,1-methyl		—	1·22M HClO$_4$	Long and Schulze, 1964
-,1-p-dimethyl-ammoniumbenzyl		~ −1·7	2·16M HClO$_4$	Long and Schulze, 1964
-,1-chloro		~ −3·4	4·17M HClO$_4$	Long and Schulze, 1964
-,1-nitro-4,6,8-trimethyl		—	5·06M HClO$_4$	Long and Schulze, 1964
-,1 cyano		~ −6·8	8·36M HClO$_4$	Long and Schulze, 1964
1,3,5-Trimethoxy-benzene	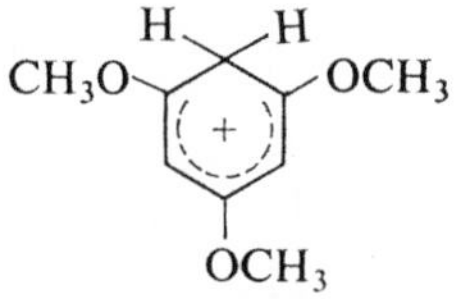	−5·1	7M HClO$_4$	Long and Schulze, 1964 Kresge and Chiang, 1961a
Heptalene	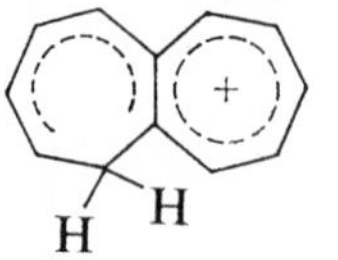 ?	⩾ +7	—	H. J. Dauben and Bertelli, 1961

[1] Hinman and Lang, 1964.

Table 4.12—*continued*

Base dissolved	Carbonium ion	pK	Acid conc. for half-ionization	Source
Hexamethyl-benzene		—	90·5% H_2SO_4	Kilpatrick and Hyman, 1958
Mesitylene		—	94·5% H_2SO_4	Kilpatrick and Hyman, 1958
1,1-Diphenyl-ethylene	$Ph_2\overset{+}{C}$—CH_3	—	71% H_2SO_4	Deno, Groves and Saines, 1959
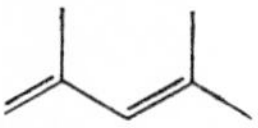 (diene structure)	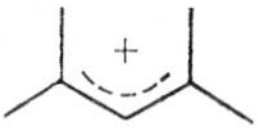 (carbonium ion structure)	—	73% H_2SO_4	Deno, Bollinger *et al.*, 1963
Mixed dienes	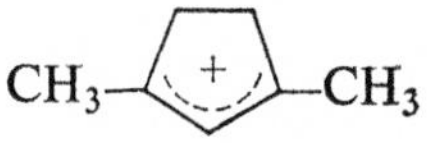 CH_3—(cyclopentenyl cation)—CH_3	—	35% H_2SO_4	Deno, Bollinger *et al.*, 1963
Mixed dienes	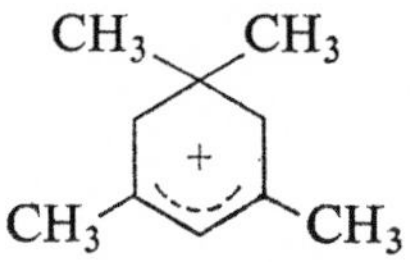 (tetramethyl cyclohexenyl cation structure)	—	50% H_2SO_4	Deno, Bollinger *et al*, 1963
Mixed dienes	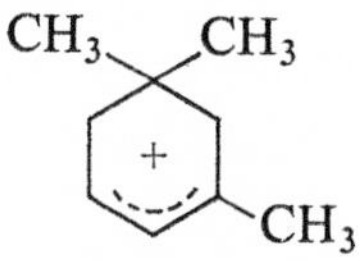 (trimethyl cyclohexenyl cation structure)	—	80% H_2SO_4	Deno, Bollinger *et al.*, 1963
Mixed dienes and/or alcohols	 CH_3—(cyclopentenyl with cyclopropyl)	—	12% H_2SO_4	Deno, Richey *et al.*, 1965
Mixed dienes and/or alcohols	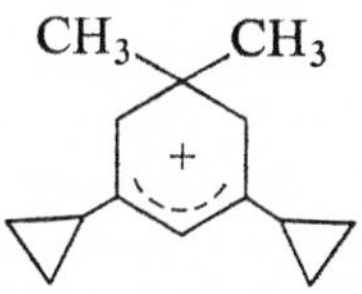 (dimethyl dicyclopropyl cyclohexenyl cation structure)	—	1·2% H_2SO_4	Deno, Richey *et al.*, 1965

but even within this rather narrow family of bases it has proved impossible to find an acidity function common to all its members. Indicator measurements on substituted azulenes have been carried out with the same objective.[1] For

[1] Long and Schulze, 1964.

the case of arylolefins as bases it has been proposed[1] that the activity coefficient ratio f_B/f_{BH^+} could be approximated to f_{ROH}/f_{R^+}, where ROH is a J_0-indicator. This allows us to combine Equations (4.11) and (4.15) to get (4.20).

$$J_0 - \log a_{H_2O} = pK_{BH^+} + \log \frac{[B]}{[BH^+]} \qquad (4.20)$$

This function (which has been designated H_R') is an improvement on H_0 in expressing the acidity-dependence of the protonation of olefins but, in the light of present experience in the systematic exploration of acidity functions for protonation on carbon, its general utility may be doubted.[2] The resolution of this general problem probably requires a more sophisticated approach to the subject of interactions in solution.

Pending such proper understanding of the equilibria some workers prefer to indicate the basicity of a compound by merely stating the acidity of the medium (expressed either as a percentage composition of the medium or as a value of a specified acidity function) at which the indicator base is exactly half-converted to its conjugate acid. Relative basicities of different indicators stated in this manner are rough guides only, for they relate to no clearly defined common standard state, but probably suffice to establish the sign and approximate magnitude of substituent effects.

The literature thus contains a great deal of information concerning the acidity of media in which protonation on a carbon atom of olefins, dienes and aromatic compounds occurs but, with the exceptions noted above, the information is not sufficiently quantitative to inspire confidence in the significance of detailed structural effects on basicity. The painstaking compilation of data by Arnett[3] confines itself, for all compounds of this type, to a statement of the percentage composition of aqueous sulphuric acid in which the compounds are thought to be half-ionized. Table 4.12 gives a selection of such data. For some entries in the table it is not known what conjugate base is in equilibrium with the carbonium ion. These carbonium ions were generated from a mixture of dienes, and a diene mixture is said to be recoverable from acid solutions by careful dilution, but the chemical composition of the latter mixture has not been determined. Because of the chemical instability of solutions of intermediate acidity (for reasons, see p. 80), the investigation of these systems is not easy. The results are only a rough guide to carbonium ion stabilities, and the reader is referred to the original work for detailed discussion and values for a number of other related ions.[4] Finally, there is in some cases uncertainty whether the carbonium ion is in equilibrium mainly with olefin or with an alcohol. This is also indicated in the Table.

[1] Kresge and Chiang, 1961a.
[2] Schubert and Quacchia, 1962; Kresge, Barry et al., 1962.
[3] Arnett, 1963.
[4] Deno, Bollinger et al., 1963.

4.1.6 DISTRIBUTION AND VAPOUR PRESSURE MEASUREMENTS

The successful use of indicator measurements requires both forms of the indicator to dissolve in the acidic solvent system, and many neutral hydrocarbon bases are not soluble enough for this purpose. On the other hand, carbonium-ion salts are soluble, so that the solubility of a basic substance should increase with the acidity of the medium, i.e. with progressive conversion of the base to the soluble protonated form. The determination of basicity by solubility measurements, i.e., the distribution of a sparingly soluble substance between the solid state and the ionic form in solution, suffers from practical disadvantages.[1] On the other hand, the distribution of sparingly soluble bases between an inert solvent (in which the ions do not appreciably dissolve) and an acidic phase (in which the neutral base does not appreciably dissolve) has long been used as a method for separating organic bases and for the determination of protolytic equilibrium constants, such as the basicity constant of aniline. The successful application of this principle to hydrocarbon bases by use of more highly acidic solutions[2] provided the first method for the quantitative study of carbonium-ion formation by protonation. Concentrations are conveniently measured by spectrophotometry, and the inert phase can also be analysed by gas chromatography.[3] Such measurements can be translated into pK values of bases only if the distribution coefficients of the neutral base species between the two phases can be determined or if a reasonably good estimate of its magnitude can be made. Even where this information is not available the measurements may have some value in the comparison of the basicity of similar compounds, e.g. azulenes,[4] or arylethylenes.[5]

For the determination of the basicities of aromatic hydrocarbons which are even more feebly basic, hydrogen fluoride can be used as the acidic phase which extracts the base from an organic phase (carbon tetrachloride or n-heptane).[6] The acidity of the hydrofluoric acid phase can be adjusted over a wide range, either by addition of alkali fluoride, which decreases the acidity, or by addition of BF_3 which stabilizes fluoride ions according to Equation

$$BF_3 + F^- \rightarrow BF_4^-$$ (4.21)

(4.21). The equilibrium constant of reaction (4.21) has been measured,[7] and a very wide range of basicities can therefore be determined, with due regard to

---

[1] Hammett and Chapman, 1934.

[2] McCaulay and Lien, 1951.

[3] Arnett, Wu et al., 1962.

[4] Plattner, Heilbronner and Weber, 1949; 1950; Plattner, Fürst and Marti, 1949.

[5] Gold and Tye, 1952b; cf. Deno, Groves and Saines, 1959.

[6] McCaulay and Lien, 1951; H. C. Brown and Brady, 1952; Mackor, Hofstra and van der Waals, 1958b.

[7] Mackor, Hofstra and van der Waals, 1958a.

activity coefficients in the ionic media. Results on alkyl-substituted aromatic hydrocarbons[1] (Table 4.6) and on unsubstituted condensed aromatic hydro-carbons[2] (Table 4.13) have been obtained in this way. The correlation of the former set of data with conductivity measurements[3] (Table 4.6) leaves no doubt that the interaction responsible for the extraction of hydrocarbon into the acid phase produces ions. It is known from NMR measurements that some of the ions produced in this way are definitely carbonium ions in which a proton becomes attached to a ring position (to produce a tetrahedral $>CH_2$ group).[4] The regularity of the dependence of the basicity on structure further suggests that a common process is observed throughout these series. However, some doubts concerning this have been expressed since a CH_2 group is not detectable in the product of the interaction of naphthalene with acid by infrared spectral measurements.[5] Analogous basicity measurements have also been carried out with other related acid systems.[6]

Table 4.13. *Selected values of equilibrium constants for protonation of polycyclic aromatic hydrocarbons in HF and HF-BF$_3$ from distribution and vapour pressure measurements*[a]

Hydrocarbon	σ_A/σ_{HA^+}	log K_{eq}[b]	log K_{chem}[c]
Benzene (1)[d]	6	−9·4	−10·2
Biphenyl (3)	6	−5·5	−6·3
Triphenylene (7)	6	−4·6	−5·4
Naphthalene (2)	4	−4·0	−4·6
Phenanthrene (4)	4	−3·5	−4·1
Chrysene (8)	2	−1·7	−2·0
Pyrene (11)	4	+2·1	+1·5
Dibenz[*a*,*h*]anthracene (10)	2	2·2	1·9
Benz[*a*]anthracene (9)	2	2·3	2·0
Anthracene (5)	2	3·8	3·5
Perylene (13)	4	4·4	3·8
Naphthacene (6)	4	5·8	5·2
Benzo[*a*]pyrene (12)	1	6·5	6·5

[a] Mackor, Hofstra and van der Waals, 1958a.

[b] $K_{eq} = \dfrac{[AH^+][F^-]}{[A]} \dfrac{\gamma_{\pm}^2}{\gamma_A}$.

[c] $K_{chem} = K_{eq}\sigma_{HA^+}/\sigma_A$ (σ is the symmetry number; see Paragraph 4.2.3).

[d] Numbers in parentheses refer to Figure 5.2.

[1] McCaulay and Lien, 1951; Mackor, Hofstra and van der Waals, 1958b.
[2] Mackor, Hofstra and van der Waals, 1958a.
[3] Kilpatrick and Luborsky, 1953.
[4] MacLean, van der Waals and Mackor, 1958.
[5] Perkampus and Baumgarten, 1964b.
[6] H. C. Brown and Pearsall, 1951; H. C. Brown and Wallace, 1953a.

A related technique which has been used to supplement the distribution measurements with hydrofluoric acid is that of vapour pressure measurements in ternary systems $HF\text{-}BF_3$-base as a function of composition,[1] i.e., distribution (though not of the base) between solution and vapour. As a result of protonation of the comparatively involatile base the vapour pressure of the $HF\text{-}BF_3$ pair is reduced. Because of the high acidity of the $HF\text{-}BF_3$ combination this method has been successful for very weak bases (e.g. toluene). If extended to the related $HF\text{-}SbF_5$ system, it could conceivably provide quantitative data on even weaker bases.

However, the serious disagreement between McCaulay and Lien's results and the apparently more refined measurements due to Mackor, Hofstra and van der Waals[1] (Table 4.6) is disturbing, though both sets of results agree as to the order of the basicities. The technique has also been used with hydrogen chloride by itself as the volatile acid, but in this case a looser association between the acid and aromatic molecules is the cause of the vapour pressure reduction. The method therefore requires independent evidence concerning the nature of the interaction.[2]

4.1.7 EMF Measurements

The successful use of a galvanic cell reversible with respect to carbonium ions has provided a promising source of quantitative data on carbonium-ion equilibria (see Paragraph 2.5.3). The EMF measurements allow the standard free energy change $\Delta G°$ (and equilibrium constant K) of reactions (4.22) to be

$$R^+ + \tfrac{1}{2}(Ph_3C \cdot CPh_3) \rightarrow Ph_3C^+ + \tfrac{1}{2}(R\text{—}R) \qquad (4.22)$$

measured for a series of substituted triphenylmethyl cations R^+ (present as fluoroborates). Such data are reproduced in Table 4.14.

Table 4.14. *Values of K and $\Delta G°$ for reaction* (4.22) *of substituted triphenylmethyl cations* (*EMF measurements in acetonitrile*)[a]

p-substituents in phenyl rings of R^+			K	$\Delta G°$
—	—	—	(1)	(0·0)
F	—	—	0·98	0·1
CH_3	—	—	$3·6 \times 10^{-2}$	2·0
OMe	—	—	$2·0 \times 10^{-4}$	5·1
OMe	OMe	—	$3·7 \times 10^{-8}$	8·8
OMe	OMe	OMe	$1·7 \times 10^{-9}$	12·0
NMe_2	—	—	$6·5 \times 10^{-12}$	15·2
NMe_2	NMe_2	NMe_2	$3·1 \times 10^{-18}$	23·9

[a] Jenson and Taft, 1964.

[1] McCaulay and Lien, 1951; Mackor, Hofstra and van der Waals, 1958a,b.
[2] H. C. Brown and Brady, 1949, 1952.

4.2 Rates of Carbonium-ion Formation

4.2.1 THE STATUS OF RATE MEASUREMENTS IN RELATION TO CARBONIUM-ION STABILITY

It was pointed out in paragraph 4.1.2 that, for equilibrium measurements, the reactants and products of the reaction are reference marks for any expressions of stability of the ions. A similar point can be made concerning the kinetic methods, and need not be re-stated in detail. However, the situation is basically more complicated.

Arguments about the stability of carbonium ions dependent on rate measurements fall into two broad categories. The first type of argument is concerned with rates of reactions of carbonium ions and generally amounts to the proposition that for analogous modes of reaction a less stable carbonium ion will be

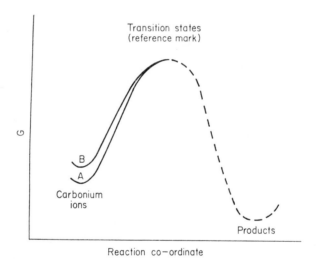

FIG. 4.3. Free energy profiles for conversion of carbonium ions to products.

destroyed more rapidly. What this implies is that the transition state, whatever the cause of its instability relative to the reactant carbonium ion, has substantially lost the carbonium character of the reactant and that the energy of the transition state is less influenced by structural variation than that of the carbonium ion. The situation is sketched in Figure 4.3, illustrating the difference in reaction rate of two carbonium ions (A, B) on this supposition.

The second kind of argument is concerned with rates of formation of carbonium ions and it is equivalent to the idea that a more stable ion will be formed more rapidly from a given type of parent molecule. The rate comparison now measures the free energy difference between the parent molecule and the transition state leading to the carbonium ion, and it is a measure of carbonium-ion stability only in so far as the energies of related transition states run parallel to the respective energies of carbonium ions. The correspondence will be closer the more the transition state resembles the carbonium ion, as indicated in Figure 4.4, illustrating the cause of different reaction rates for this case.

This generalization is a special case of what is often referred to as Hammond's postulate,[1] according to which a transition state and an unstable intermediate

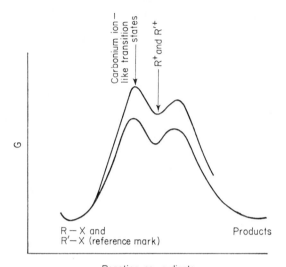

FIG. 4.4. Free energy profiles for carbonium ion formation.

which occur during a reaction process and which have nearly the same energy will be interconverted with only a small reorganization of molecular structure.

In a reaction conforming to the potential energy profile of Figure 4.4 the reaction velocity is determined by the ionization step, i.e. the transition states for any processes following the ionization are lower than the supposedly carbonium ion-like transition state.

Both Figures 4.3 and 4.4 include the reference mark with respect to which the energy of the carbonium ion (or carbonium ion-like transition state) is in fact measured. For example, when we say that a carbonium ion R^+ is more stable than R'^+ on the ground that the ionization $R-X \to R^+ + X^-$ is more rapid than the corresponding ionization of $R'-X$, we could be more explicit and say that, *relative* to the parent molecule $R-X$, the transition state $R^+ \ldots X^-$ is more stable than the transition state $R'^+ \ldots X^-$ is relative to $R'-X$.

The second argument has an important corollary. If the carbonium ion R^+

[1] Hammond, 1955.

lies close in energy to the transition state $R^+ \ldots X^-$ for its formation, this means that the energy of the carbonium ion is not greatly changed by the approach of the nucleophilic group X^- up to the transition-state distance. This means, in turn, that *changes* in X can exert only a minor influence on the stability of $R^+ \ldots X^-$. This conclusion can be stated in the form of the rule that the less stable a carbonium ion is, the less susceptible its reaction velocity will be to structural variations in the nucleophilic reagent X^-, or the less *selective* it will be in its reactions with a series of alternative nucleophilic reagents.

It is evident from these considerations that kinetic arguments about carbonium ion stabilities can be criticized on the ground that they are, at best, fair approximations. However, they cannot be disregarded for it is precisely on this seemingly insecure evidence that the main structural effects on the stability of simple carbonium ions were first recognized. Conversely, the ability to make correct predictions of relative reaction rates, and of the composition of products formed by reaction with competing reagents, from known relative stabilities of carbonium ions is clearly useful. Naturally, the approximations involved will be better in some cases than in others, and it should cause no surprise that qualitative or semi-quantitative information is all that can be expected.

The first general method, based on relative reactivities of different carbonium ions, is rarely of practical utility for, if a carbonium ion is sufficiently stable to be present in solution in analytically controlled concentration (as is required for kinetic studies), it is easier to apply one of the equilibrium methods. Experiments along these lines are therefore chiefly of interest in different connexions. A comparison of the rates of hydride abstraction by the triphenylmethyl cation and its 4,4′,4″-trimethoxy analogue[1] (in which the latter ion is found to be *ca.* 1000 times less reactive) confirms the relative stabilities inferred from equilibrium studies. On the other hand, di(4-methoxyphenyl)methyl cations react slightly more rapidly than triphenylmethyl cations, whereas indicator measurements on the corresponding alcohols indicate that the former ions are more stable. The discrepancy can be rationalized as a steric effect but indicates the care required in the interpretation of such results.[2]

4.2.2 $S_N 1$ REACTIONS

Comparisons based on rates of formation of carbonium ions are the most important kinetic method. There are fairly distinct areas and phases of its application. The first of these concerns the simple aliphatic ions for which alternative methods of experimentally assessing their stability in solution have not, so far, succeeded, although equilibrium studies in antimony pentafluoride or a similar solvent system might be fruitful. Some independent information

[1] Bartlett and McCollum, 1956.
[2] See also Diffenbach, Sano and Taft, 1966.

about such systems in the gas phase is available from ionization potentials but this was certainly not available during the early formative years of carbonium ion chemistry and is not immediately applicable to solutions.

The earliest kinetic studies in this field were mostly directed towards the mechanistic distinction between S_N1 and S_N2 reactions (Section 2.6). As a result of this work, it is thought that solvent systems such as aqueous ethanol and, particularly, formic acid are very favourable to the S_N1 mechanism to the virtual or complete exclusion of the S_N2 mechanism in most cases. Studies with the aim of measuring ionization velocities and the effect of structural variation on them have therefore generally employed these reactive media. Table 4.15 lists some relative rates obtained under such conditions.

Table 4.15. *Relative rates of solvolyses. Alkyl bromides in (a) formic acid (ca. 0·5 % water) and (b) 80 % aqueous ethyl alcohol (v/v)*

	Temp. (°C)	Me	Et	n-Pr	i-Pr	t-Bu	neo-Pentyl	Ref.
(a) {	95°	0·64	(1)	0·69	—	—	0·57	a
	100·2°	0·58	(1)	—	26	~10^8	—	b
(b)	55°	2·5	(1)	—	1·7	7200	—	c

[a] Dostrovsky and Hughes, 1946.
[b] Bateman and Hughes, 1940.
[c] Bateman, Cooper et al., 1940.

There are several reasons why the interpretation of these numerical values is complicated somewhat beyond the basic principles discussed above.

The most obvious experimental issue is the question whether all the compounds listed in fact react by a unimolecular mechanism or whether nucleophilic attack by the solvent is involved to a certain extent. One might think that this point could be settled by comparing the relative reaction velocities in different ionizing solvents. Such experiments do indeed confirm the order

$$t\text{-Bu} > i\text{-Pr} > \text{Et}$$

for the solvolysis rates, although the rate ratios are sensitive to the nature of the solvent. Formolysis of t-butyl bromide at 25° is estimated to be some 10^6 times more rapid than formolysis of i-propyl bromide[1] and this rate ratio is sometimes regarded as characteristic of solvolyses in which the nucleophilic activity of the solvent has no influence on the reaction rate (i.e. a "pure" S_N1 or "limiting" solvolysis). Lower rate ratios are held to indicate solvolysis by a mechanism having some S_N2 character.[2] In ethanol–water mixtures, for example, the order Me > Et, inverted from the sequence in formic acid, is found. Since substituents generally affect the rates of typical bimolecular

[1] Streitwieser, 1956, p. 615.
[2] E.g. Jensen and Ouellette, 1961.

(S_N2) reactions in the reverse direction of the order for S_N1 reactions, one may therefore conclude that the solvolysis for methyl bromide in ethanol–water is largely, if not entirely, bimolecular and that even in formic acid there may be a bimolecular contribution to the rate. The rate ratio $CH_3Br/C_2H_5Br = 0.6$ therefore represents an upper limit for the S_N1 process. A procedure much less open to doubt would be to study non-solvolytic unimolecular reactions in ionizing solvents. Such experiments would allow the kinetic order of the reaction with respect to another solute to be established. All solvolytic measurements suffer from the inherent weakness that this most direct criterion concerning the molecularity of the reaction is not available. (Whether the nucleophilic participation of the solvent in reactions which are not entirely unimolecular should be described as a concurrent reaction or in terms of an intermediate mechanism is one of the problems that have arisen in consequence but which does not affect the strictly unimolecular rates which are our main concern in the present context.)[1]

In view of the remarks about the opposed structural effects on the rates of typical S_N1 and S_N2 reactions, the point should perhaps be made that this rate variation cannot be used as an infallible criterion of reaction mechanism in nucleophilic substitution reactions. Reactions which, from other evidence, are known to be bimolecular may give the reactivity sequence stated above for unimolecular reactions.[2] The implication is that these bimolecular reactions have transition states with some carbonium-ion character, i.e. that departure of the anion has progressed further than attachment of nucleophile to the carbonium centre.

Because of the preference for a planar arrangement of the bonds attached to a carbonium centre, carbonium ions in which the attainment of a planar or near-planar arrangement is impossible or energetically difficult are not expected to be stable. Tertiary halides are a class of compounds usually disposed towards unimolecular solvolysis. However, when the halogen is attached to a tertiary carbon atom which occupies a bridgehead position in a small bicyclic system, the carbonium ion generated would have such an unfavourable non-planar structure because coplanar bonds to the carbonium centre would require considerable deformation of the rings. The first demonstration of the correctness of these considerations was based on a kinetic fact, namely the observation that 1-apocamphanyl chloride (**4.7**) was solvolysed too slowly for the reaction to be detectable.[3] The total lack of reactivity in aqueous ethanol solution, even in the presence of potassium hydroxide or silver nitrate, indicates that both S_N1 and S_N2 mechanisms are very difficult, the latter because the cyclic structure prevents rearward attack by a nucleophilic reagent.[4] The

[1] Cf. Winstein, Grunwald and Jones, 1951; Gold, 1956b.
[2] Conant, Kirner and Hussey, 1925.
[3] Bartlett and Knox, 1939.
[4] Bartlett, 1951.

conclusion that the low S_N1 reactivity was due to the difficulty of forming a planar bridgehead ion has found support from ionization-potential measurements[1] and their approximate correlation with the rates of unimolecular solvolysis of the bromides.[2] Other factors may also be important: unfavourable non-bonded interactions (e.g. between the bridgehead carbon atoms in **4.7**) may be involved.[3]

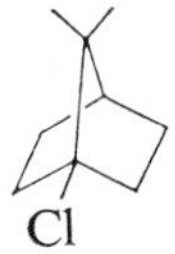

(4.7)

However there are also marked differences in reactivity between other bridgehead halides which are expected to have very similar conformational strain effects.[4] Despite their low rate of formation, 1-adamantyl cations (**4.8**) appear nevertheless to be quite stable in $SbF_5\text{-}SO_2$.[5]

(4.8)

It was pointed out above (Paragraph 4.2.1) that ionization rate measurements lead to stabilities of carbonium ion-like transition states relative to the stability of the parent molecules. Normally, structural effects on the stability of alkyl halides are considered less important than the effects on the carbonium ions, and, as in the preceding example, a sequence of rates is frequently thought of also as a sequence of intrinsic stabilities of carbonium ions. This reasoning is seriously wrong if the formation of a carbonium ion is substantially assisted by steric strain in the parent molecule. The increase in bond angles on going from tetrahedral to trigonal co-ordination allows an increase in the distances between non-bonded parts of the molecule and hence a decrease in the steric strain. An increase in rate on going from a less congested to a more congested starting structure may therefore reflect a substituent effect on properties of the reactants more than on properties of transition states related to carbonium

[1] Franklin and Field, 1953.
[2] Doering, Levitz et al., 1953.
[3] Gleicher and Schleyer, 1967.
[4] R. C. Fort and Schleyer, 1964a,b; Grob, Schwarz and Fischer, 1964.
[5] Schleyer, Fort et al., 1964.

ions.[1] The relevant information about the reactant molecules could be obtained by thermodynamic measurements, in particular heats of combustion, but this appears to be a somewhat neglected area of research. In the absence of reliable information of this kind it is difficult to gauge the importance of this "steric acceleration."[2]

A superficially clear case for steric acceleration is provided by a comparison of the unimolecular solvolysis rates of p-nitrobenzoates of hindered alcohols (in dioxane–water, 60:40 by weight, at 40°):[3]

$(t-Bu)_3C$	$(t-Bu)_2C.i-Pr$	$t-BuC(i-Pr)_2$	$(i-Pr)_3C$
31	8·3	8·5	1

The case becomes less straightforward once it is appreciated that the aliphatic solvolysis products are in each case olefins with a rearranged skeleton. This opens up several possible explanations for the rate sequence. Perhaps the most plausible of these assumes that the ionization does not lead to a carbonium ion of the same structure as the alkyl group in the ester. The occurrence of the simultaneous rearrangement can then be taken to be indicative of the fact that the unrearranged skeleton is not the most stable transition state, so that the rate comparison has nothing to do with the relief of steric strain by the opening out of the t-Bu—C—t-Bu bond angles. Of course, it may be argued that the rearrangement is also caused by steric strain, i.e. that even the planar unrearranged carbonium ion is too congested a structure so that further relief is obtained by its rearrangement.

This problem, whether the carbonium ion has a rearranged structure from that of its progenitor and whether partial rearrangement has taken place in the transition state leading to its formation, is a difficult one, and this difficulty has given rise to much controversy about so-called non-classical carbonium ions. This topic is treated more fully in Chapter 7. Its implications may be significant even in simple systems. For example, rearrangement to i-propyl systems seems to be the general consequence of generating carbonium ions from an n-propyl compound.[4] The most probable explanation of the fact that the rate of the S_N1 solvolysis of n-propyl bromide is very similar to that of ethyl bromide is that the hydride migration has not progressed up to the formation of the transition state and that the primary carbonium ion is probably the first ion produced. Anomalously large solvolysis rates are generally observed in rearranging systems of some complexity and congested struc-

---

[1] It is also possible for ionization to be hindered by steric effects. In particular, such hindrance is thought to arise in congested molecules in which the direction of departure of the leaving group is severely constrained by a rigid molecular frame, as in certain endo-substituted endo-norbornyl esters (see p. 233).

[2] H. C. Brown and Fletcher, 1949; H. C. Brown and Stern, 1950; F. Brown, Davies et al., 1951.

[3] Bartlett and Stiles, 1955.

[4] Gold and Satchell, 1963b.

ture for which either an explanation in terms of release of steric strain or rearrangement in the transition state (neighbouring-group participation) is superficially acceptable. Rate comparisons in such systems are therefore some- what enigmatic guides to the stability of carbonium ions: they reflect the energy difference between a strained parent molecule and a less strained but possibly partially rearranged carbonium ion-like transition state.

This kind of ambiguity does not apply in similar measure to solvolysis rate comparisons between alkyl, allyl and arylalkyl compounds under unimolecular conditions. The following relative rate constants (compiled by Streitwieser)[1] for the solvolysis at 50° of the respective chlorides in 80% aqueous ethanol are thought to reflect mainly the relative stabilities of the unrearranged carbonium ion-like transition states:

i-propyl	allyl	benzyl	α-phenylethyl	t-butyl	diphenylmethyl
0·70	52	100	7400	8200	$\sim 10^7$

4.2.3 SUBSTITUENT EFFECTS: σ^+- AND σ^*-VALUES

σ^+-*Values*. The second main application of rate measurements in relation to carbonium ion stability builds on the experience gained in the detailed study of the ionization reactions of alkyl halides. By comparing the solvolysis rates, in 90% aqueous acetone at 25°, of cumyl chlorides (**4.9**) with different substituents in the aromatic ring, one can measure the influence of substitutents Y in stabilizing the transition state for a structure strongly disposed to unimolecular reactions.

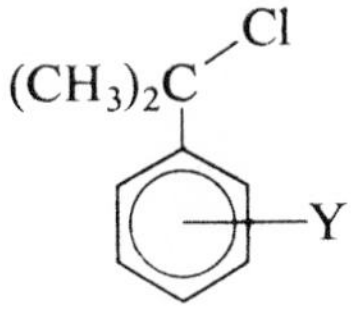

(**4.9**)

The system is well chosen[2] in that it appears to be free from complications due to steric effects, except when the substituent Y occupies an *ortho* position, and also because the solvolytic reactions do not lead to rearranged products. The effect of other ionizing solvents was investigated and shown to lead to similar substituent effects.[3] H. C. Brown and his school, to whom these measurements are due, used the results to define substituent constants σ^+ which are intended to give a measure of the effect of substituent groups on the stability of carbonium ions and carbonium ion-like structures. The definition

[1] Streitwieser, 1956b.
[2] H. C. Brown and Okamoto, 1957.
[3] Okamoto, Inukai and Brown, 1958.

of σ^+ in terms of the rate coefficients for unsubstituted and substituted cumyl chlorides (k_H and k respectively), is Equation (4.23).

$$\log (k/k_H) = \rho\sigma^+ \qquad (4.23)$$

The equation is a modification of Hammett's $\rho\sigma$ rule [Equation (4.24)],[1] which attempted to provide a general correlation of rates and equilibrium

$$\log (k/k_H) = \rho\sigma \qquad (4.24)$$

constants of side-chain reactions of m- and p-substituted benzene derivatives, irrespective of the polar character of the reaction. The parameter ρ characterizes the reaction, and σ is characteristic of the substituent group and its position in the ring. The limitations of the procedure are revealed by the

Table 4.16. *Substituent effects on solvolysis rates of t-cumyl chlorides*[a]

	k/k_H			σ^+	
Substituent	*ortho*	*meta*	*para*	*meta*	*para*
H	(1)	(1)	(1)	(0)	(0)
OMe	105	0·610	3360	0·047	−0·778
SMe	—	0·192	553	0·158	−0·604
Ph	—	0·320	6·52	0·109	−0·179
Me	3·63	2·00	26·0	−0·066	−0·311
Et	2·07	1·94	22·0	−0·064	−0·295
i-Pr	0·847	1·87	18·8	−0·060	−0·280
t-Bu	—	1·85	14·4	−0·059	−0·256
SiMe$_3$	—	0·895	0·806	0·011	0·021
F	0·0502	0·0251	2·14	0·352	−0·073
Cl	0·00786	0·0156	0·305	0·399	0·114
Br	0·00606	0·0144	0·208	0·405	0·150
I	0·0110	0·0233	0·244	0·359	0·135
CO$_2$H	—	0·0345	0·0124	0·322	0·421
CO$_2^-$(K$^+$)	—	1·35	1·28	−0·028	−0·023
CO$_2$Me	—	0·0212	0·00605	0·368	0·489
CO$_2$Et	—	0·0217	0·00650	0·366	0·482
CF$_3$	—	0·00441	0·00106	0·520	0·612
CN	—	0·00279	0·00102	0·562	0·659
NO$_2$	—	0·000871	0·000257	0·674	0·790
NMe$_3^+$(Cl$^-$)	—	0·0220	0·0131	0·359	0·408

[a] Stock and Brown, 1963.

fact that, as more data have become available, it has been found necessary to abandon the view that a single substituent constant is adequate for all reactions, and a number of modified sets of substituent constants have been proposed to deal with specific classes of reactions. The first published attempt to derive substituent parameters for "electron deficient" reactions was based on the

[1] Hammett, 1935; for more recent reviews see Jaffé, 1953; Ritchie and Sager, 1964.

Beckman rearrangement of substituted acetophenone oximes.[1] The σ^+-values (derived from the cumyl chloride hydrolyses) represent the set of parameters considered applicable for the correlation of equilibrium constants of carbonium-ion forming equilibria and rate constants of reactions with carbonium ion-like transition states according to Equation (4.23). The value of the reaction constant ρ ($\equiv -4\cdot54$ in 90 % acetone–water at 25°) is chosen so as to connect the σ^+-values to the σ-values proposed by Hammett for the general correlation of substituent effects in different types of organic reactions according to Equation (4.24). (For the reasoning underlying this choice, see the review by Stock and Brown.[2]) Table 4.16 lists the relative rates and σ^+ constants thus obtained.

The interest of σ^+ constants to us lies in the fact that they attempt to remove the discussion of substituent effects away from specific examples and to cast the information in a more general form. Whether this goal is attainable, i.e. whether it is possible to define a single set of σ^+-values that is applicable to different reactions and equilibria, simply by using Equation (4.23) with different values for ρ, has often been debated.[3] The question is not one to which a simple yes–no answer can be given.[4] Of course, Equation (4.23), like the original Hammett $\rho\sigma$ rule [Equation (4.24)] cannot be exact, as Hammett[5] himself clearly pointed out. What is now under discussion is whether it represents a sufficiently good approximation to give predictions that are useful for a specific purpose. There are undoubtedly many cases where σ^+-values have been found useful, and estimates of σ^+ based on arylmethanol–arylmethyl cation equilibria[6] do not differ significantly from the parameters derived from the solvolyses of cumyl chlorides. Several reactions in which the formation of carbonium ions is plausibly considered to be the rate-determining process show $\rho\sigma^+$ correlations with large negative values of the reaction parameter ρ. These include the solvolysis of substituted diphenylmethyl p-nitrobenzoates in aqueous acetone ($\rho = -4\cdot12$ to $-3\cdot69$);[7] the *cis–trans* isomerization of cinnamic acids, which goes by way of hydration of the double bond and for which $\rho = -4\cdot3$,[8] the formation of cinnamic acids by the corresponding dehydration ($\rho = -4\cdot6$)[9] and the hydration of styrenes ($\rho = -3\cdot42$)[10] and phenylpropiolic acids ($\rho = -4\cdot79$).[11] Additional examples of correlations with σ^+ are the

---

[1] Pearson, Baxter and Martin, 1952; Ritchie and Sager, 1964.
[2] Stock and Brown, 1963.
[3] Cf. Ritchie and Sager, 1964.
[4] van Bekkum, Verkade and Webster, 1959.
[5] Hammett, 1935.
[6] Deno and Schriesheim, 1955; Deno and Evans, 1957.
[7] Silver, 1961a.
[8] Noyce and Avarbock, 1962.
[9] Noyce, King *et al.*, 1962.
[10] Schubert, Lamm and Keeffe, 1964.
[11] Noyce, Matesich *et al.*, 1965.

equilibrium constants for the protonation of substituted benzoic acids,[1] the rates of decomposition of diaryldiazomethanes catalysed by toluene-p-sulphonic acid,[2] of the Claisen rearrangement of allyl aryl ethers,[3] the decarboxylation of anthranilic acids,[4] the gas-phase pyrolysis of arylethyl acetates (see Paragraph 4.2.4), and, more surprisingly, the base-catalysed condensation of malononitrile with benzaldehydes,[5] and some free-radical reactions.[6] It may however, be doubted whether the inference that the corresponding transition states have carbonium-ion character is always justified.[7] It is likewise clear that the prediction of reaction rates from σ^+-values is in some cases inadequate,[8] and extended equations, with a larger number of parameters, have been discussed as possible improvements.[7]

The finding that there is a parallelism between σ^+-values and mass-spectrometric ionization potentials of substituted benzyl radicals[9] suggests that σ^+-values do capture—at least partially—a fairly fundamental property of carbonium ions: it also underlines very clearly the relevance of ionization potentials to the discussion of more complex processes (see Paragraph 4.1.3).

The value of the reaction constant ρ measures the susceptibility of a reaction to substituent effects. If we maintain that the chief stabilizing action of a substituent group is that of charge dispersal (see Section 5.2), we would expect the formation of the fully charged gaseous cation to be accompanied by the largest negative ρ-value. This prediction is borne out by the ionization potentials of benzyl radicals given in Table 4.3 ($\rho = -20$). The fact that ρ-values of most carbonium ion-forming reactions in solution are considerably smaller (cf. $\rho = -4 \cdot 54$ for t-cumyl chlorides) then implies that the charge concentration in the solvated transition state of such a reaction is considerably less than that of a free gaseous ion.

The main and very successful application of σ^+-values has been in the discussion of electrophilic aromatic substitution and side-chain reactions of aromatic compounds,[10] so that the comparison between different reactions involves not only transition states which show varying degrees of resemblance to carbonium ions but also structurally different carbonium ions. For example, formulae **4.10** and **4.11** represent the transition state (and the related

[1] Stewart and Yates, 1960.
[2] Bethell and Callister, 1963b.
[3] White and Fife, 1961.
[4] Dunn and Prysiazniuk, 1961.
[5] Patai and Israeli, 1960.
[6] Huyser, 1960; Bartlett and Rüchardt, 1960.
[7] Ritchie and Sager, 1964.
[8] Fox and Kohnstam, 1964.
[9] Harrison, Kebarle and Lossing, 1961.
[10] Stock and Brown, 1963.

carbonium ion) relevant to the S_N1 reaction of benzyl chloride, formulae **4.12** and **4.13** the corresponding structures for aromatic nitration.

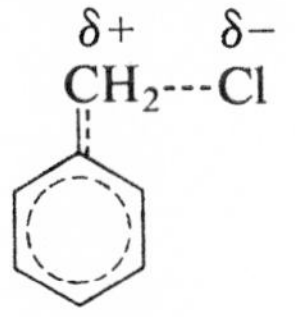

$$\overset{\delta+}{C}H_2\overset{\delta-}{\cdots}Cl$$

(4.10)

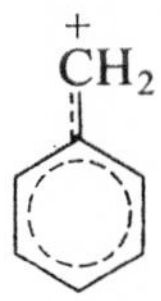

$$\overset{+}{C}H_2$$

(4.11)

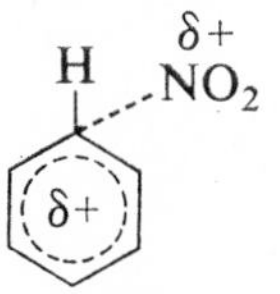

$$H\underset{\quad}{\overset{\delta+}{\cdots}}NO_2$$

(4.12)

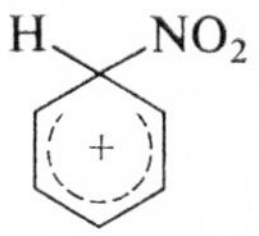

$$H\underset{\quad}{\diagdown}NO_2$$

(4.13)

The fact that carbonium ion-like structures are found in the transition states of many organic reactions is, of course, an added reason for the great general interest taken in the chemistry of carbonium ions although superficially they represent merely a rather special class of organic species.

σ^*-*Values.* The effect of substituent groups on reaction rates for aliphatic compounds has been approached along similar lines. Basically, this is a much more complex problem because of the lack of rigidity of the system and the greater proximity of the substituents to the reaction site. For these reasons the electrical effects of the substituents are complicated by steric ones. Considerable effort has gone into the problem of separating the two types of effect, and a treatment due to Taft[1] has achieved a good deal of success also for carbonium ion reactions.

The procedure, based on a much earlier proposal by Ingold,[2] starts from a comparison of rates of acid- and base-catalysed ester hydrolyses. These two types of hydrolysis are thought to involve similar mechanisms for simple methyl or ethyl esters, with transition states of rather similar structure but different charge distribution. Consequently substituent groups may be considered to exert similar steric effects in acid and base hydrolysis. On the other hand the polar requirements of acid and base hydrolysis will be different and, accordingly, their rates should show a different susceptibility to the inductive effects of substituent groups. Taft therefore expressed the polar effect of groups by the parameter σ^*, defined by Equation (4.25),

$$\sigma^* = \frac{1}{2 \cdot 48} [\log (k/k_0)_B - \log (k/k_0)_A] \tag{4.25}$$

where k and k_0 relate respectively to substituted and unsubstituted esters, and the subscripts B and A signify basic and acidic conditions of hydrolysis. The constant $2 \cdot 48$ is a scaling factor introduced so as to make the numerical values of σ^* similar in size to the Hammett substituent constants σ. The value of σ^* should be a measure of the polar substituent effect, divorced from steric (and resonance) effects.

[1] Taft, 1952, 1953, 1956.
[2] Ingold, 1931.

The justification of the procedure (which is subject to several provisos) lies in the reasonable correlation[1, 2] of a number of aliphatic substitution reactions according to a modified Hammett $\rho\sigma$ relation

$$\log (k/k_0) = \rho^*\sigma^* \qquad (4.26)$$

(sometimes called the Taft-Ingold equation) and by the apparent additivity of substituent effects σ^*. In the context of the subject of this book it is interesting that several carbonium ion-forming reactions obey Equation (4.26), with the implication that steric effects are nearly constant for the particular group of structures studied within each set. These reactions include[2] the solvolysis of tertiary alkyl halides in 80% aqueous ethanol ($\rho^* = 3\cdot29$). Significantly, lower ρ^*-values are observed for bimolecular aliphatic substitution reactions in solution.

Table 4.17. σ^*- and E_s-values of alkyl substituent groups[a]

	σ^*	E_s
H	$+0\cdot490$	—
CH_3	$0\cdot000$	$0\cdot00$
C_2H_5	$-0\cdot100$	$-0\cdot07$
$n\text{-}C_3H_7$	$-0\cdot115$	$-0\cdot36$
$i\text{-}C_3H_7$	$-0\cdot190$	$-0\cdot47$
$n\text{-}C_4H_9$	$-0\cdot130$	$-0\cdot39$
$i\text{-}C_4H_9$	$-0\cdot125$	$-0\cdot93$
$t\text{-}C_4H_9$	$-0\cdot300$	$-1\cdot54$
$neo\text{-}C_5H_{11}$	$-0\cdot165$	$-1\cdot74$
$(C_2H_5)_2CH$	$-0\cdot225$	$-1\cdot98$

[a] Taft, 1956.

The σ^*-values (Table 4.17) reproduce the sequence of inductive effects given in earlier, more qualitative formulations of the electronic theory of organic chemistry. For alkyl groups, the effects of chain-lengthening and branching are completely in line with previous deductions.[3]

The idea that polar substituent constants can be assigned invariant values is an assumption which, in first approximation, has been sufficiently successful to gain widespread acceptance. We shall therefore not pursue the question whether further improvement in linear free energy correlations might be obtainable through the use of a separate set of σ^*-values applicable to carbonium ion-forming reactions by analogy with the distinction between σ and σ^+ substituent constants. The validity of such proliferation of $\rho\sigma$ correlations has recently been reviewed.[4]

[1] Taft, 1953.
[2] Streitwieser, 1956a.
[3] See, for example, Ingold, 1953.
[4] Ritchie and Sager, 1964.

Taft's analysis has similarly suggested that characteristic steric effects may be assigned to substituent groups. For reasons which have already been outlined (Section 3.1) this assumption is probably less justifiable than the corresponding treatment of polar effects. However, the approach has some predictive value, which presumably is confined to reactions with a relatively small or constant amount of steric hindrance.

Briefly,[1] Taft considers that substituent effects in acid-catalysed ester hydrolysis are a measure of the steric effect alone (since they are very similar for groups of the same size but quite different polar characteristics).[2] The steric effect of a group is therefore defined by Equation (4.27).

$$\log (k/k_0)_A = E_s \qquad (4.27)$$

It then follows from Equations (4.25) and (4.27) that the substituent effect on basic hydrolysis, where both electronic and steric effects operate, must be given by

$$\log (k/k_0)_B = E_s + 2 \cdot 48 \sigma^*$$

The E_s-values thus obtained bear a reasonable relation to the bulk of the groups concerned, and show no trend with the values of the corresponding σ^* constants.

For a reaction series in which polar effects are constant (or small) the linear free energy law for steric effects is

$$\log (k/k_0) = \delta E_s \qquad (4.28)$$

where the reaction constant δ is a relative measure of the susceptibility of the reaction to the steric requirements of the substituents. However, this condition is unlikely to be met in carbonium ion-forming or -destroying reactions, since we expect polar influences always to be important in such cases.

Equation (4.26) has been used for the detection of abnormal effects of substituents on velocities of carbonium ion-forming reactions in systems where the formation of bridged ions is a possibility (see Paragraphs 7.2.1, 7.5.1).

4.2.4 HETEROLYTIC REACTIONS IN THE GAS PHASE

The pyrolysis reactions of a number of alkyl halides in the gas phase have been found to be homogeneous unimolecular elimination processes leading to olefin and hydrogen halide. There is a qualitative parallelism between the substituent effects on the rates of these gas-phase eliminations and on those of the unimolecular solvolyses (leading to both substitution and elimination) of the same halides in polar solvents.[3] For this and similar reasons it has been suggested that there is a mechanistic analogy between these two types of reaction and that elongation of the carbon–halogen bond, with polarization in the

---

[1] For the full exposition of the theory, see Taft, 1956.

[2] In correlations of rate constants for acid-catalysed hydrolysis of *m*- and *p*-substituted benzoate esters with Hammett σ-constants, ρ is close to zero. Thus the polar effect of the substituents is small.

[3] Maccoll and Thomas, 1955a,b,c; Harden and Maccoll, 1955.

5

$\overset{\delta+}{C}$—$\overset{\delta-}{H}$al characterizes the transition state for pyrolysis. More recently, it has explicitly been proposed that this transition state can be represented as an intimate ion pair, i.e. as a pair of fully formed ions held together by electrostatic forces.[1]

Of the considerable number of kinetic features that have been listed as being in support of a common mechanism for pyrolysis and solvolysis[2] the effects of alkyl substituents in α- and β-positions are especially plausible for they do not find a ready explanation in terms of a homolytic mechanism for pyrolysis. It is found that α-methylation strongly enhances the rate so that, for example, the following rate sequence obtains

$$t\text{-BuCl} > i\text{-PrCl} > \text{EtCl}$$

There is a weaker effect of β-methylation, in the same sense, so that

$$s\text{-Bu} > n\text{-PrCl} > \text{EtCl}$$

Again, as in unimolecular reactions in polar solvents, Wagner-Meerwein rearrangements are sometimes observed. Thus, in the pyrolysis of neopentyl chloride, products derived from t-pentyl chloride account for the larger part of the reaction.[3] The pyrolysis of isobornyl chloride likewise gives mostly a rearranged product (camphene). Rearrangement to tricyclene and camphene predominates in the decomposition of bornyl chloride.[4]

On the other hand, the analogy between pyrolysis and unimolecular solvolysis in polar solvents breaks down in one respect, in that the gas-phase reaction involves *cis*-elimination,[5] whereas *trans*-elimination occurs in polar solvents. Whilst this was at first regarded as a difficulty,[6] a reason for the difference is suggested by more recent work on the stereochemistry of the ionic addition of hydrogen halides in non-polar solvents.[7] This reaction, being the reversal of elimination, must have the same transition state as elimination by an ionic mechanism. It has been found that *trans*-addition is a characteristic of ionic addition only in polar solvents; in the non-polar solvent pentane the addition of deuterium bromide to acenaphthylene is still polar in character but nearly 90% of the addition product is the *cis*-isomer.[8] It follows that hydrogen halide elimination under these conditions should mainly be from *cis*-positions. It is also more likely that a gas-phase reaction will resemble a solution reaction in a non-polar solvent rather than the same reaction in a polar solvent. For these reasons, the *cis*-character of the gas-phase elimination no longer appears

[1] Ingold, 1957; Maccoll, 1965.
[2] Maccoll, 1964.
[3] Maccoll and Swinbourne, 1964.
[4] Bicknell and Maccoll, 1961, 1965.
[5] Barton, 1949.
[6] Maccoll, 1965.
[7] Dewar and Fahey, 1963a,b,c.
[8] Dewar and Fahey, 1963a.

to be anomalous. The stereochemical results in the addition reaction are interpreted in terms of the stability of ion pairs between carbonium ions and anions.

The pyrolysis reactions of alkyl esters are likewise *cis*-eliminations of olefins and have the character of polar reactions. The polar nature of the transition state, in which the alkyl group acquires carbonium ion-like character and the carboxylate becomes partially anionic, has been demonstrated by the effects of substituents in both halves of the molecule. In simple alkyl esters (acetates or formates) the sequence[1] t-Bu > i-Pr > Et is again found, reflecting the order of stability of the corresponding carbonium ions, but the relative rate differences are smaller than for the halides, and the reactivity of t-butyl esters follows the order dichloroacetate > chloroacetate > acetate which is the order of the stabilities of the anions (or of the strengths of the corresponding acids).[2] However, the polar requirements of the two moieties have been established in more detail by studies of the effects of substituents in aromatic rings attached either in the alcohol or in the acid component of the ester. Thus the rate of pyrolysis of ethyl[3] and isopropyl benzoates[4] is increased by the presence of electron-withdrawing substituents. The reaction velocities are well represented by $\rho\sigma$-relationships. σ^0-Values[5] (substituent constants thought to express inductive effects only) give the best fit. The corresponding ρ-values are 0·33 for the isopropyl esters and 0·20 for the ethyl esters. A similarly good fit is obtained in the related pyrolysis of ethyl phenyl carbonates, for which $\rho = 0·19$.[6] The effect of *ortho*-substituents is the same as that of *para*-substituents for the ethyl and isopropyl benzoates,[7] indicating that there can be but little steric hindrance. Excellent correlations between reaction velocities and substituent constants σ^+ hold for 1-aryl-2-phenylethyl acetates, 1-arylethyl acetates, and 2-arylethyl acetates.[8] These indicate that the stability of the corresponding carbonium ion is also decisive for the stability of the pyrolysis transition state.

Whilst these extensive studies on esters, chiefly due to G. G. Smith and his school, clearly establish the importance of some charge separation in the transition state, the ρ-values also permit us to estimate that the charges are but slightly developed. By contrast with the values of −0·66 and −0·62 for 1-arylethyl and 1-aryl-2-phenylethyl acetates, i.e. for substitution in a 1-aryl ring, the ρ-values of S_N1 solvolysis of aryldimethylmethyl (t-cumyl) chlorides (where the substituents are likewise in a 1-aryl ring) are in the region of −4·5.

[1] Maccoll, 1959.
[2] Emovon, 1963.
[3] G. G. Smith, Jones and Brown, 1963.
[4] G. G. Smith and Jones, 1963.
[5] Taft, 1960a.
[6] G. G. Smith, Jones and Taylor, 1963.
[7] G. G. Smith and Brown, 1964; D. A. K. Jones and Smith, 1964.
[8] G. G. Smith, Bagley and Taylor, 1961; Taylor, Smith and Wetzel, 1962.

(The precise value depends slightly on the solvent used.[1]) More exact conclusions from the magnitude of the ρ-values of pyrolyses are made difficult by the fact that they are significantly dependent on temperature.[2]

It can similarly be concluded that the polarity of the transition state for the pyrolysis of alkyl halides is not very great though apparently more pronounced than in ester pyrolysis. Maccoll[3] has pointed out that there is a linear relationship between the activation energy of this reaction and the heterolytic bond dissociation energy (see Table 4.4) for a number of alkyl chlorides and bromides. However, the slope of the line is only 0·28, indicating that the transition state is not much like a free carbonium ion. (Of course, such an extreme view of the transition state has never been seriously entertained.) The difference between activation energies and heterolytic bond dissociation energies can be rationalized as the coulombic attraction energy between carbonium and halide ions.[4]

The geometry of the transition state for ester pyrolysis is usually taken to involve a six-membered ring,[5] and the reaction is thought to proceed thus:

$$
\begin{array}{ccc}
\displaystyle \begin{array}{c}
\mathrm{C-C} \\
/ \quad\ \ \backslash \\
\mathrm{O} \qquad \mathrm{H} \\
\backslash \\
\mathrm{C=O} \\
| \\
\mathrm{R}
\end{array}
&
\longrightarrow
\left[\ \begin{array}{c}
\mathrm{C\cdots C} \\
\mathrm{O} \qquad\qquad \mathrm{H} \\
\mathrm{C\cdots O} \\
| \\
\mathrm{R}
\end{array}\ \right]^{\ddagger}
&
\longrightarrow
\begin{array}{c}
\mathrm{C=C} \\
\mathrm{O} \qquad\ \mathrm{H} \\
\backslash\ \ / \\
\mathrm{C-O} \\
| \\
\mathrm{R}
\end{array}
\end{array}
$$

The idea of the cyclic transition state is, of course, connected with the *cis*-character of the elimination.[6] Whilst such a transition state is very plausible, this sterochemical evidence does not, in the light of the considerations of the *cis*-elimination from alkyl halides noted above, look as convincing now as it did a few years ago.

In the context of the present chapter the significance of the gas-phase experiments lies in the way in which they permit the order of stabilities of polar transition states and hence presumably of carbonium ions to be quantitatively established under conditions where subsituent effects cannot be modified through hydrogen-bonding or other modes of interaction with a solvent. On the other hand, the transition state still involves interaction between its (completely or partially) cationic or anionic halves and, if the interpretations that have been placed on the observations are correct, there is thus a possibility that the gas-phase work may lead to experimental values for the energetics of some of these interactions. Experiments in this field thus promise to become

[1] Okamoto, Inukai and Brown, 1958.
[2] Taylor, Smith and Wetzel, 1962.
[3] Maccoll, 1962.
[4] Maccoll and Thomas, 1955a.
[5] Hurd and Blunck, 1938.
[6] DePuy and King, 1960.

an even more significant link between ionization potentials and the energetics of S_N1 solvolysis reactions.

4.2.5 AROMATIC HYDROGEN-ISOTOPE EXCHANGE

The aromatic substitution reaction most closely related to carbonium ions is electrophilic hydrogen-isotope exchange. This reaction represents one of the main applications of kinetic measurements to the study of carbonium ion stabilities. In essence the hydrogen exchange in an aromatic compound catalysed by an acid HA involves two kinetically important steps, shown in Equation (4.29) for the replacement of deuterium by protium in benzene under conditions in which the exchange proceeds essentially in one direction only,

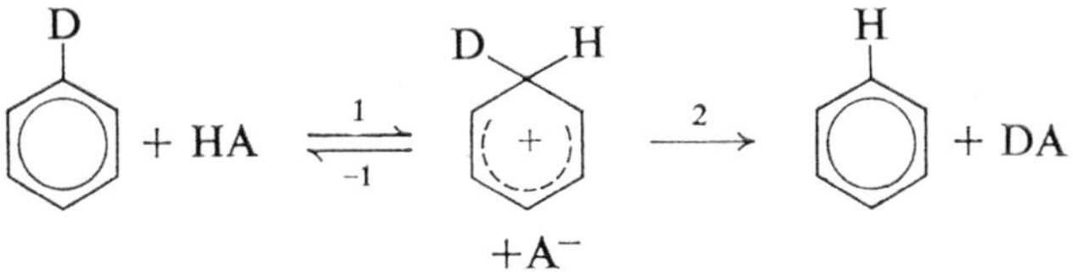

(i.e. when the abundance of deuterium in the reaction medium and therefore in the catalysing acid is very small).[1] The first-order rate constant λ for isotope exchange is accordingly given by Equation (4.30), since the intermediate

$$\lambda = \frac{k_1 k_2}{k_{-1}+k_2} [HA] \qquad (4.30)$$

carbonium ion will not be present in high concentration under conditions where the exchange is a slow reaction. The rate constant k_1 relates to the formation of the carbonium ion. The factor $k_2/(k_{-1}+k_2)$ represents a kinetic isotope effect and, whilst this is expected to vary somewhat with the nature of the aromatic substrate,[2] the change is regular and the reported extreme values for it are 0·23 and 0·10. Subject to this factor, the exchange rates therefore measure the rates of proton attachment to isotopically labelled aromatic compounds.

In the case of this reaction it is possible to make an approximate estimate of the degree to which the transition state resembles the carbonium ion intermediate. In aqueous acids, aromatic hydrogen exchange has been shown (for several substrates) to be subject to general acid catalysis.[3] The catalytic coefficients k_{HA} are related to the dissociation constants K_{HA} of the respective acids according to the Brönsted catalysis law [Equation (4.31)].

$$\log k_{HA} = \alpha \log K_{HA} + \text{constant} \qquad (4.31)$$

[1] The experimental evidence has recently been reviewed by Gold, 1964; Batts and Gold, 1964.

[2] Melander and Olsson, 1956.

[3] Kresge and Chiang, 1959, 1961b; Colapietro and Long, 1960; Challis and Long, 1963; Schulze and Long, 1964; R. J. Thomas and Long, 1964.

The constant α is a measure of the degree of proton transfer in the transition state and, in the case of reactive aromatic substrates (1,3,5-trimethoxybenzene, for example), has a value close to one-half.[1] The implication is that the proton is half-transferred in the transition state.

This interpretation of the value of the Brönsted exponent requires that the exchange rate constants for different aromatic substrates and the same concentration of catalysing acid should be related to the basicities (K_B) of the aromatic compounds according to Equation (4.32).

$$\log \lambda = \alpha \log K_B + \text{constant} \qquad (4.32)$$

If it is justified to assume α to a value close to one-half, it would then follow that the relative basicities of feebly basic aromatic hydrocarbons (to form carbonium ions by protonation on carbon) can be calculated from measurements of exchange velocities in strongly acidic media at fixed values of H_0. It similarly follows that the relative stabilities of isomeric carbonium ions formed by protonation at different aromatic carbon atoms of the same compound can be derived from the relative rates of exchange at these different nuclear positions, provided there are no specific stereochemical differences near the reaction site of the aromatic substrate, so as to invalidate the Brönsted law.[2] This condition may approximately be satisfied in the absence of *ortho*-substituents.

Some of the other limitations of the procedure should be apparent from the previous remarks about acidity functions (Paragraph 4.1.5). Although H_0 is *intended* to be a measure of the acidity of the medium towards any electrically neutral base, this is found not to be strictly correct: ionization ratios of indicators of different structure do not show the same dependence on the composition of an acid mixture. This lack of parallelism implies that the relative basicities and even the apparent order of basicities of two indicators may change with changing medium.

In exchange reactions, i.e. in the equilibrium between base and transition state, analogous factors operate, and relative reactivities depend on the medium used. Because exchange velocities can be measured over a very wide range of values (and hence over a much wider range of acidities than indicator ionization ratios), it is possible to observe this medium effect even by merely changing the composition of a water–mineral acid mixture. The reasons for this anomaly may in part be connected with the possibility of general acid catalysis even in highly acidic media.[3]

Table 4.18 reproduces some results which illustrate the dependence of relative exchange rates of hydrocarbons on the acidic medium used. They convey some indication of the dubious reliability that still attaches to estimates

[1] Kresge and Chiang, 1961b.
[2] Cf. R. J. Thomas and Long, 1964.
[3] Kresge, Hakka *et al.*, 1965.

of *small* differences in relative basicity based on exchange rates. One can be more confident about the significance of larger rate differences. For example, the larger rate of detritiation of toluene-*p-t* compared with the *m*-isomer indicates that methyl substitution in the 3-position of a completely cisoid pentadienyl cation is more stabilizing than methyl substitution in the 2-position.

More dramatic medium effects on reactivity are found if relative exchange rates in an anhydrous hydrogen halide solvent are compared with an aqueous

Table 4.18. *Relative rates of detritiation of aromatic substrates in acidic media at 25°[a]*

	Medium A[b]	Medium B[c]
Benzene-t_1	(1)	(1)
Toluene-*o*-t_1	541	330
-*m*-t_1	9·2	7·2
-*p*-t_1	702	313
t-Butylbenzene-*o*-t_1	—	393
-*m*-t_1	32	23·7
-*p*-t_1	863	387
Biphenyl-2-t_1	133	52
-3-t_1	—	0·68
-4-t_1	143	52
Naphthalene-α-t_1	1079	370
-β-t_1	127	62

[a] Eaborn and Taylor, 1961.
[b] $CF_3.CO_2H$-H_2O-H_2SO_4 (95·31:2·21:2·48 mole per cent).
[c] $CF_3.CO_2H$-H_2O-$HClO_4$ (92·04:5·45:2·51 mole per cent).

acid. This is intelligible since the reaction observed is a proton transfer from an acid to the aromatic compound and the change in medium will now cause the nature of the transition state to change. Such change of the transition state may involve not only the actual stoichiometric composition but also the extent of proton transfer.

However, because exchange can be measured over a very wide range of velocities, it is possible to confine a comparison of reactivities to a single medium. (Because ionization ratios of indicators cannot be measured over a similar range it is not possible analogously to compare the basicities of a range of indicators in a single medium.) There is evidence that specific structural effects associated with the interaction between substrate, acid and medium, other than those connected with the basicity of the substrate, are probably small in exchange reactions. Relative values of exchange velocities in a single medium are therefore likely to provide roughly the correct sequence of the relative basicities of aromatic molecules, i.e. of the stabilities of carbonium ions relative to aromatic molecules, even when these stabilities are very low and therefore not measurable by other techniques. The difficulty of a more precise treatment is apparent from Equation (4.32). The required factor α is so far known only for a few, very reactive aromatic substrates in dilute aqueous acid, and its value may change when substrates of drastically different reactivity are employed. More seriously, systematic comparisons of exchange reactivity have generally employed non-aqueous acid media for which no information concerning α is available. The seriousness of this lack of information is underlined by the fact that relative measurements in different media are significantly different, which indicates that α is indeed a sensitive function of the solvent. By comparison with these uncertainties, the small change in the isotope effect as a result of substrate variation and the resultant uncertainty of the precise relationship between the rates of exchange and protonation are insignificant.

There is, however, some evidence for the reality of Equation (4.32) for correlating base strength with exchange constants, at least over a short range of basicities. For example, the rate constants for deuterium exchange at the 10-position of monomethylbenz[a]anthracenes in a medium composed of deuterioacetic acid, sulphuric acid and p-chlorotoluene (in the weight proportion 10:1:5) are related to the basicities of these substrates (measured spectrophotometrically in hydrofluoric acid) according to Equation (4.32).[1] The slope α of the logarithmic graph again has a value close to one-half but, in view of the change in medium between the two sets of results, the significance of this value is not certain. Similar correlations—though sometimes with different slopes—have been reported for methylbenzenes[2] and for polycyclic aromatic hydrocarbons.[3] Where such correlations exist, it is possible to interpolate the basicities of aromatic compounds from measured exchange rates.

4.2.6 OLEFIN HYDRATION

The kinetics of the acid-catalysed addition of water to olefins bears a somewhat similar relationship to olefin–carbonium ion equilibria as aromatic hydrogen exchange does to the equilibria between aromatic hydrocarbons and the carbonium ions which are their conjugate acids. The mechanism of the reaction in aqueous solution involves proton transfer from the catalysing acid to olefin in the rate-limiting step, by which we mean that in the transition state the proton occupies a position *en route* from the catalysing acid to the site which it occupies in the product alcohol. Detailed kinetic studies have not systematically explored a wide range of structural changes in the olefin and it is

---

[1] Dallinga, Smit and Mackor, 1958.
[2] Mackor, Smit and van der Waals, 1957.
[3] Dallinga, Verrijn Stuart *et al.*, 1957.

not certain that the conclusions about mechanism, which are in the main derived from work on isobutene, styrene, α-methylstyrene[1] and closely related compounds, are necessarily valid for all olefins.

The formation of the carbon–oxygen bond of the alcohol is considered to be subsequent to and not synchronous with the proton transfer, so that the product of the rate-limiting step is cationic. In view of the comparatively high stability of t-butyl, $\overset{+}{PhCHMe}$, and $\overset{+}{PhCMe_2}$ cations (the products of adding just a proton to isobutene, styrene and α-methylstyrene, respectively) it is plausible to assume that it is these carbonium ions which are the cationic products of the rate-limiting step of hydration.

This model should allow us to proceed from relative hydration rates of structurally similar olefins to their relative basicities, on the basis of Equation (4.32), as soon as reliable values of α become available. In the case of isobutene α is only slightly less than unity.[2] It is already known that p-substituent groups in styrene influence the hydration rate according to their σ^+-values.[3] Since α is less than unity, the basicities of the styrenes must cover a larger range of values than their rates of hydration.

The addition of the proton to the olefin is here considered to be the rate-limiting step which precedes the attachment of the hydroxyl group. This discussion should therefore be applicable, with minor modifications, to other addition reactions to olefins which share the same initial process but in which the carbonium ion is then converted into different products. A limited comparison between methoxy-substituted ethylenes is possible on this basis.[4]

4.2.7 ISOTOPE EFFECTS

Although a number of experiments on primary isotope effects of carbonium-ionization reactions have been reported, the position is still not satisfactory, mainly because of the very small size of heavy-atom isotope effects.

The replacement of protium in the organic substrate by deuterium in general leads to a significant reduction in the rate of carbonium-ion formation. The effect is still fairly small but, because the comparison concerns such closely similar systems, can often be measured with reasonable precision. According to the position of the deuterium substitution, one speaks of α- and β-hydrogen isotope effects. Substitution of several deuterium atoms magnifies the effect. In the case of t-butyl chloride the replacement of all nine hydrogen atoms by deuterium causes a *ca.* 2·4-fold rate reduction.[5] The rate reduction corresponds to a destabilization of the carbonium ion-like transition state.

[1] Boyd, Taft *et al.*, 1960; Gold and Kessick, 1965a,b; Schubert and Lamm, 1966; Deno, Kish and Peterson, 1965.

[2] Gold and Kessick, 1965a,b.

[3] Schubert, Lamm and Keeffe, 1964.

[4] Gold and Waterman, 1967; Kresge and Chiang, 1967.

[5] Frisone and Thornton, 1964; Hakka, Queen and Robertson, 1965.

5*

Much of the discussion of these effects, especially the β-hydrogen isotope effect, has been concerned with the question of the origin of the stabilizing influence of methyl substituents on carbonium ions, i.e., whether it is more appropriate to describe this as an inductive or as a hyperconjugative effect. Although a great deal of thought has been devoted to this issue,[1] it is still not altogether clear to what extent this distinction is operationally significant for alkyl compounds and to what extent it is merely linguistic. Carbonium ions with α-phenyl groups tend to be more stabilized by CH_3 groups in *ortho* and *para* positions than by CD_3 groups, whereas there is practically no difference between the effects of CH_3 and CD_3 groups in *meta* positions. It would appear that in these particular circumstances an explanation couched in terms of hyperconjugation corresponds more closely to established usage.[2]

4.3 Survey of Stable Carbonium Ions

Many typical carbonium ions have already been mentioned in the preceding sections of the book by way of illustration of principles. However, whereas some ions received mention, others were neglected simply because they did not seem to lend themselves so well for this purpose. The present brief section seeks to redress the balance somewhat by looking at the whole field from the point of view of the nature of the ions, irrespective of whether their formation occurs by a particularly interesting reaction or whether their study has proved of notable importance.

The first class of carbonium ions to receive intensive study were triphenyl-methyl cations and their close relatives. A very large number of triphenylmethyl cations with substituents in the aromatic ring are known, many of them in the form of crystalline salts. Diphenylmethyl cations are considerably less stable; solutions in aqueous sulphuric acid decompose rapidly,[3] but they can be prepared and kept in SbF_5-SO_2 at low temperatures,[4] as can methyl-substituted benzyl cations.[5] In all these cases nuclear substituents exert a profound effect on the stability, dimethylamino, methoxyl and methyl substituents being especially effective in stabilizing the ions. α-Fluorine atoms increase the stability of benzyl and diphenylmethyl cations.[6] α-Chlorine atoms may have a similar effect, in view of the reported formation of the ion **4.14** on dissolution of 2,4,6-trimethylbenzotrichloride in sulphuric acid.[7] Increased stability is also found in trixenyl (tri-*p*-biphenylyl)methyl cations. By

[1] For extensive reviews, see Dewar, 1962; Halevi, 1963.

[2] Shiner and Verbanic, 1957; E. S. Lewis, 1959.

[3] Gold and Tye, 1952a.

[4] Olah, 1964.

[5] Cupas, Comisarow and Olah, 1966.

[6] Olah, Cupas and Comisarow, 1966.

[7] Gillespie and Robinson, 1964; Deno, Friedman and Mockus, 1964; Robinson and Ciruna, 1964.

comparison with diphenylmethyl cations, xanthydryl (xanthenyl) (**4.15**) cations are much more stable, fluorenyl cations **4.16** less so. Because of the great stability of the triphenylmethyl cation it is even possible to prepare

(**4.14**)

(**4.15**)   (**4.16**)

$SbCl_6^-$ salts of doubly charged carbonium ions derived from this structure, e.g. **4.17** and its *m*-isomer.[1] The preparation of the salt of a corresponding tricarbonium ion, $1,3,5\text{-}C_6H_3(CPh_3)_3$, has also been claimed.[2]

The great stabilities of a number of more recently discovered conjugated carbonium ions were predicted from simple quantum-mechanical considerations (HMO method, see Paragraph 5.2.3), before the discovery of the ions or else explained soon after their discovery. The most remarkable prediction was that of the cycloheptatrienyl cation (**4.1**). Hückel recognized the stability of this structure in 1931;[3] its preparation was announced only as recently as 1954.[4] Other examples are the phenalenyl cation (**4.18**),[5] the

(**4.17**)   (**4.18**)

1-azulenium cation (**4.19**),[6] heptalenium cations (**4.20**),[7] and substituted cyclopropenyl cations (**4.21**).[8] These structures are the most stable carbonium ions

[1] Hart, Sulzberg and Rafos, 1963; Volz and Volz de Lecea, 1964.

[2] Volz and Volz de Lecea, 1966.

[3] E. Hückel, 1931.

[4] Doering and Knox, 1954; H. J. Dauben, Gadecki *et al.*, 1957.

[5] Gold and Tye, 1952c; Pettit, 1956.

[6] Heilbronner and Simonetta, 1952.

[7] H. J. Dauben and Bertelli, 1961.

[8] Breslow and Höver, 1960; Breslow and Chang, 1961; Breslow, Lockhart and Chang, 1961.

known and the stimulation of work in this field is one of the major achievements of the application of quantum-mechanical methods to organic chemistry. The ions **4.1** and **4.21** are examples of cyclic conjugated systems with $(4n+2)$ π-electrons (the corresponding values of n being 1 and 0 respectively). The high stability of this electronic complement was pointed out by Hückel ("Hückel's $4n+2$ rule"). Aryl derivatives of cycloheptatrienyl[1] and cyclopropenyl cations[2] are known but it seems to be more interesting that the di-n-propylcyclopropenyl cation is more stable than the diphenylcyclopropenyl cation.[3] The trichlorocyclopropenyl cation has also been prepared.[4] There is evidence that protonated cyclopropenone derivatives are to be regarded as hydroxycyclopropenyl cation derivatives.[5]

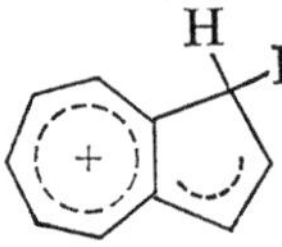

(4.19) 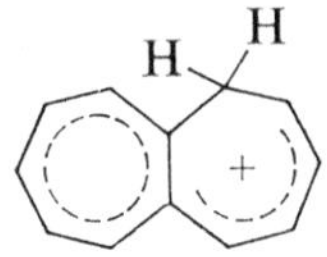   (4.20) 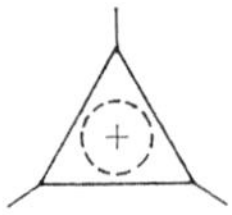   (4.21)

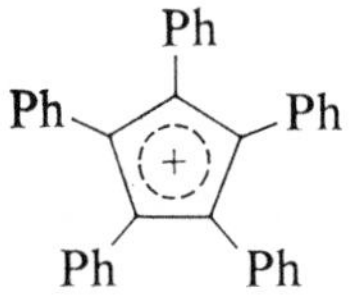

(4.22) 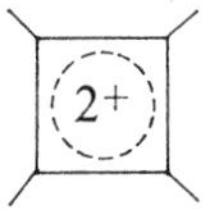   (4.23) 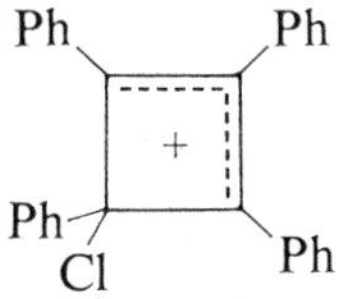   (4.24)

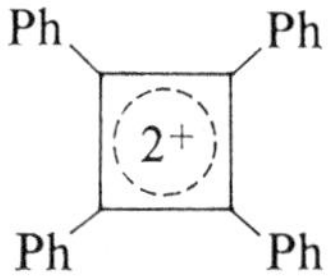

(4.25) 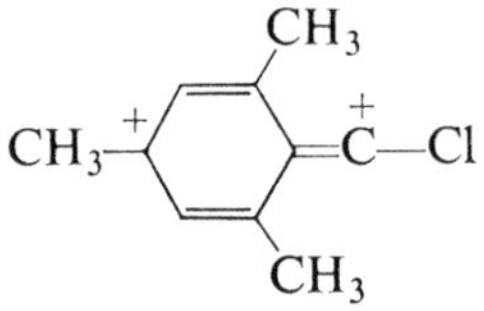   (4.26)

The cyclopentadienyl cation is not a "$4n+2$" system and not expected to be stable. Even its pentaphenyl derivative (**4.22**) can be prepared only at low temperatures. Molecular orbital theory predicts that cyclopentadienyl cations should have a low-lying triplet (diradical) state. This has been confirmed for

[1] van Helden, ter Borg and Bickel, 1962; Wilt and Piszkiewicz, 1963; Jutz and Voithenleitner, 1964.
[2] Breslow and Chang, 1961; Breslow, Lockhart and Chang, 1961.
[3] Breslow, Höver and Chang, 1962.
[4] Tobey and West, 1964.
[5] Breslow, Haynie and Mirra, 1959; Breslow and Peterson, 1960; Vol'pin, Koreshkov and Kursanov, 1959.

4.22.[1] The corresponding pentachloro-ion is a triplet in its ground state.[2] A similar possibility exists in the case of the phenyl cation.[3]

The cyclobutadienyl di-cation (**4.23**), on the other hand, is a "$4n+2$" system, and attempts have been made to prepare and prove the structure of this ion.[4] However, one of these preparations[5] was later shown to have produced the substituted cyclobutenyl cation **4.24** instead of the intended di-cation **4.25**.[6] The electrostatic repulsion in a small di-cation is here evidently too great. The same appears to be true of the supposed di-cation of structure **4.26**,[7] the evidence for which is more satisfactorily explained in terms of singly charged cations.[8]

The ion **4.24** contains a substituted allyl system in an otherwise saturated ring. A large number of cationic systems of this general type have been reported. The evidence generally does not include the preparation of crystalline salts, as in the above example,[9] but rests on spectroscopic data for solutions. Cations containing allyl groups in four-membered,[10] five-membered and six-membered rings[11] have been studied. The cyclic allyl cations are more stable than the corresponding open-chain ions, the cyclopentenyl cations being the most stable ones.[12] Methylation at the terminal positions of the allyl system greatly enhances the thermodynamic stability of both open-chain and cyclic allyl cations. The unsubstituted allyl cation and the 2-methylallyl cation can, however, be prepared in SbF_5-SO_2 solution at $-60°$.[13] The pentachloroallyl cation forms several stable solid salts.[14]

The allyl cation is the first member of the series of linear conjugated carbonium ions. Derivatives of the next member of the series, the pentadienyl cation,[15] are more stable than those of the allyl cation. In talking about the stability of these classes of ions one must be careful to distinguish thermodynamic stability with respect to precursors—which is the sense in which these systems have high stability—and stability with respect to possible secondary

[1] Breslow, Chang and Yager, 1963; Breslow, Chang *et al.*, 1967.

[2] Breslow, Hill and Wassermann, 1964; Breslow, Chang *et al.*, 1967.

[3] Taft, 1961.

[4] Freedman and Frantz, 1962; Farnum and Webster, 1963.

[5] Freedman and Frantz, 1962.

[6] Bryan, 1964; Freedman and Young, 1964.

[7] Hart and Fish, 1958, 1960, 1961.

[8] Gillespie and Robinson, 1964; Deno, Friedman and Mockus, 1964; Robinson and Ciruna, 1964.

[9] Bryan, 1964.

[10] Katz, Hall and Neikam, 1962; Katz and Gold, 1964.

[11] Deno, Richey *et al.*, 1962a, 1963; Deno, Bollinger *et al.*, 1963; Deno, Friedman *et al.*, 1963.

[12] Deno, Bollinger *et al.*, 1963.

[13] Olah and Comisarow, 1964.

[14] West and Kwitowski, 1966.

[15] Sorensen, 1964.

reaction products. In the latter sense the allyl and dienyl cations are frequently very unstable. Rearrangement of cyclic ions[1] and cyclization of linear ions[2] occur very readily, but, by the use of low temperatures, it is possible to slow down the cyclization sufficiently for the observation of the NMR spectrum of the linear pentadienyl cation.[3] Reactions which destroy carbonium ions are particularly troublesome in media containing comparable concentrations of carbonium ion and olefin (conditions which can never entirely be avoided in the formation of the carbonium ion by protonation of olefin in an acidic medium). The rate of decomposition generally passes through a maximum for equal concentrations of cation and olefin.[4] Cyclic pentadienyl systems contained in a six-membered ring are obtained by protonation of aromatic compounds (see Section 3.3). Here again methylation or anellation of the benzenoid ring increases the stability of the carbonium ions. A particularly stable member of the class is the heptamethylcyclohexadienyl ion (**4.27**).[5] Closely related

(**4.27**)   (**4.28**)   (**4.29**)

to this are the spiro-carbonium ions **4.28** and **4.29**,[6] detectable in solution at low temperature.

Protonation on a ring carbon appears to be thermodynamically favoured over protonation on the oxygen atom of phenols or aromatic ethers.[7]

The increasing stability of polyenyl cations with chain length is also shown by the phenylated series with the general formula **4.30**.

$$[Ph(CH \cdots CH)_n \cdots CHPh]^+ \qquad (\textbf{4.30})$$

The tetrafluoroborate salts for $n = 0, 1, 2, 3, 4$ have been prepared and, whereas the salt with $n = 0$ (containing the diphenylmethyl cation) is stable only below $-40°C$, the last member is stable at room temperature.[8]

Ion pairs are reported to be formed when aliphatic polyenes (e.g. β-carotene) interact with strong organic acids, such as trichloroacetic acid, in benzene and

[1] Deno, Friedman *et al.*, 1963.
[2] Sorensen, 1964, 1965; Deno and Pittman, 1964; Deno, Pittman and Turner, 1965.
[3] Olah, Pittman and Sorensen, 1966.
[4] Deno, Richey *et al.*, 1963.
[5] Doering, Saunders *et al.*, 1958.
[6] Eberson and Winstein, 1965; Olah, Namanworth, *et al.*, 1967.
[7] Kresge, Barry *et al.*, 1962; Schubert and Quacchia, 1962, 1963; Birchall, Bourns *et al.*, 1964.
[8] Hafner and Pelster, 1961.

may contain long polyenyl cations.[1] The existence of such ions now rests on firm NMR evidence.[2] The colour change which occurs on adding acid to poly-cyclopentadiene, a polymer thought to contain some conjugated double bonds, is interpreted in a similar way.[3]

The direct observation of saturated aliphatic carbonium ions has been made possible by the use of solutions of hexafluoroantimonates of carbonium ions in antimony pentafluoride solution at low temperatures. These studies, reported in a series of papers by Olah (which have been the subject of a partial review[4]) have included t-butyl,[5] 1-adamantyl (**4.8**),[6] 2-norbornyl (**4.31**),[7] and even s-propyl cations.[8]

(4.31)

Diarylalkynyl cations (**4.32**) and other acetylenic cations have been prepared in acid solutions.[9]

$$\overset{+}{Ar_2C} . C{\equiv}C—CH_3 \qquad\qquad (4.32)$$

Cyclopropyl groups have a remarkable stabilizing effect on various aliphatic carbonium ions. Several workers had noted the accelerating influence of α-cyclopropyl groups on solvolysis rates.[10] This phenomenon was at first also ascribed to the formation of rearranged carbonium ions, the driving force of the rearrangement assisting the rate of heterolysis,[11] but Hart and Sandri recognized that the results implied high stability of unrearranged alkylcyclopropylmethyl cations. The correctness of the inference has been confirmed by the preparation of stable solutions of tricyclopropylmethyl cations (**4.33**)[12] and, at low temperatures, of related ions, such as **4.34**, **4.35** and **4.36**,[13] and by the kinetics of substitution reactions.[14] It has also been shown that cyclopropyl substituents

[1] Wassermann, 1954, 1957; Bauge, Smith and Wassermann, 1962.

[2] Sorensen, 1965.

[3] A. A. Levy and Wassermann, 1965.

[4] Olah and Pittman, 1966.

[5] Olah, Tolgyesi et al., 1963.

[6] Schleyer, Fort et al., 1964.

[7] Schleyer, Watts et al., 1964.

[8] Olah, Baker et al., 1964.

[9] Richey, Philips and Rennick, 1965; Pittman and Olah, 1965c; Richey, Rennick et al., 1965.

[10] E.g. J. D. Roberts and Mazur, 1951a; Bergstrom and Siegel, 1952; Hart and Sandri, 1959; Cox, Caserio et al., 1961.

[11] Mazur, White et al., 1959; Caserio, Graham and Roberts, 1960.

[12] Deno, Richey et al., 1962b; Hart and Law, 1962, 1964.

[13] Pittman and Olah, 1965a; Deno, Liu et al., 1965.

[14] Richey and Richey, 1966.

markedly stabilize cyclic alkyl and pentadienyl cations, such as **4.37**[1] (see Table 4.12). The comparative stability of the spiro-carbonium ions **4.28** and **(4.29)** can perhaps also be associated with the presence of a cyclopropyl ring adjoining carbon atoms with partial carbonium character.

(4.33)   **(4.34)**   **(4.35)**   **(4.36)**

(4.37)

Perchlorate salts of ions in which there is a possibility of interaction between the carbonium centre and a non-adjacent olefinic bond show greater stability than corresponding saturated ions. This is one of the arguments in favour of bridged structures (Chapter 7). A particularly pertinent example is the 7-norbornadienyl cation, prepared[2] as the fluoroborate in liquid sulphur dioxide at $-70°C$ and shown by NMR measurements to have a somewhat unsymmetrical structure **4.38**.[3] A related type of ion is that produced by protonation of cyclo-octatetraene and, on the basis of its NMR spectrum, assigned the "homocycloheptatrienyl" structure **4.39**.[4]

(4.38)   **(4.39)**

[1] Deno, Richey *et al.*, 1965.
[2] Story and Saunders, 1960.
[3] Story, Snyder *et al.*, 1963.
[4] Rosenberg, Mahler and Pettit, 1962; Keller and Pettit, 1966; Winstein, Kaesz *et al.*, 1965.

5 | FACTORS GOVERNING THE STABILITY OF CARBONIUM IONS

5.1 General Considerations

It was pointed out in Paragraph 4.1.2 that the "stability" of a carbonium ion can be defined only in relative terms, i.e. with reference to another species from which the carbonium ion can be derived or to which it can revert (the reference system). In the present section we shall further examine factors which influence the stability as conceived in this way.

Systems containing carbonium ions can be stabilized by factors practically unconnected with the carbonium ion itself (or the corresponding group of atoms in its precursor) (see however, Section 3.1 for some qualifications). Effects which can be assigned to this category have already been mentioned (Sections 3.2 and 3.3) and are exemplified by the interaction of the halide ion derived from an alkyl halide with a metal halide to form a complex anion, e.g.

$$RF + SbF_5 \rightarrow R^+ + SbF_6^-$$

They will not here be discussed further.

For the purposes of arrangement of the discussion of this book the factors which are concerned with the carbonium ion are themselves divided into "internal" and "external" ones. Internal factors are those solely considered in terms of the carbonium ion framework: substituent effects are an obvious example. "External" factors concern the interaction of the carbonium ion with the solvent, with the particle carrying the negative charge and, where relevant, with a neutral residue which has separated in the formation of the carbonium ion (see Section 3.2). The division is not perfectly defined. Although the "external" factors are largely electrostatic (and to that extent truly external) it will later be shown that they are in some measure chemically specific and can affect the chemistry of the carbonium ion moiety so as to influence the nature of reaction products, for example. Such effects can also be conceived in structural terms concerned with the carbonium ion which could with some justification be termed "internal" (see Paragraphs 5.3.2, 5.3.3 and 6.1.3).

5.2 Internal Factors

The stabilities of gaseous carbonium ions relative to alkyl halides or other saturated precursors can usefully be considered to be composed of two terms, associated with the steps

$$RX \xrightarrow{\ 1\ } R\cdot + X\cdot \xrightarrow{\ 2\ } R^+ + X^-$$

Accordingly, two quantities will affect the variation of the overall energetics (i.e. the heterolytic dissociation energy) with the nature of R: (1) the (homolytic) dissociation energy of R—X, which involves rehybridization and the creation of a new atomic arrangement of the radical R with a planar trigonal arrangement of bonds about the carbon atom to which the group X was initially attached, and (2) the ionization potential of R·. As can be seen from Table 4.4 the dissociation energies of alkyl compounds are expected not to be as sensitive to the nature of R as the ionization potentials, except where there are significant steric interactions between R and X (see Section 3.1), although the situation is different for allyl, benzyl or similar systems for which the dissociation process involves a more far-reaching change of the electronic structure of the system. For all systems, the ionization potential should reflect the ability of the system to adjust itself to the removal of an electron so as to minimize the energy.

5.2.1 ELECTROSTATIC ARGUMENTS

It is known that an electrostatic charge on a macroscopic conductor is distributed over the external surface of the conductor. This is an experimental fact, discovered by Faraday, which results from the mutual repulsion of like charges. This charge repulsion must also be present in an ion and will tend to drive the cationic charge of a carbonium ion to the surface of the ion and, indeed, by interaction with the solvent, beyond it (see Section 5.3). As a consequence, a large carbonium ion should be more stable (in the gas phase) than a smaller one, simply because the charge density at its surface is less. This charge repulsion probably accounts to a large extent for the clear trend of ionization potentials of related radicals to decrease as the size of the radical (and ion) increases (Table 4.3).

The effects of substituents in larger ions, at positions well removed from the atom at which the change in hybridization and stereochemistry occurs, can be understood in similar terms. For such substituents (at p-positions in benzyl, diarylmethyl and triarylmethyl cations, for example) the stability of the ion relative to its uncharged precursor can be interpreted by the ability of the substituent group to accept the positive charge at the surface of the ion. Sub-stituents described as electron-attracting, such as chlorine, tend to oppose this charge dispersal by binding the electrons which, for cation stabilization, should be released towards the carbonium centre. Electron-repelling substituents at the periphery will conversely stabilize the carbonium ion. As the success of the σ^+ parameters in expressing substituent effects on carbonium ions implies (Paragraph 4.2.3), this generalization holds—with minor reservations—for all phenomena reflecting carbonium-ion stabilities, including the ionization potentials of substituted benzyl radicals.

For instance, the difference in ionization potentials between methyl and t-butyl radicals, i.e. the enthalpy change of the reaction (5.1) can be roughly

$$\overset{\bullet}{C}H_3 + CMe_3^+ \rightarrow CH_3^+ + \overset{\bullet}{C}Me_3 \qquad (5.1)$$

calculated if we assume methyl and t-butyl cations to be electrically charged spheres of conductor having as radii the *maximum* covalent distances from the carbonium centres to the surface of the peripheral hydrogen atoms (1.37Å and 2.45Å respectively). The result (53 kcal mole^{-1}) compares with the experimental value (58 ± 2 kcal mole^{-1}, Table 4.3). The assumptions about the geometry of the particles can obviously be improved upon, but such refine-ment of this calculation would hardly be justified since structural effects on the stability of carbonium ions are more subtle. If the size of the ion were the sole determining factor for carbonium ions composed only of C and H atoms, the ionization potentials of these ions should follow directly from their dimensions, and Table 4.3 clearly shows that this is not so. The analogy with the macroscopic conductor is imperfect (a) because a carbonium ion is not composed of uniform material but contains regions of varying affinity for electrons, roughly indicated by the different atoms (different not only on account of their chemical nature but also because of different co-ordination numbers, or valence states), and (b) because the distribution of electrons in a particle of molecular dimensions is subject to the restrictions of quantum mechanics. As a result the charge of the carbonium ion is not confined to the peripheral atoms of the ion but is distribu-ted over the entire ion in a non-uniform pattern. The delocalization of the charge away from the carbonium centre, with resultant electrification of other atoms is sometimes referred to as internal charge dissipation.

The reality of the charge dissipation is most readily demonstrated by the chemical shifts in the NMR spectra of carbonium ions. The low proton screen-ing-constants generally observed in carbonium ions are a consequence of the low electron density on the hydrogen atoms.

5.2.2 GENERAL AIMS OF QUANTUM-MECHANICAL CALCULATIONS ON CARBONIUM IONS

As yet, the exact correlation of charge densities and screening constants is not possible, although several useful suggestions for such correlations have been made (Section 2.3). It follows that there is at present no absolutely reliable physical measurement by which one can test more sophisticated (quantum-mechanical) calculations of charge distribution either in electrically neutral molecules or in charged species such as carbonium ions. The experimental situation is however slightly better in the case of conjugated systems than for saturated species. In the former type of system, it has been recognized for some time that quantum-mechanical calculations of chemical reactivity at alternative sites within the same molecule, for reactions in which reactivity is thought to be linked to charge density, can successfully be correlated with experimental observations (as given, for example, by the isomer distributions or partial rate factors for substitution at the different positions of aromatic compounds).[1] It is even more significant that certain equilibrium constants involving conjugated molecules and bond lengths can be both measured and predicted from calculation. The empirical success of a large number of such calculations[2] leads us to believe that the physical model used in them has a basis in reality and that the approximations involved are not too violent. In turn we are led to accept that other statements about the molecules—based on the same method of calculation—are justified although these statements cannot as yet be tested to a significant accuracy. As will be shown below, some of the verifiable calculations are directly concerned with carbonium ions so that we may optimistically expect the same type of calculation to produce sensible answers for the charge distribution within conjugated carbonium ions. Because of the wider possibilities for testing theory which conjugated systems offer they have generally proved more attractive to theoreticians than saturated systems for which ionization potentials are the chief experimental facts with which theoretical treatments can be compared. We shall therefore consider first the quantum-mechanical results for charge distributions and energies of conjugated carbonium ions.

To chemists conditioned by classical valency rules the resonance description of conjugated systems offers qualitatively the simplest account of their stability and of the charge dispersal. In this formulation of theory the stability of allylic cations is attributed to resonance between the equivalent canonical structures **5.1** and **5.2** in which the double bond, formed by overlap of carbon $2p$-orbitals, occupies alternative positions for the same arrangement of the nuclei. In its mathematical elaboration, which is outside the scope of this book, this valence-bond theory leads to values of the energy of the real molecule relative

$$RCH{=}CH{-}\overset{+}{C}HR \qquad\qquad R\overset{+}{C}H{-}CH{=}CHR$$

$$\textbf{(5.1)} \qquad\qquad\qquad \textbf{(5.2)}$$

to that of a hypothetical molecule with the fixed-bond structure of formula **5.1**. The great stability of ions such as the triphenylmethyl cation is then

[1] Greenwood and McWeeny, 1966.
[2] Streitwieser, 1961.

associated with the very large number of valence bond structures of comparable energy that can be written for it (e.g. **5.3, 5.4, 5.5**).

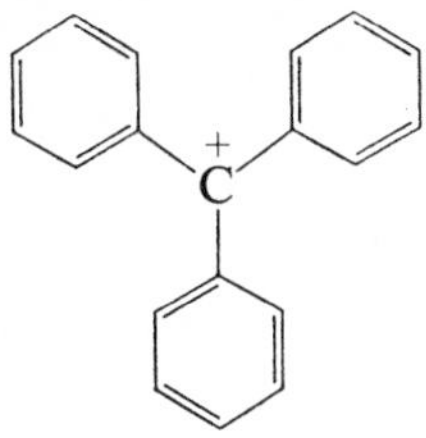

(5.3) 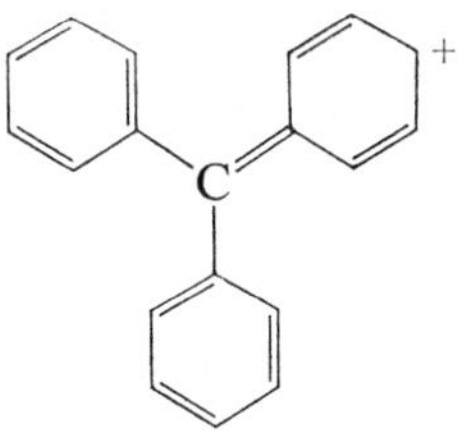   **(5.4)** 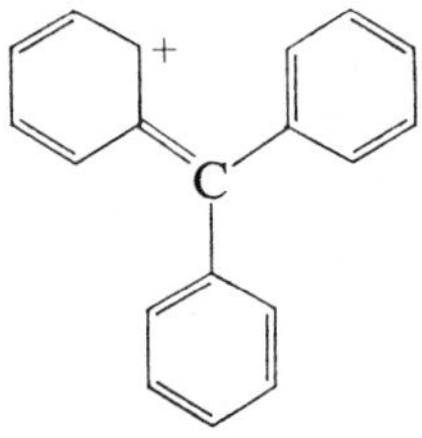   **(5.5)**

The theory also offers a ready explanation for the distribution of the charge. For example, the equivalence of the two structures **5.1** and **5.2** implies that equal charges should be found at the two terminal carbon atoms of the allylic system. However, because the calculations tend to become complicated as the number of carbon atoms in the conjugated system increases, the method has been much less widely used than the molecular orbital method to be discussed in Paragraph 5.2.3.[1] The simple method introduced by Hückel[2] ("HMO method") has had remarkable successes, not only in the detailed interpretation of carbonium-ion equilibria but also in the recognition of the so-called "$4n+2$ rule" which led to the discovery of some important carbonium-ion systems (see Section 4.3). This success has to some extent led to a disregard for the intrinsic weaknesses of the method. These are perhaps more apparent in HMO calculations of spectra and charge distributions than in the calculations of resonance stabilization.

Charge distribution and stability are related properties, although the connexion may not be transparently obvious in a mathematically complex theory. Both properties can be calculated on the basis of theoretical models of carbonium ions but, because their connexion is not a direct one, models which are successful in predicting energies need not be equally satisfactory for the calculation of charge densities.

The following paragraphs consider carbonium ions in the light of HMO theory and indicate the application of some extensions of the HMO method to carbonium ions. A more general exposition of the application of quantum mechanics to organic molecules can be found in a number of recent textbooks on that subject.

5.2.3 THE HMO METHOD FOR CONJUGATED CARBONIUM IONS

The Hückel molecular-orbital (HMO) method[2] is the most widely used approximation for conjugated molecules. In this the σ-electrons are

---

[1] See, however, Simonetta and Heilbronner, 1964.
[2] E. Hückel, 1931.

considered to be localized and to have a total energy which is an additive property of the component bonds of the system, whereas the π-electrons occupy nonlocalized orbitals. The energies of the individual one-electron π-orbitals are then calculated by a variation method and hence, by feeding all π-electrons of the system pairwise into the two-electron molecular orbitals proceeding in order of increasing energy, the total π-electron energy of the system is obtained. These molecular orbitals are linear combinations of atomic orbitals ("LCAO"). Considering a system of n conjugated carbon atoms one can write, for each of the n molecular orbitals,

$$\psi = c_1\phi_1 + c_2\phi_2 + \ldots c_n\phi_n \qquad (5.2)$$

where the coefficients c express the contributions of each of the atomic $2p_z$ orbitals (n in number). As there are n molecular orbitals ψ, each of which contains n coefficients c, there are in all n^2 values of c, and all of these can be obtained from the calculation which leads to the π-electron energy values. The details of these calculations are fully described in textbooks.[1]

The energies are obtained in terms of two parameters, α and β, termed respectively the Coulomb and resonance integrals. The numerical value of α is not required in simple applications of the theory; that of β is, in HMO calculations, usually deduced by comparison of some calculated and experimental energies. In the electronic ground state of the molecule, the n π-electrons occupy the levels with the lowest energies that are available. Since only two electrons may, according to the Pauli exclusion principle, occupy an orbital, the upper half of the levels in a molecule (with an even number of conjugated atoms) will be vacant. (This is illustrated in Figure 5.1 for 1,3-butadiene.) The square of

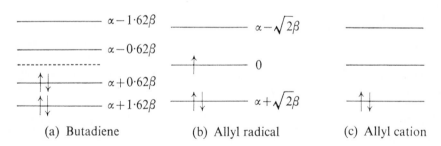

(a) Butadiene   (b) Allyl radical   (c) Allyl cation

FIG. 5.1. Energy levels in alternant π-electron systems according to HMO method.

each coefficient c is a measure of the electron population at a particular carbon atom arising from an electron in the respective molecular orbital. The total π-electron population at each position (or conjugated carbon atom) in the molecule can be calculated as the sum of these squares for all occupied orbitals (half-weight being given to orbitals occupied by a single electron), normalized

[1] Streitwieser, 1961; Hanna, 1965; Peacock, 1965; Phillips, 1965.

so that the total for all positions is equal to the number of electrons in the system. For an electrically neutral alternant conjugated system (i.e. one without odd-membered rings) the population is exactly one π-electron per position.

The method is directly applicable to ordinary conjugated molecules (i.e. those with an even number n of conjugated atoms and π-electrons) as well as to free radicals (in which n is an odd number). The main difference between these two cases in HMO theory is the occupancy of the highest filled level. When n is even, all filled levels ($n/2$ in number) contain a pair of electrons; when n is odd, $(n-1)/2$ levels contain a pair and the highest occupied level contains a single electron.

The calculation of the HMO energy levels and hence of the total energy of a conjugated system does not involve prior knowledge or calculation of charge distribution, and can be carried out without explicit reference to that charge distribution. Early quantum-mechanical calculations on carbonium ions concerned themselves with the π-electron energy of conjugated carbonium ions relative to uncharged conjugated molecules from which the carbonium ions could be formed. These energy differences could therefore be approximately related to equilibrium constants for the formation of carbonium ions. The possibility of calculating equilibrium constants for the formation of carbonium ions by this method was pointed out by Wheland[1] but, in the absence of suitable experimental data, was not then pursued further. By the same method the stability of a number of carbonium ions was predicted before their actual discovery (see Section 4.3).

Applied to the formation of carbonium ions by proton addition to unsaturated or aromatic systems, $B + H^+ \rightarrow BH^+$, the calculations take the form[2]

$$\Delta E = E_{BH^+} - E_B - E_{H^+} \tag{5.3}$$

$$= (E_\pi)_{BH^+} - (E_\pi)_B + \text{constant} \tag{5.4}$$

The approximation in Equation 5.4 assumes constancy of the contribution of σ-electrons to the energy difference. For a reaction in solution ΔE is in practice indistinguishable from ΔH. Consequently

$$\Delta H \simeq \Delta E_\pi + \text{constant} \tag{5.5}$$

The calculated values of ΔE_π in the present problem always take the form $-(2\alpha + L_r^+ \beta)$. The constant coefficient of α arises from the diminution of the total number of π-electrons by two. As far as the π-electrons are concerned, the calculation can also be thought to correspond to the process of reducing the π-electron framework by the carbon atom to which the proton is added,

[1] Wheland, 1934, 1942.
[2] Gold and Tye, 1952c.

the total π-electron population of BH^+ being two less than that of B, as if two π-electrons had been removed from B and localized at the site of proton addition. Consequently the coefficient L_r^+ can be referred to as a *cation localization energy*.[1]

For a series of similar acid-base reactions at the same temperature the entropy term $T\Delta S$ is likely to have a fairly constant value, so that

$$\Delta G° = -RT\ln K_{chem} = \Delta E_\pi + \text{constant} \qquad (5.6)$$

Expressed in this way, the equilibrium constant K_{chem} refers to proton addition at a single specified position. However, this is not the experimental equilibrium constant K_{eq} if alternative equivalent sites for proton addition are available: K_{chem} and K_{eq} then differ by a statistical factor.[2] This statistical correction, which can also be thought of as an entropy contribution, is systematically applied by the inclusion of symmetry numbers σ:[3]

$$K_{chem} = K_{eq} \frac{\sigma_{BH^+}}{\sigma_B} \qquad (5.7)$$

These calculations of carbonium-ion equilibria[4] by the HMO method were successful in several respects. They correctly reproduced the relative stabilities of isomeric carbonium ions formed from hydrocarbon bases by protonation, i.e. the preferred site of protonation if several alternatives exist. For example, they confirmed that the ion **5.6** should be more stable than **5.7**. They also

(5.6)   (5.7)

explained the decreasing stability of carbonium ions (relative to parent olefins along the series

$$\overset{+}{Ph_2C}.CH_3 > \overset{+}{Ph_2C}.CH_2Ph > \overset{+}{Ph_2C}.CHPh_2$$

At the same time the calculations pointed out the great stability of the phena-lenyl cationic system[4,5] (**5.8**) which is present in the carbonium ion **5.9** and thus accounts for the high basicity of benzo[a]pyrene[4] that permits isolation of this hydrocarbon by sulphuric acid extraction.[6]

[1] The terminology and sign convention adopted follows Streitwieser's (1961) suggestion. Alternatively $-L_r^+\beta$ is also called by this name.
[2] Mackor, Hofstra and van der Waals, 1958a.
[3] S. W. Benson, 1958.
[4] Gold and Tye, 1952c.
[5] For a review of phenalenes, see Reid, 1965.
[6] Berenblum, 1945.

For the same reason[1] indeno[2,1-a]phenalene (**5.10**) is a basic hydrocarbon:[2] the product of proton addition is the carbonium ion **5.11**.[3] Very similar calculations[4] confirmed the relative basicity of naphthalene and azulene and the position of proton addition in azulene.

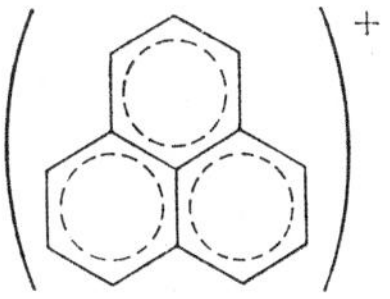

(**5.8**) 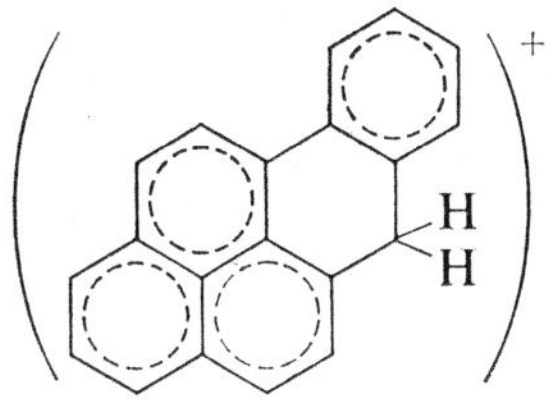   (**5.9**)

A systematic comparison of HMO calculations of this type with experimental data[5] later demonstrated far-reaching agreement for proton adducts of unsubstituted polycyclic aromatic hydrocarbons (Figure 5.2). The deviations from the correlation line which are noticeable for peri-condensed hydrocarbons are reduced in the SCF-refinement (see Paragraph 5.2.5) of the calculation.[6] The subject has been reviewed in detail by Perkampus.[7]

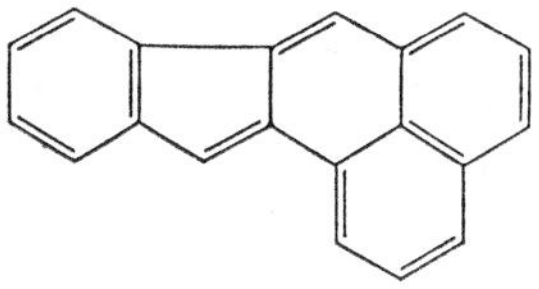

(**5.10**) 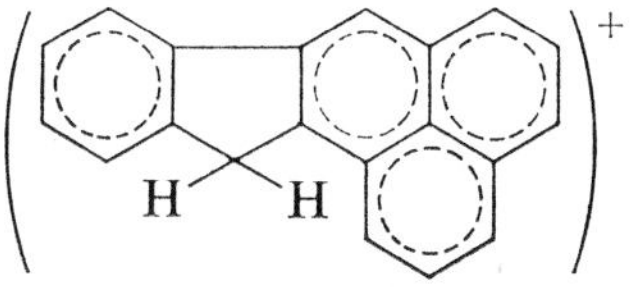   (**5.11**)

HMO calculations have also been successfully applied to the carbonium ion-forming equilibria

$$RCl \rightleftharpoons R^+ + Cl^- \tag{5.8}[8]$$

and

$$ROH + H^+ \rightleftharpoons R^+ + H_2O \tag{5.9}[9]$$

for which experimental data relating to conjugated cations R^+ are available (see Paragraph 4.1.5). The general principles of the calculations are the same. An additional assumption is required to deal with the Cl and OH substituents in the parent molecules: so far, as a first step, it has been assumed that the

[1] Zahradnik and Michl, 1965.
[2] Aitken and Reid, 1956.
[3] Bonthrone and Reid, 1966.
[4] Heilbronner and Simonetta, 1952.
[5] Mackor, Hofstra and van der Waals, 1958a.
[6] Dallinga, Verrijn Stuart *et al.*, 1957.
[7] Perkampus, 1966.
[8] Streitwieser, 1952.
[9] Gold, 1956a; Streitwieser, 1961, pp. 363–7.

influence of these groups can be neglected. The fact that the correlations are not perfect in these cases may, in part, be connected with this, but perhaps a more serious weakness of the calculations is the neglect of steric influences (see Paragraph 5.2.4). In addition, the effect of solvation energies may also be involved (see Paragraph 5.3.2).

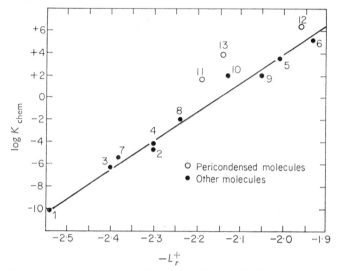

FIG. 5.2. Plot of log K_{chem} against $-L_r^+$, after Mackor, Hofstra and van der Waals, 1958a. (For key to compounds, see Table 4.13, p. 86.)

When the π-electron energy differences for RCl and R^+ are compared with rates of carbonium ion-forming reactions (or, more accurately, their free energies of activation) one would expect to find a reasonable correlation if the transition state is very much like the carbonium ion. The fact that the transition state cannot be the carbonium ion itself, but must have an intermediate electronic arrangement, should result in smaller rate differences than would correspond to the energy difference between RCl and R^+. On the assumption that entropy differences are unimportant for a series of related chlorides, such a comparison of measured and calculated rate ratios (or, what comes to the same thing, the value which has to be assumed for the parameter β in order to match calculated and measured rates) should give some indication of the carbonium ion character of the transition state, i.e. the extent to which the system has gone over towards a carbonium ion in the transition state.[1]

The application of the HMO method to charge distribution in carbonium ions rests on the assumption that the electron removed from a free radical in the notional formation of a carbonium ion is a π-electron and that its removal has no repercussions on the σ-electrons. The carbonium ion therefore differs from

[1] Dewar and Sampson, 1956, 1957.

the corresponding radical only by lacking the odd electron in the highest filled level. In alternant radicals the orbital which thus becomes vacant has antinodes at alternate positions, the first one being at a terminal position of any chain or side-chain of the ion. Since the parent radical, being an electrically neutral species, contained a population of one π-electron on each carbon atom it follows that the "hole" created by the removal of an electron from the most energetic orbital (i.e. the charge of the carbonium ion) must be distributed amongst the positions which correspond to antinodes of the highest occupied level of the radical. Conversely, no charge is to be found, according to this approximation, at the other (i.e. nodal) positions. In fact, the HMO charge distribution in alternant carbonium ions can be found by simple arithmetic[1] without knowledge of the energy levels or of other molecular orbitals. One makes use of the theorem that the coefficients c (of the radical's highest occupied orbital) corresponding to the nearest-neighbour atoms (either two or three in number) surrounding a nodal position must add up to zero.

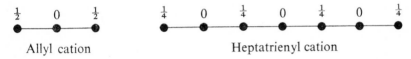

Allyl cation   Heptatrienyl cation

Fig. 5.3. Schematic charge densities in alternant carbonium ions according to HMO method.

The charge distributions of very simple carbonium ions that have been calculated by the HMO technique are shown in Figure 5.3. The result for the allyl cation predicts the charge to be shared between the two ends of the molecule, with no charge at the centre. In the heptatrienyl cation the charge appears to be equally shared amongst the odd-numbered carbon atoms of the chain. Intuitively, this charge distribution must seem to be wrong, for electrostatic repulsion is expected to tend to drive the charge more towards the ends of the ion.

The fact that a considerable part of the charge in polyenyl cations resides at atoms other than those at the extremes of the molecule is, of course, not in doubt. To give a fairly simple demonstration, one can compare the chemical shifts of the methyl protons for ions of the series[2]

$$(Me_2C\cdots CH\cdots (CH\cdots CH)_n\cdots CMe_2)^+ \qquad (n = 0\text{–}5)$$

which, because of their similar chemical surroundings in all members, are probably a fair reflection of charge density. There is a regular change towards larger screening as the chain length increases, which implies that a larger fraction of the cationic charge is associated with the non-terminal positions when more such positions are present.

[1] Longuet-Higgins, 1950.
[2] Sorensen, 1965.

The HMO calculations also lead to the so-called "bond orders" for the bonds of the conjugated system. These values are intended to express the bond multiplicity and their importance lies in the fact that they are empirically related to bond lengths, though the correlation is not perfect. The lengths found in crystallographic studies for the bonds of the three-membered ring of the triphenylcyclopropenyl cation (**5.12**)[1] and for the bonds linking the central carbon atom to the phenyl rings of the triphenylmethyl cation,[2] are in qualitative agreement with the theoretical prediction. In both cases the bond lengths indicate appreciable double-bond character. The reported lengths are $1 \cdot 373 \pm 0 \cdot 005$ and $1 \cdot 454 \pm 0 \cdot 018$ Å, which may be compared with the C—C bond lengths of $1 \cdot 54$, $1 \cdot 39$ and $1 \cdot 335$ Å for ethane, benzene and ethylene respectively.

5.2.4 THE EXTENT OF PLANARITY OF CONJUGATED CARBONIUM IONS

The delocalization of $2p$-electrons (π-electrons), which is a cardinal feature of all quantum-mechanical treatments of conjugated systems, is possible through the overlap of the atomic $2p_z$-orbitals which occurs in planar conjugated

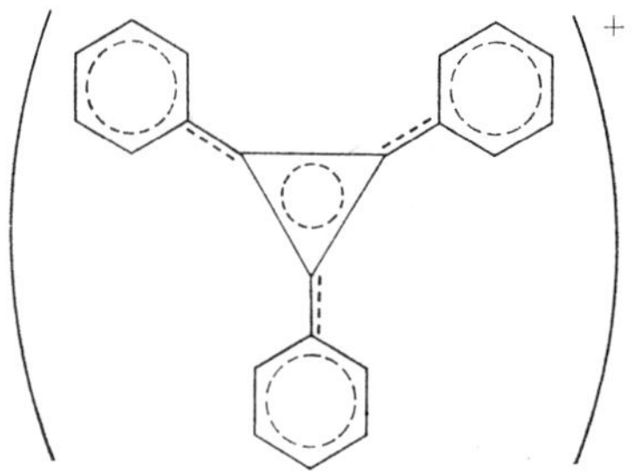

(**5.12**)

systems of carbon atoms. Overlap is reduced if a bond is twisted, with an accompanying reduction in the stability of the molecule.[3] It follows that conjugated systems will tend to be coplanar but, for steric reasons, exact planarity cannot always be achieved. Small deviations from planarity do not greatly increase the energy of the system.

The difficulty has long been known to exist in the case of the triphenylmethyl cation.[4] A planar structure, as drawn in formula (**5.3**), for example, is impossible because the *ortho*-hydrogen atoms of the phenyl groups would interfere with each other. This congestion can be relieved by rotating the phenyl groups about the bond joining them to the central carbon atom. Several problems arise in consequence: (a) are all rings twisted in the same sense, so as to produce a

[1] Sundaralingam and Jensen, 1966.
[2] Gomes de Mesquita, MacGillavry and Eriks, 1965.
[3] Pauling and Corey, 1951; Dewar, 1952.
[4] G. N. Lewis, Magel and Lipkin, 1942.

propeller-like structure, or is one ring twisted in the opposite sense to the other two; (b) are all rings twisted through the same angle; and (c) is it possible to recognize optical isomerism in carbonium ions because of the handedness of the propeller? Both electronic[1] and infrared spectra[2] indicate that the ion has D_3 symmetry. Crystallographic results for the perchlorate[3] also support this symmetry, with a twist angle of *ca.* 32°. The symmetrical propeller form is therefore the preferred structure, but in solution at ordinary temperatures one would expect that the pitch of the propeller is variable and that racemization occurs readily.

The preference of conjugated carbonium ions for planar arrangements is also strikingly confirmed by the accurate X-ray crystallographic study of the triphenylcyclopropenyl ion (5.12),[4] in which the phenyl rings are somewhat further apart than in the triphenylmethyl cation. As a result the system can approach planarity more closely. The twist angles of the three rings are 7·6, 12·1 21·2°, the inequality being attributed to differences in packing about the phenyl groups in the solid.

In view of the experimental evidence for D_3 symmetry in the triphenylmethyl cation, not much weight can now be attached to the indirect reasons which were previously advanced in favour of other structures. (A summary and criticism of these arguments has been given.[5])

5.2.5 Substituent Effects and Modifications of the HMO Method for Conjugated Carbonium Ions

The effect of substituents, especially methyl and methylene groups, on the stability of carbonium ions derived from aromatic systems is not easily introduced into the HMO method in an entirely convincing manner. Methyl and other alkyl substituents stabilize carbonium ions. Qualitatively, these effects can be allowed for by semi-empirical adjustment of the parameters α and β,[6] and this procedure was followed in early calculations[7] on the basicity of methylazulenes. From more complete treatments[8] and the comparison of calculated basicities of methylbenzenes with experimental values[9] it appears that the inductive effect of the methyl group as a substituent in the pentadienyl cation is

[1] Chu and Weissman, 1954; Ng and Adam, 1964.
[2] Sharp and Sheppard, 1957.
[3] Gomes de Mesquita, MacGillavry and Eriks, 1965.
[4] Sundaralingam and Jensen, 1966.
[5] Bethell and Gold, 1958c.
[6] Pullman, Mayot and Berthier, 1950.
[7] Heilbronner and Simonetta, 1952.
[8] Muller, Pickett and Mulliken, 1954; Ehrenson, 1961, 1962; Dewar, 1963; Flurry and Lykos, 1963.
[9] McCaulay and Lien, 1951; Kilpatrick and Luborsky, 1953; Mackor, Hofstra and van der Waals, 1958b.

more important than hyperconjugation.[1] In discussions of this problem, as in other quantum-mechanical calculations, it is sometimes in dispute whether the inadequacy of some calculated results stems from the imperfections of the intended physical model or the unintentional imperfections due to the approximations inherent in the quantum-mechanical method used. Conversely, the success of a particular treatment does not necessarily establish the correctness of the supposed physical model.

In the calculation of π-electron energy levels (and charge distribution) by the HMO method, one assumes that each π-electron moves in the Coulomb force field of a rigid framework of equidistant identical charge centres corresponding to the carbon atoms of the conjugated system and in a uniform field of the other electrons. The assumption that all carbon atoms r of the π-system are identical is embodied in the use of a constant Coulomb integral α ($\alpha \equiv \int \phi_r \mathbf{H} \phi_r$); the assumption that all C—C distances between atoms r and s in the conjugated system are the same further leads to the use of a constant resonance integral β ($\beta \equiv \int \phi_r \mathbf{H} \phi_s$). The errors inherent in these assumptions appear to a large extent to be self-cancelling or else reduced by suitable choice of the value of β, since calculations of resonance energies of conjugated molecules by the HMO method have unquestionably had a great deal of success.

However, charge distributions in carbonium ions calculated by the HMO method indicate quite clearly that there *are* differences between the carbon atoms of a conjugated carbonium ion, and the inequality of charges suggests that the assumption of equal Coulomb integrals must be much less satisfactory for a carbonium ion than for a neutral molecule. The method thus appears to lack self-consistency.

Various modifications of the HMO method have therefore been made which aim to remove this defect. In addition to the improbable charge distribution which the HMO method yields, the individual π-electron energy levels of carbonium ions are clearly incorrect. An example is the energy difference between radicals and the corresponding carbonium ions produced by loss of an electron in the highest occupied level of the radical. This energy difference corresponds to the ionization potential of the radical. The HMO method predicts ionization potentials of all alternant radicals to have the same value, corresponding to the Coulomb integral α, but this prediction is clearly not borne out by the measured ionization potentials (Table 4.3).

In a self-consistent field (SCF) modification of the molecular orbital treatment the consequences of coulombic repulsion between the charges on the conjugated framework are explicitly taken into account,[2] and this method reproduces correctly the observed trend of the ionization potentials (decreasing as the conjugated system becomes more extensive).[3] In effect, the calculation

[1] Cf. Streitwieser and Nair, 1959.
[2] Brickstock and Pople, 1954; Pople, 1957.
[3] Hush and Pople, 1955.

no longer assumes the other electrons to exert a uniform average field but the actual field corresponding to the orbitals they occupy.

A rather simpler modification ("Wheland-Mann method" or "ω-technique"), in which electron repulsion is introduced into the HMO method by relating the Coulomb integral α to the charge density for each carbon atom of the conjugated system, similarly improves energy calculations.[1] The introduction of

Table 5.1. *Calculated cationic charge densities for alternant conjugated carbonium ions according to different methods of calculation*[a]

Benzyl cation	HMO	ω	SCF
α	0·57	0·41	0·50
1	0	0·08	−0·13
2(*o*)	0·14	0·13	0·14
3(*m*)	0	0·05	0·07
4(*p*)	0·14	0·15	0·23
β-Phenylallyl cation			
α	0·50	0·41	0·47
β	0	0·12	−0·07
1	0	0	−0·20
2(*o*)	0	0·02	−0·02
3(*m*)	0	0	0·10
4(*p*)	0	0·01	0·18
Triphenylmethyl cation			
α	0·31	0·22	0·25
1	0	0·03	−0·15
2(*o*)	0·08	0·06	0·05
3(*m*)	0	0·02	0·06
4(*p*)	0·08	0·06	0·19

[a] Taken from Streitwieser, 1961, pp. 360–1.

coulombic repulsion generally results in the expected greater concentration of cationic charge at the periphery of the ion. Streitwieser[2] has collected the results of charge-density calculations by these three techniques for benzyl, β-phenylallyl and triphenylmethyl cations. A summary is given in Table 5.1. The large negative charges appearing in the SCF calculations by Pople's method are surprising and Streitwieser has cited other reasons why the charge distributions calculated by the ω-technique seem more satisfactory than those obtained from the SCF treatment. The ω-technique has also been used as a refinement in the calculation of cation localization energies.[3]

The positive-charge distribution $p > m > o$ predicted by the SCF method for

[1] Streitwieser, 1961, p. 115.
[2] Streitwieser, 1961, pp. 360–1.
[3] Streitwieser, Brauman and Bush, 1963.

the triphenylmethyl cation parallels the sequence of screening constants in the proton resonance spectrum,[1] but another view of the NMR spectra[2] regards the charge densities on o- and p-positions to be roughly the same and the difference between the o- and p-proton screening constants to be attributable to the screening effect of neighbouring phenyl groups which are twisted (40°) out of planarity.[3] The most recent estimate of the twist angle is 32°.[4]

It should be noted that the percentage differences between charge densities calculated by different MO methods (Table 5.1) appear greatest for the positions carrying only small charges: the predictions agree well as to which atom of the ion will be the most highly charged position.

It is evident that models which are satisfactory for predicting total energies may prove less adequate for calculations of charge densities. Calculations of total energy may average out errors affecting individual electronic levels, whereas charge distribution is more sensitively dependent on the correctness of the wave functions of the higher occupied levels. Similarly, spectral transitions, i.e. differences between energy states of the system, depend even more critically on the correctness of the highest occupied and lowest unoccupied electronic levels of the system. It is likely, therefore, that models which satisfactorily predict the position of electronic transitions and ionization potentials will be more reliable for prediction of charge distribution. Less sophisticated models may however suffice for predictions of total stability.

Of course, the HMO method is based on a very simple model of the molecule and possible refinements in the technique are not confined to the inclusion of electron repulsion. We cannot concern ourselves with this general problem here, since the discussion would not be of particular relevance to carbonium ions as distinct from conjugated systems in general.

A refinement which seems of particular importance for conjugated carbonium ions is configuration interaction. The electronic configuration (or molecular wave function) expressed by the allocation of electrons to the lowest available spin orbitals in accordance with the Pauli exclusion principle corresponds to the configuration of lowest energy, but in this refinement of the theory it is no longer taken to be the same as the ground state of the system. A wave function of even lower energy can be constructed by taking a linear combination of configurations, i.e. by mixing together the lowest-energy configuration and configurations corresponding to higher-energy values. The contribution of higher-energy (or excited) configurations rapidly fall off with increasing energy. There is furthermore a symmetry restriction on the configurations which can interact. It has been pointed out[5] that configuration interaction is particularly

[1] Dehl, Vaughan and Berry, 1959.
[2] Farnum, 1964
[3] Sandel and Freedman, 1963.
[4] Gomes de Mesquita, MacGillavry and Eriks, 1965.
[5] Colpa, MacLean and Mackor, 1963.

significant in alternant carbonium ions because the energy-spacing of the configurations is such that a doubly-excited configuration (i.e. one derived by promoting two electrons from the highest occupied level of the carbonium ion to the next level) makes a significant contribution to the ground-state wave function. The effect of this refinement on the charge distribution is slight (Table 5.2). The calculated charge distribution is intermediate between the predictions of the ω-technique and the SCF method without configuration interaction. However, the effect on the individual energy levels of the system is more significant and the energies of electronic spectral transitions are more correctly predicted by this method.

Table 5.2. *Cation charge densities in the allyl cation according to different MO methods*

	HMO	ω-technique[a]	SCF[b]	Configuration interaction[b]
Atom 1 or 3	0·500	0·439	0·494	0·462
Atom 2	0	0·142	0·011	0·077

[a] From Streitwieser, 1961, p. 116.
[b] From Colpa, MacLean and Mackor, 1963.

5.2.6 ALIPHATIC CARBONIUM IONS

By comparison with the very large volume of theoretical work on systems involving conjugated carbonium ions, alkyl cations have received a relatively small amount of attention. Some of these studies have been detailed and thoughtful but their contribution to the development of the subject of carbonium ions, judged—as all theories must be—on their predictive value, has not been large. In this respect most of the studies have been largely assessed by their success in reproducing the observed ionization potentials of radicals. At the moment these constitute the least ambiguous quantitative experimental information about aliphatic carbonium ions. However, since even a very crude electrostatic model is reasonably successful in this respect (see Paragraph 5.2.1), this is not a particularly impressive test of sophisticated theories. This position is unlikely to remain so for long: the preparation of reasonably stable solutions of aliphatic carbonium ions that has been achieved (see Section 4.3) should bring in its train measurements of equilibrium constants and other physical properties against which theories can be tested.

The stabilization of aliphatic carbonium ions brought about by methyl substitution has been ascribed to an inductive effect or to hyperconjugation (see also Paragraph 4.2.7). In the hyperconjugation model[1] the principal resonance

[1] Muller and Mulliken, 1958, and references given by them. This paper should be consulted for a full statement of the treatment.

6

structure of the ethyl cation is written as **5.13**, the H_3 group constituting a triply-bonded quasi-atom, and this is stabilized by resonance with the structure **5.14**.

$$H_3 \equiv C - \overset{+}{C} \underset{\diagdown H}{\overset{\diagup H}{}} \qquad \overset{+}{H_3} = C = CH_2$$

$$\textbf{(5.13)} \qquad\qquad\qquad \textbf{(5.14)}$$

Muller and Mulliken's calculation[1] is semi-empirical, in that it involves an adjustable proportionality constant which allows the Coulomb integral on each atom or quasi-atom to be linearly related to the charge on that atom. As is implied by the resonance structure **5.14**, the carbon–carbon bond has, according to this model, some double-bond character. This prediction may be more diagnostic of the correctness of the model than the ability of the calculation to reproduce, with suitable assumptions, the ionization potentials.[2] The analysis of infrared spectra of aliphatic carbonium ions should throw some light on this question, and values of force constants that support some double-bond characters of the C—C bonds in the t-butyl cation have been reported (see Paragraph 2.3.2).

The unorthodox bonding implied by the assumption that hyperconjugation is important in carbonium ions is paralleled by the theories of bonding in boron hydrides. The analogy between boron and the isoelectronic carbonium carbon has already been remarked upon (Section 1.2).

In view of the interest in the possible existence of bridged carbonium ions (Chapter 7), various molecular-orbital calculations have been performed on molecular models involving unconventional (or "non-classical") arrangements of carbon and hydrogen atoms. Simonetta and Winstein[3] suggested that overlap of the p-orbital of C(3) and the vacant p-orbital on C(1) in "homo-allylic" cations of the type **5.15** could be treated by a slight modification of the

$$\underset{4}{\overset{\diagup}{\text{C}}} = \underset{3}{\overset{\diagdown}{\text{C}}} \underset{\diagdown \text{C}}{\overset{2}{\diagup}} \underset{1}{\overset{+}{\text{C}} -}$$

$$\textbf{(5.15)}$$

HMO method in which the resonance integral between C(1) and C(3) is assigned a smaller value ($k\beta$) than that usually assumed for neighbouring atoms of a conjugated system (β). The approach thus treats the ion **5.15** as if it were a slightly misbehaved allyl cation and leads to the conclusion that the 1–3 interaction lowers the energy of the system. The value of k is estimated from the overlap between p-orbitals at C(1) and C(3).[4]

---

[1] Muller and Mulliken, 1958.
[2] See also Hanazaki, Hosoya and Nagakura, 1963; Melton and Joy, 1965.
[3] Simonetta and Winstein, 1954.
[4] See also Pilar, 1958, 1959.

The same procedure can be applied to other relative positions of a double bond and a vacant p-orbital as, for example, in the 7-norbornenyl cation (5.16):[1]

(5.16)

The relevant conjugated structure is now a misbehaved cyclopropenyl cation, with reduced resonance integrals between C(7) and the other two atoms C(2), C(3). The extension of this treatment to cyclopropylmethyl and cyclobutyl-methyl cations[2] and to various bridged carbonium-ion structures, including those without any formal double bond,[3] and the estimation of steric strain in these systems have been reviewed. A problem which is basic to the application of molecular orbital theory to these ions concerns the absence of σ-electrons from the pseudo-bonds between C(1) and C(3) in **5.15** or between C(2) and C(7) in **5.16**, i.e. the π-electrons are not in a potential field due to a combination of nuclei and σ-electrons as is present in conjugated systems. Similarly, the comparison of alternative skeletal structures by the HMO method, attempting to assess the relative stability of bridged and unbridged formulae, for example, is suspect: ions of different geometry present different potential fields and contributions to the bonding energy from terms other than the π-electron energy. These difficulties are not easily assessed. There is, however, no reason to doubt that such interactions "across space" lead to stabilization. It is more difficult to be certain of their size and to know whether they are indeed responsible for "non-classical" effects, especially on reaction velocities (see Chapter 7).

An even more audacious empirical method of calculation (termed "an extended Hückel theory"),[4] in which interactions between $1s$ electrons of hydrogen and $2s$ and $2p$ electrons of carbon are considered and the energy of the system is minimized as in the variation treatment used by Hückel, has also been applied to carbonium ions.[5] At their present stage of development, the calculations are mainly directed towards structural problems. By systematically repeating the computations for many internuclear distances and conformations (including unconventional structures) one aims to find the most stable molecular geometry. Charge distributions and energies are also generated by the computer programs used. The great complexity of the model necessitates inspired assumptions, the full implications of which require closer examination.

[1] Woods, Carboni and Roberts, 1956.
[2] Howden and Roberts, 1963.
[3] Piccolini and Winstein, 1963.
[4] Hoffmann, 1963.
[5] Hoffmann, 1964a,b; Trahanovsky, 1965.

The predictive value of the approach has not yet been adequately tested. Dewar and Marchand[1] regard such calculations as "valueless, except in a very qualitative sense". The issue at the moment lies in the precise significance of the term "very qualitative".

5.3 External Factors

5.3.1 INTRODUCTION: SOME ELECTROSTATIC CONSIDERATIONS

The formation of gaseous carbonium ions by heterolysis of neutral molecules requires high energies (Table 4.5): heterolytic reactions in the gas phase are not easily observed (Paragraph 4.2.4; see, however, Paragraph 4.1.3). In solution, organic reactions involving carbonium-ion formation are much more frequently found. The high energy required for heterolysis seems to be offset by interaction between the ions and their surroundings, in particular solvent molecules and other ions. These interactions may be regarded as ways of achieving external dissipation of the charge on the carbonium ion.

The physical chemistry of ionic solvation and interionic interactions in solution is quite highly developed, information coming from conductimetry, potentiometry, etc. These methods are again appropriate to solutions of stable carbonium ions but are inadequate for the study of carbonium ions formed as fleeting intermediates (Chapter 2). Because of differences in experimental approach, theoretical concepts and terminology tend to be somewhat different in this field. For example, the concept of "ion pairs" as developed by Bjerrum to describe the conductance of electrolytes in solution in solvents of low dielectric constant is not directly helpful in interpreting the kinetic and stereochemical features of, say, acetolyses of alkyl arenesulphonates, which Winstein also discusses in terms of "ion pairs", though these are now defined somewhat differently.

The main reason for the difference in approach lies in the life-times of the solute ions. In discussing properties of solutions of stable ions it is usual to treat the interactions of an ion with solvent molecules and other ions as time averages, for the fluctuations in these interactions occur over very short time intervals compared to the life-time of an ion or to the time-scale of thermodynamic measurements. However, the life-time of an unstable carbonium ion may be short in relation to these fluctuations. In consequence, a short-lived ion may never achieve the type of surroundings that a stable ion experiences—at least on the average—simply because the time needed for the surroundings to adjust themselves to the newly generated ion so as to produce optimum stabilization is longer than the life-time of the ion. We thus see at the outset why the physical chemistry of electrolytes may prove inadequate for some problems of carbonium ions, although we would expect it to be no less successful in its

[1] Dewar and Marchand, 1965.

applications to stable carbonium ions than in applications to other stable ions *in the same solvents.*

These problems are met in aggravated form when the rates of formation of carbonium ions are considered, for the carbonium ion-like transition states are, in their very nature, transient entities. In addition, one is faced with the question of how much like a carbonium ion a particular transition state is. This makes it the more unfortunate that comparatively little experimental evidence concerning the solvation and ion association of stable carbonium ions is available, for we are forced to supplement our knowledge from the effects on reaction velocities, the most closely related properties for which abundant information is available.

It is instructive to start our discussion by applying the laws of electrostatics to a simple model of a carbonium ion, the so-called "sphere in continuum" model. The free energy associated with the inhomogeneous electric field surrounding a spherical ion, of radius R and charge q, is $q^2/2R$ in the gas phase, and $q^2/2RD$ in a structureless medium of dielectric constant D. The change in the free energy on transferring the ion from the gas phase to the dielectric medium is thus:

$$\Delta G = -\frac{q^2}{2R}(1-1/D) \qquad (5.10)$$

In Equation (5.10) (often referred to as the Born equation) ΔG can be equated with the free energy of solvation of the ion. Amongst other things, we ignore in this type of calculation (a) dielectric saturation in the vicinity of the ion, and (b) the free energy change due to disruption of the solvent structure by the ion (ΔG_c). Dielectric saturation is usually regarded as unlikely for carbonium ions because of their large size, which reduces the intensity of the electrical field surrounding them.[1] Disruption of solvent structure is important, but, for a series of ions of similar size, the effect should be approximately constant. Thus, in comparisons between such ions, the major factor determining the solvation energy will be electrostatic. In general, however,

$$\Delta G_{solv} = -\frac{q^2}{2R}(1-1/D) + \Delta G_c \qquad (5.11)$$

and

$$\Delta S_{solv} = -\frac{q^2}{2R}\frac{d}{dT}\left(\frac{1}{D}\right) - \Delta S_c \qquad (5.12)$$

Since $d(1/D)/dT$ is usually positive, the first term in the expression for ΔS_{solv} is negative, i.e. the electrostatic effect of introducing the ion into the solvent is order-producing. However, the total effect will also depend on the sign and magnitude of the entropy change due to the creation of a cavity in the solvent structure to accommodate the ion (ΔS_c).

According to Equation (5.11) the interaction between the ion and the solvent should be strongest for small R and large D. Generally speaking, the solvation

---

[1] Mason, 1958, but see Paragraph 5.3.3.

energies of carbonium ions will therefore be smaller than those of singly charged metallic cations. Furthermore, carbonium ions will be less stabilized and thus more difficult to form as the dielectric constant of the medium is decreased. ΔG_{solv} and ΔS_{solv} refer to the interaction of an ion with the entire surrounding space, but it may readily be shown (by comparing values of ΔG for spheres of radius R and $2R$) that one half of the electrostatic part of each of these quantities refers to interaction between the ion and the solvent in a spherical shell of thickness R immediately surrounding the ion. Thus the greatest ordering effect will be exerted on those solvent molecules actually in contact with the ion, the solvent dipoles orienting themselves so as to minimize the effect of the charge. Beyond this primary solvation sheath the effect will diminish quite rapidly.

In an analogous fashion, the field of an ion will impose a certain degree of order on other ions present in solution so that, on average, a carbonium ion will be surrounded by an excess of negatively charged ions ("ionic atmosphere"). For dilute solutions of large ions in solvents of high dielectric constant this phenomenon is adequately described in terms of the Debye-Hückel theory. At higher concentrations or, what is particularly relevant to the discussion of organic reactions, in solvents of low dielectric constant, the situation is less well understood. For here the energy of electrostatic interaction between the ion and the solvent is small, but that between ion and ion, depending as it does on D^{-1}, gains in importance relative to the disordering effect of purely thermal energy. In contrast to the non-specific long-range interaction between ions involved in the ionic-atmosphere model, a reasonably satisfactory description of the physical properties (e.g. conductivity, spectra) of solutions of ions in media of low dielectric constant uses the model of aggregation of ions into pairs, triple ions and larger clusters. We shall see (Paragraph 6.2.4) that there is evidence from carbonium-ion chemistry which seems to require not only a specific interaction between the constituents of these aggregates but that the ions have a particular spatial arrangement.

The "sphere in continuum" model of carbonium ion solvation represents a gross oversimplification in several respects:

(a) The geometrical model of carbonium ions as uniformly charged spheres is obviously too naïve (see Section 5.2).
(b) There is evidence[1] that the assumption that the solvent is structureless is inadequate in discussions of ionic interactions.
(c) For carbonium ions in solution, internal and external modes of charge delocalization mutually interact (see Paragraph 5.3.2).

Finally, it must again be emphasized that carbonium ions in solution are accompanied by an equal number of counter-ions. It is therefore impossible to study carbonium ions in solution in isolation: for example, the free energy of ionization of a molecule RX will include the solvation energies of both R^+ and

[1] Eigen, 1957.

X^-. Only by restricting comparisons to systems with the same X is it possible to investigate the effect of structure on the stability of R^+. The influence of the solvent on the stability or rate of formation of carbonium ions is never a function of its interaction with R^+ alone, and, from a purely thermodynamic point of view, even a separation of solvation energies into cationic and anionic contributions (Table 5.3) cannot be verified. On the other hand, the *chemical* effects of solvation, as indicated by the composition or stereochemistry of reaction products derived from the carbonium ion, frequently result from the interaction with the cation only, and thus afford an approach to the study of solvation which is denied to us by thermodynamic methods.

In this section we shall concern ourselves with conclusions derivable from studies of stable carbonium ions and from rates of carbonium-ion formation. More information comes from studies of the reactions of carbonium ions (e.g. stereochemical studies) and these are dealt with in Chapter 6.

5.3.2 SOLVATION OF CARBONIUM IONS

The nature of the interaction between carbonium ions and the solvent. It is generally agreed that solvolysis of t-butyl chloride in water or alcohols involves rate-determining heterolysis of the carbon–chlorine bond. However, the rate depends on the solvent used: for example it is much greater in water than in alcohols. This solvent effect can be taken to imply that solvent molecules are somehow concerned in the heterolysis, at least to the extent of solvating the incipient ions. However, the principal reaction product is the result of substitution, i.e. of direct chemical involvement of the solvent. A more specific interaction between carbonium ion and solvent must therefore come into play at some stage. The question is at what stage this occurs.

To take one extreme point of view, one could make a sharp distinction between the electrostatic, solvating function of the solvent—which alone is involved in the formation of the carbonium ion—and its nucleophilic function which is responsible for covalency formation during a subsequent phase of the substitution. Solvation of carbonium ions is thus seen as a non-directional electrostatic interaction of the ion with solvent molecules, though, clearly, the intensity of the interaction around a non-spherical, non-uniformly charged carbonium ion cannot be the same at all points. Further, the solvating molecules are not regarded as permanently associated with a particular ion but rather as continually undergoing exchange with molecules from the bulk of the solvent.

A different point of view, equally extreme in the opposite sense, has been advanced in order to account for the high degree of inversion of configuration observed in certain unimolecular substitutions of organic halides (Paragraph 6.2.4). According to this, no distinction is drawn between solvation and nucleophilic attack on carbonium ions. The solvated ion is represented as **5.17**, in which there is partly or wholly covalent attachment of two solvent molecules (S) to the carbonium centre by overlap of the two lobes of its vacant p-orbital with suitable filled orbitals of the solvent molecules.[1] The C—S bonds are regarded as being weaker than the other bonds in **5.17**, facilitating exchange processes. The similarity of **5.17** to the conventional representation of the transition state in S_N2 displacements is obvious.

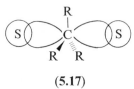

(5.17)

By a small change of either of these points of view, structure **5.17** may be regarded as representing one instantaneous arrangement of the ion R_3C^+ in relation to certain surrounding species. The difference between the two approaches therefore lies essentially in the interpretation of the bonding between the central ion and the solvation sheath. The distinction between electrostatic and covalent bonding is not always clear even for stable inorganic ions:[2] the borderline between electrostatic solvation and aquation appears to be as diffuse as for most classifications in solution chemistry.

Energetics of solvation. Definitions. The ionization of an organic molecule RX in the gas phase (g) and in solution (s) is represented in Figure 5.4,

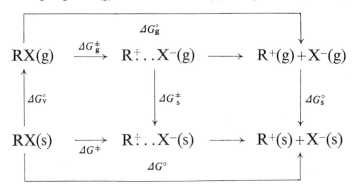

FIG. 5.4. Free energy cycles for ionization of organic molecules in the gas phase and in solution.

$R^+ \ldots X^-$ being the transition state of ionization and R^+ and X^- the infinitely separated ions. The solvation energy of the carbonium ion R^+ is thus that part of ΔG_s° due to transfer of R^+ from the state of rest in the gas phase to solution in the solvent in question.

From Figure 5.4 it is evident that

$$\Delta G^{\circ} = \Delta G_g^{\circ} + \Delta G_s^{\circ} + \Delta G_v^{\circ} \tag{5.13}$$

[1] Doering and Zeiss, 1953; Streitwieser, 1956b.
[2] Hunt, 1963.

The ease with which appreciable equilibrium concentrations of carbonium ions are formed in solution compared with the gas phase rests in large measure on the importance of ΔG_s°, but, as we shall see, the solvation energy of RX, ΔG_v°, can also play an important part. Figure 5.4 also yields Equation (5.14).

$$\Delta G^{\ddagger} = \Delta G_g^{\ddagger} + \Delta G_s^{\ddagger} + \Delta G_v^\circ \qquad (5.14)^1$$

Equations (5.13) and (5.14) have usually been employed to estimate ΔG° or $\Delta G^{\ddagger}$ and related quantities from electron impact data and calculated values of ΔG_s°, rather than for the derivation of solvation energies of carbonium ions. The most successful treatment along these lines is that of Franklin[2] who estimated ΔH_s° and ΔS_s° using semi-empirical equations[3] which fitted the known thermodynamic data for solvation of alkali metal and halide ions.[4] Some of Franklin's values are given in Table 5.3.

Table 5.3. *Theoretical estimates of enthalpies (kcal mole^{-1}) and entropies (cal mole^{-1} deg^{-1}) of solvation for alkyl cations*[a]

Ion	Ionic radius[b] (Å)	H$_2$O $-\Delta H_s^\circ$	H$_2$O $-\Delta S_s^\circ$	CH$_3$OH $-\Delta H_s^\circ$	CH$_3$OH $-\Delta S_s^\circ$
CH$_3^+$	1·75	61	2	66·4	23·6
CH$_3$.CH$_2^+$	2·05	54	0	59·0	21·7
CH$_3$.CH$_2$.CH$_2^+$	2·18	50	0	56·0	20·9
(CH$_3$)$_2$CH$^+$	2·38	46	0	52·5	19·9
(CH$_3$)$_3$C$^+$	2·80	40	0	46·0	18·2

[a] Franklin, 1952.
[b] Average value estimated from models and converted to an "effective radius" by addition of a solvent-dependent constant (0·85Å in water and 0·64Å in methanol).

Most discussions of carbonium-ion solvation have been based on semi-empirical treatments of solvent effects on rates of carbonium-ion formation and the derived activation parameters, particularly the entropy of activation. For the purpose of discussing the effects of changing the reaction medium, it is convenient to transform Equation (5.14) into

$$\delta_m \Delta G^{\ddagger} = \delta_m \Delta G_s^{\ddagger} + \delta_m \Delta G_v^\circ \qquad (5.15)^5$$

[1] The alternative forms $k = k_0 f_{RX}/f^{\ddagger}$ and $k = k^\circ h_{RX}/h^{\ddagger}$ are sometimes employed. Here k is a velocity constant in solution, k_0 that in a reference solvent and k° that in the gas phase. h's are Henry's Law constants and f's activity coefficients.
[2] Franklin, 1952; cf. A. G. Evans, 1946.
[3] Latimer, Pitzer and Slansky, 1939.
[4] Latimer and Slansky, 1940; Slansky, 1940.
[5] Applying Equation (5.15) to a specific case:
$\Delta G^{\ddagger}$ (methanol) $- \Delta G^{\ddagger}$ (water) $= \Delta G_s^{\ddagger}$ (methanol) $- \Delta G_s^{\ddagger}$ (water) $+ \Delta G_v^\circ$ (methanol) $- \Delta G_v^\circ$ (water).

6*

where δ_m is an operator signifying the change in $\Delta G^{\ddagger}$, etc., resulting from a change in the composition of the reaction mixture[1] and $\delta_m \Delta G_g^{\ddagger}$ is necessarily zero. Equations (5.13) and (5.14) can be transformed in an analogous fashion to take account of the influence of changes in the reactant structure by use of the operator δ_R. Thus, for example

$$\delta_R \Delta G^{\circ} = \delta_R \Delta G_g^{\circ} + \delta_R \Delta G_s^{\circ} + \delta_R \Delta G_v^{\circ} \qquad (5.16)^2$$

Effect of the structure of the carbonium ion. The main structural effect in this context is on the distribution of the positive charge. As we have noted earlier, this will lead to a non-uniform interaction of the ion with the solvent at different points on its periphery. It will be particularly apparent for conjugated carbonium ions. An electrostatic treatment,[3] a simple elaboration of the Born equation [Equation (5.10)], regards the solvation energy as the sum of contributions from interaction of discrete centres of positive charge individually with the medium, viz.

$$\Delta G_s^{\circ} = - \sum_r \frac{q_r^2 \, e^2}{2R} (1 - 1/D) \qquad (5.17)$$

where q_r is the positive charge on the rth carbon atom (which in some cases has been calculated by MO theory), and R the effective radius of the charged centre. The treatment satisfactorily accounts for the variation in stability of triarylmethyl cations relative to the corresponding radicals, assumed to be unsolvated, using reasonable values for R (in formic acid, 0·88Å; in sulphur dioxide, 0·75Å).

The choice of triarylmethyl cations for this test of the electrostatic theory of structural effects is a particularly happy one. Examination of triarylmethanol-triarylmethyl cation equilibria in aqueous sulphuric acid shows that experimental values of ΔG° and ΔS°, both of which vary widely according to the nature of substituent groups, fit Equation (5.12).[4] This indicates that the behaviour of triarylmethyl cations is adequately described in most cases by simple electrostatic considerations. The anomalous behaviour of nitro-substituted triphenylmethyl cations suggests that more specific (e.g. hydrogen-bonding) interactions between carbonium ions and the solvent may occur in some cases, as has been recognized for other organic cations.[5]

In other respects the success of Mason's treatment is probably partly fortuitous, since it assumes that the centres of charge are situated in an isotropic dielectric medium. However, the carbonium ion itself occupies a significant proportion of the space around the centre of charge and this must reduce

---

[1] Leffler and Grunwald, 1963.

[2] Applying Equation 5.16 to a specific case:
$$\Delta G^{\circ}(\text{RCl}) - \Delta G^{\circ}(\text{R'Cl}) = \Delta G_g^{\circ}(\text{RCl}) - \Delta G_g^{\circ}(\text{R'Cl}) + \Delta G_s^{\circ}(\text{RCl}) - \Delta G_s^{\circ}(\text{R'Cl}) +$$
$$\Delta G_v^{\circ}(\text{RCl}) - \Delta G_v^{\circ}(\text{R'Cl})$$

[3] Mason, 1958; Grinter and Mason, 1964a.

[4] Arnett and Bushick, 1964.

[5] Taft, 1960b; Deno, Berkheimer *et al.*, 1959; Arnett and Bushick, 1964.

the interaction with solvent molecules. Steric inhibition of solvation is a well-documented phenomenon in the field of acid-base equilibria, for example, and there is evidence that it has consequences in carbonium-ion chemistry. Thus, increasing the size of α-substituents in organic halides increases the entropy of activation in carbonium-ion formation, probably by restricting access of solvent molecules to the developing positive centre.[1] The variation with change of solvent of the effect of a p-t-butyl substituent relative to p-methyl on the rate of acid-catalysed hydrogen isotope exchange in aromatic compounds (Table 4.18) can probably be attributed in part to steric inhibition of solvation of the adjacent positive centre by the t-butyl group.[2] Other examples have been given.[3]

Bearing these limitations of the treatment in mind, one can use Equation (5.17) to interpret certain aspects of structural effects on rates of carbonium-ion formation in solution. To take a simple example, allyl chloride undergoes unimolecular solvolysis in formic acid at 25° only 26 times faster than n-propyl chloride[4] despite the extra stability due to allylic resonance expected in a carbonium ion-like transition state. If differences of solvation energy of the reactants and of entropy of the ions in the gas phase are neglected, Equation (5.16) can be re-written as

$$\delta_R \Delta G^{\ddagger} \simeq \delta_R \Delta G^{\circ} = \delta_R \Delta H_g^{\circ} + \delta_R \Delta G_s^{\circ} \tag{5.18}$$

where δ_R now signifies the change from n-propyl to allyl.

From the kinetic data $\delta_R \Delta G^{\ddagger} \simeq 2$ kcal mole^{-1} and, from the data of Table 4.4, $\delta_R \Delta H_g^{\circ} = 35$ kcal mole^{-1}, whence $\delta_R \Delta G_s^{\circ} = -33$ kcal mole^{-1}, i.e. the free energy of solvation of the propyl cation is greater than that of the allyl cation by 33 kcal mole^{-1}. Equation (5.17) can be modified to express structural changes in the carbonium ion, giving

$$\delta_R \Delta G_s^{\circ} = -\delta_R \sum_r \frac{q_r^2\, e^2}{2R}\, (1-1/D) \tag{5.19}$$

Assuming no structural effect other than on charge distribution, and regarding the positive charge as localized on one terminal carbon atom in the propyl cation and divided equally between the two terminal carbon atoms in the allyl cation, one obtains

$$\delta_R \Delta G_s^{\circ} = -\frac{e^2}{2R}\, (1-1/D)\, [1^2 - 2(\tfrac{1}{2})^2]$$

$$= -\tfrac{1}{2}\Delta G_s^{\circ}\ \text{(propyl cation)}$$

$$= -25\ \text{kcal mole}^{-1}\ \quad \text{(from Table 5.3)}$$

In view of the assumptions the agreement of this value with that obtained using Equation 5.18 is as good as can be expected. This explanation of the

[1] A. G. Evans and Hamann, 1951.
[2] Eaborn and Taylor, 1961.
[3] Hyne and Wills, 1963.
[4] Vernon, 1954.

kinetic data in terms of differential solvation seems preferable to the alternative proposal[1] that there is little charge delocalization in the transition state for ionization of allyl chloride.

Whatever one's reservations about the details of such calculations it is evident that the interaction between ion and solvent is affected not only by the size but also the distribution of charge in the ion. It follows, conversely, that the solvating power of the solvent will influence the charge distribution in the carbonium ion. This question should in principle be amenable to experimental study, most obviously by nuclear magnetic resonance spectroscopy (cf. Paragraph 2.3.1).

Effect of the solvent. Cycloheptatrienyl iodide (**5.18**) absorbs light in the visible region of the spectrum at a wavelength which is strongly dependent on the nature of the solvent (e.g. $\lambda_{max} = 346$ mμ in water, 572 mμ in methylene chloride).[2] Excitation is thought to occur to an excited state resembling the structure **5.19** in which an electron has been transferred from the iodide ion

(5.18)   (5.19)

to the carbonium ion. This type of process is termed charge transfer (see Paragraph 5.3.4). Values of the excitation energy (E_T) in a variety of solvents are recorded in Table 5.4.

Table 5.4. *Values of E_T (kcal mole^{-1}) for cycloheptatrienyl iodide at 25°*[a]

Water	82·7	Acetonitrile	58·3
Methanol	70·9	Acetone	53·0
Ethanol	66·6	Methylene chloride	50·0
Isopropyl alcohol	64·5		

[a] Kosower, 1964.

The values of E_T increase with increasing solvent polarity: this is attributed largely to greater solvation of the ground state (**5.18**). Indeed, if it is assumed that the solvation energy of **5.19** is zero or constant, the solvent effect on the solvation energy of the carbonium iodide is given by $\delta_m \Delta G_s^\circ = \delta_m E_T$. In principle, ΔG_s° itself could be determined if the upper state is unsolvated. The energy for conversion of **5.19** into **5.18** in the gas phase can be calculated from available data (viz., ionization potential of the cycloheptatrienyl radical = 152 kcal mole^{-1};[3] electron affinity of iodine = 74 kcal mole^{-1}) to be 78 kcal mole^{-1}. This

[1] Franklin and Lumpkin, 1951.
[2] Kosower, 1964.
[3] Harrison, Honnen *et al.*, 1960.

calculated value (which applies to the *least* polar medium, namely the gas phase) is *larger* than all but one of the measured E_T-values, which indicates the shortcomings of the assumptions.

It may be noted that energies for a similar charge-transfer transition in the pyridinium iodide **5.20** (Z-values)[1] are larger than E_T-values in the same solvent by a constant amount (~ 12 kcal mole^{-1}), suggesting that the principal contributor to $\delta_m E_T$ is the variation in solvation energy of the iodide ion. Since the iodide ion is smaller than the two cations, this is to be expected on the basis of the Born equation (5.10).

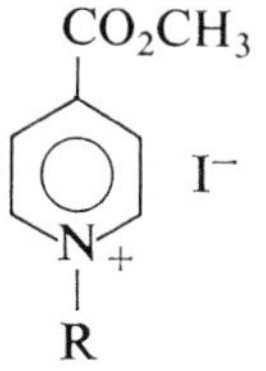

$$\underset{\text{(5.20)}}{\text{CO}_2\text{CH}_3 \text{ ring with N}^+\text{—R, I}^-} \qquad (R = CH_3, C_2H_5)$$

Because of the absence of direct data on the energetics of solvation of stable carbonium ions, solvent effects on rates of carbonium-ion formation have often been used to obtain such information. A qualitative theory of solvent effects,[2]

Table 5.5. *Rate constants and activation parameters for unimolecular solvolysis of t-butyl chloride at 25°[a]*

Solvent	$10^7 k$ (sec^{-1})	$\Delta H^{\ddagger}$ (kcal mole^{-1})	$\Delta S^{\ddagger}$ (cal mole^{-1} deg^{-1})
Water	$2\cdot7 \times 10^5$	$23\cdot2$	$+12\cdot2$
Formic acid	$1\cdot1 \times 10^4$	$21\cdot0$	$-1\cdot9$
Formamide	$3\cdot7 \times 10^2$	$22\cdot4$	$-3\cdot8$
Methanol	$7\cdot2$	$24\cdot9$	$-3\cdot1$
Acetic acid	$2\cdot2$	$25\cdot8$	$-2\cdot5$
Ethanol	$1\cdot0$	$26\cdot1$	$-3\cdot2$

[a] Winstein and Fainberg, 1957.

founded on the assumption that charge–solvent interaction is the dominant influence on the rate (through $\Delta H^{\ddagger}$) achieved considerable success. The data in Table 5.5 illustrate the effect of solvent changes on the rate and activation parameters for ionization of t-butyl chloride. Leaving aside the results for water, it is evident that decreasing "polarity" of the solvent (see below) is associated almost entirely with increasing $\Delta H^{\ddagger}$. $\Delta S^{\ddagger}$ remains virtually con-

[1] Kosower, 1958.
[2] Ingold, 1953.

stant, as predicted, and small.[1] It follows that the change in "orderedness" of the system in reaching the transition state is affected little by the nature of the solvent, although the change in the strength of the substrate–solvent interaction is. However, in water, a solvent having a much more ordered structure than the other solvents in Table 5.5, the transition state is apparently much less ordered than the ground state, owing to disruption of the solvent structure in the vicinity of the ionic transition state. It is evident that $\Delta S^{\ddagger}$ cannot be a guide to the change in the degree of order in the substrate and primary solvation sheath alone: account must be taken of the interaction of the solvated substrate with other solvent molecules and in particular its influence on solvent structure.

Equation (5.15) shows that the solvent effect on both ground and transition states must be considered. Since $\Delta G_v^{\circ} = -RT \ln h_{RX}$ (where h_{RX} is the Henry's law constant for RX in a given solvent), $\delta_m \Delta G_v^{\circ}$ is obtainable, at least in principle. Table 5.6 indicates how the solvent effect on the free energy of activation of t-butyl chloride in a number of pure solvents is made up of effects on the ground and transition states. For the change from methanol to ethanol or acetic acid both these effects are positive implying *increased* ground-state solvation and a somewhat greater *decrease* in transition-state solvation. For the change to aqueous solution, the increase in reaction rate is largely determined by the reduction in ground-state solvation energy though the solvation of the transition state is increased.

Table 5.6 *Solvent effects on ground and transition state solvation energies (kcal mole^{-1}) in the solvolysis of t-butyl chloride at 25°[a]*

Solvent	$\delta_m \Delta G^{\ddagger}$	$\delta_m \Delta G_v^{\circ}$	$\delta_m \Delta G_s^{\ddagger}$	$\delta_m E_T$[b]
Methanol (Standard)	(0·0)	(0·0)	(0·0)	(0·0)
Ethanol	1·28	0·53	0·75	4·3
Acetic acid	0·75	0·15	0·60	4·4
Water	−6·25	−4·09	−2·16	−11·6

[a] Winstein and Fainberg, 1957.
[b] From Table 5.4.

It is noteworthy that $\delta_m \Delta G_s^{\ddagger}$ parallels $\delta_m E_T$ more closely than it parallels $\delta_m \Delta G^{\ddagger}$, but values of $\delta_m \Delta G_s^{\ddagger}$ are much smaller than values of $\delta_m E_T$, which indicates that the interaction between the transition state and the solvent is weaker than that between cycloheptatrienyl iodide and the solvent.

In mixed solvents the difficulties of interpreting solvent effects on rates of carbonium-ion formation are aggravated by the possibility of selective solva-

[1] Values of $\Delta S^{\ddagger}$ close to zero have been suggested as characteristic of unimolecular solvolysis, much lower values being expected for bimolecular solvolyses because of the "freezing" of a solvent molecule in the transition state (Long, Pritchard and Stafford, 1957; Taft, Purlee et al., 1955; Schaleger and Long, 1963).

tion of ions by one of the components of the solvent mixture.[1] Available data suggest that changes in ground-state solvation energy increase in importance as the water content of aqueous organic solvents increases.[2] Observed values of $\Delta H^{\neq}$ in aqueous alcoholic media pass through a minimum value at 80–90 volume % water and this can be accounted for in the case of t-butyl chloride by changes in ΔH_v°,[3] although solvent effects on the transition state may need to be explicitly considered with other substrates.[4] Indeed, in these media the transition state for solvolysis of t-butyl chloride behaves in much the same way as a typical 1 : 1 electrolyte, e.g. $(CH_3)_4N^+Cl^-$, for which the variation of the partial molar heat of solution is small.[5] Other, less securely based evidence for the importance of ground state solvation comes from values of $\Delta C_p^{\neq}$ and solvent deuterium-isotope effects.[6]

Measure of solvent polarity. We have made use of the concept of polarity and solvating power in the foregoing discussion in a qualitative way. The problem of devising an adequate quantitative measure is by no means resolved and, indeed, may not have a perfectly general solution.

If we look upon carbonium-ion solvation as an electrostatic phenomenon, then the dielectric constant (D) becomes the obvious measure of solvating power (see, however, p. 138). While it would be generally accepted that the sequence t-butyl alcohol ($D=12\cdot2$), isopropyl alcohol ($D=18\cdot3$), ethanol ($D=24\cdot3$), methanol ($D=32\cdot6$) and water ($D=78\cdot5$) is one of increasing polarity, the place to be allotted to non-hydroxylic solvents, such as acetone ($D=20\cdot5$), acetonitrile ($D=37\cdot5$) and dimethyl sulphoxide ($D=48\cdot9$) is less certain. Nevertheless the best-known purely electrostatic theory of solvent effects which has also been applied to rates of carbonium-ion formation[7] is formulated in terms of the dielectric constant. However its success is confined to comparisons of closely similar solvents, e.g., binary mixtures over narrow composition ranges.[8]

As indicated above, E_T- and Z-values derived from spectroscopic measurements are logically the most appropriate empirical measure of solvent polarity for carbonium-ion chemistry. However, in discussions of rates of carbonium-ion formation two other measures (of "ionizing power") have been used: the

[1] Hyne, 1960, 1963; Hyne, Wills and Wonkka, 1962.

[2] Featherstone, Jackson and Kohnstam, 1963.

[3] Winstein and Fainberg, 1957; Arnett, Duggleby and Burke, 1963; Arnett, Bentrude, *et al.*, 1965; Arnett, Bentrude and Duggleby, 1965; Arnett and McKelvey, 1965.

[4] Hyne and Wills, 1963; Hyne, Golinkin and Laidlaw, 1966.

[5] Arnett, Bentrude *et al.*, 1965.

[6] For example, Kohnstam, 1962; Robertson, 1964; Moelwyn-Hughes, Robertson and Sugamori, 1965; Leffek, Robertson and Sugamori 1965; Martin and Robertson, 1966; but see Hulett, 1964.

[7] Kirkwood, 1934; see also Scatchard, 1939.

[8] Fainberg and Winstein, 1956b.

Y-value, defined as the logarithm of the titrimetric (acidimetric) rate of solvolysis of t-butyl chloride at 25° relative to that in 80 % ethanol-water,[1] and the logarithm of the velocity constant for the production of titratable acid from **5.21** at 75° (log k_{ion}).[2] The latter measure has the advantage that it is believed

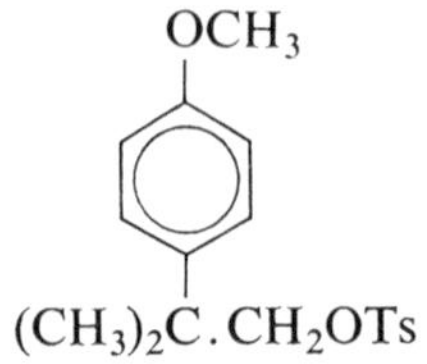

$$OCH_3$$

$$(CH_3)_2C.CH_2OTs$$

(5.21)

to be uncomplicated by the effects of recombination of ion-pair intermediates (see Paragraph 5.3.3) and thus to reflect more accurately the ionizing power of the medium. Some values of these quantities are listed in Table 5.7.

Table 5.7. *Measures of solvent polarity at* $25^{\circ a}$

Solvent	D	Z (kcal mole^{-1})	Y	log k_{ion} (75°)
Water	78·5	94·6	3·493	−1·180
Formic acid	57·9	—	2·054	−0·929
Methanol	32·6	83·6	−1·090	−2·796
Ethanol	24·3	79·6	−2·033	−3·204
Acetic acid	6·2	79·2	−1·639	−2·772
i-Propyl alcohol	18·3	76·3	−2·73	—
Acetonitrile	37·5	71·3	—	−4·221
t-Butyl alcohol	12·2	71·3	−3·26	—
Dimethyl sulphoxide	48·9	71·1	—	−3·738
Dimethylformamide	36·7	68·5	—	−4·298
Acetone	20·5	65·7	—	−5·067
Methylene chloride	8·9	64·2	—	—
Dimethoxyethane	3·5–6·8	62·1	—	—
Tetrahydrofuran	7·4	—	—	−6·073
Diethyl ether	4·2	—	—	−7·3
Iso-octane	1·9	60·1	—	—

^{a} Reichardt, 1965.

5.3.3 INTERACTION OF CARBONIUM IONS WITH OTHER IONS

Non-specific interaction. Information concerning the stabilization of carbonium ions by non-specific interaction with other ions has generally been gleaned from studies of the influence of salts on rates of carbonium-ion formation. The presence of ions in solution usually promotes the reaction and this has been interpreted as indicating that the carbonium ion-like transition state is additionally stabilized, compared with reaction in the absence of salts, by

[1] Grunwald and Winstein, 1948.
[2] S. G. Smith, Fainberg and Winstein, 1961.

formation of an "ionic atmosphere".[1] This model leads to a simple electrostatic theory.[2] The velocity constant (k) for unimolecular heterolysis of a reactant RX in the presence of added salt is related to that in the absence of salt by the Brönsted-Bjerrum equation:

$$k = k_0\, \gamma_{RX}/\gamma^{\ddagger} \tag{5.20}$$

Here γ is an appropriate activity coefficient which can be related to the ionic strength (I). The treatment is the analogue of the Debye-Hückel theory, modified to describe the ionic distribution around a dipolar species.[3] Equation (5.17) thus becomes

$$k = k_0\, \text{antilog}_{10}\left(0\cdot912 \times 10^{16}\, \frac{\sigma I}{D^2 T^2}\right) \tag{5.21}$$

where $\sigma = z^2 d$, z being the charge (expressed as a multiple of e) and d the charge separation in the dipolar transition state. (D is the dielectric constant of the medium and T the temperature.) In practice a more complex equation is necessary to deal with S_N1 reactions to take account of purely chemical reactions between the intermediate carbonium ion and saline additives. (e.g. the "common-ion effect", Section 2.6). Experimental results for a number of substrates RX fit the theory with values of the adjustable parameter σ which are reasonable and which vary in a rational way with the structure of R.[4]

Equation (5.21) leads to two important predictions concerning the interaction of carbonium ion-like transition states and other ions:

(i) It should increase in importance with decreasing dielectric constant, D.

(ii) For salts of a given charge type, the effect should be independent of the chemical identity of the ions.

The results of Table 5.8 give the parameters of the equation $k = k_0 (1 + b[\text{LiClO}_4])$ where k is the rate constant for ionization of (5.21) in the presence of lithium perchlorate in a variety of solvents.[5] In broad terms, prediction (i) is borne out despite the neglect of ion-pairing of the added salt.[6] The anomalous position of acetic acid in the series of solvents warns of the inadequacies of the simple electrostatic theory and more sophisticated interpretations of the results are possible.[7] Prediction (ii) is not fulfilled: for example, the rate of solvolysis of 4-chlorodiphenylmethyl chloride in 80 % acetone–water increases linearly with the concentration of lithium perchlorate, but is affected little by tetrabutylammonium perchlorate.[8]

[1] Ingold, 1953.
[2] Bateman, Church et al., 1940.
[3] Kirkwood, 1939.
[4] Ingold, 1953; Golomb, 1959a, b.
[5] Winstein, Smith and Darwish, 1959.
[6] Golomb, 1959b.
[7] Winstein, Friedrich and Smith, 1964.
[8] Winstein, Hojo and Smith, 1960.

The inadequacies of the simple electrostatic theory of salt effects are in large measure due to neglect of the effect of the added ions on γ_{RX}. In favourable cases, e.g. t-butyl chloride in water,[1] γ_{RX} can be determined by solubility measurements and $\gamma^{\ddagger}$ from rate studies at constant substrate activity (e.g. by use of solutions saturated with RX). The effects of different salts on both γ_{RX} and $\gamma^{\ddagger}$ group themselves according to the charge type of the salt, but within each group there are variations dependent upon the identity of the salt. The electrostatic effect is thus accompanied by a second, salt-dependent medium effect, which has been identified with the influence of the salt on the internal pressure of the solvent. The qualified success of the electrostatic theory is attributable to cancellation of this specific effect in the ratio $\gamma_{RX}/\gamma^{\ddagger}$.

Table 5.8. *Parameters of the equation* $k = k_0 \, (1 + b \, [LiClO_4])$ *for ionization of* (5.21)[a]

Solvent	Temper-ature (°C)	$10^5 k_0$ (sec^{-1})	b	D
Acetic acid	50	11·9	12·2	6·2
Dimethyl sulphoxide	75	18·2	0·0	48·9
Dimethylformamide	75	4·96	1·4	36·7
Acetic anhydride	75	3·41	47·1	—
Acetone	75	0·86	47	20·5
Caprylic acid	75	0·43	461	—
Ethyl acetate	75	0·113	553	6·0
Tetrahydrofuran	75	0·085	482	7·4
Ether[b]	50	0·0006	$2·98 \times 10^5$	4·2

[a] Winstein, Smith and Darwish, 1959.
[b] Results better represented by an equation having an additional, higher-order term in the salt concentration (Winstein, Friedrich and Smith, 1964).

Ion association. Electrostatic theory.[2] For a system of spherical, non-polarizable ions in a structureless dielectric medium (dielectric constant, D), the probability of finding an ion B at a distance r from ion A is given by

$$P = \frac{Nc}{1000} \exp\left(\frac{-z_A z_B e^2}{Dr \, kT}\right) 4\pi r^2 dr \qquad (5.22)$$

where c is the ionic concentration, z_A, z_B are the ionic charges, e the electronic charge, k is Boltzmann's constant, N Avogadro's number and T the temperature. For ions of like sign, P is very small: for oppositely charged ions P passes through a minimum value when the ionic separation is

$$r_{min} = \frac{z_A z_B}{2DkT} e^2 \qquad (5.23)$$

[1] Clarke and Taft, 1962a, b.
[2] Bjerrum, 1926.

Their energy of electrostatic interaction is then $2kT$. At separations greater than r_{min} the thermal energy of the ions is greater than the electrostatic energy and the ions can be regarded as free. The converse is true for separations less than r_{min}, the two ions behaving as essentially a single species or ion-pair. Typical values of r_{min} for $1:1$ electrolytes are $3·6$ Å in water, 45 Å in acetic acid and 120 Å in benzene. In media of low polarity, two ions can be regarded as an ion-pair on this definition even though they are separated by one or more solvent molecules. The method of calculation may, however, be too simple[2] if one is dealing with ions in which the charge is broken up between different sites in media for which the calculated r_{min} is of the order of molecular diameters.

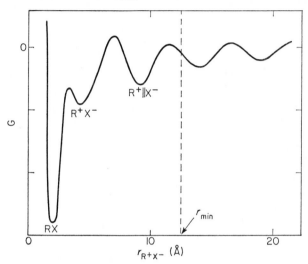

FIG. 5.5. Energy profile for ionization and dissociation of organic molecules in solution. ($D=20$. The separation of the scale marks of the ordinate corresponds to an energy of the order of 10 kcal mole^{-1}.)

Let us now consider the approach of an anion X^- to a carbonium ion R^+—a process known to involve a small but finite activation energy in solution[1] —in a medium for which r_{min} is considerably greater than the combined ionic radii. At infinite separation the two ions are free and each is solvated. Approach of the ions at this stage is restricted by the small energy barrier to diffusion through the medium. As the ions approach, the energy of the system is reduced by the amount of their mutual electrostatic interaction. When only one or two solvent molecules separate the ions a fairly shallow energy minimum is reached (labelled $R^+\|X^-$ in Figure 5.5). Because of dielectric saturation in the space between the ions, the force of attraction is large, but it is known from relaxation studies on inorganic salts that removal of solvent molecules from between

[1] Hawdon, Hughes and Ingold, 1952.

[2] For a critical account of theoretical treatments of ion association, see Szwarc, 1965.

the components of such an ion pair requires a substantial amount of energy.[1] Removal of the intervening solvent molecules yields by stages a pair of ions in contact (R^+X^-). This will be peripherally solvated, and collapse to the covalent molecule requires a small amount of activation energy. The sequence is shown diagrammatically in Figure 5.5[2] where only a single potential barrier has been indicated between $R^+\|X^-$ and R^+X^-. If r_{min} is much larger than the diameter of a solvent molecule, several such barriers, corresponding to the extrusion of successive intervening solvent molecules, will exist. The principle of microscopic reversibility requires that heterolysis of RX follow the same course in reverse. In media of high dielectric constant r_{min} can be so small that heterolysis of RX yields electrostatically free ions directly.

Evidence for ion-pair formation in carbonium-ion reactions. Experimental evidence for ion association involving carbonium ions comes from conductivity and spectrophotometric measurements of equilibrium constants and from kinetic data. The equilibrium methods have already been described (Paragraphs 4.1.4 and 4.1.5). We deal now with kinetic evidence.

We have seen how, in substitution and elimination reactions of a molecule of the type RX, the observation of a rate reduction by added common ions, X^-, provides strong evidence for the intermediate formation of carbonium ions (Paragraph 2.6.3). Such an effect is observable only if the anion formed in heterolysis interchanges with similar anions in the reaction medium at a rate which is rapid compared with the life-time of the carbonium ion, so that the rate of recombination of R^+ and X^- is proportional to the concentration of X^-. Ion-pair formation should thus be demonstrable if recombination can be shown to be independent of the concentration of common anion since the rate of reversion of ion-pairs to covalent molecules proceeds without intervention of the ions of added electrolyte. The problem is two-fold, viz. to demonstrate the occurrence of both ionization and recombination. This can be achieved if the substrate RX is capable of isomerization when ionized: examples of the methods employed are as follows:

(i) Allylic rearrangement: transformation of **5.22** to **5.23** during acetolysis of the tertiary isomer occurs at a rate independent of the concentration of added chloride ion.[3]

$$(CH_3)_2CCl.CH:CH_2 \qquad (CH_3)_2C:CH.CH_2Cl$$
$$\textbf{(5.22)} \qquad\qquad\qquad \textbf{(5.23)}$$

(ii) Wagner-Meerwein rearrangement: conversion of **5.24** to the more reactive isomer **5.25** occurs during acetolysis but not formolysis or ethanolysis of the former.[4] In other cases isotopic labelling may be necessary to demonstrate the occurrence of such rearrangements.[5]

[1] Eigen and Tamm, 1962; Atkinson and Kor, 1965.
[2] Cf. Grunwald, 1954.
[3] W. G. Young, Winstein and Goering, 1951.
[4] Winstein and Schreiber, 1952b.
[5] E.g. Jenny and Winstein, 1958; Winstein, Friedrich and Smith, 1964.

$PhCHMe.CH_2.O.SO_2$⟨○⟩Br $MeCH.CH_2Ph$
                                    |
                                    $O.SO_2$⟨○⟩Br

(5.24)   (5.25)

(iii) Rearrangement of the anionic moiety: when the leaving group, X^-, is an ambident nucleophile, e.g., $R.CO_2^-$,[1] SCN^-,[2] $R.CO.S^-$,[3] or RSO_2^-,[4]; rearrangement can occur by ionic recombination at the alternative nucleophilic centre. In the case of carboxylate ions, ^{18}O-labelling is of course necessary.

(iv) Loss of optical activity: racemization of optically active 4-chlorodiphenylmethyl chloride occurs prior to unimolecular solvolysis in acetic acid[5] (see below).

Combinations of these procedures are sometimes used in special circumstances, e.g. allylic rearrangement, rearrangement of the leaving group and loss of optical activity.[6] Circumstantial rather than direct evidence that isomerization is the result of ionization is usually advanced: other, intramolecular mechanisms for isomerization not involving carbonium-ion formation are sometimes possible.

Loss of optical activity proves to be particularly useful in the study of ion-pair formation in solvolyses. The reaction velocity can be determined by measurements of optical activity (α) as a function of time [Equation (5.24)] as well as by acidimetric titration [Equation (5.25)].

$$(+)\text{-RX} \xrightarrow[\text{SOH}]{k_\alpha} (\pm)\text{-ROS} + (\pm)\text{-RX}$$

$$k_\alpha = (2 \cdot 303/t) \log (\alpha_0/\alpha_t)$$

(5.24)

$$\text{RX} \xrightarrow{k_t} \text{ROS} + \text{HX}$$

$$k_t = (2 \cdot 303/t) \log [V_\infty/(V_\infty - V_t)]$$

(5.25)

[V = Titration volume. Subscripts refer to time.]

While in good solvating solvents $k_\alpha = k_t$, it is often found that in less polar solvents—acetic acid is a particularly good example—k_α exceeds k_t. For example, for *threo*-3-phenyl-2-butyl toluene-*p*-sulphonate[7] (5.26), k_α/k_t is 1·18 in formic acid (25°), 2·05 in ethanol, and 4·4 in acetic acid (75°), the ratios being

[1] Goering and Levy, 1962.
[2] Fava, Iliceto *et al.*, 1965.
[3] S. G. Smith, 1962.
[4] Darwish and Preston, 1964.
[5] Winstein, Gall *et al.*, 1960.
[6] Goering, Pombo and McMichael, 1963; Goering, Doi and McMichael, 1964.
[7] Where necessary the terms *threo* and *erythro* are employed with the usual extended definition: the *erythro*-diastereo isomer is that for which there is an eclipsed conformation with at least two sets of similar substituents in line.

little affected by added common ion.[1] The similarity of activation parameters for the two rates suggests that both processes involve as a first step ionization to an ion pair (5.27), the collapse of which yields racemic starting material and no titratable acid. However, acid formation must arise from reaction of the carbonium ion with solvent, and this step is expected to be facilitated by dissociation of the ion-pair to free ions. Ion pairs themselves can also react with solvent. This is shown by the observation that, while added common ion reduces k_t at low concentrations by removing free carbonium ions, it does not completely suppress solvolysis.[2]

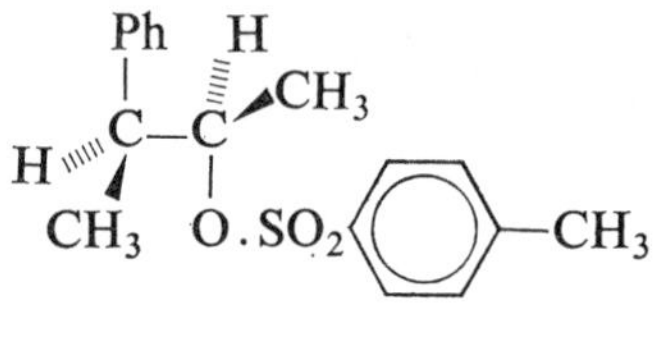

(5.26)

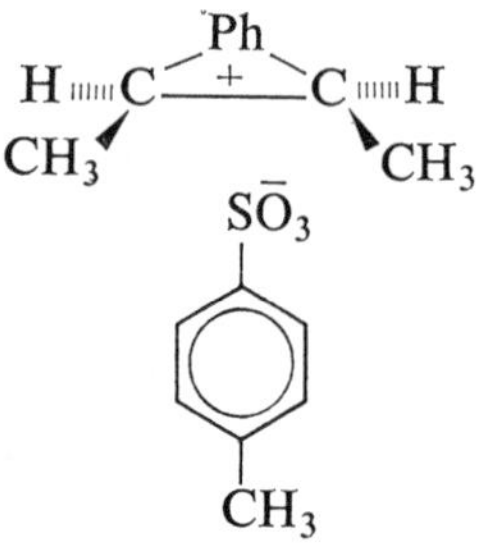

(5.27)

Most of the early examples of this phenomenon involved substrates thought to yield bridged carbonium ions, e.g. 5.27[3] from 5.26. Later work revealed that ion pairs were formed in solvolyses where bridging was most unlikely, e.g. diarylmethyl halides which had been used in early studies of mass-law effects in solvolyses. However, it is clear that excess racemization is more likely in the case of ions such as 5.27 since relatively little movement of the component ions is necessary to bring them to a symmetrical arrangement: for other carbonium ions, racemization may require migration of the leaving group to the opposite face of the cation, the time involved offering greater opportunity for dissociation and solvolysis. In all cases, however, k_α represents a minimum value for the rate of ionization of RX to the ion pair since recombination with

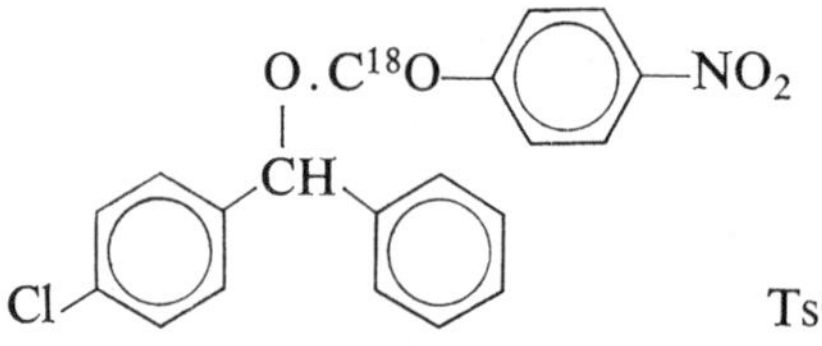

(5.28)

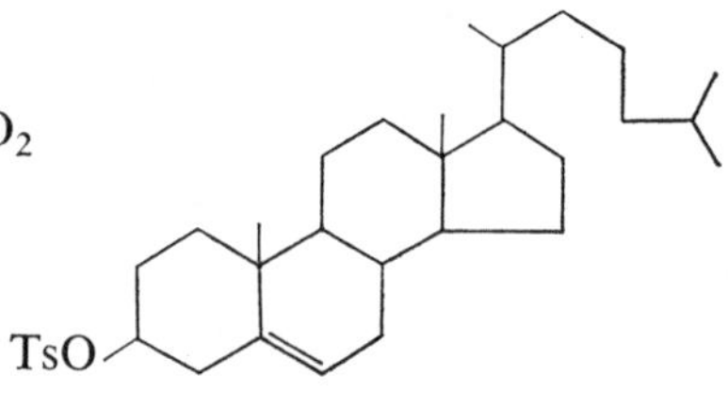

(5.29)

[1] Winstein and Schreiber, 1952a.
[2] Winstein, Clippinger et al., 1956.
[3] Winstein and Schreiber, 1952; Winstein and Trifan, 1952a,b (see Chapter 7).

retention of configuration remains undetected. Indeed, the specific rate of equilibration of ^{18}O in optically active, carbonyl oxygen-labelled 4-chloro-diphenylmethyl p-nitrobenzoate (**5.28**) is 2·3 times that of racemization, indicating that in this case ion-pair return with ^{18}O-equilibration occurs with predominant retention of configuration.[1]

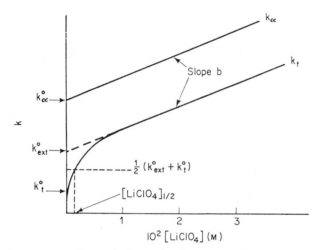

FIG. 5.6. Salt effects on poliarmetric (k_α) and titrimetric (k_t) rate constants for solvolysis.

The evidence so far presented requires only one type of ion-pair inter-mediate for its rationalization. That two types exist follows from the influence of added salts on k_α and k_t. The form of results is shown schematically in Figure 5.6, in which a number of parameters are defined, for lithium perchlorate in acetic acid. Thus k_α increases linearly with increasing lithium perchlorate concentration,[2] and k_t behaves similarly for certain substrates, e.g. **5.26**.[3] This linear rate increase is often referred to as the "normal" salt effect. With other substrates, e.g. **5.29**,[4] k_t increases much more rapidly at very low salt concentrations ($\sim 0·01M$) than at higher concentration. This is sometimes described as a "special" salt effect. Some values of the parameters of Figure 5.6 for **5.29** are given in Table 5.9.

Since the addition of lithium perchlorate reduces k_α/k_t but not to unity, there appear, in the absence of added salts, to be two types of ion pair, both of which can return to starting material with loss of optical activity. The added salt can interact with one of these two types, reducing its return, and, at suffi-

[1] Goering and Levy, 1964.
[2] Winstein and Robinson, 1958.
[3] Winstein, Clippinger et al., 1954; Fainberg and Winstein, 1956a, c.
[4] Winstein, Clippinger et al., 1954.

ciently high salt concentration, suppressing it completely. The residual difference between k_α and k_t is then due to the collapse to starting material of the ion-pairs of the other type.[1]

Observations such as these can be interpreted in terms of the two types of ion-pair intermediate considered on p. 151. The complete reaction scheme is shown in Figure 5.7[2] together with the accepted terminology and symbolism.

Table 5.9. *Parameters of the special salt effect on the titrimetric rate constants for acetolysis of cholesteryl toluene-p-sulphonate* (**5.29**) *at* 25°

Salt	k°_{ext}/k°_t	$10^5[LiClO_4]_{\frac{1}{2}}$(M)	b	Ref.
Lithium perchlorate	2·3	4	28	*a*
Perchloric acid	2·4	6	28	*b*
Diphenylguanidinium perchlorate	2·3	40	12	*b*
Lithium acetate	2·3	200	2	*b*

[a] Winstein, Clippinger *et al.*, 1954.
[b] Winstein and Clippinger, 1956.

The action of lithium perchlorate is thus regarded as replacement of X^- in the solvent-separated ion pair by ClO_4^- which, owing to its low nucleophilicity and the rapid ionization of any covalent perchlorate ester ($RClO_4$) formed,[3] effectively reduces ion pair return to RX and enhances k_t. Support for this explanation is provided by the following observations. The "special" salt effect is associated with longer-lived carbonium ions. It is observed only in systems where ion-pair return occurs, but conversely the occurrence of such return does not necessarily produce the special effect. Trapping of solvent-separated ion pairs is not restricted to perchlorates: acetates (Table 5.9), bromides[4] and azides[5] can capture the intermediate as ROAc, RBr or RN_3. Common ions, however, do not give rise to the "special" effect. Indeed, common ions can suppress the "special" effect of, say, perchlorate ion when both types of ion are present, even in cases where no common-ion effect is ordinarily observed ("induced common-ion rate depression").[6] Conventional steady-state treatment of the scheme of Figure 5.7 yields equations which fit the observed kinetic behaviour in the solvolysis of a number of substrates.[4,6]

[1] Winstein and Robinson, 1958.
[2] Winstein, Clippinger *et al.*, 1956.
[3] Ehret and Winstein, 1966.
[4] Winstein, Klinedinst and Clippinger, 1961.
[5] Goering and Levy, 1964.
[6] Winstein, Klinedinst and Robinson, 1961.

The extent to which the two types of ion-pair and the free carbonium ion take part in solvolytic reactions depends in part upon the organic structure in question. The longer the life-time of the carbonium ion intermediates the greater

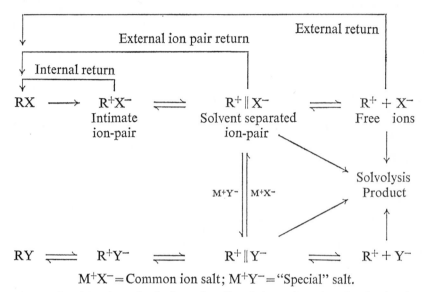

$M^+X^- = $ Common ion salt; $M^+Y^- = $ "Special" salt.

FIG. 5.7. Winstein's scheme for the formation, dissociation and reaction of carbonium ion-pairs in solvolytic reactions.

is the likelihood of formation of the solvent-separated ion-pair and the dissociated ions. The role of the solvent is more complex. This may be illustrated by examining the influence of acetic anhydride on the kinetics of acetolysis of *threo*-3-*p*-methoxyphenyl-2-butyl *p*-bromobenzenesulphonate (**5.30**) as shown

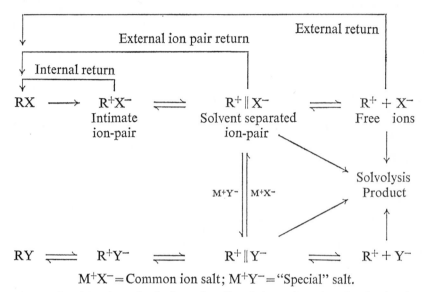

(5.30)

in Table 5.10. Thus the addition of acetic anhydride steadily reduces the rate constant for formation of intimate ion-pairs (k_α°), but causes the titrimetric rate constant to pass through a maximum. Moreover, the magnitude of the special salt effect of added lithium perchlorate, indicated by k_{ext}°/k_t°, is progressively reduced by added acetic anhydride while, at the same time, common-ion rate depression, which is not observed in acetic acid, becomes increasingly apparent. These effects may be interpreted by distinguishing the ability of a solvent to promote ionization from its ability to bring about dissociation of ionic aggregates. On this basis acetic acid would appear to be a better ionizing solvent but a poorer dissociating solvent than acetic anhydride. Thus in acetic acid internal return from ion pairs is very important: addition of acetic anhydride reduces the rate of formation of ionic intermediates but increases the extent to which they are dissociated.

Table 5.10. *Kinetic data for the acetolysis of* threo-3-p-*methoxyphenyl*-2-*butyl* p-*bromobenzenesulphonate* (**5.30**)[a]

Solvent	AcOH(25°)	50%AcOH-Ac$_2$O(25°)	Ac$_2$O(50°)
$10^7 k_\alpha^\circ$(sec^{-1})	798	578	442
$10^7 k_t^\circ$(sec^{-1})	196	318	107
k_α°/k_t°	4·1	1·8	4·1
k_{ext}°/k_t°	2·58	1·56	1·47
%ROAc from solvent-separated ion-pair	100	21	3
%ROAc from dissociated ion	0	79	97

[a] Winstein, Baker and Smith, 1964.

Analogous ionization schemes, involving two types of ion-pair, have been successful in interpreting observations not only in other areas of carbonium ion chemistry[1] but also in fields well removed from that of carbonium ions.[2]

In aprotic media ion solvation is less good than in hydroxylic solvents, even when the dielectric constant is quite high (Paragraph 5.3.2)[3] and ion-pair formation thus becomes more important. Despite experimental difficulties (Section 2.6), particularly in aprotic solvents of very low dielectric constant, e.g. benzene (where no consistent account even of the experimental facts has yet been given),[4] clear evidence for ion-association has been obtained both from studies of the heterolysis of neutral molecules[5] and in the protonation of olefins.[6]

[1] E.g. Bethell and Howard, 1966; Diaz and Winstein, 1966.

[2] E.g. Griffiths and Symons, 1960; Blandamer, Gough and Symons, 1966; Hogen-Esch and Smid, 1966a, b.

[3] Parker, 1962.

[4] Compare for example, Hudson and Saville, 1955, Swain and Kreevoy, 1955; Hughes, Ingold *et al.*, 1957a; Keefer and Andrews, 1962.

[5] Recent references to the more important investigations are: (benzene) Swain and Kreevoy, 1955; Swain and Pegues, 1958; Hughes, Ingold *et al.*, 1957b; (ether) Winstein, Friedrich and Smith, 1964; (acetic anhydride) Winstein, Baker and Smith, 1964; (acetone) Winstein and Appel, 1964; Swain and Tsuchihashi, 1962; (acetonitrile) Iliceto, Fava *et al.*, 1961, Fava, Iliceto *et al.*, 1965.

[6] Dewar and Fahey, 1963a, b, c, 1964).

5.3.4 CHARGE TRANSFER

A more recently recognized charge-dispersing interaction between carbonium ions and other species is charge-transfer complex formation with suitable one-electron donors (D:), e.g. halide ions or aromatic hydrocarbons. The stability of the complex of R^+ and $D:$ is thought to stem from the contribution to the resonance hybrid of a limiting structure in which the donor has transferred *one* electron to the carbonium ion, i.e., $R \cdot D \cdot^+$.[1]

The anion-dependent colour of the cycloheptatrienyl halides both in the solid state and in solution is attributable to such charge transfer.[2] The use of absorption spectral measurements on solutions of the iodide in discussions of solvent polarity is described in Paragraph 5.3.2. In contrast with the perchlorate and tetrafluoroborate, cycloheptatrienyl halides readily undergo oxidation and thermal and photo-chemical decomposition.[3] Complexes in which charge transfer to the cycloheptatrienyl cation is from aromatic hydrocarbons, e.g. anthracene, are detectable spectrophotometrically[4] and there is evidence that olefins also can act as donors.[5]

Studies at present are largely restricted to the cycloheptatrienyl cation, but it seems likely that charge transfer interaction may have a bearing on the behaviour of less stable carbonium ions.[6] Thus the triphenylmethyl cation will accept an electron from ferrocene in nitromethane solution, forming the triphenylmethyl radical (detectable by its reaction with oxygen to form triphenylmethyl peroxide) and ferricinium ion (detectable by its colour).[7] The fate of free radicals formed in processes such as this depends on the reaction conditions: dimerization is sometimes observable.[8] In favourable cases charge transfer can lead to the formation of identifiable radical cations[9] and to polymerization of olefins.[10]

---

[1] Mulliken, 1950, 1952a, b.

[2] Doering and Knox, 1954; Doering and Krauch, 1956; Harmon, Cummings *et al.*, 1962a,b; Harmon and Davis, 1962; Harmon, Alderman *et al.*, 1965.

[3] Harmon, Alderman *et al.*, 1965.

[4] Feldman and Winstein, 1961.

[5] Conrow, 1961; Bawn, Fitzsimmons and Ledwith, 1964.

[6] Kosower, 1956; Colter, Wang *et al.*, 1964; for a general account of the role of charge-transfer complexes as reaction intermediates, see Kosower, 1965.

[7] Hawthorne, 1956.

[8] R. W. Murray and Kaplan, 1966.

[9] Ledwith and Sambhi, 1965.

[10] Bawn, Fitzsimmons and Ledwith, 1964.

6 | REACTIONS OF CARBONIUM IONS

6.1 Introduction

6.1.1 CARBONIUM IONS AS ELECTROPHILES

According to our definition of the term (Chapter 1), a carbonium ion can always be represented by at least one valence bond structure in which one carbon atom is trivalent and carries the positive charge. Because of the vacant orbital on this, the carbonium carbon atom, the site will be electrophilic and the ion as a whole will be classed as an electrophile. With few exceptions (Paragraph 5.3.4), all reactions of carbonium ions may be thought of as the attack of the carbonium centre on electron pairs, which, in appropriate circumstances, can be non-bonded, π-bond and σ-bond electrons (Table 6.1). In this Chapter we shall, for purposes of classification, treat carbonium ion reactions as attack of the carbonium centre on electron pairs of various types, rather than as reactions of the carbonium ion as a whole. Thus olefin formation (E1 elimination) is regarded (Table 6.1) as an intramolecular attack of the carbonium centre on the electrons of a β-situated carbon-hydrogen σ-bond, rather than as a reaction of the carbonium ion with a non-bonded electron pair on the base B.

The observed products of reactions of carbonium ions depend on whether the primary products, formally represented in Table 6.1, can react further. All the processes in Table 6.1 are, in principle, reversible and certain of them yield a new carbonium ion which may have opportunities for further reactions of the types listed. In all cases, the reactions can be intramolecular, the carbonium ion itself providing an electron pair suitably situated for reaction. Certain aspects of these intramolecular reactions are dealt with in Chapter 7.

6.1.2 THE REACTION PRODUCTS

Carbonium ions are often highly energetic intermediates, and this has two important consequences:

(i) A number of alternative reaction paths are usually available to them.

(ii) The reactions of carbonium ions are mostly too rapid for direct kinetic study.

Often the relative proportions of the various reaction products can be measured, but these *need* not necessarily reflect the relative rates of the primary competing processes. The reversibility of the processes listed in Table 6.1 can lead to thermodynamic control of reaction products (i.e. formation of products in proportion to their stability relative to each other *under the reaction conditions*). Thus, Friedel-Crafts alkylation of toluene by methyl halides catalyzed by aluminium chloride, which at $0°$ yields predominantly the expected *o*- and *p*-xylenes, affords almost exclusively the thermodynamically favoured *m*-isomer at $104°$.[1] Again, olefin formation from carbonium ions often occurs under conditions sufficiently acidic for the product to be re-protonated: where more than one olefin can be formed, an equilibrium mixture of olefins then results. In such circumstances, determination of the product proportions provides no information on the reactivity of the carbonium-ion precursor.

When the carbonium ion-consuming steps of a reaction are irreversible, the product proportions are directly related to the velocities of the competing processes, represented by Equation (6.1) (see also Section 2.6).

$$R^+ + X_1 \xrightarrow{k_1} P_1; \; R^+ + X_2 \xrightarrow{k_2} P_2; \ldots R^+ + X_n \xrightarrow{k_n} P_n \qquad (6.1)$$

Assuming that R^+ is kinetically free, we may write

$$d[P_i]/dt = k_i[R^+][X_i]$$

and

$$\sum^n (d[P_i]/dt) = [R^+]\sum^n k_i[X]_i$$

so that

$$d[P_i]/\sum^n (d[P_i]) = k_i[X_i]/\sum^n k_i[X_i] \qquad (6.2)$$

If the concentrations of the reactants X remain effectively constant throughout the course of the reaction, Equation 6.2 can be integrated giving, for the product composition at any stage of reaction,

$$[P_i]/\sum^n [P_i] = k_i[X_i]/\sum^n k_i[X_i] \qquad (6.3)$$

For a pair of product-forming steps yielding P_i and P_j the result becomes

$$[P_i]/[P_j] = k_i[X_i]/k_j[X_j]$$

[1] Norris and Rubinstein, 1939. The question whether carbonium ions are involved in this particular reaction (cf. p. 181) is not germane to the point of this illustration.

Table 6.1. *Reactions of carbonium ions*

Electron pair type	Source of electrons	Typical reactions	Formal representation
A. Non-bonded	(i) Anions (e.g. halide, carboxylate, etc.)	Unimolecular nucleophilic substitution at aliphatic carbon	 $\mathrm{C^{+}} \; X^{-} \longrightarrow \; \mathrm{C-X}$
	(ii) Electrically neutral molecules containing atoms with non-bonded electrons (e.g. alcohols, amines)	Unimolecular solvolysis	 $\mathrm{C^{+}} \; \ddot{O}\!\!<^{R}_{H} \longrightarrow \; \mathrm{C}{-}\overset{+}{O}\!\!<^{R}_{H}$
B. π-Bond	(i) Olefins	Cationic polymerization	 $\mathrm{\sim\!\!C^{+}} \; \mathrm{C{=}C} \longrightarrow \; \mathrm{\sim\!\!C{-}C{-}\overset{+}{C}{-}}$
	(ii) Aromatic compounds	Friedel-Crafts and related reactions	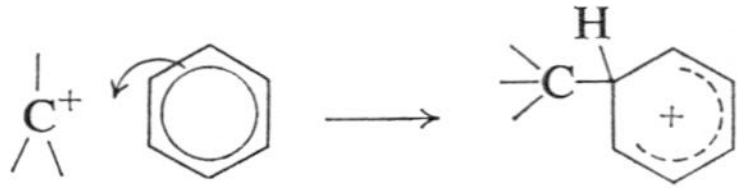 $-\overset{+}{\mathrm{C}}\!< \; + \;\bigcirc \longrightarrow$

C. σ-Bond

(i) C—H bonds (inter- and intramolecular reaction)

(a) Olefin formation

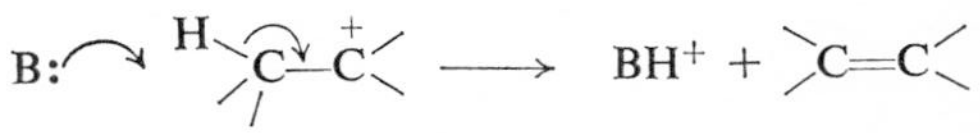

$$B: + H-\overset{|}{\underset{|}{C}}-\overset{+}{\underset{|}{C}}- \longrightarrow BH^+ + C=C$$

(b) Hydride transfer

$$\overset{|}{\underset{|}{C}}{}^+ + H-R \longrightarrow \overset{|}{\underset{|}{C}}-H + R^+$$

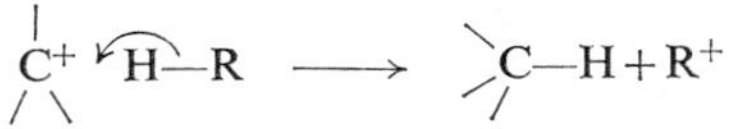

(ii) C—C bonds (intramolecular reaction)

(a) Wagner-Meerwein and related rearrangements

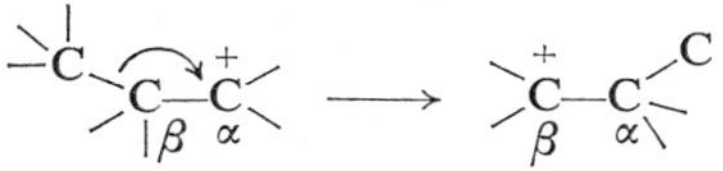

$$\overset{|}{\underset{|}{C}}-\overset{+}{\underset{\beta}{C}}-\overset{}{\underset{\alpha}{C}} \longrightarrow \overset{+}{\underset{\beta}{C}}-\overset{|}{\underset{\alpha}{C}}-C$$

(b) Fragmentation

$$\ddot{X}-\overset{|}{\underset{|}{C}}-\overset{|}{\underset{|}{C}}-\overset{+}{\underset{|}{C}}- \longrightarrow \overset{+}{X}=C + C=C$$

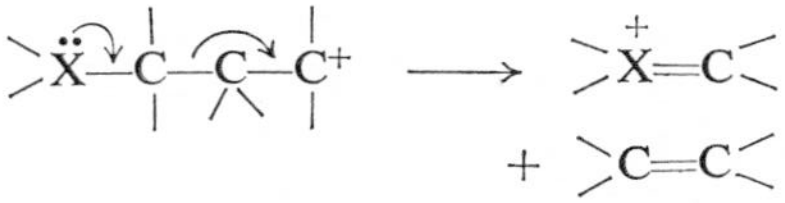

so that relative values of the velocity constants of two individual carbonium ion reactions can be determined from the relative concentrations of their products. This basic approach is of course applicable to any type of reactive intermediate provided only that the products whose proportions are compared are formed irreversibly. The procedure can be readily adapted to yield differences in activation parameters.

6.1.3 CHEMICAL CONSEQUENCES OF CHARGE DELOCALIZATION

The principal modes of charge dispersal were classified in Chapter 5 as (a) internal (electrical induction, conjugation and related phenomena), and (b) external (solvation, ion association and charge transfer). Both types of charge delocalization can be important in determining the fate of the carbonium ion. We may regard the external factors as secondary, since the interaction between the carbonium ion and its surroundings will depend upon the degree of charge delocalization possible within the ion. Nevertheless these external factors can exert important modifying influences on the effects of internal delocalization.

Internal charge dispersal shows the most clear-cut chemical effects when it leads to the formation of carbonium centres at sites other than that from which a leaving group departed. For example, allylic cations, can react with nucleophiles at one of two carbonium centres. Thus unimolecular hydrolysis of each of the isomeric allylic halides (**6.1** and **6.2**) yields the same mixture of α, α- and γ,γ-dimethylallyl alcohols, indicating that the two reactions share a common intermediate allylic cation represented by the canonical forms (**6.3a** and **6.3b**).

$$(CH_3)_2C:CH.CH_2Cl \qquad (CH_3)_2CCl.CH:CH_2$$
$$\textbf{(6.1)} \qquad\qquad\qquad \textbf{(6.2)}$$

$$(CH_3)_2C:CH.CH_2^+ \longleftrightarrow (CH_3)_2C^+.CH:CH_2$$
$$\textbf{(6.3a)} \qquad\qquad\qquad \textbf{(6.3b)}$$

More often, however, somewhat different product proportions are obtained from isomeric reactants of this type. Representative data are given in Table 6.2. The difference in yield of one of the products from a pair of isomeric reactants is sometimes referred to as the "product spread". Generally, the unrearranged product is formed to a larger extent from the primary halide if the other isomer is a secondary or tertiary halide, and the product spread decreases with increasing carbonium-ion stability (as judged by solvolytic reactivity) and increasing solvent polarity. While product spread may be due in part to the incursion of S_N2 substitution, particularly with the less reactive of the isomeric reactants, the dominant factor is probably the proximity of the leaving group to the carbon atom from which it has just departed at the time of attack by the

Table 6.2. *Percentage of primary product in the solvolysis of allylic chlorides at 25°[a]*

Compound	EtOH	EtOH/Ag$_2$O	H$_2$O	H$_2$O/Ag$_2$O	HOAc/AgOAc	Equilibrium
CH$_3$.CH:CH.CH$_2$Cl ⎫	91[b]	70[c]	55	45	60	~80[c]
CH$_3$.CHCl.CH:CH$_2$ ⎬	53[b]	46[c]	36	34	56	
(CH$_3$)$_2$C:CH.CH$_2$Cl. ⎫	48	35	15	17	55	~90[c]
(CH$_3$)$_2$CCl.CH:CH$_2$ ⎬	30	20	15	16	55	

[a] DeWolfe and Young, 1956, 1964.
[b] At 78°.
[c] Note that kinetic control leads to a preponderance of the thermodynamically less stable product (Catchpole, Hughes and Ingold, 1948); see Paragraph 4.1.1.

7

solvent. The field of the anion polarizes the allylic cation, rendering the nearby carbon atom the more electrophilic centre and thus favouring the formation of unrearranged product. Thus external charge-dispersing factors modify the effects of internal delocalization of the charge.

Examples of related effects of internal charge-delocalization in so-called bridged carbonium ions are given in Chapter 7.

Inductive charge spreading, because it does not produce new carbonium centres, does not have such straightforward chemical consequences. Instead, the inductive effect reduces the intensity of the electric field surrounding the carbonium centre, modifying its external interactions with solvent molecules, anions and other potential reaction partners and consequently reducing the rate of its reactions with nucleophiles. We have previously pointed out that low reactivity is to be expected of a thermodynamically stable ion. The fact that this low reactivity can likewise be described as a consequence of the low charge density at the reactive site of the carbonium ion again illustrates the underlying connexion between charge dispersal and stabilization of the ion.

The solvation of the carbonium ion should have a qualitatively similar effect on reactivity as the inductive effect. However, except for unimolecular reactions of carbonium ions, the effect of solvation on the nucleophiles and corresponding transition states must also be considered explicitly in any discussion of reactivity. The qualitative theory of Ingold[1] gives general guidance: for example, the charge destruction indicated by the process

$$R^+ + X^- \rightarrow R^{\delta+} \ldots X^{\delta-}$$

should be impeded more than the charge dispersal in

$$R^+ + X \rightarrow R^{\delta+} \ldots X^{\delta+}$$

by a change to a more solvating solvent. However, it must be remembered that, in general, solvents do not interact equally strongly with anions and cations.

We have previously (Paragraph 5.3.3) discussed some of the chemical effects of inter-ionic forces. In addition they can, in conjunction with solvent effects, modify the steric course of carbonium-ion reactions (see Paragraph 6.2.4).

6.1.4 INFLUENCE OF THE SOURCE OF THE ION ON CARBONIUM-ION REACTIONS

The reactions of carbonium ions are modified to some extent according to the nature of the reactant molecules from which the ions are derived. The largest differences are usually observed between carbonium ions produced in simple heterolyses,

$$RX \rightarrow R^+ + X^-$$

and those produced in nitrous acid deamination

$$RNH_2 \rightarrow RNH \cdot NO \rightarrow RN_2OH \rightarrow RN_2^+ \rightarrow R^+ + N_2,$$

[1] Ingold, 1953, p. 345.

particularly in aprotic media.[1] Thus deamination often yields a greater variety of products, and, in appropriate cases, the products have different stereochemistry and show different patterns of skeletal rearrangement compared with simple heterolysis reactions, e.g. of organic halides. The behaviour is that expected of carbonium ions of high reactivity which discriminate little between potential reaction partners: the epithets "hot" or "unsolvated" have sometimes been applied to these carbonium ions. Specific examples of this behaviour, which is not restricted to carbonium ions obtained by deamination, will be given in the sequel.

We shall adopt the mechanism for nitrous acid deamination outlined above,[2] recognizing, however, that it is not universal. Thus loss of nitrogen from $CH_3 . CH_2O . CO . CH_2N_2^+$ occurs only on attack by a nucleophile[3] and without formation of a carbonium ion. The extent to which such S_N2 reactions occur with other diazonium ions, for which the corresponding carbonium ion is more stable than $^+CH_2 . CO . OR$, is still uncertain.[4] There is even doubt about the formation of the diazonium ion itself in certain cases, e.g., from primary s-alkylamines $(RR'CH . NH_2; R,R' = alkyl)$.[5]

It has been suggested that carbonium ions formed from diazo and diazonium precursors are highly energized because their formation is fast and exothermic.[6] This suggestion replaces the original problem by a more general one: how is the energy of a common transition state divided between two simultaneously formed products? Huisgen's hypothesis, that a carbonium ion will be particularly unstable when the simultaneously formed particle (the nitrogen molecule in this instance) is especially stable, is an attractive one but is not by itself an explanation.

The consequences of this high potential energy of the carbonium ion are manifold. Thus, energy barriers, so high as to prevent some reactions of carbonium ions obtained by simple heterolysis, can be surmounted by carbonium ions formed in deamination. Further, the life-time of the energized carbonium ion will be very short, comparable to the time for rotation about a carbon–carbon single bond in some cases. As a result, the conformation in which a carbonium ion reacts may be the most stable conformation of its precursors rather than the most stable conformation of the ion, leading to unusual migratory aptitudes in rearrangement.[7] The solvation sheath, surrounding the carbonium ion and providing a proportion of the reaction partners, may also not be that most appropriate to the carbonium ion because

---

[1] Bayless, Friedman et al., 1965; Bayless, Mendicino and Friedman, 1965.

[2] Ridd, 1961.

[3] Albery and Bell, 1961; Hammett, 1940, p. 288; J. D. Roberts, Regan and Allen, 1952.

[4] Streitwieser and Schaeffer, 1957a; Streitwieser, 1957; Ridd, 1961.

[5] Maskill, Southam and Whiting, 1965; Whiting, 1966.

[6] Huisgen and Reimlinger, 1956a,b.

[7] Cram and McCarty, 1957; see pp. 214–215.

of the short period of time available for the solvent molecules to accommodate themselves to it: unusual stereochemical results may thus arise.[1]

6.2 Attack of Carbonium Centres on Non-bonded Electron Pairs

6.2.1 INTRODUCTION

This reaction is the reverse of carbonium-ion formation by heterolysis of electrically neutral or positively charged molecules. Reaction partners are typical nucelophiles: they can be anions, e.g. halide ions, or neutral molecules, e.g. alcohols, and they may have more than one nucleophilic centre (Paragraph 5.3.3)

$$R^+ + Cl \rightarrow RCl$$

$$R^+ + EtOH \rightarrow R.\overset{+}{O}{\overset{H}{\underset{Et}{\diagdown}}} \rightarrow ROEt + (H^+)$$

The reaction with anions yields initial products which are electrically neutral. With alcohols and amines, for example, proton loss from the first-formed oxonium or ammonium ion occurs readily (Paragraph 3.1.2) in a subsequent step. In cases where the nucleophilic atom does not bear hydrogen (e.g., ethers) the first-formed ion may be stable; indeed it may be more stable than the carbonium ion. For example, the addition of the triphenylmethyl cation to diethyl ether in nitromethane solution

$$Ph_3C^+ + Et_2O \rightleftharpoons Ph_3C.\overset{+}{O}Et_2$$

is a reversible reaction, the equilibrium constant of which can be determined.[2] In other cases, the oxonium ion produced in the first step may decompose giving a different positively charged species.[3] Thus cyclic ethers, such as tetrahydrofuran, polymerize under the influence of carbonium-ion initiators.[4] In these cases the oxonium ion cleaves to produce a new carbonium ion which can attack a further ether molecule, viz.

$$R^+ + O\!\!\bigcirc \longrightarrow R\!\!-\!\!\overset{+}{O}\!\!\bigcirc \longrightarrow RO(CH_2)_3CH_2^+$$

$$RO(CH_2)_3CH_2^+ + O\!\!\bigcirc \longrightarrow RO(CH_2)_4\!\!-\!\!\overset{+}{O}\!\!\bigcirc \longrightarrow$$

$$RO(CH_2)_4O(CH_2)_3CH_2^+$$

etc.

[1] Ridd, 1961; but see Mills, 1953, Huisgen and Reimlinger, 1956a; Huisgen and Rüchardt, 1956a,b; Streitwieser, 1957; Streitwieser and Schaeffer, 1957a; Streitwieser and Coverdale, 1959.

[2] W. B. Smith and Rao, 1961.

[3] Olah and O'Brien, 1967.

[4] E.g. Meerwein, Delfs and Morschel, 1960; Müller and Huber-Emden, 1961; Bawn, Bell et al., 1965.

Nucleophilic activity and basicity are related properties. Proton transfer from carbonium ions to species having non-bonded electron pairs, to give (usually) olefins, may thus constitute an important reaction competing with co-ordination of the carbonium centre to the nucleophile (see Paragraph 6.4.2).

The rapidity of the attack of carbonium ions on non-bonded electron pairs renders kinetic investigation extremely difficult, except in the special case of triarylmethane dye cations (see Paragraph 6.2.3). Most of the available information on the reactivity of carbonium centres with non-bonded electrons has been obtained from proportions of products formed in competing reactions [Equation (6.3)]. In S_N1 reactions displaying a common-ion rate retardation, ratios of rate constants for reaction of the carbonium ion with the common ion and with another nucleophile, usually the solvent, can be derived using the methods outlined in Section 2.6. The reaction of the carbonium centre with a hydroxylic solvent is usually regarded as occurring by collapse of its primary solvation sheath, though some of the experimental evidence[1] has been challenged.[2]

Considering the importance of this class of reactions, relatively little systematic investigation, covering a range of carbonium ion structures, has been reported. In particular, information on the energetics of the reaction is sparse: such results as there are support the view that the reaction is highly exothermic, with a low activation energy, and involves a transition state which resembles the reactant carbonium ion and nucleophile more closely than the primary reaction product. It should be borne in mind that the stabilization of the carbonium ion by the solvent and other ions (Section 5.3) has not always been explicitly considered in discussions of, for example, structural influences on the course of the reaction.

6.2.2 THE INFLUENCE OF THE NUCLEOPHILE

Reactivities ($\log k_{rel}$) of a range of nucleophiles having non-bonded electron pairs towards triphenylmethyl cations relative to that of water are given in Table 6.3. All show high nucleophilic activity, the most notable values being those for azide ion (because it is the highest),[3] hydroxide ion (because it illustrates the effect of proton removal from the nucleophile) and aniline (because it is so high for a neutral molecule having its lone pair in conjugation with a benzene ring).

The reactivity of a nucleophile towards any given reagent depends upon the combination of a number of properties of the nucleophile.[4] The following factors have been considered explicitly:

(i) Basicity.
(ii) Polarizability.

[1] Bateman, Church et al., 1940.
[2] Golomb, 1959a,b; E. A. Hill, 1965.
[3] But see E. A. Hill, 1965.
[4] Edwards and Pearson, 1962; Hudson, 1962; R. G. Pearson, 1963.

(iii) Availability of electron pairs on atoms adjacent to the nucleophilic atom (sometimes referred to as the "α-effect").

(iv) Steric effects.

(v) Interaction with the solvent and other species, e.g. counter-ions.

Table 6.3 includes values of parameters related to some of these properties: ΔpK_a^{HN}, the relative acidity of the conjugate acids of the nucleophiles, measures basicity; $[R]_\infty$ the molar refraction for light of infinite wavelength, averaged over all directions, is a measure of polarizability; E° is the standard electrode

Table 6.3. *Reactivity of nucleophiles towards triphenylmethyl cations (relative to water)* [a, b]

Nucleophile,N	$\log k_{rel}$	ΔpK_a^{HN}	$\Delta\log [R]_\infty$	ΔE°	n
H_2O	0·00	0·00	0·00	0·00	0·00
$CH_3.CO_2^-$	3·04[c]	6·46	—	0·95	2·72
Cl^-	3·49	~ −3	0·389	1·24	3·04
N_3^-	4·95	6·46	—	1·58	4·00
OH^-	3·99	17·5	0·143	1·65	4·20
SCN^-	4·11	1·00	—	1·83	4·77
$S_2O_3^{2-}$	3·49	3·60	—	2·52	6·36
$C_6H_5NH_2$	3·57	6·28	—	1·78	4·49

[a] Values of $\log k_{rel}$ (Swain, Scott and Lohmann, 1953) determined in water–dioxan–acetone (6:2:92 by weight) at 25°, assuming no volume change on mixing the solvents in the calculation of $[H_2O]$: values of other parameters taken from a more extensive compilation (Leffler and Grunwald, 1963, pp. 247, 253).

[b] Symbols are defined in the text on this page.

[c] In 85% by weight acetone–water at −34°.

potential for the equilibrium $2N^z \rightleftharpoons (N_2)^{z+2} + 2e^-$, which models the formal oxidation of the nucleophile when it reacts with an electrophile. A more direct, empirical measure of nucleophilic activity is provided by n, the value of $\log(k_N/k_{H_2O})$ for bimolecular substitution in methyl bromide. Clearly there is poor correlation of $\log k_{rel}$ with any one of these parameters:[1] linear combinations[2] would improve matters. The failure of the correlation with basicity is somewhat unexpected: co-ordination of a proton to the electron pair of the nucleophile could be regarded formally as a model for the attachment of the carbonium ion, though solvation and steric effects would obviously be very different. Polarizability would not be expected to be very important in reactions at a carbonium centre because of the low electron density at the reaction site.

Relatively little attention has been devoted to steric effects on nucleophilic reactivity towards carbonium ions. The greater nucleophilic activity of fluoride

[1] E.g. Swain and Scott, 1953.
[2] Edwards, 1954, 1956.

compared with bromide ion towards t-butyl cations in sulphur dioxide has been attributed to steric causes[1] and the reactivities of aliphatic alcohols towards diarylmethyl cations in acetonitrile appear to fall in a steric order.[2] In the latter case, compression between the alkyl group and the hydroxyl hydrogen atom in the transition state is presumably responsible, but this should be partly allowed for in ΔpK_a.[3]

Interaction of the nucleophile with the solvent can be expected to be of profound importance in modifying the reactivity of the nucleophile towards a carbonium ion. Thus the order of reactivity of halide ions in the dipolar aprotic solvent dimethylformamide is that of electronegativity, the reverse of the situation in hydroxylic solvents.[4] Ion-pairing will also be an important influence on anionic nucleophiles in certain circumstances. Generally speaking, the influence of the medium is likely to be complex. Qualitatively we should expect that the process $R^+ + X^- \to R^{\delta+} \ldots X^{\delta-}$ would decrease in importance relative to that of $R^+ + Y \to R^{\delta+} \ldots Y^{\delta+}$ as the ion-solvating power of the medium increases.[5] However, experimental evidence on this point is conflicting.[6] Simple electrostatic theories along the lines indicated in Paragraph 5.3.3 cannot be properly tested, but are evidently inadequate, in part probably because they neglect ion-association which is known to be important in the solvents used.[7]

6.2.3 EFFECT OF CARBONIUM-ION STRUCTURE ON REACTIVITY

The range of carbonium-ion structures systematically investigated in reactions with non-bonded electron pairs is quite small. Table 6.4 contains values of the reactivities of azide ion relative to water (obtained by the competition method) and chloride ion relative to water (from mass law constants, α, see Section 2.6) with a range of carbonium ions of widely different thermodynamic stability in aqueous acetone. As expected, the more stable carbonium ions tend to be more discriminating between competing nucleophiles (cf. p. 89–90). In the limit of infinite carbonium-ion reactivity, reaction should occur at every collision, reaction rates would be diffusion-controlled and relative reactivities would be unity. That this trend exists is shown by the behaviour of the very reactive intermediate thought to be $C_6H_5^+$, obtained by unimolecular decomposition of benzenediazonium ion $C_6H_5N_2^+$ in water at $100°$, for which k_{Cl^-}/k_{H_2O} is $2 \cdot 5$.[8]

A similar conclusion can be reached from the data in Table 6.5 in which mass-law constants, $(\alpha = k_{Cl^-}/k_{H_2O}(H_2O))$ obtained from the kinetics of

[1] Bunton, Greenstreet et al., 1954a,b.
[2] Bethell and Howard, 1966.
[3] Bartlett and McCollum, 1956.
[4] Weaver and Hutchison, 1964.
[5] Ingold, 1953, p. 345.
[6] Bateman, Church et al., 1940; Golomb, 1959b.
[7] Golomb, 1959a,b.
[8] E. S. Lewis, 1958.

Table 6.4. *Relative reactivities of azide ion, chloride ion and water towards carbonium ions in* 90% *acetone–water[a]* (v/v)

Carbonium ion	Temp.	$k_{N_3^-}/k_{H_2O}$	Temp.	k_{Cl^-}/k_{H_2O}	pK_{R^+}[b]
$C_6H_5)_3C^+$	$-34°$	110,000[c]	$-34°$	3100[c]	$-6·63$
$(p\text{-}CH_3C_6H_4)_2CH^+$	$0°$	240	$0°$	600	$-10·4$
$(C_6H_5)_2CH^+$	$25°$	200	$25°$	120[d]	$-13·3$
	$50°$	180			
$(CH_3)_3 C^+$	$50°$	3·9	$25°$	180[e]	—

[a] Swain, Scott and Lohmann, 1953; but see also E. A. Hill, 1965; Sneen, Carter and Kay, 1966.
[b] From Table 4.9.
[c] 85% Acetone–water.
[d] 80% Acetone–water.
[e] 5% Ethanol–water.

hydrolysis of diarylmethyl halides in aqueous acetone, are compared with relative rates of hydrolysis.[1] Thus low rates of hydrolysis and low values of α go together. The high value of α for 4-phenyldiphenylmethyl chloride may indicate that high polarizability provides additional stability (and discrimination) for the carbonium ion but not for the transition state leading to its formation.

Table 6.5. *Mass law constants* (α) *and relative rates of hydrolysis* (k) *for the hydrolysis of substituted diphenylmethyl chlorides in* 70% *acetone–water at* 0°[a]

Substituent	α (l.mole^{-1})	k
4-NO$_2$	0·71	0·00045
4-C$_6$H$_5$,4'-NO$_2$	1·52	0·0101
—	2·08	(1·00)
4-C$_6$H$_5$	8·43	8·15

[a] Bailey, Fox *et al.*, 1966.

Analogous substituent effects have been found for the directly measured velocity constants for reaction of cations of the type **6.4** with hydroxide ion and water, the so-called "alkaline fading of triphenylmethane dyes" (Table 6.6).[2] The rate constants generally increase with increasing electron withdrawal by m- and p-substituents, and these cations, very stable by virtue of the two p-NMe$_2$

[1] Bailey, Fox *et al.*, 1966; earlier, less reliable values of α are given by Bensley and Kohnstam, 1955.

[2] Similar measurements on a series of less stable triarylmethyl cations are reported by Diffenbach, Sano and Taft, 1966.

substituents, discriminate between hydroxide ion and water about ten times more effectively than the unsubstituted triphenylmethyl cation. The marked rate reduction by o-substituents is attributable to steric hindrance.

Once again the least satisfactory feature of some of the results just described

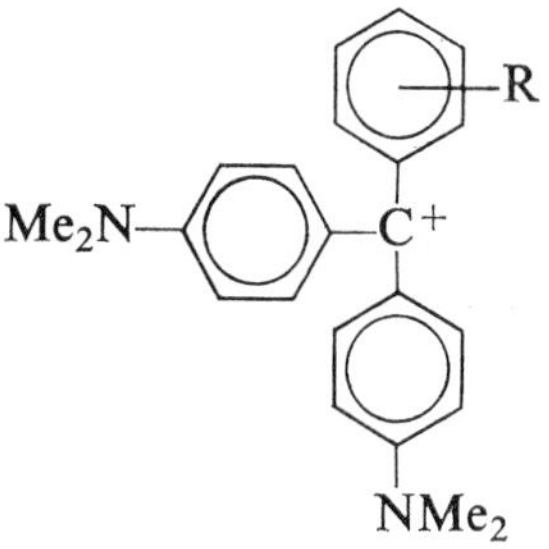

(6.4)

Table 6.6. *Velocity constants for reaction of Malachite Green derivatives with hydroxide ion and water in aqueous solution at 20°. (Ionic strength: 0·5)*

Substituent R in 6.4	$10k_{OH^-}$ (l.mole^{-1}sec^{-1})	$10^4k_{H_2O}$ (sec^{-1})	Ref.
H[i]	5·28	1·08	a
p-NMe$_2$[j]	0·69	0·06	b
o-OMe	0·48	0·30	c
m-OMe	0·30	1·04	a
m-OH	1·95	1·09	a
o-F	1·78	0·39	d
p-F	6·75	0·92	e
o-Cl	0·22	0·021	f
m-Cl	8·03	1·02	g
p-Cl	7·33	1·00	e
o-Br	0·18	0·011	f
m-Br	7·77	1·02	g
p-Br	7·38	0·97	e
o-I	0·09	0·003	f
m-I	7·43	0·88	g
p-I	7·27	0·82	e
p-NMe$_3^+$	14·5	1·04	h

[a] Cigén, 1961a.
[b] Cigén, 1958.
[c] Cigén, 1961b.
[d] Cigén and Ekström, 1963a.
[e] Cigén and Ekström, 1963c.
[f] Cigén and Ekström, 1963b.
[g] Cigén and Ekström, 1964.
[h] Cigén, 1960.
[i] Malachite Green.
[j] Crystal Violet.

7*

is the lack of information regarding the association of the carbonium ion with counter-ions, which could be important.[1]

6.2.4 STEREOCHEMISTRY

Reaction at an asymmetric carbon atom. Most data on this topic refer to carbonium ions formed in $S_N 1$ reactions at an asymmetric carbon. The observed behaviour is summarized in Ingold's "$S_N 1$ Rule",[2] enunciated on the basis of a limited number of experimental results, viz. "*Mechanism $S_N 1$, proceeding through a carbonium ion, involves racemization, together, in general, with an excess of inversion, unless a configuration-holding group is present, when configuration is predominantly retained*". Discussion of reactions in which, as a result of neighbouring-group participation, retention is the major stereochemical result is deferred until Chapter 7. Retention due to restricted rotation about the bond linking the carbonium carbon atom to an aryl substituent in a free triarylmethyl cation is also known.[3]

Substitution at an asymmetric carbon atom involving carbonium-ion formation had earlier been predicted by Lowry to involve retention[4] and by Kenyon to involve inversion of configuration.[5] On a naïve modern view, transformation of the tetrahedral bond arrangement of sp^3-hybridized carbon to the planar arrangement of sp^2-hybridized carbon creates a plane of symmetry in the carbonium ion: thus substitution products should be racemic. Generally, however, predominant inversion is found. Some typical observations from unimolecular solvolyses of organic halides are given in Table 6.7. Evidently, though the nature of the solvent has some effect, the dominant influence is the structure of the carbonium ion. Inversion increases in the series α-phenylethyl < 3,7-dimethyl-3-octyl < 2-octyl, i.e. secondary arylalkyl < t-alkyl < s-alkyl, the order of decreasing thermodynamic stability of the carbonium ion. A simple explanation of the stereochemical course of the reaction[6] is that reaction of the carbonium ion with the solvent occurs soon after the energy barrier for carbonium ion formation has been surmounted. Although heterolysis is complete, the leaving group is still close to one face of the carbonium ion, shielding it from solvent attack, which now occurs predominantly from the opposite face, leading to inversion of configuration. Clearly, the more stable the carbonium ion, the longer its life-time and the more chance there is for the leaving group to diffuse away, permitting attack from both sides with equal probability.

---

[1] Sneen, Carter and Kay, 1966.
[2] Ingold, 1953, p. 381.
[3] Murr and Santiago, 1966.
[4] Lowry, 1925.
[5] Kenyon and Phillips, 1930; Kenyon, Lipscomb and Phillips, 1930.
[6] Cowdrey, Hughes *et al.*, 1937; Ogg and Polanyi, 1935; but see also Winstein, 1939; Streitwieser, 1955.

Table 6.7. *Inversion during unimolecular solvolysis of alkyl derivatives*

Alkyl halide	Solvent	Temp.	% Inversion (net)	Ref.
2-n-Octyl bromide	60% (v/v) EtOH-H$_2$O	60°	66 (hydrolysis)	a
			74 (ethanolysis)	a
3,7-Dimethyl-3-octyl chloride	80% (v/v) Acetone-H$_2$O	60°	21	b
	Methanol	60°	34	b
3,7-Dimethyl-3-octyl acetate	70% (v/v) Acetone-H$_2$O/H$^+$	76°	19	c
α-Phenylethyl chloride	80% (v/v) Acetone-H$_2$O	70°	1·9	d
	60% (v/v) Acetone-H$_2$O	70°	5·4	d
	Acetic acid	50°	15	e
	Water	20°	17·5	d

[a] Hughes, Ingold and Masterman, 1937.
[b] Hughes, Ingold et al., 1950.
[c] Bunton, Hughes et al., 1950.
[d] Hughes, Ingold and Scott, 1937.
[e] Steigman and Hammett, 1937.

Attempts to make this qualitative interpretation more precise stem from Hammett's suggestion[1] that the first intermediate in $S_N 1$ reactions should be regarded as an ion pair[2] which reacts with solvent molecules with inversion at the carbonium centre or dissociates to free ions yielding racemic products. This model can be elaborated[3] by assuming that there is a specific number, n, of solvation sites surrounding the carbonium ion. One of these sites is occupied by the leaving group in the first-formed ion pair. Solvolysis at this stage (velocity constant, k), by collapse of the solvation sheath[4] gives predominantly inverted product. Alternatively, ion-pair dissociation (velocity constant k') gives a symmetrically solvated carbonium ion and hence racemic product. A simple kinetic treatment combined with the observed fractional excess of inverted product yields values of $n + k'/k$: for example, values of about 6 are observed for α-phenylethyl chloride in a variety of solvents, the approximate constancy suggesting that this is the value of n (i.e. $n \gg k'/k$). However, it is now recognized that ion-association phenomena are more complex than considered in this model, and in particular, that racemization can occur prior to solvent intervention (see Paragraph 5.3.3). In cases of substitution by ionic nucleophiles, both the carbonium ion and the nucleophile may be present as ion pairs. The reaction may then be envisaged[5] as occurring by way of ionic quadruplets and raises the question[6] of isomerism in such structures, e.g. 6.5 and 6.6.

$$R^+X^-M^+Y^- \qquad\qquad R^+Y^-M^+X^-$$

$$\textbf{(6.5)} \qquad\qquad\qquad \textbf{(6.6)}$$

Investigation of acid-catalysed oxygen exchange and racemization of s-butyl alcohol[7] indicates that the intermediate carbonium ion reacts always so as to yield inverted product, a result which might be thought more appropriate to reaction through a bimolecular transition state. Application of the method described above gives a solvation number, n, of 2. This corresponds to one extreme view of carbonium-ion solvation in general, the so-called "structural hypothesis", according to which only two solvation sites need be considered (see Paragraph 5.3.2). On this view the stereochemical course of carbonium-ion reactions is pictured as in Figure 6.1. The first intermediate carbonium ion is solvated by the leaving group and a solvent molecule. This can revert to starting material of retained configuration[8] or yield solvolysis product which is inverted. Competing with these processes is a frontside displacement

[1] Hammett, 1940, p. 127.

[2] The term "encumbered carbonium ion" is sometimes used in cases where the leaving group is electrically neutral (Boyd, Taft et al., 1960).

[3] Grunwald, Heller and Klein, 1957.

[4] Ingold, 1953, p. 367; but see Golomb, 1959a,b.

[5] Streitwieser and Walsh, 1965.

[6] Hughes, Ingold et al., 1957b.

[7] Bunton, Konasiewicz and Llewellyn, 1955.

[8] Cf. Goering and Levy, 1964.

of the leaving group by another solvent molecule to give the symmetrically solvated carbonium ion and hence racemic product. In support of this view, the degree of inversion in, for example, methanol solution is *decreased* by addition of solvents such as dioxan, acetonitrile and nitromethane (but not benzene and chloroform) which can, by co-ordination, stabilize the "pentacovalent" intermediates.[1] Added salts appear to function similarly.[2]

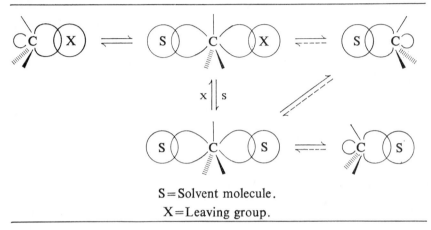

S = Solvent molecule.

X = Leaving group.

Fɪɢ. 6.1. Stereochemical course of solvolysis according to the "Structural Hypothesis."

The structural hypothesis lays emphasis on the ability of weakly nucleophilic species to react with the carbonium ion (or with RX itself)[3] to give predominantly inverted products which are unstable under the reaction conditions and can heterolyse again. The net effect of such repeated inversions in competition with simple S_N1 solvolysis by the hydroxylic solvent is to increase the degree of racemization. Whether such phenomena are to be classed as solvation or reactions of carbonium ions is a matter of individual preference.

Reactions of allyl cations. Substitution reactions of allylic compounds without rearrangement (cf. Paragraph 6.1.3) can give rise to several stereochemical results. As for other carbonium-ion reactions, substitution by the S_N1 mechanism at an asymmetric allylic carbon atom leads to racemization with a small excess of inversion.[4]

However, in reactions of allylic systems where *cis–trans* isomerism occurs, there is the additional stereochemical possibility that unrearranged substitution product may have been converted from one geometrical isomer to the other. In the allyl cation, π-electron delocalization reduces the bond order in the β-γ

[1] Doering, Streitwieser and Friedman, 1956; Streitwieser and Schaeffer, 1957a,b; Streitwieser and Andreades, 1958.

[2] Streitwieser and Walsh, 1963, 1965.

[3] Weiner and Sneen, 1965a,b.

[4] Arcus and Kenyon, 1938; Arcus and Smith, 1939; Airs, Balfe and Kenyon, 1942.

bond, and this should facilitate rotation about this bond (Figure 6.2).[1] An explicit test of this hypothesis, using *cis*-crotyl chloride (**6.7**) in aqueous silver nitrate, showed (after allowing for intramolecular rearrangement of the starting material) that there is $99 \pm 1\%$ retention of the original *cis* stereochemistry in

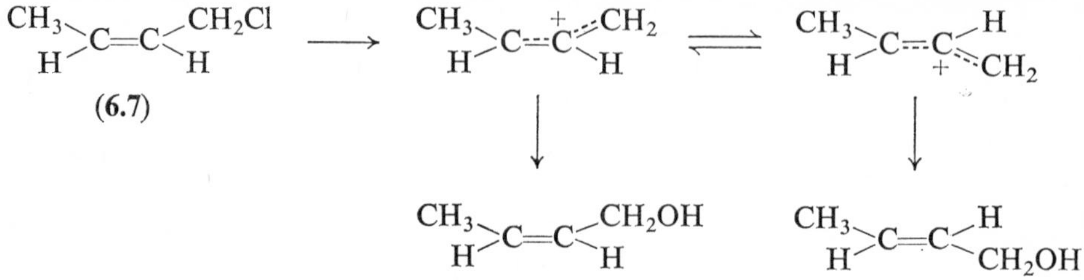

$$CH_3 \underset{H}{\overset{}{>}}C=C\underset{H}{\overset{CH_2Cl}{<}} \longrightarrow CH_3 \underset{H}{\overset{}{>}}C\overset{+}{=}C\underset{H}{\overset{CH_2}{<}} \rightleftharpoons CH_3 \underset{H}{\overset{}{>}}C=C\underset{+\ CH_2}{\overset{H}{<}}$$

(**6.7**)

$$CH_3 \underset{H}{\overset{}{>}}C=C\underset{H}{\overset{CH_2OH}{<}} \qquad CH_3 \underset{H}{\overset{}{>}}C=C\underset{CH_2OH}{\overset{H}{<}}$$

$(99 \pm 1\%$ of unrearranged products)
+rearranged products
$(CH_3 . CH(OH) . CH:CH_2)$

FIG. 6.2. Stereochemical course of solvolysis of *cis*-crotyl chloride.

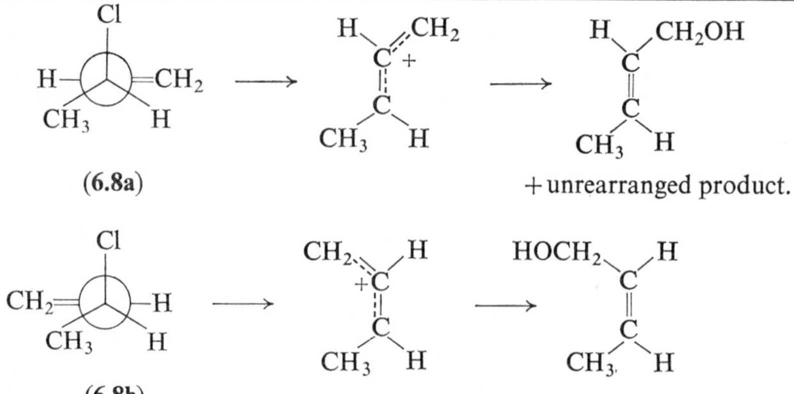

(**6.8a**)

+unrearranged product.

(**6.8b**)

FIG. 6.3. Stereochemical course of solvolysis of α-methylallyl chloride.

the unrearranged part of the solvolysis product.[2] The rearranged product of reaction of allyl cations may be either *cis* or *trans*: for example, α-methylallyl chloride (**6.8**) hydrolyses in aqueous silver nitrate to give a mixture of crotyl alcohols in which the *trans*-isomer predominates. This result is explicable[3] in terms of the preferred conformation of the starting material (**6.8a**) which yields an allylic cation in which rotation is not possible before reaction with nucleophile (see Figure 6.3).

    [1] Cf. Winstein 1951; Hoffmann and Olofson, 1966.
    [2] W. G. Young, Sharman and Winstein, 1960: see also, Sleezer, Winstein and Young, 1963; W. G. Young and Franklin, 1966.
    [3] de la Mare, 1963.

It would be interesting to know whether *cis–trans* interconversion is possible in longer-lived allyl cations.

6.3 Attack of Carbonium Centres on π-Bond Electrons

6.3.1 INTRODUCTION

The attack of carbonium centres on π-bond electrons may be represented: $X:Y + R^+ \rightarrow {}^+X\!-\!Y\!-\!R$. We shall concern ourselves largely with those reactions in which the π-bonded atoms are sp^2-hybridized carbon, the reaction then being the conversion of one carbonium ion into another. The product ion can react either with further π-electrons or in some other way (Paragraph 6.1.1), depending on its structure and environment. The reaction products are usually determined by the relative rates of these competing processes, though the relative stability of possible products can sometimes be important.

Two general reactions of great practical importance fall in this province. One, corresponding to reaction of the product carbonium ion with further olefinic π-electrons, is cationic vinyl polymerization, and the other, more important for aromatic π-electrons, in which the product carbonium ion loses a positively-charged fragment, is substitution, i.e. aromatic alkylation. A comprehensive account of these reactions is beyond the scope of this book.[1] We shall concern ourselves here with the structural and environmental factors which influence the reactivity of carbonium ions towards π-bond electrons. Important intramolecular reactions of carbonium centres with π-electrons are mentioned in Section 7.4.

6.3.2 AROMATIC ALKYLATION

Nature of the reaction. The reaction of carbonium ions with aromatic π-electrons (e.g., of benzene) can be represented

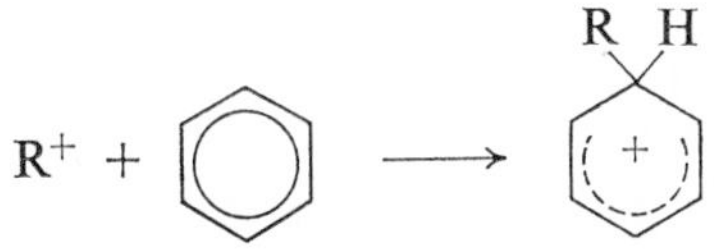

$$(6.9)$$

The product ion (see Chapter 3), sometimes referred to in this context as a σ-complex, readily gives up a proton from the tetrahedral carbon atom. The overall reaction is thus aromatic alkylation.

Aromatic alkylation under the influence of acidic catalysts, generally known as the Friedel-Crafts reaction, is of wide application in organic chemistry and chemical technology. Under the influence of Lewis or Brönsted acids, typically $AlCl_3$, BF_3, H_2SO_4, HF, nuclear alkylation of aromatic compounds can be

[1] For exhaustive reviews see Plesch, 1963, and Olah, 1963.

carried out using alkyl halides, alcohols, olefins and acetylenes (provided a source of protons is available), esters of organic and inorganic acids, ethers, aldehydes and ketones, mercaptans, sulphides, thiocyanates and even paraffins. It has long been recognized, from the effects of substituents in the aromatic compound on orientation and reactivity, that the reaction falls in the class of electrophilic aromatic substitution. Somewhat less certain is the nature of the intermediates involved, particularly the nature of the electrophile.

Evidence for the existence of ions of the type **6.9** has already been given. For example, such ions can be detected spectroscopically in solution (Section 2.3). In favourable cases it is possible to isolate and characterize salts which are stable at low temperatures but which decompose to give the alkylated aromatic compound at higher temperatures (e.g., **6.10**)[1]. The so-called "red oils" which sometimes separate during Friedel-Crafts alkylation have the composition of aromatic solvates of similar salts.[2]

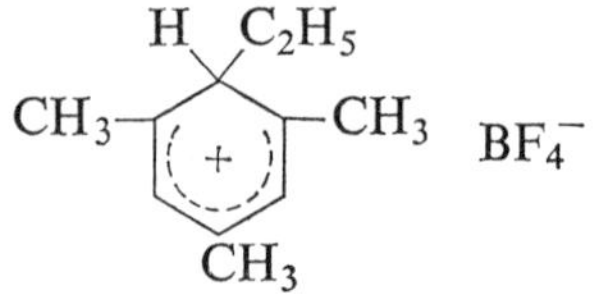

(**6.10**)

Kinetic studies of aromatic alkylation indicate that the rate-determining step is the formation of the σ-complex (**6.9**)[3]. Thus, under a wide variety of conditions, the reaction rate is given by

$$v = k[\text{Alkylating agent}][\text{Aromatic compound}]\phi$$

where ϕ is a function of the catalyst concentration, often simply the concentration itself.[4] Moreover, proton loss from the σ-complex is not kinetically significant. Deuterium substitution in the aromatic compound at the site of alkylation has little[5] or no[6] effect on the rate.

The kinetic form of the reaction does not usually enable the electrophile to be identified. However, in the case of diphenylmethylation of mesitylene and anisole in acetic acid (catalyzed by mineral acids, zinc chloride or boron trifluoride), the function ϕ has been shown also to determine the degree of reversible conversion into carbonium ions of indicator molecules having a

[1] Olah and Kuhn, 1958.

[2] Baddeley, Holt and Voss, 1952; H. C. Brown and Pearsall, 1952; H. C. Brown and Wallace, 1953b; Lieser and Pfluger, 1960.

[3] But see Olah, Flood et al., 1964.

[4] See for example, H. C. Brown and Grayson, 1953; Hart and Cassis, 1954; Jungk, Smoot and Brown, 1956; Bethell and Gold, 1958a,b.

[5] Olah, 1965.

[6] Bethell and Gold, 1958a.

similar constitution to the alkylating agent.[1] The function can therefore be determined spectrophotometrically and media with the same value of ϕ (irrespective of their chemical composition) yield identical values of the rate constant k.[2] This is in agreement with the view that the rate-limiting reaction involves attack of a carbonium ion on the aromatic compound, i.e.

$$v = k_2[R^+][ArH] \tag{6.4}$$

Whilst there is strong physical evidence for the formation of carbonium ions from typical alkylating agents under the influence of Friedel-Crafts catalysts (Chapter 3), the evidence for carbonium-ion involvement in alkylation is often less direct. For example, the alkyl group from the alkylating agent is sometimes found to have undergone skeletal rearrangement and other reactions (e.g. fragmentation) typical of carbonium ions. The earliest example is Gustavson's observation that aluminium chloride-catalysed alkylation of benzene with n-propyl chloride gives isopropylbenzene.[3] Alkylating agents that are optically active by virtue of asymmetry at the potential carbonium centre usually give a largely racemic alkylated product, though with a small but perceptible degree of inversion of configuration.[4] The formation of symmetrical complex anions, such as $AlCl_4^-$ has been shown by chlorine isotope scrambling between alkyl chloride and aluminium chloride during alkylation[5] although this need not be evidence for carbonium ion formation.[6]

On the other hand, the following results for Friedel-Crafts alkylations with primary alkyl halides and metal halide catalysts do not accord very well with the simple interpretation of the reaction in terms of attack on the aromatic compound by a carbonium ion. At low temperatures alkylation of benzene by n-propyl chloride and aluminium chloride gives largely n-propylbenzene, i.e. the product *without* rearrangement of the alkyl group.[7] Methylation of toluene by methyl bromide and iodide gives *different* isomer proportions, viz. CH_3Br:o-xylene, 53·7%; m-xylene, 17·3%; p-xylene, 28·9%. CH_3I: o-xylene, 48.3%; m-xylene 11·9%; p-xylene, 39·8%,[8] suggesting different effective alkylating species for the two halides. Alkylation by primary halides under given conditions is some four powers of ten times *slower* than by secondary and tertiary halides: for the reaction of alkyl bromides with toluene in the presence of gallium bromide the reaction is of the first order in each reagent and the sequence of relative rates is[9] methyl, 1; ethyl, 13·7; n-propyl, 15·9;

[1] Bethell and Gold, 1958a,b; Gold and Riley, 1960, 1962.

[2] Bethell and Gold, 1958b; Gold and Riley, 1960.

[3] Gustavson, 1878.

[4] Price and Lund, 1940; Burwell and Archer, 1942; Burwell, Elkin and Shields, 1952; Hart, Spliethoff and Eleuterio, 1954; Streitwieser and Stang, 1965.

[5] Fairbrother, 1937, 1941.

[6] E.g. Oulevey and Susz, 1961.

[7] Ipatieff, Pines and Schmerling, 1940.

[8] H. C. Brown and Jungk, 1956.

[9] Smoot and Brown, 1956.

i-propyl, 3×10^5; t-butyl 8×10^5. This order parallells the conductivity of the corresponding complexes formed between alkyl fluorides and boron trifluoride.[1] The electrophilic species formed from methyl and ethyl bromides and aluminium bromide is more selective (and therefore presumably more stable) than that formed from i-propyl bromide under similar conditions, i.e. the reverse of the expected order of carbonium stabilities.[2] While such evidence might be regarded as indicating that primary carbonium ions are of low intrinsic stability and therefore show high reactivity even when in the form of tight ion pairs, the reaction can be formulated as a bimolecular nucleophilic substitution by the aromatic compound on the alkylating agent, the leaving group of which is specifically solvated by the metal halide catalyst.[3] The transition state of the reaction is represented in **6.11**. The stereochemical consequence of such a mechanism, potentially observable using an α-deuteriated primary alkyl group, should be complete inversion of configuration, but the necessary experiment has yet to be carried out.

(**6.11**)

The reactivity of aromatic compounds. Aromatic compounds can be regarded as multident nucleophiles: their overall reactivity represents the sum of the reactivities of the nucleophilic sites. Kinetic data on aromatic alkylation are comparatively scarce, a consequence of the kinetic complexity of typical Friedel-Crafts reaction mixtures. Most information has therefore been derived from competitive experiments in which two aromatic compounds compete for a small quantity of electrophile. Such experiments give relative values of overall reactivity (K), usually referred to benzene. When these are combined with product isomer ratios, the reactivity of individual nuclear positions relative to a single position in benzene can be obtained. This quantity is called the partial rate factor, the symbols o_f, m_f and p_f signifying the values for *ortho-*, *meta-* and *para-*positions in a mono-substituted benzene. The procedure is widely employed in studies of aromatic reactivity generally.[4] Its application to aromatic alkylation is straightforward in principle but needs particular care because, under typical reaction conditions, the reaction products can undergo further reactions, such as positional isomerization,[5] rearrangement of alkyl

[1] Olah, Kuhn and Olah, 1957.
[2] H. C. Brown and Jungk, 1956.
[3] Brown and Grayson, 1953; Jungk, Smoot and Brown, 1956.
[4] Ingold, 1953, p. 243.
[5] Allen and Yats, 1961.

substituents, dealkylation, disproportionation and hydride transfer.[1] Under sufficiently severe conditions the reaction products may be thermodynamically controlled[2] and then give no information about reactivities.

Table 6.8 gives some typical results for a series of monosubstituted benzenes. The pattern of these results accords well with the qualitative electronic theory of substituent effects on electrophilic aromatic substitution.[3] However, many common aromatic substituents, e.g. $-NR_2$, $-NO_2$, $-CO.R$, possess non-bonded electron pairs which can co-ordinate with the acidic catalyst used in aromatic alkylation. Discussions of reactivity in such cases are complicated by the deactivating effect of such complexing. In some polysubstituted aromatic compounds specific interactions between substituents may further complicate the phenomena.[4] Superimposed steric effects of substituents affect chiefly substitution in the *ortho*-positions. (Compare, for example, o_f/p_f for fluoro-, chloro- and bromobenzenes in Table 6.8).

Values of log m_f and log p_f derived from Table 6.8 correlate well with σ^+ (Paragraph 4.2.3), as would be expected for a transition state structure close to 6.9. The value of the reaction constant, $-2\cdot4$, is one of the least negative of ρ-values for electrophilic aromatic substitutions (cf. uncatalysed bromination, $-12\cdot1$; Friedel-Crafts acetylation, $-9\cdot1$; nitration, $-6\cdot0$).[5] This relative insensitivity of the ethylation reaction to substituents in the aromatic nucleus suggests that the electrophile is highly reactive and therefore rather indiscriminate in its choice of reaction sites. In many electrophilic aromatic substitutions the ability of the electrophile to discriminate in its choice of aromatic compound ("substrate selectivity") parallels its ability to discriminate between different nuclear positions in a given aromatic compound ("positional selectivity").[6] This can be formalized in the so-called Selectivity Relation[5] according to which, for a given substituted benzene, log $p_f = b$ log(p_f/m_f) where b is a constant characteristic of the substituent. The results of Table 6.8 fit this Selectivity Relation. However, other results[7] (Table 6.9) show low selectivity between aromatic compounds but high selectivity between nuclear positions. The parallelism between overall reactivities of aromatic compounds in such reactions and π-complex stability has led to the suggestion that the substrate selectivity is determined by relative rates of π-complex formation and positional selectivity by relative rates of conversion of the π- to a σ- complex.[8] The

[1] E.g. Baddeley, Holt and Voss, 1952; Sharman, 1962; R. M. Roberts, Baylis and Fonken, 1963; R. M. Roberts, Khalaf and Greene, 1964; R. M. Roberts and Shiengthong, 1964.

[2] E.g. Norris and Rubinstein, 1939; McCaulay and Lien, 1952.

[3] Ingold, 1953, Chapter 6; Norman and Taylor, 1965.

[4] E.g. Bethell, Gold and Riley, 1959.

[5] Stock and Brown, 1963.

[6] H. C. Brown and Nelson, 1953.

[7] Olah, Kuhn and Flood, 1962a,b; Olah, Flood et al., 1964; Olah, Flood and Moffatt, 1964a,b; Olah and Overchuk, 1965.

[8] Olah, Flood et al., 1964.

Table 6.8. *Relative reactivities (K), isomer distributions, and partial rate factors in ethylation of substituted benzenes by ethyl bromide/gallium bromide in ethylene dichloride at 25°[a]*

Compound	K^b	Products (%)			o_f	m_f	p_f
		ortho	meta	para			
Toluene	2·33	38·4	21·0	40·6	2·69	1·47	5·70
Biphenyl	1·81	33·3	25·6	41·1	0·905[c]	0·695[c]	2·23
Fluorobenzene	0·282	42·9	13·7	43·4	0·364	0·116	0·738
Chlorobenzene	0·214	42·2	15·9	41·9	0·271	0·102	0·588
Bromobenzene	0·133	24·0	21·8	54·2	0·096	0·087	0·433

[a] H. C. Brown and Neyens, 1962a,b.
[b] For benzene, $K = 1$.
[c] Contains an additional statistical factor of two.

Table 6.9. *Alkylation of methylbenzenes by i-propyl bromide/aluminium chloride in nitromethane at 25°[a]*

Aromatic compound	K	Products (%)					Relative basicity[b]	
		2-	3-	4-	5-	6-	$HCl(\pi)$	$HF\text{-}BF_3(\sigma)$
Benzene	1·0	—	—	—	—	—	0·61	Small
Toluene	2·03	46·7	14·7[c]	38·6	—	—	0·92	0·01
o-Xylene	2·21	—	45·8	54·2	—	—	1·13	2
m-Xylene	2·80	—	—	89·4	10·6	—	1·26	20
p-Xylene	2·70	100	—	—	—	—	1·00	1·0
1,2,3-Trimethylbenzene	4·31	—	—	65·2	34·8	—	1·46	~40
1,2,4-Trimethylbenzene	3·25	—	—	—	58·5	41·5	1·36	40
1,3,5-Trimethylbenzene	0·35	100	—	—	—	—	1·59	2800

[a] Olah, Flood et al., 1964.
[b] Brown and Brady, 1952.
[c] Corresponds to deactivation of the *meta*-position by the methyl substituent.

factors which determine whether or not the reaction obeys the Selectivity Relation still remain to be specified.

The influence of carbonium-ion structure on reactivity. For a mechanism in accordance with Equation (6.4) the observed velocity constant for formation of an ion such as **6.9** will be the product of an equilibrium constant for the formation of the carbonium ion from the alkylating agent and the specific rate of attack (k_2) of this intermediate on the aromatic compound. For a given aromatic compound, values of the latter constant for different carbonium ions are measures of carbonium-ion reactivity.

Table 6.10. *Reactivities and partial rate factors for alkylation of toluene (solvent) by alkyl bromides and gallium bromide at 25°*

Alkyl group	K	o_f	m_f	p_f	$\log(p_f/m_f)$	Ref.
Methyl	5·70	9·51	1·70	11·8	0·842	a
Ethyl	2·47	2·84	1·56	6·02	0·587	a
i-Propyl	1·82	1·52	1·41	5·05	0·554	b
Benzyl	4·00	4·91	2·32	9·43	0·609	c

[a] H. C. Brown and Smoot, 1956.
[b] Choi and Brown, 1959.
[c] H. C. Brown and Bolto, 1959.

Sometimes direct kinetic study of aromatic alkylation permits analysis along these lines. Thus, sulphuric acid-catalysed alkylation of mesitylene by diphenylmethanol has been found to be some 2–3 times more rapid than by 4,4′-dichlorodiphenylmethanol under a particular set of conditions, in which only a small fraction of the alcohol is converted to carbonium ion. However, when allowance is made for the substituent effect on the pre-equilibrium, the dichlorodiphenylmethyl cation is found to be nearly twice as reactive as the unsubstituted ion.[1] Thus the pre-equilibrium is more important than the rate constant for carbonium-ion attack in determining the overall reaction rate.

More often, however, the equilibrium constant for carbonium-ion formation is eliminated by carrying out competitive reactions, either between two aromatic compounds or between the available nuclear positions of one aromatic compound. Conclusions about the carbonium ion are then deduced from its selectivity (see above). Some typical data are given in Table 6.10.

Both substrate selectivity (K) and positional selectivity [measured by $\log(p_f/m_f)$] indicate that the order of reactivity of the alkylating species is i-propyl > ethyl > benzyl > methyl, very different from that expected for

[1] Bethell and Gold, 1958a.

carbonium ions, viz. methyl > ethyl > i-propyl > benzyl. Such observations suggest that the electrophile in the primary alkyl cases may not be a carbonium ion (see p. 181), but a rigorous argument on this would also require some consideration of the stabilizing influence of the environment, since this is expected to vary with cation structure (Paragraphs 5.3.2 and 5.3.3).

6.3.3 REACTION OF CARBONIUM IONS WITH OLEFINS

Scope and nature of the reaction. This family of reactions, embracing the alkylation of olefins and paraffin hydrocarbons and cationic vinyl polymerization, is of considerable commercial importance in the petrochemical and polymer industries. Evidence that carbonium ions are intermediates in these reactions can be summarized as follows: (i) the reaction conditions are such as are known to bring about carbonium-ion formation from molecules of similar constitution to the reactants; (ii) the reactions can be initiated by addition of pre-formed carbonium salts to olefins; (iii) typical carbonium-ion rearrangements take place; (iv) polymerization, e.g., of styrene under certain conditions, is sometimes accompanied by formation of a colour similar to that of simpler carbonium ions of similar constitution; (v) the kinetic form of cationic vinyl polymerization is consistent with the view that carbonium ions are the propagating species. Some aspects of this evidence will be enlarged on later.

The usual reaction of carbonium ions with olefins leads to addition rather than substitution products, viz.

$$R^+ + \ \overset{\textstyle >}{\ }C:C\overset{\textstyle <}{\ } \longrightarrow R{-}\overset{|}{\underset{|}{C}}{-}\overset{|+}{\underset{|}{C}} \overset{N}{\longrightarrow} R{-}\overset{|}{\underset{|}{C}}{-}\overset{|}{\underset{|}{C}}{-}N,$$

where N is any available nucleophile, and both steps are, in principle, reversible. Substitution does occur, however, in the reaction of carbonium ions with "active methylene" compounds, e.g. the conversion of **6.12** into **6.13**. The mechanism of this reaction is co-ordination of the ion with the enol form of the reactant followed by proton loss from the oxonium ion.[1]

$$CH_2(CO.NH_2)_2 \qquad\qquad Ph_3C.CH(CO.NH_2)_2$$
$$(6.12) \qquad\qquad\qquad (6.13)$$

$$H_2N.CO.CH:C{\overset{OH}{\underset{NH_2}{<}}} \ \overset{Ph_3C^+}{\underset{}{\rightleftharpoons}} \ H_2N.CO.\underset{\underset{CPh_3}{|}}{CH}.C{\overset{\overset{+}{O}H}{\underset{NH_2}{<}}}$$

The identity of N depends to some extent on the source of the carbonium ion: for example, treatment of ethylene with t-butyl chloride and aluminium

[1] Patai and Dayagi, 1962b; see also Patai and Dayagi, 1962a; Patai, Dayagi and Friedlander, 1962; N. W. Jordan and Elliott, 1962.

bromide gives a mixture of 1-chloro- and 1-bromo-3,3-dimethylbutanes by reaction of the intermediate carbonium ion (**6.14**) with the mixed tetrahaloaluminate ion $AlClBr_3^-$.[1] The olefin itself can on protonation provide the carbonium ion which initiates reaction. In alkylation of paraffins, the protonated olefin abstracts a hydride ion from the paraffin (see Section 6.4), and the resultant carbonium ion then reacts with a further olefin molecule to give the product ion which is destroyed by further hydride abstraction. Thus isobutane and ethylene in the presence of $AlCl_3/HCl$ or BF_3/HF afford a complex mixture of products, the hexane fraction of which contains **6.15**.[2] The major com-

$$(CH_3)_3C.CH_2.CH_2^+ \qquad (6.14)$$

ponents are, however, hydrocarbons **6.16** and **6.17** in which skeletal rearrangement has evidently occurred. The rather unusual course of these rearrangements is discussed in Paragraph 6.4.3.

$$(CH_3)_3C.CH_2.CH_3 \qquad\qquad (CH_3)_2CH.CH(CH_3)_2$$
$$(6.15) \qquad\qquad\qquad\qquad (6.16)$$
$$(CH_3)_2CH.CH_2.CH_2.CH_3$$
$$(6.17)$$

In some cases of alkylation of olefins by carbonium ions from alkyl halides, a second olefin molecule may act as nucleophile **6.18**:[3] can thus be obtained from ethylene and i-propyl chloride. In favourable circumstances, successive reaction with many olefin molecules occurs, and the product is polymeric. Indeed all reactions of carbonium ions with olefins can be regarded as cationic polymerization with varying degrees of polymerization. In general the average degree of polymerization, $\overline{DP}$, i.e. the average number of

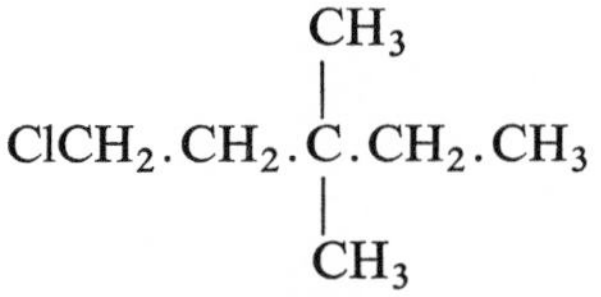

$$\begin{array}{c} CH_3 \\ | \\ ClCH_2.CH_2.C.CH_2.CH_3 \\ | \\ CH_3 \end{array}$$
$$(6.18)$$

monomer (olefin) units in the product, is given by the expression $\overline{DP} = v_p/(v_t + v_{tr})$, where v signifies reaction velocity and the subscripts p, t, and tr refer to propagation and termination steps of polymerization and to transfer reactions of the propagating species severally:

Propagation:

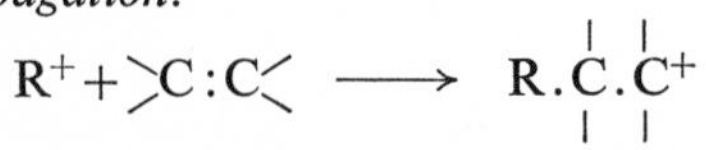

$$R^+ + {>}C:C{<} \longrightarrow R.\overset{|}{C}.\overset{|}{C^+}$$

[1] Schmerling, 1945; Schmerling and West, 1952.
[2] Grosse and Ipatieff, 1943.
[3] Schmerling, 1945; V. A. Miller, 1947; Schmerling and Meisinger, 1953.

Termination:

$$R^+ + X^- \longrightarrow RX$$

or $\quad R^+ + ZX_{n+1}^- \longrightarrow RX + ZX_n \ [ZX_n = \text{metal halide catalyst}]$

Transfer:

$$\text{R.CH.}\overset{|}{\underset{|}{\text{C}}}{}^+ + X^- \longrightarrow R{-}\overset{|}{\underset{|}{\text{C}}}:\text{C}{\Big\langle} + HX \quad \left.\begin{array}{c} \\ \\ \\ \\ \\ \\ \\ \end{array}\right\} \begin{array}{l}\text{Proton}\\ \text{loss}\end{array}$$

$$\text{R.CH.}\overset{|}{\underset{|}{\text{C}}}{}^+ + {\Big\rangle}\text{C}:\text{C}{\Big\langle} \longrightarrow R{-}\overset{|}{\text{C}}:\text{C}{\Big\langle} + H\overset{|}{\underset{|}{\text{C}}}{-}\overset{|}{\underset{|}{\text{C}}}{}^+$$

$$\text{R.}\overset{|}{\underset{|}{\text{C}}}.\overset{|}{\text{C}}{}^+ \longrightarrow R^+ + {\Big\rangle}\text{C}:\text{C}{\Big\langle} \qquad \text{Fragmentation}$$

$$\text{R.}\overset{|}{\underset{|}{\text{C}}}.\overset{|}{\text{C}}{}^+ + RH \longrightarrow \text{R.}\overset{|}{\underset{|}{\text{C}}}.\overset{|}{\text{CH}} + R^+ \qquad \text{Hydride abstraction}$$

With these possible modes of reaction, it is not surprising that a variety of products covering a wide range of molecular weights is obtained. The complexity is increased by the possibility of skeletal rearrangement of the intermediate carbonium ions. High molecular-weight polymers are usually obtained at low temperatures when propagation is much more rapid than termination and transfer reactions.

Cationic vinyl polymerization. The range of monomers which undergo cationic polymerization is much narrower than that found for radical polymerization. The principal groups of monomers are styrenes and vinyl ethers. Isobutene is the only simple olefin which readily forms high polymers by cationic polymerization: other α-olefins, though highly reactive towards carbonium ions, yield only low molecular-weight products because of the great importance of transfer processes.

Cationic polymerization is generally initiated by a Brönsted acid or by a Friedel-Crafts catalyst in conjunction with a source of protons, termed the co-catalyst and typically water, an alcohol or carboxylic acid. Polymerization occurs with great rapidity even at very low temperatures and the rate of disappearance of monomer (M) usually fits an equation of the form:

$$-d[M]/dt = k_{\text{obs}}[M]^n[\text{Catalyst}][\text{Co-catalyst}] \qquad (6.5)$$

where the exponent n is in the range 1–3 and is commonly 2. This is consistent with a reaction scheme in which carbonium ions, probably in the form of ion pairs,[1] are the chain carriers, viz.

Initiation:

$$M + \text{catalyst} + \text{co-catalyst} \xrightarrow{k_i} HM^+X^-$$

Propagation:

$$HM^+X^- + M \xrightarrow{k_p} HM_2^+X^- \to \to \ldots HM_r^+X^-$$

[1] Biddulph, Plesch and Rutherford, 1965; Veselý, 1961.

Termination:

$$HM_r^+X^- \xrightarrow{k_t} HM_rX$$

Transfer:

$$HM_r^+X^- \xrightarrow{k_{tr}} M_r + HX$$

Using the steady-state approximation and assuming that initiation is much slower than propagation and chain termination, $k_{obs} = k_p k_i/(k_t + k_{tr})$ and $n = 2$; $\overline{DP}$ can be shown to be $k_p[M]/(k_t + k_{tr})$. Thus from the variation of k_{obs} and $\overline{DP}$ with monomer concentration, k_i can be measured absolutely. The other constants, notably k_p, are obtainable only as ratios. Values of k_p can be obtained in the perchloric acid-catalysed polymerization of styrene in 1,2-dichloroethane or methylene chloride, since initiation appears to be very fast and termination absent.[1] The concentration of the propagating species appears to be that of the catalyst, giving the kinetic equation

$$-d[M]/dt = k[HClO_4]_0[M].$$

The chain carrier in this case is probably the expected carbonium ion **6.19** (perhaps in equilibrium with the corresponding perchlorate ester).[2] Criticism[3] of this carbonium-ion mechanism, based largely on electronic spectra of reaction mixtures, is invalid.[4]

The structure of the polymers formed in carbonium ion reactions is that expected if the more stable of the two possible product cations is formed in the propagation stage. Thus poly-isobutene consists of monomer units linked head to tail although this is a more strained structure than a head–head–tail–tail arrangement.[5] Polystyrene also shows the regular head-to-tail arrangement, presumably as a result of successive attachment of the chain carrier to the β-carbon atom of the side chain, forming a benzylic cation (**6.19**). The same structure would be achieved by successive reactions at the α-carbon atom giving **6.20**, but this is inconsistent with the red colour of polymerizing styrene under certain conditions,[6] and the observed structural effects on reactivity (see p. 192).

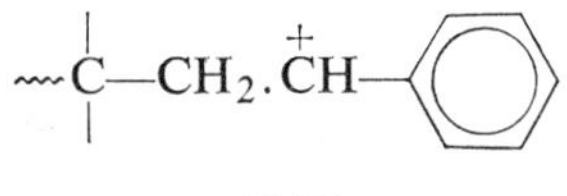

(**6.19**) 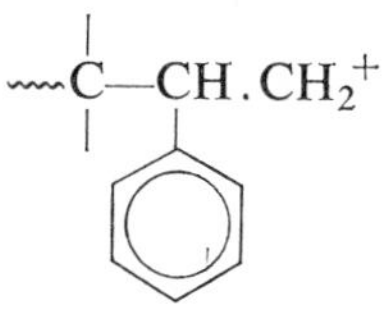   (**6.20**)

[1] Pepper and Reilly, 1962; see also Hayes and Pepper, 1961.
[2] D. O. Jordan and Treloar, 1961; Bywater and Worsfold, 1966.
[3] Gandini and Plesch, 1964, 1965a; see also G. R. Brown and Pepper, 1965.
[4] Hanazaki and Nagakura, 1965; Olah, Pittman *et al.*, 1966a; Higashimura, Kanoh and Okamura, 1966; Bywater and Worsfold, 1966; Bertoli and Plesch, 1966.
[5] R. M. Thomas, Sparks *et al.*, 1940.
[6] D. O. Jordan and Treloar, 1961.

In some cases polymers are obtained in which the monomer units are 1,3-rather than 1,2-linked owing to the occurrence of hydride or alkyl shifts.[1] For example, reaction of **6.21** with aluminium chloride/ethyl chloride at low temperatures gives polymeric material in which the repeating unit is **6.22**.[2] Evidently rearrangement occurs more rapidly than propagation in this system.

$$(CH_3)_3C.CH=CH_2$$

$$\begin{array}{c} CH_3 \\ | \\ -C-CH.CH_2- \\ | \quad | \\ CH_3 \ CH_3 \end{array}$$

(6.21)   (6.22)

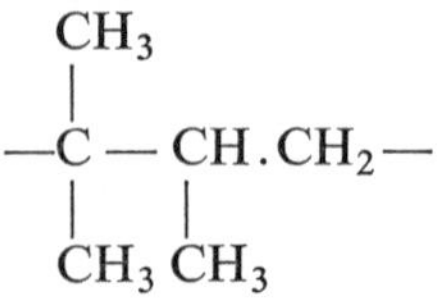

If, in forming the polymer, asymmetric carbon atoms are produced, there arises the possibility that they will all have the same configuration (isotactic polymer), alternating *d*- and *l*-configurations (syndiotactic) or random configurations (atactic) along the polymer chain.[3] Stereoregularity is observable in some cationic vinyl polymerizations, an example being boron trifluoride-catalysed polymerization of isobutyl vinyl ether.[4] This can be interpreted in terms of a configuration-holding interaction between the ether oxygen atom of the antepenultimate monomer unit in the polymeric propagating species and the carbonium centre (see Paragraph 7.2.1) giving **6.23**. The next monomer unit is then attached from a direction opposite to that of the C^+—O "bond".[5]

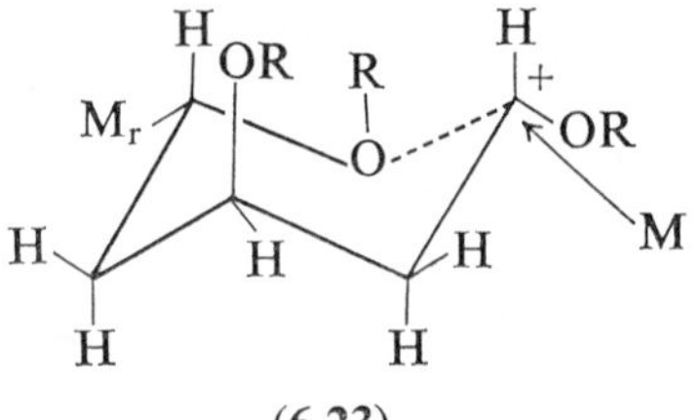

(6.23)

Olefin structure and reactivity. Stabilization of the positive charge on the product carbonium ion appears to be the important factor in determining the direction of addition of cations to unsymmetrical olefins, and calculations have been made of the energy changes involved on the basis of mass-spectrometric data.[6] Protonation of olefins can also be regarded as a model for the reaction of carbonium ions with olefinic π-electrons (Paragraph 4.2.6).

[1] E.g. Kennedy and Thomas, 1962, 1963; Kennedy, 1964; Wanless and Kennedy, 1965; for a review, see Kennedy and Langer, 1964.
[2] Kennedy, Elliott and Hudson, 1964.
[3] Bawn and Ledwith, 1962.
[4] Schildknecht, Zoss and McKinley, 1947; Schildknecht, Gross and Zoss, 1949.
[5] Cram and Kopecky, 1959; Cram, 1960.
[6] Greensfelder, 1955.

For polymerizing systems, the obvious index of reactivity, k_p is not generally directly accessible (see p. 189). Values of k_p relative to that of a standard monomer can, however, be obtained by the study of co-polymerization.[1]

If two monomers, M_1 and M_2 are present in a polymerizing mixture, both will be incorporated into the polymer chains in amounts determined by the velocities of their reactions with the carbonium centre. The velocity constant for such reactions of a given monomer will, to a first approximation, depend on whether the terminal monomer unit is M_1 or M_2. If the chains are long, so that monomer consumption can be considered in terms of propagation reactions only, and the steady state approximation can be used, it can be shown[2] that

$$\frac{d[M_1]}{d[M_2]} = \frac{[M_1]}{[M_2]} \left\{ \frac{[M_2] + [M_1]\, k_{11}/k_{12}}{[M_1] + [M_2]\, k_{22}/k_{21}} \right\} \qquad (6.6)$$

where k_{11} and k_{12} are velocity constants for reaction of carbonium ions having terminal M_1 units with M_1 and M_2 respectively, and k_{22} and k_{21} are similar constants for carbonium ions having terminal M_2 units. From the monomer ratio in the copolymer, values of monomer reactivity ratios, k_{11}/k_{12} ($\equiv r_1$) and k_{22}/k_{21} ($\equiv r_2$), can be derived.

Three limiting situations exist:

(i) $r_1 r_2 \gg 1$: monomers react only with end-groups of the same type, i.e. co-polymerization does not occur;

(ii) $r_1 r_2 = 0$: monomers react only with end-groups of the opposite kind, i.e. M_1 and M_2 alternate along the polymer chain;

(iii) $r_1 r_2 = 1$: $k_{11}/k_{12} = k_{22}/k_{21}$: a given monomer is equally reactive towards the two types of end group, i.e. M_1 and M_2 are randomly distributed along the polymer chain ("ideal co-polymerization").

In the last case, since monomer reactivity is independent of the cationic centre involved, values of r_1 (or $1/r_2$) can be used as measures of the intrinsic reactivity of olefins with carbonium ions. Some representative values, relative to styrene as standard (M_2), are given in Table 6.11. The experimental error in values such as these can be quite large. It therefore complicates the discussion of temperature, solvent and anion effects on relative reactivities. Substantial variation of reactivity ratios is sometimes found when solvent and catalyst are changed,[3] and ion-pairing may be responsible for deviations from ideal co-polymerization.[4]

[1] See, for example, Cundall, 1963.

[2] Mayo and Lewis, 1944; see also, Melville, Noble and Watson, 1947; Goldfinger and Kane, 1948.

[3] Overberger and Kamath, 1959; Dunphy and Marvel, 1960; Tobolsky and Boudreau, 1961; G. R. Brown and Pepper, 1963.

[4] G. R. Brown and Pepper, 1963.

The relative reactivity of *m*- and *p*-substituted styrenes (e.g. Table 6.11) can be satisfactorily correlated by use of σ^+-values (Paragraph 4.2.3) with a reaction constant (ρ) of about -2.[1] This provides confirmation of the earlier deduction that the propagating carbonium ion in styrene polymerization is a benzylic cation. In contrast to the sensitivity of olefin reactivity to polar influences, steric effects appear to be small. This is the reverse of the situation in radical polymerization and points to a considerable difference in transition state geometry.[2]

Table 6.11. *Olefin reactivity towards carbonium ions from monomer reactivity ratios in cationic polymerization*[a,b]

Olefin	Relative reactivity	Olefin	Relative reactivity
Vinyl ethers	High	*o*-Chlorostyrene	0·6–0·2
p-Dimethylaminostyrene	200	*trans*-β-Methylstyrene	0·46
p-Methoxystyrene	100	*p*-Bromostyrene	0·4
p-Methoxy-α-methylstyrene	8	*p*-Chlorostyrene	0·4
Isobutene	4	Vinyl acetate	0·4
Acenaphthylene	3·3	*cis*-β-Methylstyrene	0·3
p-Methylstyrene	1·5	*m*-Chlorostyrene	0·3
p-Ethylstyrene	1·2	Isoprene	0·12
m-Methoxystyrene	1·1	Chloroprene	0·06
α-Methylstyrene	1·0	*m*-Nitrostyrene	0.05
Styrene	(1·0)	Butadiene	0·02

[a] Cundall, 1963.
[b] In nitrobenzene solution at 0–25°.

6.3.4 ATTACK OF CARBONIUM CENTRES ON C—X MULTIPLE BONDS

Attack of carbonium centres on the π-electrons of multiple bonds between carbon and another element such as nitrogen or oxygen usually leads to alkylation of the hetero-atom. Since such atoms often possess non-bonded electron pairs, the reaction can be classified either as reaction with these electrons or as reaction between the carbonium ion and the π-electrons of the multiple bond. We have chosen the latter course because in its formal representation

$$R^+ + \underset{\ddots}{>}C{=}\ddot{X}{-} \longrightarrow \overset{+}{>}C{-}XR{-}$$

[1] Okamoto and Brown, 1957; Overberger, Arond, *et al.*, 1952; see also Dunphy and Marvel, 1960.
[2] Overberger, Tanner and Pearce, 1958.

the subsequent reactions of the product cation seem to be more readily intelligible. The possibility of resonance in the product cation (6.24) gives it a measure of stability.

$$\text{>C}^+\text{--}\ddot{\text{X}}\text{R--} \quad \longleftrightarrow \quad \text{C}\text{=}\overset{+}{\text{X}}\text{R--}$$

(6.24)

The reaction of carbonyl groups with hydrogen ion is well established but reaction with carbonium ions is relatively rare. An example is found in the acid-catalysed reaction of diphenyldiazomethane with solvent dimethylformamide which gives, after hydrolysis, diphenylmethyl formate:[1]

$$\text{Ph}_2\text{CN}_2 \rightarrow \text{Ph}_2\text{CH}^+ \xrightarrow{\text{CHO}\cdot\text{NMe}_2} \text{Ph}_2\text{CHO}\cdot\text{CH}:\overset{+}{\text{N}}\text{Me}_2 \rightarrow \text{Ph}_2\text{CHO}\cdot\text{CHO}$$

Nucleophilic attack by carbonyl oxygen on carbonium centres has been inferred from studies of racemization and radio-chlorine exchange of 4-chlorodiphenylmethyl chloride in acetone and dimethylformamide (and acetonitrile, see below)[2] and intermediates corresponding to (6.24) are isolable from reactions of carbonyl compounds and trialkyloxonium fluoroborates.[3] Alternative interpretations in terms of bimolecular displacement can be envisaged to explain the racemizing influence of acetone in solvolytic reactions.[4]

The N-alkylation of nitriles,[5] referred to in some cases as the Ritter reaction, is probably the most notable synthetic reaction in this category. The product is a substituted amide:

$$\text{R}^+ + \text{R}'\text{C}\equiv\text{N} \longrightarrow \text{R}'\text{C}^+\text{=NR} \longrightarrow \text{R}'\text{CO}\cdot\text{NHR}$$

The intermediacy of carbonium ions is usually inferred from the source of the alkyl group and the reaction conditions, i.e. alkene or alcohol with mineral acid,[6] alkyl halide with metal halide[7] or silver ion,[8] and the occurrence of rearrangement in the alkyl group.[9] In certain instances the intermediate nitrilium salt is isolable.[7] However, the expected rearrangement does not always occur[10] and it is possible that in some cases alkylation occurs without formation of a carbonium ion (cf. aromatic alkylation), e.g.

$$\text{R}'\text{CN} + \text{R}\overset{+}{\text{O}}\text{H}_2 \longrightarrow \text{R}'\text{C}^+\text{=NR} + \text{H}_2\text{O}.$$

[1] Bethell and Callister, unpublished observations.

[2] Winstein, Appel, et al., 1965.

[3] Meerwein, Borner et al., 1956.

[4] Weiner and Sneen, 1965a,b.

[5] Möller, 1957.

[6] Wieland and Dorrer, 1930; Ritter and Minieri, 1948; Ritter and Kalish, 1948; F. R. Benson and Ritter, 1949.

[7] Meerwein, Laasch et al., 1956.

[8] Cast and Stevens, 1953.

[9] Jacquier and Christol, 1957; Laurent and Mison, 1962; Christol, Laurent and Solladie, 1963.

[10] Christol, Laurent and Mousseron, 1961.

For the sulphuric acid-catalysed reaction of t-butyl alcohol with acrylonitrile at low acidities the rate is proportional to the acidity function h_0, suggesting that reaction of the nitrile with the protonated alcohol in the rate-determining step is again a plausible inference.[1]

Reaction of carbonium centres with aliphatic diazo-compounds, shown in their two most important resonance forms in **6.25**, is most appropriately considered here. In this reaction C-alkylation by the carbonium ion (R^+) occurs and nitrogen is lost forming a new carbonium ion $RR'R''C^+$, which can then react further. Co-ordination of the product ion with lone pair electrons, proton loss, fragmentation, rearrangement, and attack on a further diazo-molecule have all been observed. Thus, for example, triphenylmethyl cation with excess diazomethane in ether gives triphenylethylene and 1,2,3-triphenylpropene.[2] Protonation of diphenyldiazomethane with perchloric or arenesulphonic acids in acetonitrile gives diphenylmethyl cation which attacks a second molecule of the diazo-compound to give tetraphenylethylene.[3]

$$R'R''\overset{-}{C}\!\!-\!\!\overset{+}{N}\!\!\equiv\!\!N \;\leftrightarrow\; R'R''C\!\!=\!\!\overset{+}{N}\!\!=\!\!\overset{-}{N}$$

$$(6.25)$$

6.4 Attack of Carbonium Centres on σ-Bond Electrons

6.4.1 INTRODUCTION

We now deal with those reactions in which the carbonium centre completes its electronic octet by attack on a σ-bond electron pair, usually one forming a β-C—H or C—C bond. The interrelationship of the several important reaction types which fall in this category is shown in Table 6.12. The σ-bond electron

Table 6.12. *Reactions involving attack of carbonium centres on σ-bond electrons*

| | σ-Bond attacked | |
New bond formed	C—H	C—C
π	E1 Elimination	Fragmentation
σ	Hydride transfer	Skeletal rearrangement

pair attacked is usually part of the carbonium ion so that the reaction is intramolecular, although intermolecular hydride transfer, equivalent to electrophilic substitution at hydrogen, is well known. Intermolecular reaction of carbonium centres with carbon–carbon σ-bond electrons to form new carbon–carbon σ-bonds is also conceivable but there are no authenticated examples. Again,

[1] Deno, Edwards and Perizzolo, 1957.
[2] Whitlock, 1962.
[3] Bethell and Callister, 1963a,b.

although in principle the σ-bond electrons could bind other atoms than hydrogen and carbon to carbon, our attention will be restricted to these types.

For present purposes, the reactions will be grouped primarily according to the nature of the new bond formed at the carbonium centre, viz. (i) olefin formation, (ii) rearrangements (C—H or C—C formed), (iii) intermolecular hydride transfer (C—H formed).

6.4.2 OLEFIN FORMATION AND RELATED REACTIONS

E1 Elimination. Mechanism. The close relation of proton loss from carbonium ions and co-ordination of carbonium ions to non-bonded electron pairs (E1 and S_N1 reactions) has been recognized for a considerable time[1] (Figure 6.4). In the latter case the nucleophile reacts directly with the carbonium centre, whereas in the former the nucleophile attacks a hydrogen atom of the carbonium ion. Olefin formation occurs when this hydrogen is attached to a carbon atom β to the cationic centre. Proton loss from more remote carbon atoms is also known, e.g. nucleophilic attack on hydrogen attached to the γ-carbon atom gives a cyclopropane (see Paragraph 7.5.1).

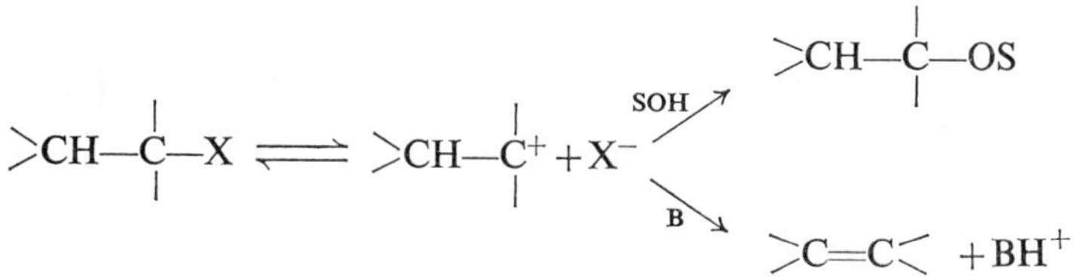

FIG. 6.4. The relationship between S_N1 and E1 reactions.

Because of their close relation, nucleophilic substitution and elimination reactions of alkyl derivatives share common kinetic criteria of unimolecularity. (Section 2.6 and Paragraph 2.7.3). Further, because the rate- and product-determining steps of the unimolecular reactions are separate, the product ratios, either [substitution product]/[elimination product] or, when the intermediate carbonium ion can afford two distinguishable olefinic products, A and B, [olefin A]/[olefin B], should be independent of the leaving group. While this is approximately so for good solvating solvents (Table 2.4), a marked dependence of both types of product ratio on the nature of the leaving group is found in less polar media, where ion-pairing is important[2] (Table 6.13).

Information concerning the mechanism of olefin formation from carbonium ions comes largely from studies of the reverse reaction, notably as the first step of acid-catalysed olefin hydration. (Paragraph 4.2.6). In this reaction

[1] Hughes, 1935b.
[2] Cocivera and Winstein, 1963.

proton transfer to the olefin is the rate-limiting step: consequently, general acid catalysis should be observable. It appears, however, that the index α in the Brönsted catalysis law is close to unity in the case of alkenes[1] and this leads to kinetic features similar to those of reactions catalysed specifically by solvated hydrogen ions, and the conclusion that the transition state of the reaction is closely similar to the intermediate carbonium ion. The principle of microscopic reversibility requires that olefin formation from carbonium ions should occur by way of the same transition state as is involved in hydration of

Table 6.13. *Influence of the solvent and leaving group on the percentage of olefin formed in the solvolysis of t-butyl derivatives*[a]

Solvent Temperature	H_2O[b] 25°	H_2O[b] 75°	C_2H_5OH[b] 75°	CH_3CO_2H[c] 75°
Leaving group: Cl	5 ± 1	$7 \cdot 6 \pm 1$	$44 \cdot 2 \pm 1$	73 ± 2
Br	5 ± 1	$6 \cdot 6 \pm 1$	$36 \cdot 0 \pm 1$	$69 \cdot 5$
I	4 ± 1	$6 \cdot 0 \pm 1$	$32 \cdot 3 \pm 1$	—
$\overset{+}{S}(CH_3)_2\overset{-}{C}lO_4$	—	$6 \cdot 5 \pm 1$	$17 \cdot 8 \pm 1 \cdot 4$	$11 \cdot 7 \pm 1$
$\overset{+}{O}H_2$	3	$4 \cdot 7$	—	—

[a] Cocivera and Winstein, 1963.
[b] 2,6-Lutidine present.
[c] Sodium acetate present.

the olefin. We may conclude, then, that proton loss from a carbonium ion occurs largely to a solvent molecule and that, at the transition state, the carbonium ion has progressed relatively little along the reaction co-ordinate leading to olefin. These deductions account nicely for certain observations on proton loss from carbonium ions. Thus, addition of bases, particularly lyate ion, usually has a negligible effect on the ratio of substitution to elimination in solvolyses, both reactions occurring by collapse of the solvation sheath of the carbonium ion (see Paragraph 6.2.1).[2] The activation energy for proton loss from a carbonium ion is usually $2 \cdot 5$–4 kcal mole^{-1} greater than for the competing co-ordination of solvent, usually reckoned to be an essentially unactivated process.[3] With such a low activation energy, proton loss cannot have progressed very far at the transition state, and this is consistent with the observation of very low kinetic deuterium isotope effects in such reactions (Table 6.14).

Additional information about the details of the reaction mechanism comes from consideration of the structure and stereochemistry of the olefinic product.

[1] Gold and Kessick, 1965a,b.
[2] For an exception see Beltramé, Bunton *et al.*, 1964.
[3] Ingold, 1953; Hawdon, Hughes and Ingold, 1952.

The effect of carbonium-ion structure. Competition from substitution makes olefin formation from carbonium ions less important preparatively than the one-step bimolecular reaction: in general, for alkyl cations, substitution predominates. Some olefin yields for reactions of t-alkyl cations are given

Table 6.14. *Kinetic deuterium isotope effects for proton removal from alkyl cations*

Substrate	Solvent	Temp.	k_H/k_D	Ref.
$CH_3.CH_2.CCl(CH_3)_2$	80% EtOH-H$_2$O(v/v)	25°	1·8	b
$CH_3.CH_2.CH(OSOCl).CH_3$	Dioxan	61·5°	1·0	c
$CH_3.CH_2.CCl(CH_3)_2$	75% AcOH-H$_2$O	57°	3·1–3·5[a]	d
	75% AcOH-H$_2$O	57°	2·5–2·8	d
$CH_3.CH_2.\overset{+}{C}N_2(CH_3)_2$	75% AcOH-H$_2$O	57°	1·5–1·6	d

[a] In the presence of silver nitrate.
[b] Shiner, 1953.
[c] Boozer and Lewis, 1954.
[d] Silver, 1961b.

in Table 6.15. From these it is apparent that proton loss occurs more readily, relative to co-ordination of the carbonium centre to solvent, in more ramified carbonium ions.

Table 6.15. *Olefin yields (%) in solvolyses of t-alkyl chlorides, RR'R"CCl, in 80% ethanol–water (v/v) at 25°*

R	R'	R"	Olefin yield[a]	Relative solvolysis rate[b]
CH_3	CH_3	CH_3	16[c]	(1·00)
CH_3	CH_3	C_2H_5	34[c]	1·63
CH_3	C_2H_5	C_2H_5	41[c]	3·10
C_2H_5	C_2H_5	C_2H_5	40	—
CH_3	CH_3	$CH_2.CH_2.CH_3$	33	—
CH_3	CH_3	$CH_2.CH_2.CH_2.CH_3$	38	—
CH_3	CH_3	$CH(CH_3)_2$	62	—
CH_3	$CH(CH_3)_2$	$CH(CH_3)_2$	78	—
C_2H_5	C_2H_5	$CH_2.CH_2.CH_3$	80	—
C_2H_5	C_2H_5	$C(CH_3)_3$	90	—
CH_3	CH_3	$CH_2.C(CH_3)_3$	65[c]	20·7

[a] H. C. Brown and Fletcher, 1950.
[b] Hughes, Ingold and Shiner, 1953.
[c] Data confirmed by Hughes, Ingold and Shiner, 1953.

8

The explanation of this trend has been much debated. Since the olefin yield increases with increasing solvolysis rate, which is attributable to steric acceleration, it can be argued that increased branching in the alkyl group makes substitution less likely because the steric compressions responsible for the acceleration of the solvolysis begin to occur in the transition state of the solvent co-ordination step.[1] Alternatively, an interpretation of the results for the simple t-alkyl cations in terms of polar effects can be advanced. According to this, the more branched cations favour elimination because there is greater electromeric (hyperconjugative) stabilization by alkyl substituents of the incipient double bond in the transition state for proton loss.[2] The polar theory does not account satisfactorily for the results for the most ramified structures in Table 6.15, but the steric interpretation of these is not the only possibility[3] (see Paragraph 4.2.2). Further study of these cases could provide quantitative information about the relative importance of the polar and steric effects.

The theory that the energy of the transition state for proton loss from an alkyl cation is largely determined by hyperconjugation of alkyl groups with the double bond which is being formed, provides a satisfactory interpretation of the observed orientation of the double bond in such reactions. If an alkyl cation is capable of producing two or more different olefin products, the one in which the double bond carries the greatest number of alkyl substituents is usually formed most rapidly and therefore to the greatest extent (Saytzeff orientation). The product is thus the most stable of the possible olefins, which is intelligible if the stability of the products is reflected in the stabilities of the transition states leading to their formation, even though these transition states closely resemble the carbonium ion in structure. It is possible that steric factors also play a part in determining the stabilities of the products and the transition states. We shall return to this point below.

From quantum-mechanical considerations, the energy of the transition state for β-proton removal from a carbonium ion should be minimized when the bond being broken and the vacant p-orbital at the carbonium centre are in the same plane. Such an arrangement can in principle always be achieved in an acyclic carbonium ion, irrespective of the conformation of the compound from which the carbonium ion is formed. However, for very reactive carbonium ions, co-ordination to a solvent molecule may occur before the arrangement appropriate to elimination has been attained, and the activation energy for proton loss is very similar to that for rotation about a carbon to carbon single bond in the lower alkanes. Two conformations of an acyclic carbonium ion from which proton loss could readily occur are shown in **6.26** For R $\neq$ S and R' $\neq$ S', two product olefins (**6.27a** and **b**) are possible, the relative amounts of which

[1] H. C. Brown and Fletcher, 1949, 1950; H. C. Brown and Okamoto, 1955; H. C. Brown and Moritani, 1955.

[2] Hughes, Ingold and Shiner, 1953; Ingold, 1953, p. 440.

[3] Hughes, Ingold and Shiner, 1953.

depend on the populations of the two conformations **6.26a** and **b** the rates of proton loss from them, and their rates of interconversion. Some results for the system in which $R=CH_3$, $S=S'=H$ and $R'=$alkyl are shown in Table 6.16.

(a)   (b)

(6.26)

(a)   (b)

(6.27)

The results make it very likely that the size of the groups R,R', S and S' determines the stereochemistry of the product olefin, probably by affecting the relative stabilities of the two conformations of the carbonium ion as well as by influencing the relative stabilities of the transition states for proton loss in

Table 6.16. *Olefinic products in E1 eliminations from* $R'CH_2.CH(OBs)CH_3$ *in anhydrous acetic acid at* $70°$[a]

R'	Product ratios		Eclipsing groups in *cis*-2-ene	
	trans-2-ene/*cis*-2-ene	1-ene/2-ene		
CH_3[b]	1·1	0·11	CH_3/CH_3	H/H
C_2H_5	1·4	0·19	CH_3/C_2H_5	H/H
$CH(CH_3)_2$	2·0	0·25	$CH_3/CH(CH_3)_2$	H/H
$C(CH_3)_3$	83	0·32	$CH_3/C(CH_3)_3$	H/H

[a] H. C. Brown and Nakagawa, 1955b.
[b] 2-Butyl toluene-*p*-sulphonate.

which the groups become more nearly eclipsed. A similar argument might be advanced to account for the greater yield of terminal olefin (Hofmann-oriented product) as the size of the β-alkyl substituent increases (Table 6.16). Indeed, terminal olefin **6.28** is the major elimination product from **6.29**.[1]

[1] Brown and Nakagawa, 1955a

This olefin is more stable than the Saytzeff product (6.30),[1] presumably because it has less eclipsing strain.

$$(CH_3)_3C.CH_2.C:CH_2 \quad (CH_3)_3C.CH_2.CBr(CH_3)_2 \quad (CH_3)_3C.CH:C(CH_3)_2$$
$$\overset{|}{CH_3}$$

(6.28)   (6.29)   (6.30)

In all discussions of this kind it should be remembered that the phenomena discussed are due to quite small differences in energy, usually less than 2 kcal mole^{-1}. With such small effects, interpretation problems are inevitable. An additional complicating factor, not specifically mentioned, is the presence of a counter-ion in the vicinity of the carbonium centre, though its effect should be nearly constant in comparisons involving always the same anion and solvent. The effect becomes important in comparisons between solvents[2] or between leaving groups.[3] For example, E1 elimination from *erythro-* and *threo-*3-deuterio-2-butyl toluene-*p*-sulphonate gives *cis-* and *trans-*2-butenes as a result of almost exclusive *cis*-elimination of toluene-*p*-sulphonic acid in acetic acid or nitrobenzene: in 80% ethanol–water *trans*-elimination predominates (Figure 6.5).[4] The explanation can be advanced that the departing anion is the most basic species present in nitrobenzene and acetic acid and that it therefore removes the nearest (*cis*) proton immediately after ionization has occurred. As might be anticipated from these results, *cis*-addition of acids (e.g., HBr) to olefins is observed in aprotic media.[5]

Fragmentation of carbonium ions. In solution, olefin formation from carbonium ions by interaction of the carbonium centre with the electrons of a $\beta\gamma$-carbon-to-carbon σ-bond is less common than by the mechanism discussed in the preceding section. In the gas phase, e.g. in the mass spectrometer, fragmentation is common, and, since extensive reviews exist (see Bibliography), will not be discussed further here. The overall reaction in solution may be represented:

$$X.\overset{|}{\underset{|}{C}}-\overset{|}{\underset{|}{C}}-\overset{|}{\underset{|}{C}}Y \longrightarrow Y^- + X.\overset{|}{\underset{|}{C}}-\overset{|}{\underset{|}{C}}-\overset{|}{\underset{|}{C}}^+ \longrightarrow X.\overset{|}{\underset{|}{C}}^+ + >C:C<$$

(i.e. the reverse of reactions discussed in Paragraph 6.3.3).

Examples are the conversion of β-pinene (6.31) to the monocyclic carbonium

[1] R. B. Turner, Nettleton and Perelman, 1958.
[2] Cocivera and Winstein, 1963, Skell and Hall, 1963.
[3] Cram and Sahyun, 1963.
[4] Skell and Hall, 1963.
[5] Dewar and Fahey, 1963a,b,c, 1964.

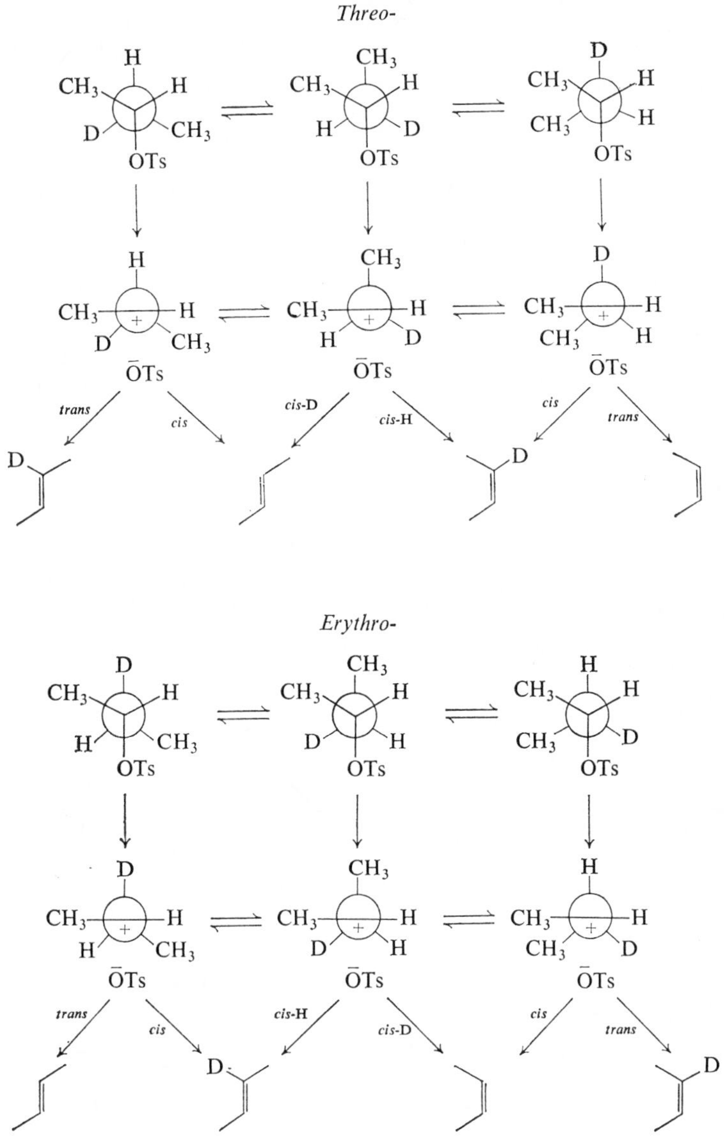

[The deuterium label permits the experimental distinction of *cis*- and *trans* elimination.]

Fig. 6.5. Stereochemistry of E1 reactions of *erythro*- and *threo*-3-deuterio-2-butyl toluene-*p*-sulphonates.

ion **6.33** on treatment with acid, presumably with intermediate formation of **6.32**,[1] and of **6.34** to cycloheptatrienyl cation and isobutene.[2]

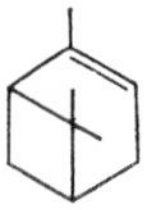

(**6.31**) 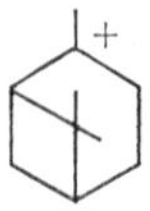   (**6.32**) 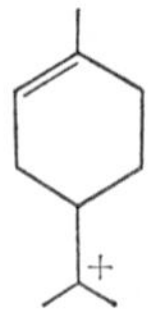   (**6.33**)

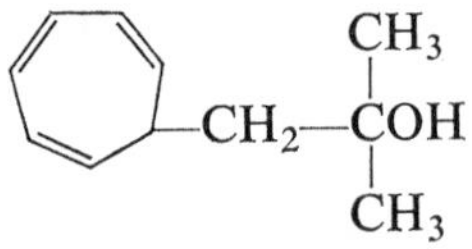

(**6.34**) 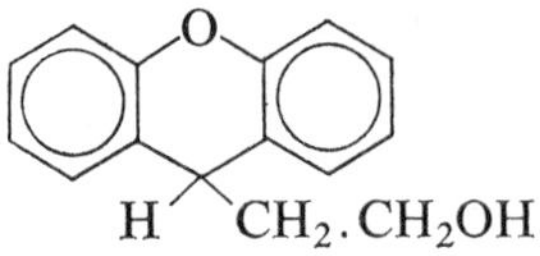   (**6.35**)   (**6.36**)

It is evident from these examples that the stability of the product cation is of great importance. This is underlined by the observation that, under given acidic conditions, **6.35**—but not **6.36**—fragments to give ethylene[3] (cf. Table 4.9 for the relative stabilities of the cations). The stability of the product cation is particularly great if an atom adjacent to the carbonium centre has non-bonded electron pairs in orbitals of symmetry appropriate for overlap with the vacant *p*-orbital on carbon. However, such a situation also increases the possibility of synchronous fragmentation reactions,[4] viz.

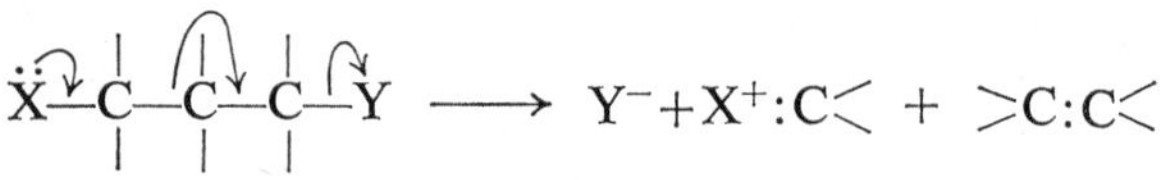

Fragmentation by way of a carbonium ion is characterized by:

  (i) a reaction rate close to that of S_N1 solvolysis of a similarly constituted molecule not containing the conjugating substituent X; and
 (ii) the occurrence of products typical of carbonium-ion reactions other than those due to fragmentation, e.g. substitution, elimination and cyclization products (Figure 6.6), the product proportions being independent of the leaving group in polar solvents.[5]

The corresponding observations for a synchronous fragmentation would be (i) rate enhancement, although this kinetic effect is sometimes difficult to

[1] Valkanas and Iconomou, 1963.
[2] Conrow, 1959.
[3] Deno and Sacher, 1965.
[4] Grob, 1959.
[5] Grob, Ostermayer and Raudenbusch, 1962.

distinguish from neighbouring-group participation in the heterolysis of the C—Y bond[1] (see Chapter 7). and (ii) 100% fragmented product.[2] Typical data illustrating the working of the criteria for carbonium ion fragmentation in solvolysis are given in Table 6.17. The rates of disappearance of all the com-

Table 6.17. *Relative rates and products of solvolysis of $XCH_2.CH_2.CY(CH_3)_2$ in 80% ethanol–water (v/v) at 40° and 56°[a]*

		—————56°—————		—————40°—————	
X	Y	Relative rate	% Fragmentation	Relative rate	% Fragmentation
$CH(CH_3)_2$	Cl	(1·0)	0	—	0
NH_2	Cl	0·99	20	—	—
$N(CH_3)_2$	Cl	0·75	50	(1·0)	43
	Br	—	—	38	45
	I	—	—	113	47
$\overset{+}{N}(CH_3)_3$	Cl	~0·01	—	—	—

[a] Grob, 1959; Grob, Ostermayer and Raudenbusch, 1962.

pounds listed are independent of the concentration of added hydroxide ion, indicating unimolecular decomposition. The rate of reaction is markedly dependent on the leaving group Y but much less affected by the nature of the γ-substituent. On the other hand the γ-substituent largely controls the extent

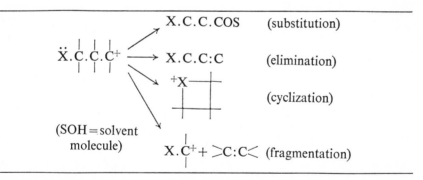

FIG. 6.6. Competing reactions of carbonium ions having α-substituents with non-bonded electron pairs.

of fragmentation. The results are consistent with initial formation of a carbonium ion, followed by fragmentation and other reactions in proportions determined by the structure of the intermediate ion.

[1] Grob, 1960; Grob and Jenny, 1960.
[2] Grob, 1959, 1960.

A further example, illustrating the importance of γ-substituents capable of conjugation and also showing that fragmentation may become possible only after rearrangement of the carbonium ion formed initially, is provided by the solvolyses of 4-toluene-p-sulphonyloxymethylquinuclidine (6.37) and its non-nitrogenous analogue (6.38) in 80% ethanol-water.[1] Thus rearrangement of the primary to the bridgehead tertiary carbonium ion occurs in both instances, but fragmentation is possible only in the heterocyclic compound (Figure 6.7).

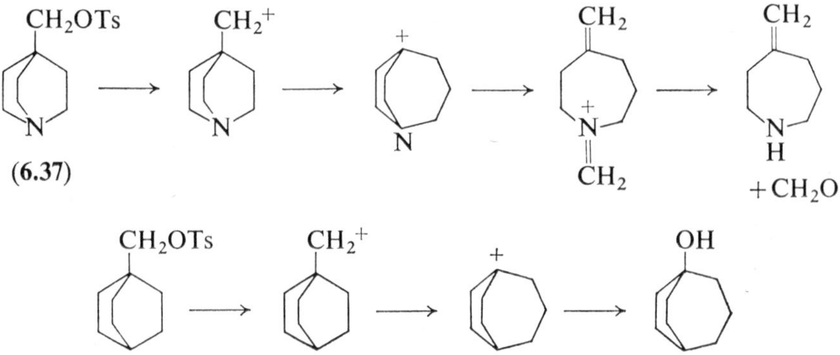

FIG. 6.7. Solvolysis of 4-toluene-p-sulphonyloxymethylquinuclidine (6.37) and its non-nitrogenous analogue.

The stereochemical aspects of carbonium-ion fragmentation are probably analogous to those discussed in E1 elimination.[2]

6.4.3 CARBONIUM-ION REARRANGEMENTS

The scope and nature of the reaction. The rearrangement of a carbonium ion, which we can represent in a fairly general way as

$$RC_\beta \cdot C_\alpha^+ \longrightarrow {}^+C_\beta \cdot C_\alpha R$$

may be regarded in two ways: the group R may be thought of as migrating from the carbon atom to which it was attached in the reactant molecule to the cationic centre, or, alternatively, the carbonium carbon atom may be considered to effect a frontside, electrophilic displacement at the atom, usually carbon or hydrogen, by which R is attached to the rest of the molecule. The former view, which is most common, leads to the concept of relative migratory aptitudes of groups. The consideration of rearrangement as an intramolecular

[1] Grob, Hoegerle and Ohta, 1962.
[2] Grob, Ostermayer and Raudenbusch, 1962.

substitution is usually restricted to cases where R is an aryl group, since there is an obvious intermolecular analogy (Paragraph 6.3.2). Carbonium-ion rearrangements are not restricted to the 1,2-shift of the group R. 1,3-Migration of hydrogen is quite common in reactions in the bicyclic monoterpenoid series, and rearrangements involving nominally even longer hydride shifts are known. These have been studied especially in cycloalkyl cations of medium ring size (8–12 carbon atoms) where the conformation of the ring brings the hydrogen and carbonium centre close together.[1]

The product of a carbonium-ion rearrangement is a second carbonium-ion, which in turn can undergo further reaction of the types detailed in the present Chapter. Until fairly recently, the rearrangement itself was not directly observable. Its occurrence was deduced by examination and correlation of the structures of the starting material, which could form the first carbonium ion, and the product, which could have arisen by further reaction of a second carbonium ion related to the first through a group migration such as that indicated above. Much of our knowledge of carbonium-ion rearrangements is derived from such circumstantial evidence.

The term carbonium-ion rearrangement involves the assumption that the reactions in which rearrangement occurs take place in a stepwise fashion, sometimes referred to as the Whitmore mechanism, namely, carbonium ion formation, rearrangement, and further reaction of the rearranged carbonium ion. Arguments have, however, been advanced that, in some instances at least, a single carbonium ion having a structure intermediate between that of the expected unrearranged and rearranged ions is involved. The question of the reality of these "bridged" or "non-classical" carbonium ions will be considered in more detail in Chapter 7. We shall only touch upon it in the present discussion.

The most common type of carbonium-ion rearrangement belongs to a wider group of reactions in which rearrangement occurs, and which is generally referred to as 1,2-shifts. An all-embracing representation of these reactions is

$$R\text{—}\overset{..}{A}\text{—}\overset{..}{\underset{..}{B}}\text{:} \;\rightarrow\; \text{:}\overset{..}{A}\text{—}\overset{..}{\underset{..}{B}}\text{—}R,$$

in which A and B represent the migration origin and terminus respectively, and the pairs of dots represent pairs of electrons which will in general form bonds to other atoms and substituent groups. The 1,2-shifts may be divided into categories depending upon the way be which rearrangement is induced. The category which includes carbonium-ion rearrangements involves initiation by generation of an electrophilic centre on atom B, viz.,

$$R\text{—}\overset{..}{A}\text{—}\overset{..}{\underset{..}{B}}\text{:} \;\rightarrow\; R\text{—}\overset{..}{A}\text{—}\overset{..}{B} \;\rightarrow\; \overset{..}{A}\text{—}\overset{..}{B}\text{—}R \;\rightarrow\; \text{:}\overset{..}{A}\text{—}\overset{..}{\underset{..}{B}}\text{—}R.$$

[1] Prelog and Traynham, 1963; Cope, Martin and McKervey, 1966.
8*

It also embraces such well-known reactions as the Beckmann rearrangement of oximes, the Hofmann degradation of amides, the Wolff rearrangement of diazoketones, and the Baeyer-Villiger conversion of ketones to esters[1] which involve migration to an electrophilic centre located on an atom other than carbon. Evidence from studies of such reactions has therefore been used by way of analogy in discussions of carbonium-ion rearrangements.

A number of groups of carbonium-ion rearrangements are often distinguished according to the structures of the reactants and products involved:

(i) *The pinacol and related rearrangements.* The acid-catalysed dehydration of pinacol (**6.39**) gives a ketone, pinacolone (**6.40**), having a rearranged carbon skeleton. Unsymmetrically substituted glycols give a number of product ketones.

$$(CH_3)_2C.C(CH_3)_2$$
$$HO \quad OH$$
$$(6.39)$$

$$CH_3.CO.C(CH_3)_3$$
$$(6.40)$$

$$(CH_3)_2C.\overset{+}{C}(CH_3)_2 \longrightarrow CH_3.\overset{+}{C}.C(CH_3)_3$$
$$OH \qquad\qquad\qquad OH$$

With trisubstituted glycols, either the tertiary or the secondary hydroxyl group may be lost in initiating the reaction. The reactions are sometimes referred to as the semihydrobenzoinic and semipinacolinic changes respectively.[2] Other, less common possibilities exist. Analogous changes occur on nitrous acid deamination of 1,2-aminoalcohols. A related reaction is the acid-catalysed conversion of a trisubstituted acetaldehyde (e.g., **6.41**) to the related ketone **6.42**.

$$Ph_3C.CHO \rightarrow Ph_3C.\overset{+}{C}HOH \rightarrow Ph_2\overset{+}{C}.CHPh \rightarrow Ph_2CH\overset{+}{C}Ph \rightarrow Ph_2CH.COPh$$
$$(6.41) \qquad\qquad\qquad\quad OH \qquad\quad OH \qquad\qquad (6.42)$$

(ii) *The dienone-phenol rearrangement.* Cyclohexadienones, on treatment with acid, are converted to phenols (e.g. **6.43** to **6.44**).

(iii) *Wagner-Meerwein (or retropinacol) rearrangement.* This group embraces all carbonium-ion rearrangements not covered in categories (i) and (ii). The course of the reaction was first elucidated by Wagner in the terpene series, but subsequent investigations by Meerwein showed that analogous rearrangements occur in a wide range of structural types. Typical examples have already been

[1] Ingold, 1953, Ch. 9; Wheland, 1957, Ch. 12; Hine, 1963, Ch. 14, 15.
[2] Tiffeneau and Lévy, 1923.

given in Paragraph 2.7.2. Special names are sometimes given to Wagner-Meerwein rearrangements under specific structural circumstances or reaction conditions (e.g. Nametkin and Dem'yanov rearrangements). We shall make no such distinctions here.

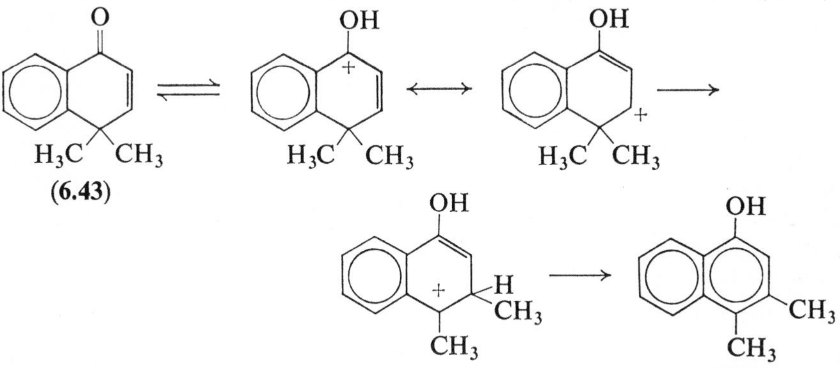

(6.43)

(6.44)

In formulating examples of these rearrangements we have indicated the mechanism in terms of plausible sequences of transformations of carbonium ions. That carbonium ions are the intermediates in these reactions is usually inferred from the reaction conditions and by structural analogies. The early work on the mechanism of conversion of camphene hydrochloride to isobornyl chloride (Section 1.4) may be cited as an example of this approach. In some instances, kinetic evidence can be advanced to show that rearrangement occurs at the carbonium ion stage of a reaction. Nuclear magnetic resonance spectroscopy, however, provides the most compelling evidence since the technique permits in favourable cases the direct observation of the intermediate carbonium ions and provides both structural and kinetic data in suitable circumstances (see Paragraph 2.3.1).

The mechanism and stereochemical course of rearrangement. In classifying the modes of intramolecular attack of carbonium centres on σ-bond electron pairs we distinguished olefin-forming reactions from rearrangements (Paragraph 6.4.1). Rearrangement could, however, be formulated as consecutive formation and alkylation (or protonation) of an olefin, viz.,

$$R-\overset{|}{\underset{|}{C}}-\overset{|}{\underset{|}{C}}{}^{+} \rightarrow R^{+} + {\textstyle >}C = C{\textstyle <} \rightarrow {}^{+}\overset{|}{\underset{|}{C}}-\overset{|}{\underset{|}{C}}-R$$

Such a mechanism is unlikely and can be ruled out in a variety of cases. Thus rearrangement and fragmentation are not usually found to occur in the same reaction: fragmentation is much less common than rearrangement. Migratory aptitudes (see p. 212) of groups do not bear any relation to their ability to exist as positive ions. In rearrangements involving migration of hydrogen, for example the conversion of $(CH_3)_2CH.CH_2^+$ to $(CH_3)_3C^+$, no deuterium is incorporated in the product when the reaction is carried out in a deuteriated solvent.[1] Similarly, no exchange of migrating hydrogen with solvent occurs in pinacol-type rearrangements.[2] It is to be concluded that the migrating group never becomes free from the rest of the carbonium ion.

Further important information concerning the mechanism of rearrangement comes from studies of the stereochemical course of the reaction. In general, stereochemical changes can occur at three sites in a rearranging molecule, the migration origin, the migration terminus and the migrating group itself. Only in the Wagner-Meerwein rearrangement can all these changes in principle be studied, and in no case has this been done in the same molecule. Indeed configurational changes in the migrating group during rearrangement have not been investigated for any carbonium-ion rearrangement. However, by analogy with the observed retention of configuration in other 1,2-shifts initiated by formation of an electrophilic centre (viz. the Beckmann, Hofmann, Curtius, Schmidt, Lossen and Baeyer-Villiger reactions),[3] no change in the configuration of an asymmetric migrating group is expected in migration to a carbonium centre.

At the migration origin and terminus, predominant inversion of configuration is observed. Two extreme examples are the exclusive Wagner-Meerwein rearrangements of camphene hydrochloride (6.45) to isobornyl chloride (6.46) and of pinene hydrochloride (6.47) to bornyl chloride (6.48). In both cases, complete inversion occurs at the migration origin (marked O in formulae 6.45–6.48) and terminus (marked T), even though both rearrangements might be thought to involve the same rearranged ion (6.49) (see Paragraph 7.5.3).

In pinacol and related rearrangements, the stereochemical course of reaction cannot be investigated at the migration origin since it becomes a carbonyl group in the product. At the migration terminus, inversion is again the rule: thus the *cis*-glycol 6.50 undergoes conversion to 6.51 more readily than the *trans*-glycol which first isomerises to 6.50 under the reaction conditions.[4]

The degree of inversion at the migration origin and terminus falls below 100% in acyclic systems. Thus for example, in the semipinacolinic deamination of stereoisomeric 1-amino-1,2-diarylpropan-2-ols (e.g. 6.52) some 25% of the 2-aryl migration occurs with retention of configuration at the migration

[1] Cannell and Taft, 1956; Coe and Gold, 1960.

[2] Mislow and Siegel, 1952; Ley and Vernon, 1957; W. B. Smith, Bowman and Kmet, 1959.

[3] Kenyon and Young, 1941; Wallis and Nagel, 1931; Jones and Wallis, 1926; Braun and Friehmelt, 1933; Wallis and Dripps, 1933; R. B. Turner, 1952; Lane and Wallis, 1941.

[4] Bartlett and Brown, 1940; R. F. Brown, 1952, 1954; R. F. Brown, Nordman and Madoff, 1952.

terminus.[1] The course of the reaction can be understood with the aid of Figure 6.8.

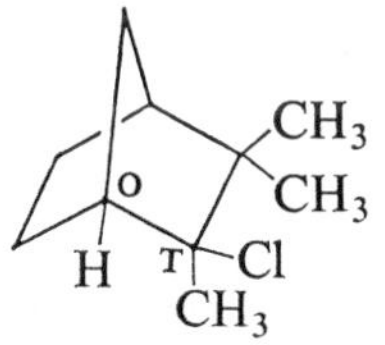

(6.45) 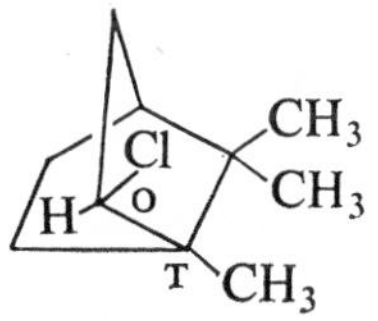   (6.46)

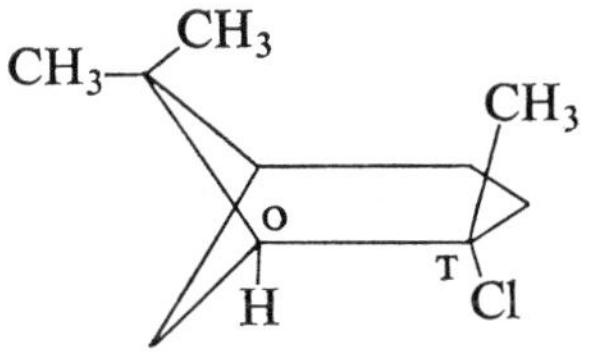

(6.47) 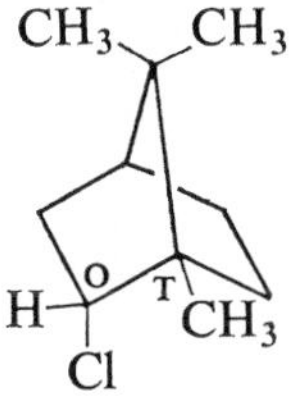   (6.48) 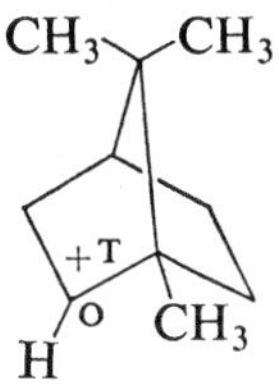   (6.49)

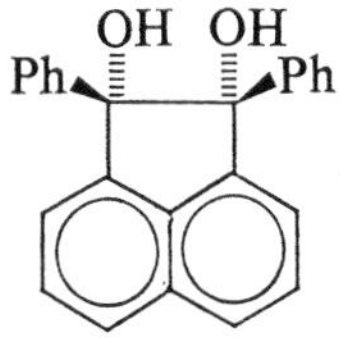

(6.50) 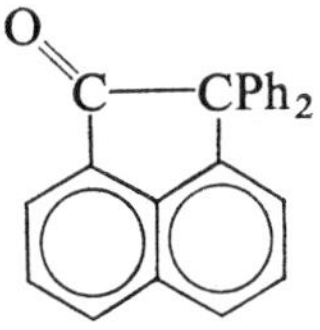   (6.51)

Of the groups attached to C(2), only Ar' is mobile and, as for other reactions of carbonium centres with σ-bond electrons, rearrangement is facilitated when the σ-orbital binding Ar' to C(2) is co-planar with the vacant p-orbital at the carbonium centre. Two conformations of the first-formed carbonium ion (6.53a and b) satisfy the requirement: 6.53a, which is closely related to the most stable conformation of the reactant, gives the ketonic product with inversion of configuration at the migration terminus, and 6.53b, obtained from 6.53a by rotation about the C(1)–C(2) bond, gives product with retention.

The generally observed predominant inversion of configuration at both the migration origin and terminus can be explained in the following way. If the migrating group (R) shifts very soon after completion of the ionization, the leaving group will still be close to the migration terminus and will shield one face of the carbonium ion. Migration will thus occur on the opposite side of the carbonium ion, inverting the configuration at the migration terminus. Any nucleophilic attack on the new carbonium centre (leading to destruction of the

[1] Benjamin, Wilder and Collins, 1961; Benjamin and Collins, 1961.

rearranged carbonium ion), for example by solvent, which occurs immediately after departure of R, will be predominantly on that face of the carbonium ion remote from R. Thus inversion will be the major steric course at the migration origin (compare Paragraph 6.2.4). Implicit in this explanation is the assumption that, in conformationally mobile systems, migration of R and destruction of the rearranged carbonium ion are faster processes than rotation about the bond linking the migration origin and terminus.[1] Little is known about the

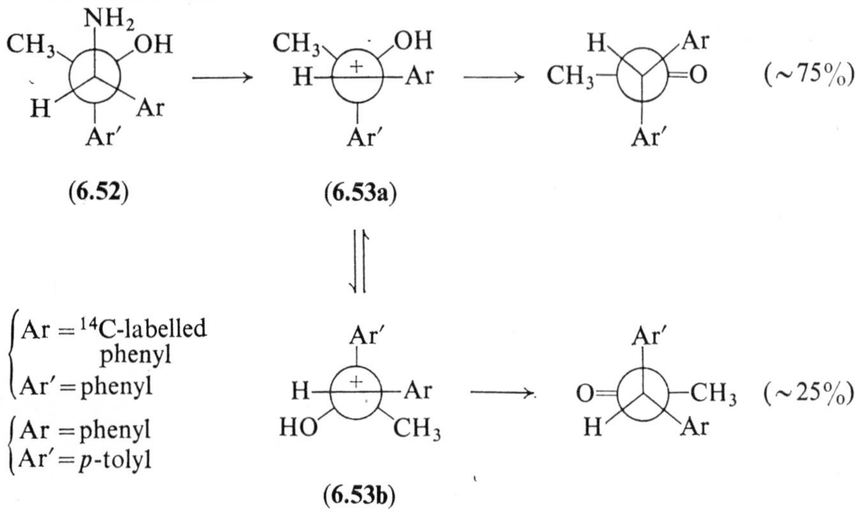

Fig. 6.8. Stereochemical course of the semipinacolinic deamination of 1-amino-1,2-diarylpropan-2-ols.

magnitude of barriers to internal rotation in carbonium ions, but some activation energies for migration of hydrogen—probably not as good a migrating group as phenyl—in carbonium ions are known. Values vary widely, but in certain cases are less than 7 kcal mole^{-1},[2] so that fairly small barriers to bond rotation in carbonium ions would explain the stereochemical results.

In some acyclic structures, for example the solvolysis of the 3-phenyl-2-butyl toluene-p-sulphonates (Paragraph 7.4.1), inversion of configuration at the migration origin and terminus is almost complete. An alternative interpretation of such inversion is that the migrating group, R in **6.54**, with its binding electrons acts as an internal nucleophile, displacing the leaving group and forming an intermediate ion in which R is bonded to both the migration origin and terminus (**6.55**). Rearrangement is then completed by nucleophilic attack at the migration origin and this is necessarily from the opposite direction to R, giving a product with inversion of configuration at both centres (**6.56**).

[1] For an extension of these ideas to bicyclic cations, see Berson and Poonian, 1966.
[2] M. Saunders, Schleyer and Olah, 1964; Brouwer, MacLean and Mackor, 1965.

Nucleophilic attack at the migration terminus yields unrearranged product with retention of configuration. The idea of a single intermediate ion in which the group R bridges the migration origin and terminus is more plausible in some cases than others. While providing an admirably simple explanation of

(6.54)   (6.55)   (6.56)

the observed changes, it raises important questions, particularly about the nature of the bridge bonds. The question of the reality of bridged ions such as **6.55** will be further discussed in Chapter 7. It is worth pointing out here, however, that the interpretation of the stereochemistry of carbonium ion rearrangements in terms of bridging accords to **6.55** the status of true intermediate, whereas, if the rearrangement involves interconverting unbridged carbonium ions, structure **6.55** would correspond to the transition state of the rearrangement process.

Structural effects on carbonium ion rearrangements. The direction of rearrangement. Generally, in reactions involving a carbonium-ion rearrangement, the product isolated contains a predominance of the compound(s) derived from the more stable of the two intermediate cations. Accordingly it is customary to represent carbonium ion rearrangements as taking place in a direction which leads to a more stable cation, that is, primary alkyl → secondary alkyl → tertiary alkyl, with suitable modification for aryl substituents, α-hetero-atoms (e.g. oxygen in the product ion in pinacol rearrangements) and special steric effects.

This commonly used generalization is probably an oversimplification. If the rate of carbonium-ion destruction is slow compared with the rate of rearrangement, the rearranged and unrearranged cations could approach an equilibrium state. The observed products would then be derived in proportions determined by the relative thermodynamic stabilities of the two carbonium ions and the velocity constants for their destruction (see Paragraph 4.1.1). If, on the other hand, the energy barrier separating the unrearranged from the rearranged ion is high relative to that which has to be surmounted to destroy the former, the product composition will be determined by the heights of the energy barriers and will be largely independent of the stability of the rearranged carbonium ion.[1]

[1] If the intermediate carbonium ion is bridged, nucleophilic attack at the bridged carbon atoms yields the rearranged and unrearranged products in proportions determined by the relative reactivities at the migration origin and terminus. In practice, reaction is predominantly at the carbon atom which would be the carbonium centre of the more stable of the two related unbridged cations (Berson, 1960) though the point of attack can sometimes be influenced by the nature of the nucleophile (Diaz, Brookhart and Winstein, 1966).

In some instances, reaction products seem to indicate that rearrangement of the intermediate carbonium ions occurs in the direction of the less stable cation. For example, treatment of butene-2 with sulphuric acid yields products derived from the t-butyl cation, and the simplest interpretation is in terms of the reaction sequence,

$$CH_3.CH:CH.CH_3 \rightarrow CH_3.CH_2.\overset{+}{C}H.CH_3 \rightarrow \overset{+}{C}H_2.CH(CH_3)_2 \rightarrow$$

$$CH_3.\overset{+}{C}(CH_3)_2$$

involving conversion of a secondary alkyl cation to a primary one. The preferred interpretation,[1] supported by isotopic labelling experiments,[2] circumvents the difficulty with an olefin alkylation-rearrangement-fragmentation sequence, viz.,

$$CH_3.CH:CH.CH_3 \rightarrow CH_3.CH_2.\overset{+}{C}H.CH_3 \xrightarrow{CH_3 \cdot CH:CH \cdot CH_3}$$

$$\rightarrow CH_3.CH_2.CH(CH_3).CH(CH_3)\overset{+}{C}H.CH_3 \rightarrow$$

$$\rightarrow CH_3.CH_2.CH(CH_3).\overset{+}{C}H.CH(CH_3)_2 \rightarrow$$

$$\rightarrow CH_3.CH_2.CH(CH_3).CH_2.\overset{+}{C}(CH_3)_2 \rightarrow$$

$$\rightarrow CH_3.CH_2.\overset{+}{C}H.CH_3 + CH_2:C(CH_3)_2 \rightarrow CH_3.\overset{+}{C}(CH_3)_2$$

Migratory aptitude. Migratory aptitude, that is, the ability of a substituent group to migrate to the carbonium centre, is a rather ill-defined concept. The term directs attention to the nature of the migrating group, but, while the group's intrinsic ability to migrate is important, other aspects of the carbonium-ion structure can be equally, if not more, important. Furthermore, external factors, such as the solvent and the catalysts employed, can modify observed migratory aptitudes, especially if a number of distinct reaction paths exist.[3]

The following internal factors can be considered to control group migration;

(i) the configuration and conformation of the starting material;
(ii) the configuration, conformation, and steric compressions at the migration origin of the unrearranged carbonium ion;
(iii) eclipsing effects in the transition state of the rearrangement step;
(iv) the electron density at the migration origin and terminus;
(v) the intrinsic migratory aptitude of the group.

Their effects will be illustrated in the sequel.

The obvious index of migratory aptitude is the *rate* of migration of a group to the carbonium centre. By direct observation of carbonium ions, using nuclear magnetic resonance spectroscopy (Paragraph 2.3.1), such rates can

[1] Karabatsos and Vane, 1963.
[2] Karabatsos, Vane and Meyerson, 1963; Hofmann and Schriesheim, 1962a,b.
[3] Collins, 1955; Collins, Rainey *et al.*, 1959.

sometimes be determined absolutely for individual migrating groups, and the results confirm that the rate of migration of a given group can change over several powers of ten, depending upon the structure of the carbonium ion.[1]

When the carbonium ion is present in very low, steady state concentration, methods based on direct observation are inapplicable. From Figure 6.9, it can be seen that, for the ion **6.57**, *relative* migratory aptitudes k_r/k_r', k_r'/k_r'' and k_r''/k_r may be evaluated from the ratios of the products P, P′ and P″ for systems in which more than one group in the ion may be capable of migration. This is the most common method of evaluating migratory aptitudes. If the steady state concentration of **6.57** can be estimated, combination with the observed

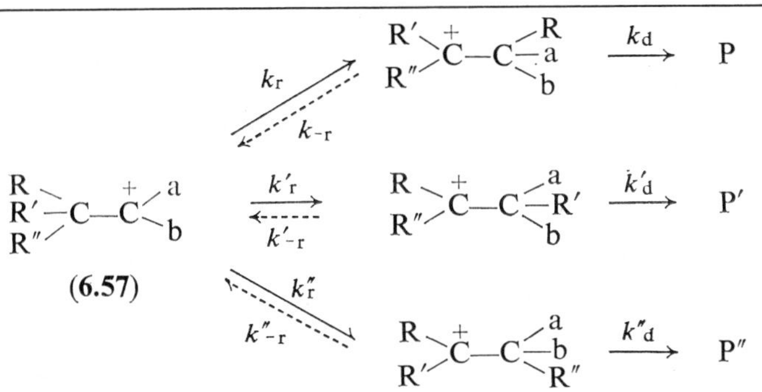

FIG. 6.9. Competitive rearrangements of a carbonium ion.

total rate of rearrangement and the product proportions yields absolute values[2] of k_r, k_r' and k_r''. These procedures are valid provided that there is no reversal of the rearrangement, i.e. $k_d \gg k_{-r}$, $k_d' \gg k_{-r}'$; $k_d'' \gg k_{-r}''$. Instances are known where the rate constant for the destruction step is a small fraction (e.g. 1/1200) of that for group migration.[3] Failure to recognize such equilibration of carbonium ions can lead to erroneous conclusions.[4]

The presence of two potential carbonium centres can present an additional complication when this method is applied to the pinacol and related rearrangements. Thus acid treatment of the unsymmetrical glycol **6.58** gives product **6.59**, by migration of a *p*-anisyl group from C_β to a carbonium centre generated at C_α, and **6.60**, by phenyl migration to a carbonium centre on C_β. It is evident that the ratio of **6.60** to **6.59** reflects not merely the relative migratory aptitudes of the phenyl and *p*-anisyl groups, but also the ability of *p*-anisyl groups to promote carbonium ion formation at C_β compared with the

[1] Brouwer, MacLean and Mackor, 1965; M. Saunders, Schleyer and Olah, 1964.
[2] See, for example, Stiles and Mayer, 1959.
[3] Raaen, Lietzke and Collins, 1966.
[4] Benjamin and Collins, 1956a,b; see also Kendrick, Benjamin and Collins, 1958; Collins and Bowman, 1959; Raaen and Collins, 1958.

ability of phenyl groups to promote carbonium-ion formation at C_α. A valid comparison of the ability of the two groups to undergo a 1,2-shift to the carbonium centre in a pinacol rearrangement could be obtained from the product ratio in the reaction of the symmetrical glycol **6.61** which also gives **6.59** and **6.60**. Some values of observed migratory aptitudes for substituted

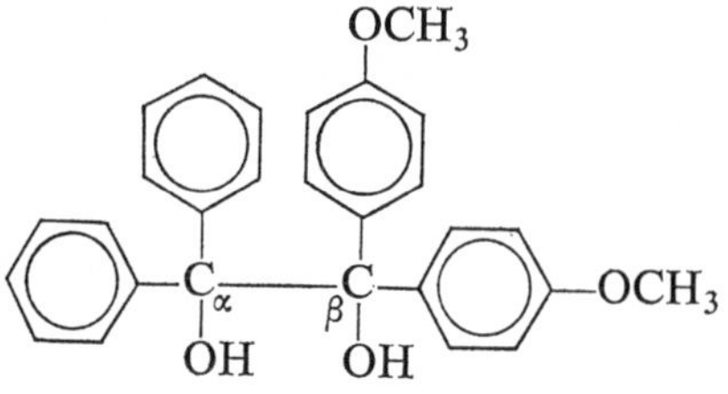

(6.58) 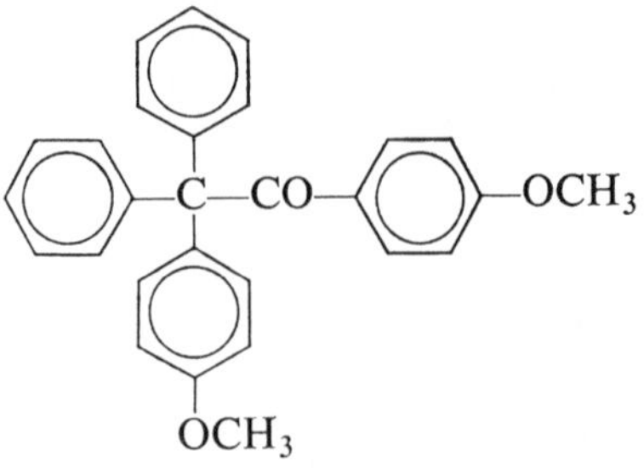   (6.59)

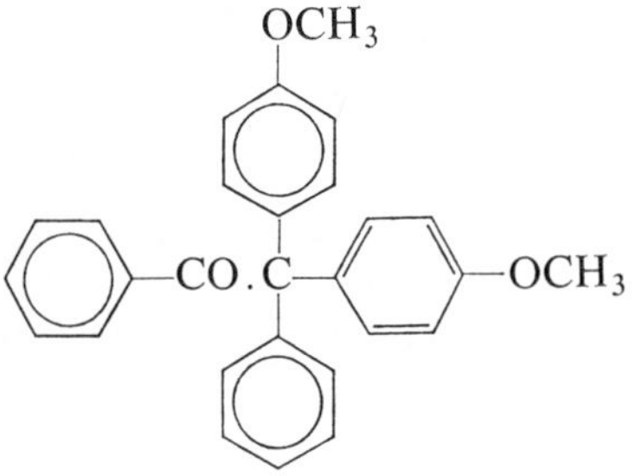

(6.60) 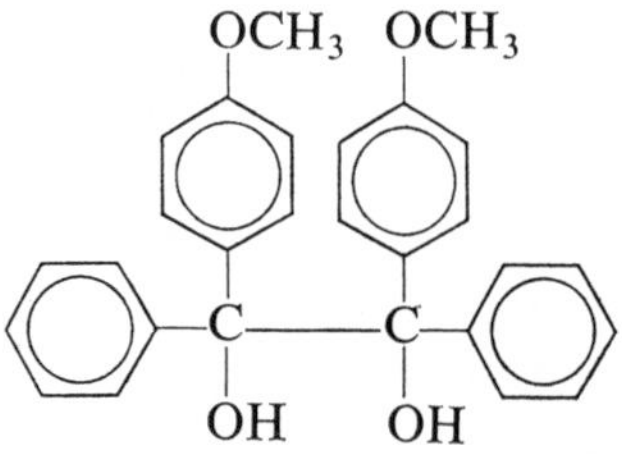   (6.61)

phenyl groups in pinacol rearrangement of symmetrical and unsymmetrical glycols are given in Table 6.18.

Even the values from symmetrical glycols must be accepted with some reservation since the configuration of the glycol (*meso-* or *dl-*) is not specified. The importance of configurational and conformational factors is illustrated by the course of the semipinacolinic deamination of the diastereoisomeric amino alcohols **6.62** ("*threo*") and **6.63** ("*erythro*"). The *threo*-compound on treatment with nitrous acid is deaminated with migration of the *p*-anisyl group giving ketone **6.64**. Under the same conditions, the *erythro*-isomer gives ketone **6.65** by exclusive phenyl migration, despite the greater intrinsic migratory aptitude anticipated for the *p*-anisyl group.[1] The explanation lies in the conformations of the reacting species[2] (see Figure 6.10). From considera-

[1] Pollack and Curtin, 1950; see also, Curtin and Pollack, 1951; Curtin, Harris and Meislich, 1952; Curtin and Meislich, 1952a,b.
[2] Benjamin, Schaeffer and Collins, 1957; Raaen and Collins, 1958.

tions of the size of the groups and the possibility of hydrogen-bonding between the adjacent amino- and hydroxyl-groups, the stability of the conformations of **6.62** is expected to decrease in the order $a > c > b$. If rearrangement and destruction of the derived carbonium ions (**6.66**) takes place more rapidly than rotation about the central carbon-carbon bond, then p-anisyl migration

Table 6.18. *Migratory aptitudes of substituted phenyl groups derived from product ratios in pinacol rearrangement of symmetrical glycols*[a]

Substituent	Migratory aptitude	Substituent	Migratory aptitude
—	$1 \cdot 00^{b}$ $(1 \cdot 00)^{b,c}$	p-CH(CH$_3$)$_2$	9
o-OCH$_3$	0·3	o-Cl	0·0
m-OCH$_3$	1·6	p-Cl	0·7 (0·75)
p-OCH$_3$	500 (0·39)	o-Br	0·0
p-OC$_2$H$_5$	500 (0·49)	p-Br	0·7
m-CH$_3$	1.95 (1·0)	o-I	0·0
p-CH$_3$	15·7 (0·96)	p-I	1·0
p-C$_2$H$_5$	5		

[a] Bachmann and Ferguson, 1934; Adkins, 1943.
[b] Standard.
[c] Values in parentheses refer to rearrangement of unsymmetrical glycols (Bachmann and Sternberger, 1934; Adkins, 1943).

will predominate. By similar reasoning **6.63c** is the most stable rotamer of the *erythro*-isomer, and the derived carbonium ion (**6.67c**) has the phenyl group in the *trans*-position, appropriate for migration. The observation that the steric course of aryl migration is the deamination of diastereoisomeric 1-amino-1-phenyl-2-arylpropan-2-ols is virtually independent of the polar nature of the migrating group (Table 7.2) is similarly explicable in terms of "ground state control" of migratory aptitude. Such control seems to be most important in nitrous acid deamination.[1]

An additional factor may favour migration of the p-anisyl group in the deamination of **6.62**. The transition states for rearrangement of the carbonium ion rotamers **6.66a** and **6.66c** will resemble **6.68** and **6.69** respectively. Clearly, the non-bonded repulsions between the eclipsed aryl substituents in **6.69** will destabilize this transition state relative to **6.68**.

[1] Cram and McCarty, 1957.

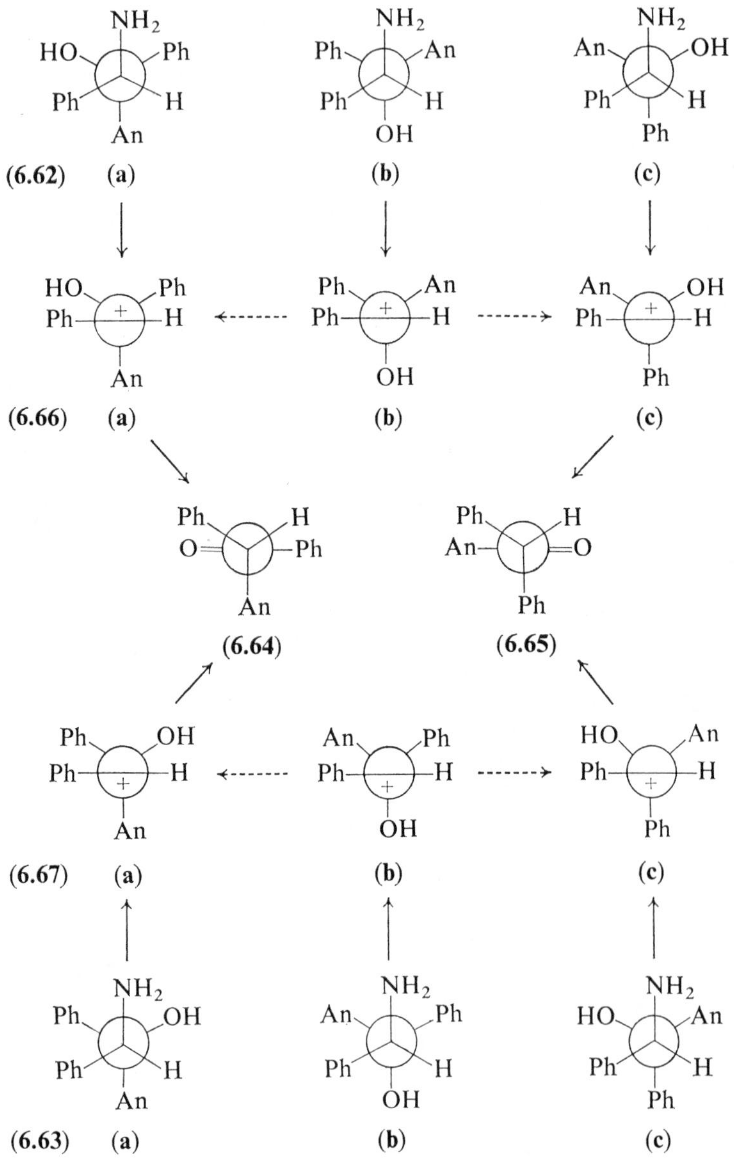

Fig. 6.10. Semipinacolinic deamination of diastereoisomeric 2-amino-1,1,2-triarylethanols (An = p-methoxyphenyl).

$$
\left[\begin{array}{c} \text{Ph} \quad\quad \text{H} \\ \text{HO} \!-\!\!\bigcirc\!\!-\! \text{Ph} \\ \text{An} \end{array} \right]^{+}
\qquad\qquad
\left[\begin{array}{c} \text{Ph} \quad\quad \text{H} \\ \text{An} \!-\!\!\bigcirc\!\!-\! \text{OH} \\ \text{Ph} \end{array} \right]^{+}
$$

(6.68) (6.69)

This effect of eclipsing in the transition state for migration should be quite general, but its importance relative to the other factors controlling migratory aptitudes is uncertain.[1] In the rearrangement of carbonium ions of the type

$$
CH_3 . CR(OH) . \overset{+}{C} (CH_3)_2 \qquad (6.70)
$$

the influence of the group R, relative to methyl, on the rate of migration of the α-methyl group is ethyl, 4·7; t-butyl, 54.[2] Evidently the effect of the eclipsing of a methyl and t-butyl group in the transition state does not outweigh the accelerating effect of greater electron density and perhaps steric compression at the migration origin.

The multiplicity of factors affecting the migratory aptitudes of groups makes it difficult to establish orders of intrinsic migratory aptitudes. In general it appears that aryl groups are most mobile, followed by hydrogen and alkyl groups. This is consistent with the requirement that, in the transition state of the 1,2-shift, the migrating group should be able to accommodate a substantial proportion of the positive charge of the carbonium ion, and some MO calculations support the sequence (cf. Section 5.2).[3] With the reservation noted above, the migratory aptitudes for substituted phenyl groups derived from the product proportions in the pinacol rearrangement of symmetrical glycols probably reflect intrinsic abilities to migrate.[4] The values for m- and p-substituted phenyl groups correlate quite well with the corresponding σ^{+}-values (Paragraph 4.2.3), with a ρ-value of about -3, confirming the importance of the contribution of structure 6.71 to the transition state of rearrangement.[5] Less symmetrical binding of the migrating group is to be expected if a substantial difference in thermodynamic stability exists between the rearranged and unrearranged ions. The low migratory aptitudes observed for o-substituted phenyl groups (Table 6.18) might seem to indicate that the energy of the transition state for the shift of such a group is raised by compressions between the o-substituent and the eclipsing groups. The preferred interpretation, in some

[1] Curtin and Crew, 1955.

[2] Stiles and Mayer, 1959.

[3] Zimmerman and Zweig, 1961.

[4] Cf. Benjamin and Collins, 1953; Collins, Ciereszko and Burr, 1953; Burr and Ciereszko, 1952.

[5] Cf. Burr, 1953, 1954; Heck and Winstein, 1957c.

cases at least,[1] is that the *o*-substituent impedes rotation about the central carbon–carbon bond in the carbonium ion, thus promoting migration of the group most favourably situated in the rotamer formed initially. This is confirmed by the reduced proportion of migration with retention at the migration terminus in deamination of (6.52) when Ar′ is an *o*-substituted phenyl group compared with that when Ar′ is a *p*-substituted group.[2]

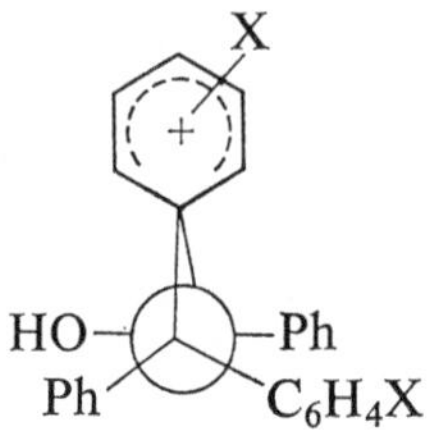

(6.71)

Intramolecular comparisons of migratory aptitudes of alkyl groups, unlike those for substituted phenyl groups, are unlikely to reflect intrinsic migratory aptitudes because of the greater variation in the size of the groups compared. By intermolecular comparison, that is, the comparison of absolute rates of migration of different individual groups in the same molecular environment (6.70), the sequence, methyl 1·0 (standard); ethyl 17, t-butyl > 4000 has been obtained.[3] Thus dispersal of positive charge, together, perhaps, with relief of non-bonded compressions in the initial carbonium ion, are again seen to be important.

The problems of intramolecular comparison of migratory aptitude exist *a fortiori* when migration of hydrogen is compared with that of other groups. Accordingly we note here only that for triphenylethylene glycol in a variety of acidic media hydrogen migrates three times more readily than deuterium, although the migratory aptitude of hydrogen relative to phenyl varies widely.[4]

6.4.4 INTERMOLECULAR HYDRIDE TRANSFER

Introduction. Reaction of carbonium centres directly with σ-bond electrons in a second molecule is commonly restricted to electrons binding hydrogen. This reaction involves transfer of a proton and two electrons from a donor molecule to the carbonium centre and is generally referred to as an intermolecular hydride ion transfer: $R^+ + XH \rightarrow RH + X^+$. It represents one example of a general class of hydride transfer reactions embracing such

[1] Raaen and Collins, 1958.
[2] Collins, Staum and Benjamin, 1962.
[3] Stiles and Mayer, 1959.
[4] Collins, Rainey *et al.*, 1959.

apparently diverse processes as, for example, the Cannizzaro and Meerwein-Pondorff-Verley reactions.[1] There exist reactions in which anionic groups other than hydride ion (e.g., CN, OR, NR_2) are transferred directly from a donor molecule to a carbonium centre. However, these reactions take place by successive co-ordination of the carbonium centre to the transferred group, followed by fragmentation, and, in some cases, the intermediate oxonium or ammonium ions are isolable.[2] Such reactions will not be discussed further.

The net transfer of a proton and two electrons to a carbonium centre can be envisaged as occurring in a number of ways. We shall be concerned only with single-step transfer of hydride ions, which, it is emphasized, never become free. Such a process is distinguishable from multistep reactions involving proton transfers by virtue of the polarities of the donor and acceptor and by the absence of hydrogen isotope exchange with hydroxylic solvents.[3]

An alternative multi-step mechanism, in which the carbonium ion accepts an electron, forming the corresponding free radical which then abstracts a hydrogen atom from a suitable source, should be readily distinguishable by examining the influence of radical traps. While such a mechanism has been excluded in certain hydride transfer reactions not involving carbonium ions,[4] explicit tests for radicals are not usually applied in studying hydride transfers to carbonium ions. Reliance is usually placed on the clean nature of the reaction, i.e., the absence of side reactions that usually accompany free radical processes.

Hydride transfer to carbonium ions is known in the gas phase,[5] but we shall restrict the present discussion to the more fully studied reactions in solution.

Scope of the reaction. Hydride ion donors may be inorganic, but are generally organic species. *A priori*, hydride transfer should be readiest from a negatively charged donor: the conditions under which carbonium ions are generated do not usually permit this. Examples are the trapping of carbonium ion intermediates in solvolyses by hydride transfer from borohydride ion[6] and the conversion of triphenylmethyl cation to triphenylmethane in formic acid by the formate ion produced in the generation of the carbonium ion from the parent alcohol.[7] Usually the donor is a neutral molecule. Some examples from the considerable range of such donors which have been employed are as follows:

(i)[8] $Ph_3C^+ + (CH_3)_2CHOH \rightarrow Ph_3CH + (CH_3)_2CO + H^+$

[1] Deno, Peterson and Saines, 1960.
[2] Meerwein, Hederich *et al.*, 1960.
[3] Baddeley and Nield, 1954; Bartlett and McCollum, 1956.
[4] Doering and Aschner, 1949, 1953.
[5] Field and Lampe, 1958; Borkowski and Ausloos, 1964.
[6] H. C. Brown and Bell, 1962; Bell and Brown, 1966.
[7] Stewart, 1957; Grinter and Mason, 1964b.
[8] Bartlett and McCollum, 1956.

(ii)[1] $(CH_3)_3C^+ + (CH_3)_2CH.CH_2.CH_3 \rightarrow$

$(CH_3)_3CH + (CH_3)_2\overset{+}{C}.CH_2.CH_3$

(iii)[2] $Ph_3C^+ + (PhCH_2)_3N \rightarrow Ph_3CH + Ph.CH\!:\!\overset{+}{N}(CH_2Ph)_2$

In cases where the hydride ion donor is a hydrocarbon, a second carbonium ion is one of the products. This reaction has been widely exploited preparatively, particularly for the synthesis of cycloheptatrienyl and related cations.[3] Such reactions are also industrially important, for example in the alkylation of isoparaffins[4] (see Paragraph 6.3.3.) and aromatic compounds.[5]

Structural effects. Intermolecular hydride transfers, particularly those involving alkyl cations, are often very rapid. Thus, hydride abstraction from isopentane by the t-butyl cation, generated from t-butyl and aluminium halides, is virtually complete in a millisecond at about room temperature.[1] The rate of hydride abstraction by more stable carbonium ions, such as the triphenylmethyl cation, is sometimes measurable by conventional means. For a number of such reactions in which the reactant cation is generated in a pre-equilibrium from the corresponding alcohol, the reaction rate is given by the expression, $v = k$ [R^+] [Donor], for the hydride donors formate ion,[6,7] xanthene[8] and i-propyl alcohol.[9] (In strongly acidic media, allowance must be made for partial conversion of basic donor molecules to their conjugate acids, since protonation destroys their donor properties.) The corresponding deuteride transfer reactions are 1·8 to 4·9 times slower, confirming that cleavage of bonds to hydrogen is involved in the rate-limiting step.[6,7,9]

Hydride transfer to carbonium ions is reversible. Where equilibrium is established, the relative stabilities of the reactant and product cations largely determine whether reaction is observable. Hydride-transfer equilibria can be used to provide quantitative information on the relative stabilities of carbonium ions.[10] Most reactions are intelligible in terms of formation of a cation of

[1] Bartlett, Condon and Schneider, 1944.

[2] Meerwein, Hederich et al., 1960.

[3] See for example, H. J. Dauben, Gadecki et al., 1957; H. J. Dauben and Bertelli, 1961a,b; Harmon, Cummings et al., 1962a,b; ter Borg, van Helden and Bickel, 1962; Wilt and Piszkiewicz, 1963.

[4] Otvos, Stevenson et al., 1951; Stevenson, Wagner et al., 1952; Hofmann and Schriesheim, 1962a,b.

[5] See for example, Pines and Arrigo, 1958; Malchick and Hannan, 1959; Serres and Fields, 1963; R. M. Roberts, Baylis and Fonken, 1963; R. M. Roberts, Khalaf and Greene, 1964.

[6] Stewart, 1957.

[7] Grinter and Mason, 1964b.

[8] Deno, Saines and Spangler, 1962.

[9] Bartlett and McCollum, 1956.

[10] Conrow, 1961.

similar or greater stability than the reactant ion (whether equilibrium is established or not).

In comparing rates of hydride transfer, other factors are also important. Thus log k for hydride transfer from xanthene to various triarylmethyl cations is a linear function of Δ pK_{R+}, effectively the negative logarithm of the equilibrium constant for the reaction:

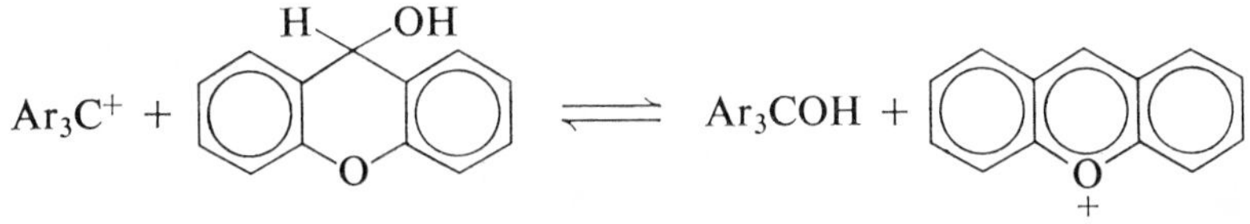

However, points for hydride abstraction by diarylmethyl cations, while still linear in Δ pK_{R+}, correspond to much faster rates.[1] The additional factor may well be steric in origin.[2] The relationship between rates of hydride transfer and K_{R+} in other hydride transfer reactions[3] can be used to estimate K_{R+} values from rate measurements.

[1] Deno, Saines and Spangler, 1962.

[2] Deno, Saines and Spangler, 1962; Bartlett and McCollum, 1956; see also Huntsman and Eggers, 1964.

[3] Grinter and Mason, 1964b; H. J. Dauben and McDonough, 1962.

7 | BRIDGED CARBONIUM IONS

7.1 Terminology

During the past quarter of a century a considerable body of evidence has accumulated which seems to require the postulation of bonding in certain carbonium ions which differs from that given in textbooks of organic chemistry published before 1939. The term "non-classical" ion has been applied to carbonium ions in which these novel bonding principles are thought to apply. Typical "non-classical" structures are **7.1** and **7.2**, where the dotted lines represent the unorthodox bonds.

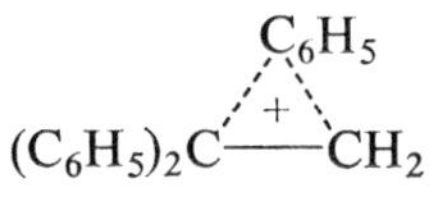

$$(C_6H_5)_2C \overset{\overset{\displaystyle C_6H_5}{\diagup \; + \; \diagdown}}{---} CH_2$$

(7.1) 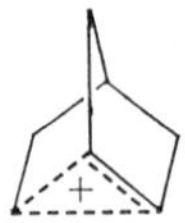   (7.2)

The essential feature of such formulae is the presence of "bridges" creating unusually disposed rings (as a rule three-membered, cf. the cyclopropenyl cation) and, for this reason, such ions are more descriptively designated as "bridged carbonium ions". We shall adopt this term, in preference to an alternative π-complex representation,[1] in the following discussion of the structures.

The use of the term "non-classical", while adequate for some purposes, has in the past tended to obstruct the proper definition of the underlying concepts. All descriptions of chemical bonding in terms of quantum mechanics are

[1] Dewar and Marchand, 1965.

"non-classical" according to the usage of that term by physicists. "Non-classical" carbonium ions can only be defined by referring to certain types of quantum-mechanical phenomena as "classical". Different workers have tended to draw the dividing line between "classical" and "non-classical" phenomena slightly differently, and the discussion of the scientific facts involved has to a large extent been overshadowed by semantic arguments. It will be evident to anyone who studies the literature of the subject in the period 1960–5 that the names "classical" and "non-classical" carbonium ions have consequently acquired emotive associations which scientific terms ought not to possess. This has led us to avoid their use and to adopt more descriptive definitions.

Of course, since all non-classical ideas—if not disproved—acquire in due course, merely through the effluxion of time, the status of classical theories, the term "non-classical" carbonium ion is bound before long to lose any claim to being a sensible description of bridged ions. We expect that other phenomena, yet to be discovered, will in turn merit that transitory epithet.

Bridging can be present in other stable or unstable organic cations that do not qualify to be called carbonium ions, e.g. **7.3** and **7.4**. Bridged *carbonium* ions is the term reserved for systems in which the bridging group is a hydrogen

$$
\begin{array}{c}
\overset{+}{NH_2} \\
\diagup \quad \diagdown \\
CH_2 \quad CH_2 \\
| \qquad | \\
CH_2 \!-\! CH_2
\end{array}
\qquad\qquad
\begin{array}{c}
Br \\
\diagup \;\overset{+}{}\; \diagdown \\
R_2C \!-\!\!-\! CR_2
\end{array}
$$

$$\textbf{(7.3)} \qquad\qquad\qquad\qquad \textbf{(7.4)}$$

atom or a hydrocarbon residue (with, perhaps, substituent groups replacing one or more of the hydrogen atoms in that residue).

For the purpose of organizing this discussion, we distinguish two types of bridged carbonium ion, those which contain a sufficient number of electrons to allow a bridged representation of the ion with normal single bonds linking all the members of the three-membered ring to be drawn, and those which are electron-deficient so that the three-membered ring must be represented either with partial bonds or as a resonance hybrid involving "no-bond" structures.[1] The first group generally embraces ions in which the bridging group contains suitably located π-electrons which can be utilized for the ring-bonding. The structure **7.1** is an example of this class, for it can be represented by the canonical structures **7.5–7.7**, or more conveniently **7.8**, in each of which a conventionally written cyclopropane ring is present. As in all chemical formulae it is, *in addition*, possible to write no-bond structures, such as **7.9** and **7.10**, and these may possibly contribute to the stability of the ring system. Ions with bridging phenyl groups have, following Cram, become known as "phenonium ions". The representation **7.8** is clearly quite analogous to the

[1] Cf. H. C. Brown, Morgan and Chloupek, 1965; W. Hückel, 1965.

formulae of the cations **7.11** and **7.12**. To that extent there is nothing
unusual (or "non-classical") about these bridged formulae. A somewhat
different problem is raised by the question of whether the pentadienyl cationic
system can in this arrangement interact with the cyclopropyl ring.

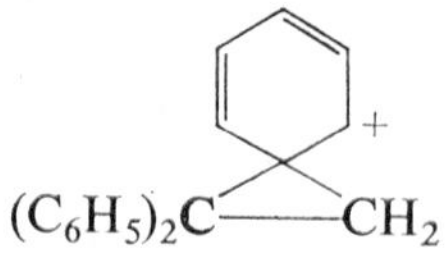

$(C_6H_5)_2C$————CH_2

(7.5)

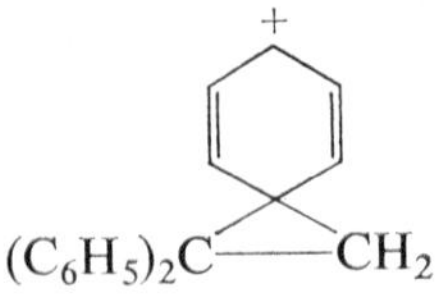

$(C_6H_5)_2C$————CH_2

(7.6)

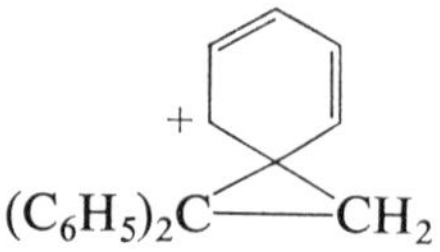

$(C_6H_5)_2C$————CH_2

(7.7)

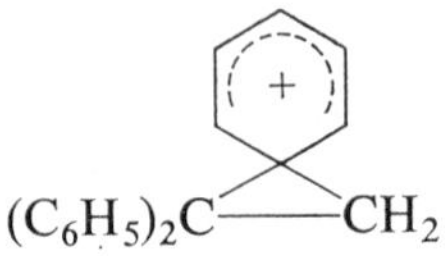

$(C_6H_5)_2C$————CH_2

(7.8)

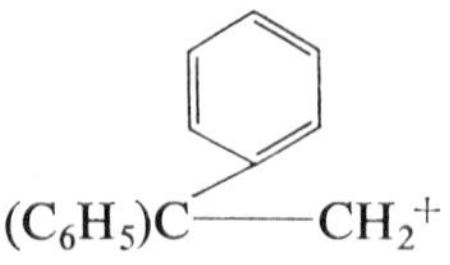

$(C_6H_5)C$————$CH_2{}^+$

(7.9)

$(C_6H_5)_2\overset{+}{C}$————CH_2

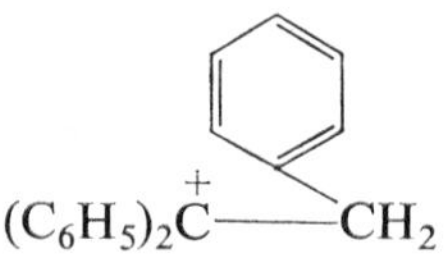

(7.10)

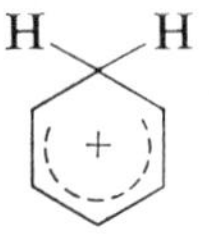

(7.11)

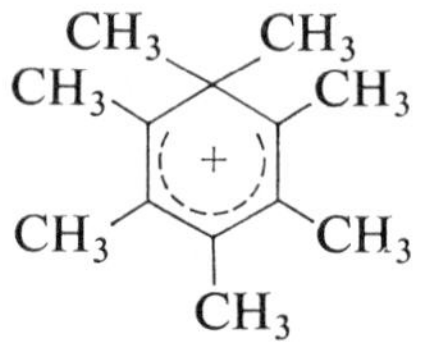

(7.12)

The structure **7.13** represents another member of this group, and is thought
to contribute to the stability of carbonium ions formed from homoallylic
systems, e.g. **7.14**.

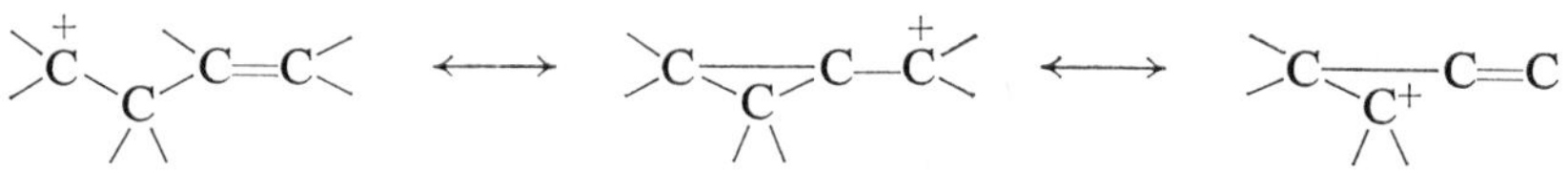

(7.13)

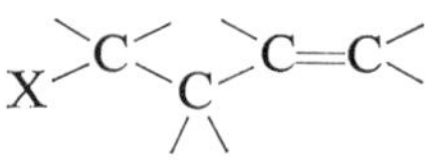

(7.14)

Formula **7.2** typifies an electron-deficient bridged carbonium ion. It has been suggested that the stability of such bicycloheptyl cations is in part due to resonance between structures **7.15** and **7.16**, i.e. the presence of bridging

(7.15)   (7.16)

across two partial sites of the cationic charge. In **7.2** the three-membered ring is indicated by partial bonds; **7.15** and **7.16** are resonating no-bond structures. None of these formulae contains a full cyclopropane ring, because the system does not possess sufficient electrons for the required number of two-electron bonds.

These representations are somewhat strange if we adopt the rules of bonding derived from electrically neutral carbon compounds. No-bond formulae, such as **7.15** and **7.16** imply in fact carbon–carbon hyperconjugation (by analogy with the electron release from carbon–hydrogen bonds by delocalization of σ-bond electrons). Relative to carbon–hydrogen hyperconjugation, this phenomenon is usually regarded as unimportant for neutral molecules but it appears not to be so for carbonium ions. Here again, the analogy between carbonium ions and boron hydrides may be pertinent, for the electron deficiency in each appears to cause unconventional types of bonding.

Whilst the foregoing paragraphs explain our definitions, we should make clear that the precise role and reality of the ions thus formulated is still, to varying degrees, under discussion (see Sections 7.3–7.6).

7.2 History

7.2.1 NEIGHBOURING-GROUP PARTICIPATION

The concept and study of bridged carbonium ions are part of the wider subject of neighbouring-group participation.[1] They developed to a large extent out of studies of bridging by neighbouring groups possessing lone pair electrons, chiefly in nucleophilic aliphatic displacements. A brief consideration of the more general topic may therefore be helpful.

We represent the course of such a reaction in Figure 7.1. The neighbouring group AB has a lone pair of electrons on the atom or group B, situated on the carbon atom β to the displaced group X. Such a β-situation is not essential, however; bridged ions having a three-, five-, or six-membered ring are particularly readily formed. In the slow step of the reaction, the leaving group X is

[1] See for example, Capon, 1964.

displaced by the lone-pair electrons on B to give the bridged ion **7.17** with Walden inversion at the α-carbon atom. (It is sometimes convenient to refer to this as AB–*n* participation, where *n* is the size of the ring formed in the bridging process.) The ion **7.17** may be stable and isolable as a salt, e.g. when AB is NH_2. It may, however, undergo further reaction with a (hydroxylic) slovent (SOH) either with retention of the bridged structure **(7.18)** or, more usually, with cleavage of the ring to give unrearranged **(7.19)** and rearranged

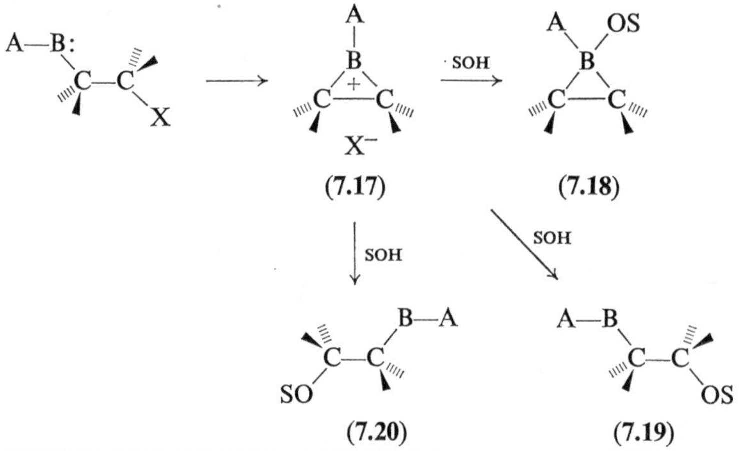

FIG. 7.1. Participation in solvolysis by a neighbouring group having a non-bonded electron pair.

(7.20) products. Because, for steric reasons, SOH attacks **7.17** from the direction opposite to the bridge, the configuration at both α- and β-carbon atoms is retained in **7.19**, while in the rearranged product an inverted configuration is found. In the absence of bridging, the unrearranged product of simple S_N1 solvolysis would be formed with inversion or complete loss of configuration at C_α. This difference thus provides a stereochemical criterion of the occurrence of bridging. Since neighbouring-group participation occurs in competition with simple substitution, the formation of bridged intermediates must be characterized by rates of solvolysis which are larger than anticipated. This phenomenon, which presupposes the ability to predict rates of solvolysis in the absence of bridging, is termed "anchimeric acceleration"[1] and provides a second important criterion of bridged-ion formation. The following examples illustrate typical procedures.

Neighbouring acetoxyl. cis-2-Acetoxycyclohexyl toluene-*p*-sulphonate **(7.21)** undergoes acetolysis $4 \cdot 5 \times 10^4$ times more slowly than cyclohexyl toluene-*p*-sulphonate and gives the *trans*-diacetate,[2] the low rate being due presumably

[1] Winstein, Lindegren *et al.*, 1953.
[2] Winstein, Grunwald *et al.*, 1948.

to electron withdrawal by the acetoxyl group. *trans*-2-Acetoxycyclohexyl toluene-*p*-sulphonate (**7.22**) is solvolysed at about one-third of the rate of the unsubstituted compound and again the product is the *trans*-diacetate, provided that potassium acetate is present. The 670-fold rate difference between the two stereoisomers is attributed to the ability of the *trans*-compound to adopt a conformation with the substituents axial, thus satisfying the stereo-electronic requirements for bridge-formation (**7.23**). This also accounts nicely for the

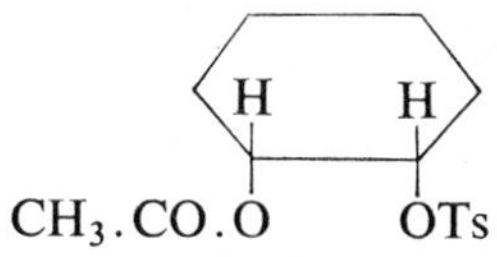

(7.21)

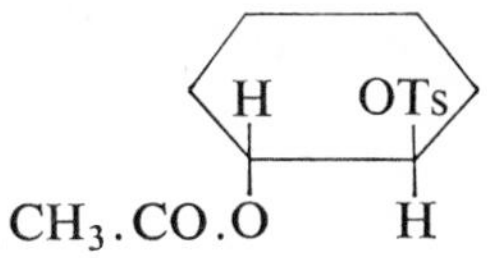

(7.22)

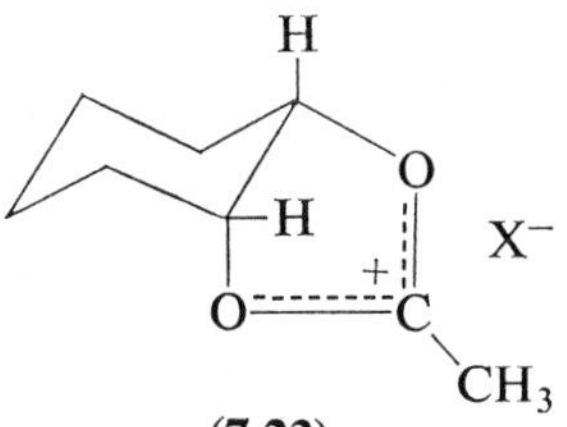

(7.23)

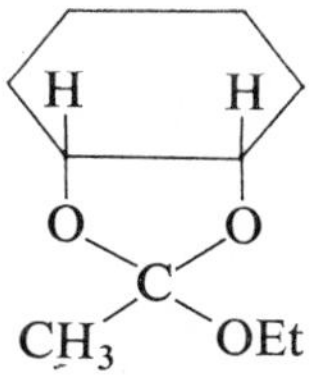

(7.24)

retention of configuration in the product from **7.22** and for the observation that acetolysis of optically active **7.22** gives racemic diacetate.[1] In ethanol **7.22** yields the orthoacetate **7.24**, and final confirmation of the intermediacy of **7.23** has been provided by its isolation $(X = BF_4)$.[2]

Neighbouring bromine. An early suggestion that bridging by neighbouring bromine was possible came in explanation of the exclusive *trans* polar addition of bromine to olefins.[3] Formation of the intermediate ion **7.4** was proposed, the bromine bridge preventing the rotation about the carbon–carbon bond possible in an unbridged ion and directing subsequent attack by bromide ion to the side remote from the bridge. Similar bridging by bromine explains the stereochemical course of the reaction of the stereoisomeric bromohydrins **7.25** and **7.26** with hydrogen bromide.[4] Thus, reaction of *threo*- and *erythro*-isomers gave the corresponding dibromides with retention of configuration but loss of optical activity. Formation of unbridged ions would have been expected to cause interconversion of *threo*- and *erythro*-configurations by rotation about the central carbon–carbon bond.

[1] Winstein, Hess and Buckles, 1942.
[2] Anderson, Friedrich and Winstein, 1963.
[3] I. Roberts and Kimball, 1937.
[4] Winstein and Lucas, 1939.

There is kinetic evidence for bridging by bromine in, for example, the solvolyses of **7.27** and **7.28**. For **7.27** the rate of acetolysis was compared with that of the *cis*-isomer, adjusted to take account of differing dipole-dipole

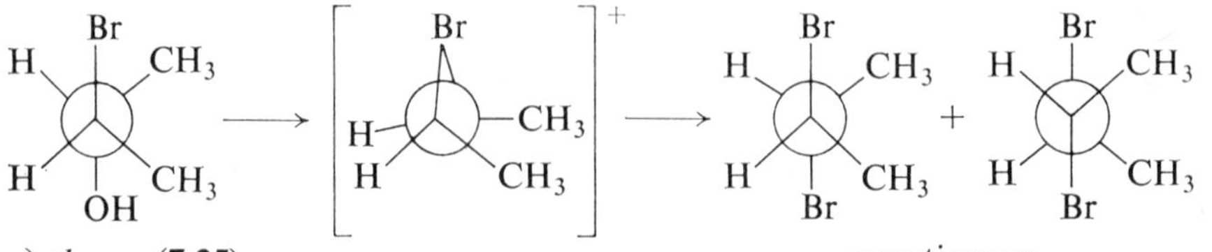

(−)-*threo*- (**7.25**)   enantiomers

                                                                        (±)-*threo*

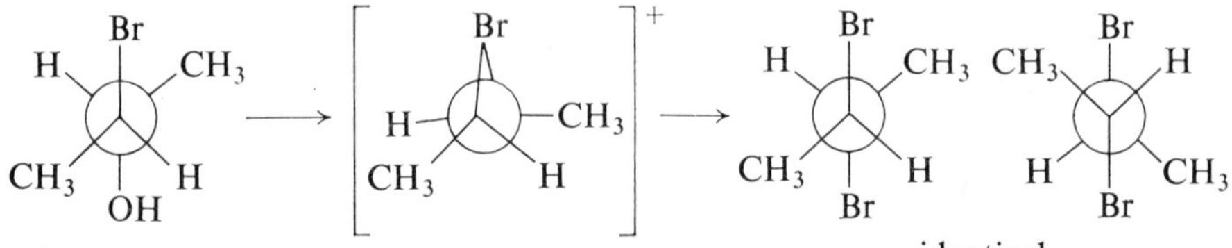

(+)-*erythro*- (**7.26**)   identical

                                                                        meso

interactions in the two compounds.[1] A 46-fold rate enhancement was established for **7.28** over the predicted rate of loss of chlorine (in the absence of bridging) according to the Taft-Ingold equation [Equation (4.26)].[2] In contrast the rate of ethanolysis of the tertiary C—Br bond in $C_6H_5 . CHBr . CH_2Br$, when compared with that for $C_6H_5 . CHBr . CH_3$ can be accounted for without

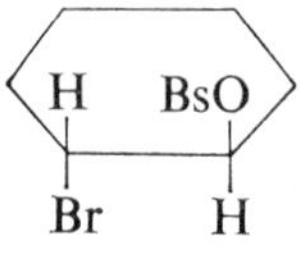

(**7.27**) 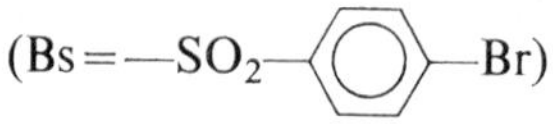 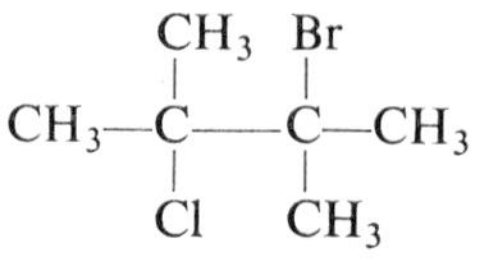   (**7.28**)

$(Bs = —SO_2—\langle\bigcirc\rangle—Br)$

postulating anchimeric acceleration,[3] presumably because heterolysis occurs so readily that the assistance of the neighbouring bromine makes a negligible contribution. The effect of the neighbouring group may be formalized by the

[1] Winstein, Grunwald and Ingraham, 1948.
[2] Streitwieser, 1956a.
[3] Winstein and Grunwald, 1946.

definition of a so-called "driving force due to participation" (L, expressed in kcal mole^{-1}) using the expression:

$$L = RT \ln (k_\Delta/k_c)$$

where k_Δ is the rate constant of the anchimerically assisted solvolysis and k_c that estimated for solvolysis if bridging were unimportant.[1] For neighbouring bromine in the solvolysis of α- and β-methyl substituted ethyl derivatives it is found that

$$L = L_0 - 2 \cdot 27 N_\alpha + 1 \cdot 79 N_\beta$$

L_0 being a constant and N the appropriate number of methyl groups, suggesting that α-methyl groups stabilize the open carbonium ion while β-methyl groups promote bridging.[2]

7.2.2 BRIDGED CARBONIUM IONS

It soon became evident that the phenomena which had led to the idea of participation in ionization by neighbouring groups with lone-pair electrons, e.g., solvolysis with retention of configuration and unusually rapid rates of ionization, could also be found in carbon skeletons not containing donor atoms. The idea of bridging by saturated hydrocarbon radicals and hydrogen, sometimes termed "synartesis",[3] and by carbon–carbon π-bond electrons grew out of this and the epithet "non-classical" was coined[4] to describe the intermediate carbonium ions.

The earliest suggestion had come from Nevell, de Salas, and Wilson[5] who, in studying the Wagner-Meerwein rearrangement of camphene hydrochloride (**7.29**) to isobornyl chloride (**7.30**; X=Cl, Y=H), pointed out that none of the more stable *endo*-chloride, bornyl chloride (**7.30**; X=H, Y=Cl), was formed. Intermediate formation of a rearranged, open carbonium ion might have been expected to yield a mixture of the two stereoisomers. A mesomeric

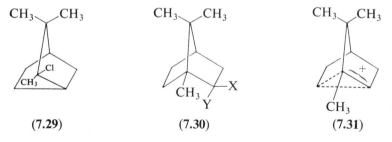

(**7.29**)   (**7.30**)   (**7.31**)

[1] Winstein and Grunwald, 1948; Winstein, Grunwald and Ingraham, 1948.
[2] Winstein and Grunwald, 1948.
[3] F. Brown, Hughes *et al.*, 1951; Ingold, 1953, p. 521.
[4] J. D. Roberts and Lee, 1951.
[5] Nevell, de Salas and Wilson, 1939.

9

intermediate ion (**7.31**) was therefore suggested to account for the observed stereospecificity.

Some seven years later it was reported that acetolysis of cholesteryl chloride (**7.32**) occurred with complete retention of configuration at C(3).[1] Assuming a unimolecular mechanism, it was suggested that the intermediate had structure **7.33**. Kinetic evidence indicating anchimeric acceleration was reported soon afterwards, and an i-cholesteryl derivative, in which the bridged structure was retained, was isolated.[2]

(7.32)   +   (7.33)

Cram's elegant investigation[3] of the acetolysis of *erythro*- and *threo*-3-phenyl-2-butyl toluene-*p*-sulphonates (see p. 240), in which, in a system of similar stereochemistry to the bromohydrins of Winstein and Lucas (see pp. 227-8), substitution products of retained configuration were obtained, completed the analogy with bridging by neighbouring lone-pair electrons. Reports of bridged carbonium ions proliferated in the chemical literature during the following years, sometimes on the flimsiest of evidence. More recently the whole concept of bridging by hydrocarbon groups has been subjected to severe criticism.[4]

Quantum-mechanical calculations were later carried out and are held to support the view that some carbonium ions may be significantly stabilized by bridging.[5] The most direct available evidence for the reality of certain (electron-sufficient) bridged ions has come from the observation of their proton magnetic resonance spectra.

The study of chemical reactions in which carbonium ions are formed as

[1] Shoppee, 1946.

[2] Winstein and Adams, 1948.

[3] Cram, 1949.

[4] E.g. H. C. Brown, 1962; W. Hückel, 1965.

[5] Theoretical considerations of the stability of bridged carbonium ions have played no decisive part in the debate concerning the reality of these structures. Calculations, usually for homoallylic systems, have been cited in favour of the idea that bridging can increase stability though the additional resonance stabilization is offset to some extent by the strain energy involved in distorting the nuclear arrangement to make such resonance possible. (See Section 5.2; Walsh, 1947; J. D. Roberts and Regan, 1953; Simonetta and Winstein, 1954; Woods, Carboni and Roberts, 1956; Howden and Roberts, 1963; Piccolini and Winstein, 1963; Hoffmann, 1964a,b; Trahanovsky, 1965; see, however, Dewar and Marchand, 1965.)

transient intermediates affords evidence of much less direct *structural* significance. Because the evidence is open to conflicting interpretations, the extent to which bridged carbonium ions are involved in such reactions requires detailed evaluation of individual cases rather than generalizations. This is the aim of the remainder of this Chapter. Sections 7.4 and 7.5 contain a survey of the main systems investigated.

7.3 Experimental Criteria of Bridged-ion Formation

The evidence upon which carbonium ion *intermediates* have been assigned bridged structures comes from four main lines of investigation:

(i) Application of physical methods.
(ii) Kinetic experiments.
(iii) Examination of the nature and proportions of reaction products.
(iv) Stereochemical observations.

7.3.1 PHYSICAL METHODS

The bridged structure assigned to certain carbonium ions requires that atomic nuclei in the ion have unusual relative dispositions. While direct observation of bond lengths and angles is possible in principle, the practical problems necessitate more subtle procedures to be used at present. Nuclear magnetic resonance spectroscopy has proved to be a most powerful tool (see Paragraph 2.3.1) and has provided firm evidence for the formation of stable bridged carbonium ions, albeit under conditions—e.g. mixtures of sulphur dioxide, antimony pentafluoride and fluorosulphuric acid at $-55°$—far removed from those in which such species have most often been postulated.[1] While such evidence answers the question of whether bridging is possible at all, nuclear magnetic resonance spectroscopy does not indicate to what extent bridging is involved in transient carbonium-ion intermediates formed during common organic reactions. Other approaches are necessary to deal with this aspect and, as we shall see, these do not provide such clear-cut evidence.

7.3.2 KINETIC DATA

Rates of reactions in which the formation of a carbonium ion is the rate-limiting step are evidence concerning the structure of the carbonium ion only if it is assumed that there is a close structural similarity between the carbonium ion and the transition complex leading to it. This is likely since, in most cases, carbonium-ion formation is an endothermic process (Hammond's postulate; see Paragraph 4.2.1).

For the formation of a bridged ion to compete successfully with formation of the corresponding open ion, the transition state leading to the bridged ion

[1] Eberson and Winstein, 1965; Olah, Namanworth *et al.*, 1967.

must have the lower energy. This is virtually equivalent to saying that bridging must be important in the transition state of the reaction (see, however, p. 235). Other things being equal, the bridged ion should therefore be formed more rapidly than anticipated for its unbridged counterpart. The relationship between the reactants, rearranged and unrearranged products and the two types of carbonium ion is shown in the form of energy profiles in Figure 7.2.

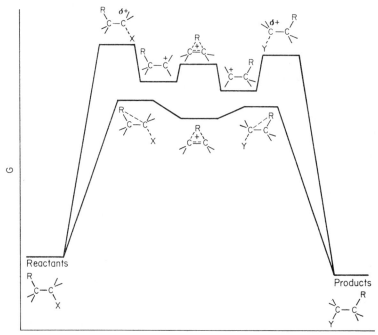

Reaction co-ordinate

FIG. 7.2. Schematic free energy profiles for nucleophilic substitution with rearrangement via bridged and unbridged carbonium ion intermediates.

The interaction of the bridging group with the α-carbon atom has the effect of dispersing the positive charge. This will reduce the interaction of the carbonium ion with solvent molecules; indeed the bridging group will occupy some space which would have been available to solvent molecules in the case of open ions. This should be reflected in a less negative entropy of activation for formation of bridged cations than for unbridged ones.[1]

In practice, the difficulty in using the rate increase as a criterion of bridged carbonium-ion formation lies in predicting the reaction rate in the absence of assistance by the bridging group, since an unexpectedly high rate may reflect lowered stability of the reactant rather than increased stability of the transition state (see p. 93). A number of approaches have been tried:

[1] E.g. Cram and Singer, 1963.

(i) Determination of the rate of the same reaction, (e.g. solvolysis) for a stereoisomer of the compound in question but one in which the configuration of the β-carbon atom is such that bridging is impossible for stereochemical reasons [cf. *cis*- and *trans*-2-acetoxycyclohexyl toluene-*p*-sulphonates, (7.21) and (7.22)].

(ii) Comparison with the rate of reaction of the compound without the bridging substituent, a suitable correction being applied for the differing polar and steric effects in the two reactions.

(iii) Use of an appropriate linear free energy relationship [e.g. the Taft-Ingold equation; Chapter 4, Equation (4.26)].

Perhaps the most sophisticated and successful method, but which is applicable only to secondary systems, falls in category (iii) and makes use of the fact that the size of the C—C—C bond angle affects the carbonyl stretching frequency in C—CO—C and also the ease of ionization C—CHX—C $\rightarrow$ C—$\overset{+}{\text{CH}}$—C in opposite directions.[1] Thus the velocity constant, in the absence of neighbouring-group assistance, for a secondary alkyl toluene-*p*-sulphonate can be estimated from the carbonyl-stretching frequency in the infrared spectrum of the corresponding ketone.[2] A more elaborate version of the same approach, due to Schleyer,[3] corrects the predicted velocity constant for torsional strain around the reaction site, changes in non-bonded interactions on forming the transition state for ionization, and polar effects. The success[4] of this method may be judged from the results in Table 7.1a. Some typical rate constants calculated by this method for compounds thought to react by formation of bridged intermediates are given in Table 7.1b. The ratio of a calculated rate constant and the corresponding observed value is thought to express the anchimeric acceleration. In a small number of cases application of this method precicts rates of solvolysis much *higher* than are observed.[5] It has been suggested[5] that this discrepancy arises from the inadequacy of one of the assumptions in Schleyer's calculations, namely that non-bonded strain in the transition state is negligible relative to that in the reactants. Indeed, the difference between the observed and calculated rates is sometimes so large that it is thought that the non-bonded strain actually *increases* on forming the transition state i.e. that there is steric hindrance of ionization. If this suggestion is correct, then Schleyer's procedure may be expected generally to overestimate the effect of steric acceleration (and hence to underestimate anchimeric acceleration).

[1] Schleyer and Nicholas, 1961; for reservations about the validity of correlations of solvolysis rate constants and carbonyl stretching frequencies, see Davis, Grosse and Ohno, 1967.

[2] Foote, 1964.

[3] Schleyer, 1964a,b.

[4] For reservations, see H. C. Brown and Muzzio, 1966.

[5] H. C. Brown, Rothberg *et al.*, 1966.

Even when such effects of non-bonded strain are not important, Schleyer's method, cannot, in individual cases, be relied on to predict an unassisted solvolysis rate to better than ± 1 log unit, but there is a clear division between the two halves of Table 7.1. In general, then, the observation of a small (less than ten-fold) enhancement of the observed rate over the rate predicted by any of the methods outlined above should not *by itself* be taken as indicative of bridged-ion formation.

There are other possible causes for unusually high rates in certain structures, and care must be exercised in interpreting a rate enhancement, determined by comparison of the reaction rate with that of a related model compound, in terms of bridged ions. To be specific, one should be certain (a) that the reaction mechanism is the same for both compounds, (b) that the model compound does not react unusually slowly, perhaps because of steric effects, such as angle strain, and (c) that the unexpectedly rapid rate is not explicable in terms of steric acceleration. Schleyer and Foote's approach attempts to overcome the last two of these difficulties. An added complication arises in organic solvents where, owing to the strong inter-ionic interactions, the phenomena of ion-pairing and internal return occur (Paragraph 5.3.3). Observed, titrimetric velocity constants can then be composites of constants for ionization, dissociation and ionic recombination reactions. Since the degree to which this

Table 7.1. *Velocity constants* (25°) *for acetolysis of secondary alkyl toluene-p-sulphonates* (k_{rel})[a] *calculated by Schleyer's method*[b]

Compound	$\nu_{C=O}$ (cm^{-1})	log k_{rel} Calc.	log k_{rel} Obs.	$\log(k_{rel}^{obs}/k_{rel}^{calc})$[c]
a. Unassisted acetolysis				
Cyclohexyl	1716	−0·1	(0·00)	0·1
7-Norbornyl	1773	−7·0	−7·00	0·0
endo-2-Norbornyl	1751	−0·2	+0·18	0·4
endo-2-Norbornenyl	1745	−1·0	−1·48	−0·5
2-Butyl	1721	−0·3	+0·53	0·8
3-Methyl-2-butyl	1718	+0·6	+0·93	0·3
3,3-Dimethyl-2-butyl	1710	+1·5	+0·62	−0·9
b. Anchimerically assisted solvolysis				
anti-7-Norbornenyl	1780	−8·8	4·11	12·9
syn-7-Norbornenyl	1780	−8·9	−3·28	5·6
Cyclobutyl	1791	−4·2	0·99	5·2
exo-2-Norbornenyl	1745	−1·4	2·42	3·8
exo-2-Norbornyl	1751	−0·6	2·71	3·3

[a] Relative to cyclohexyl toluene-*p*-sulphonate.
[b] Schleyer, 1964a,b.
[c] $\log(k_{rel}^{obs}/k_{rel}^{calc}) \equiv$ log (anchimeric acceleration).

complication occurs varies from one structure to another, simple comparison of titrimetric velocity constants could lead to erroneous conclusions. Finally, rate enhancement could be explained without invoking the formation of bridged *intermediates* if the first carbonium ion formed had a rearranged (but open) structure of greater stability than that of the open carbonium ion which would have been formed by simple ionization. On this basis the reaction involves a bridged transition state which leads to a rearranged (open) ion. Such an explanation is not possible for structures which show rate enhancement but for which rearranged and unrearranged ions are identical and therefore necessarily of equal stability (e.g. 3-phenyl-2-butyl and norbornyl systems).

Conversely, two sets of circumstances can be envisaged in which bridged ions are formed at rates no different from those predicted for unassisted reactions: (a) bridging is unimportant in the transition state though it is a stabilizing influence on the intermediate formed from it; (b) ionization leads to an unbridged ion which is subsequently transformed, in an activated process, to the bridged intermediate.

7.3.3 THE REACTION PRODUCTS

For the structure of certain products to be relevant to the question of the structure of the intermediate, the formation of the reaction products must be kinetically controlled. The strongest evidence of this kind in favour of bridged ions is the detection of products in which the bridge ring (usually three-membered) is retained, e.g. the formation of an i-cholesteryl derivative from **7.32** or of **7.35** from **7.34**[1] (cf. the formation of the orthoester **7.24** from

(7.34)　　　　　　　(7.35)

trans-2-acetoxycyclohexyl toluene-*p*-sulphonate). In most cases, however, the bridged structure does not persist in the product which is instead a mixture of unrearranged and rearranged compounds. This product composition in itself is not evidence of a bridged *intermediate*, since interconversion of open carbonium ions would bring about the same result. It can be seen from Figure 7.2 that the transition state for such interconversion of the open ions has a bridged arrangement of nuclei. The indications are that the relative proportions of rearranged and unrearranged (i.e. like the reactant in Figure 7.2) products formed by reaction of a nucleophile with a bridged intermediate are similar to those expected for rapidly interconverting unbridged ions,[2] the

[1] J. D. Roberts, Lee and Saunders, 1955.
[2] Berson, 1960.

determining factor being the relative heights of the energy barriers separating
the bridged ion from the products. (See also the footnote on p. 211.)

7.3.4 STEREOCHEMISTRY

The observation of nucleophilic substitution at a saturated carbon atom
with retention of configuration has been taken as strong evidence in support
of bridged carbonium-ion formation. It might, however, be the result not of
bridging, but of steric (including conformational) factors affecting the product-
determining step.

In some cases the alternative interpretation can clearly be shown to be
correct. This may be illustrated by reference to reactions of the 1,2,2-triphenyl-
ethyl system. Phenonium-ion formation, though conceivable in such compounds, does not occur, presumably because of the stability of simple benzylic

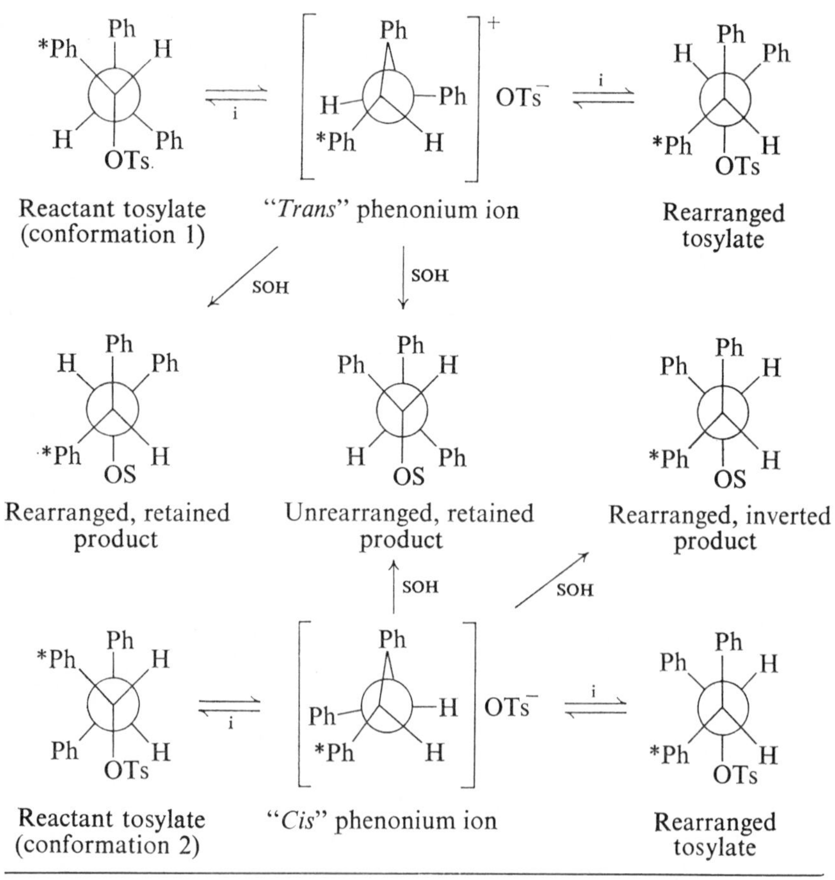

Reactant tosylate   "*Trans*" phenonium ion   Rearranged
(conformation 1)   tosylate

Rearranged, retained   Unrearranged, retained   Rearranged, inverted
product   product   product

Reactant tosylate   "*Cis*" phenonium ion   Rearranged
(conformation 2)   tosylate

FIG. 7.3. Solvolysis of 1,2,2-triphenylethyl derivatives by way of bridged carbonium ions.
(i = internal return)

cations (see Section 4.3), yet substitution takes place predominantly with retention of configuration. The evidence, in outline, is as follows:

Solvolysis of 1,2,2-triphenylethyl toluene-p-sulphonate gives the corresponding substitution and elimination products and, by using isotopically labelled starting material, it can be shown that a part of the product results from phenyl migration. In formolysis, the mole fraction (x) of rearranged product from C(1)-labelled toluene-p-sulphonate is $1/2$, and that (y) from starting material labelled in the 1-phenyl group is $2/3$, i.e. complete scrambling. In acetolysis, statistical redistribution is approached but incomplete.[1] Now, if solvolysis takes place entirely through bridged ions (Figure 7.3), the *trans*-phenonium ion should be preferentially formed because of its reduced eclipsing strain compared with the *cis*-ion. Internal return would produce rearranged and unrearranged toluene-p-sulphonates which, on subsequent re-ionization, would form phenonium ions in which the same phenyl group forms the bridge. Since there is no migration of the original 1-phenyl group, the situation for 1-labelled and 1-phenyl-labelled esters is identical and x should equal y. The observed redistribution, with $y > x$, could be explained in terms of bridged ions only if *cis*- and *trans*-phenonium ions were formed with equal frequency *and* if internal return were much more rapid than reaction of the bridged ions with the solvent. Both of these conditions are unlikely, particularly the latter in formic acid, and consequently the only alternative is that solvolysis takes place by formation of an unbridged ion which undergoes rearrangement and reaction with solvent at comparable rates.[2] Results from deamination of 1,2,2-triphenyl-ethylamine[3] and radiochemical isomerization of the acetate, labelled in the 1-phenyl and acetate groups and at C(1)[4] confirm this. However, the situation appears to be quite different in SbF_5-FSO_3H at $-60°$. For solutions of 1,2,2-triphenylethanol, the NMR spectra indicate that hydride shift (to form the stable tertiary ion $PhCH_2.CPh_2^+$) is more rapid than phenyl migration.[5]

Now, by use of optically active 1,2,2-triphenylethyl derivatives, it can be shown that the substitution products are of predominantly retained configuration, 8% *net* retention in acetolysis, 28% in hydrolysis, and as high as 50% in deamination.[6] The degree of retention is still, however, much below that observed in certain reactions, in which bridging is thought to be important, e.g. $> 90\%$ in acetolysis of 3-phenyl-2-butyl toluene-p-sulphonate (see p. 240). Figure 7.3 shows that, if bridged ions are the only intermediates involved in the reaction of 1,2,2-triphenylethyl derivatives, the inverted product should be

---

[1] Bonner and Collins, 1953; Collins and Bonner, 1955.

[2] Collins and Bonner, 1955.

[3] Bonner and Collins, 1956; see also Collins, Christie and Raaen, 1961; Collins and Benjamin, 1963.

[4] Bonner and Collins, 1955.

[5] Olah, Pittman *et al.*, 1966b.

[6] Collins, Bonner and Lester, 1959.

9*

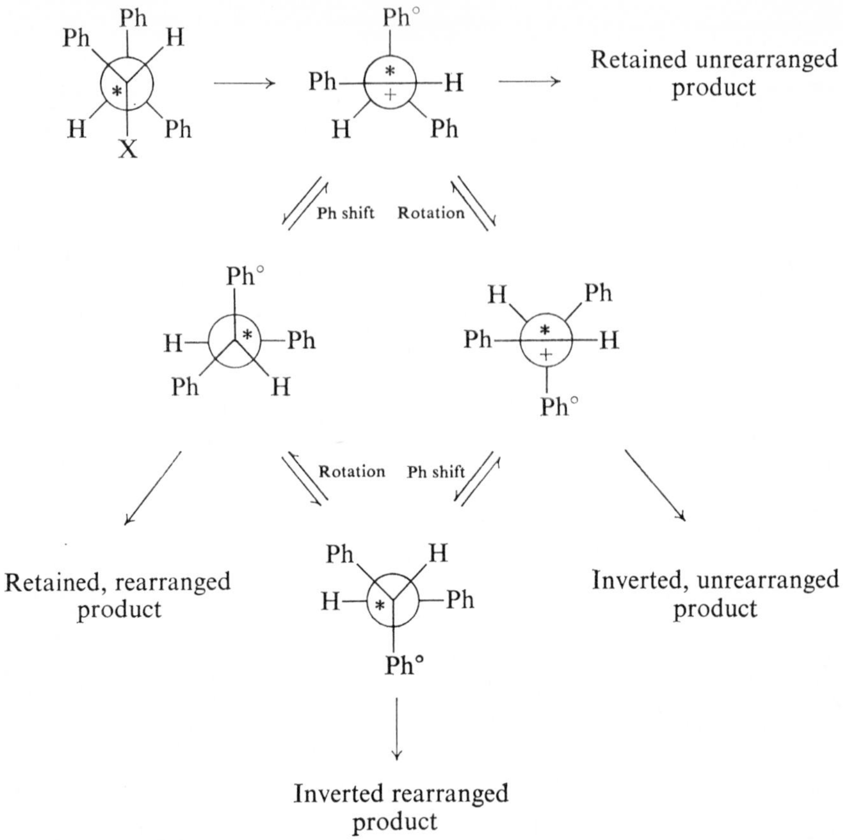

Fig. 7.4. Solvolysis of 1,2,2-triphenylethyl derivatives by way of unbridged carbonium ions.

totally rearranged. While, in deamination at least, more rearrangement is found in inverted than in retained product, this is far from complete ($\sim 30\%$). Thus bridged ions cannot be the sole intermediates, nor can the results be explained in terms of partial reaction through bridged and unbridged intermediates. The best explanation is shown in Figure 7.4. Models indicate that nucleophilic attack on the open ions is for steric reasons restricted to the direction opposite to the phenyl groups marked Ph°. The predominant retention can then be accounted for if phenyl migration or reaction of the ion with solvent is more rapid than rotation about the central carbon–carbon bond in the ion.

Similar studies rule out bridging as an important factor in other systems. Thus in the semipinacolic deamination of optically active 1,1-diphenyl-1-hydroxy-2-propylamine, stereospecifically labelled in one of the phenyl groups, some 12% phenyl migration takes place with retention of configuration at the

Table 7.2. *Steric course of deamination of* 1-amino-1-phenyl-2-arylpropan-2-ols *in 25% aqueous acetic acid* (v/v) *at room temperature*

2-Aryl	% Inversion at migration terminus		Ref.
	erythro[a]	threo[b]	
Phenyl	73	—	c
p-Tolyl	74	43	d
p-Anisyl	77	41	e
o-Anisyl	96	55	e

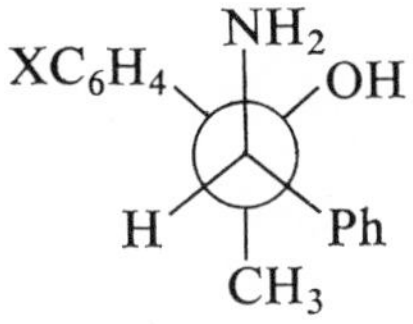

[c] Benjamin, Wilder and Collins, 1961.
[d] Benjamin and Collins, 1961.
[e] Collins, Staum and Benjamin, 1962.

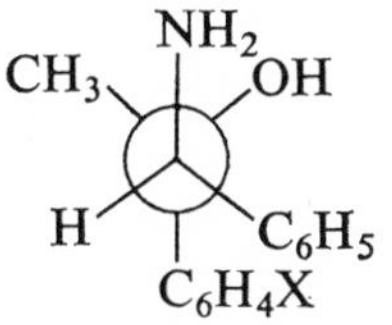

migration terminus.[1] This result implies approach of the migrating group from the direction from which the amino group was lost. Since front-side displacement is unlikely, the retained product must be formed from unbridged carbonium ion precursors. Phenonium-ion formation could explain the predominant inversion, although it might have been expected to lead to an even higher proportion of inverted product. Moreover, in deamination of 1-amino-1-phenyl-2-aryl-propan-2-ols, the degree of inversion at the migration terminus is scarcely influenced by polar effects of substituents in the 2-aryl group (Table 7.2). Polar effects would be expected to have a marked influence on the ability of the aryl group to form a bridged ion. These results, including the greater degree of inversion in *erythro*- than *threo*-compounds, are explicable in terms of unbridged ions in which phenyl migration and collapse are more rapid than rotation about the central carbon–carbon bond.

7.4 Electron-sufficient Bridged Carbonium Ions

7.4.1 ARYL-BRIDGED IONS

The 3-phenyl-2-butyl system has been widely studied, both in solvolytic and related reactions and under conditions where carbonium ions are stable. We begin with it because a range of techniques has been applied in attempts to decide whether bridging is important, although no firm decision can yet be reached. 3-Phenyl-2-butyl derivatives possess two asymmetric carbon atoms: there are thus two sets of diastereoisomers, termed *erythro* and *threo*, each being an enantiomeric pair.

[1] Benjamin, Schaeffer and Collins, 1957.

Formolysis of optically active *threo*-3-phenyl-2-butyl toluene-*p*-sulphonate gives, in addition to olefinic products, racemic *threo*-formate, whereas *erythro*-starting material yields *erythro*-formate with complete retention of optical purity.[1] The formation of the substitution products without appreciable interconversion of *threo*- and *erythro*-isomers indicates that rotation about the bond between C(2) and C(3) in the intermediate carbonium ion (or ions) is much slower than the 1,2-shift of the phenyl group and the attack of the external nucleophile. Moreover, rearranged product must have been formed with inversion of configuration at both the asymmetric centres, the unrearranged product arising by substitution with retention. The course of the nucleophilic substitution can simply be rationalized by the scheme shown in Figure 7.5, in which the intermediate phenyl-bridged ions **7.36** and **7.37** are the precursors of both rearranged and unrearranged products. Because of its plane of symmetry **7.36**, formed from the *threo*-toluene-*p*-sulphonate, yields racemic substitution product, but the product from **7.37** retains its optical activity.

Acetolysis of the two toluene-*p*-sulphonates gives essentially similar results,[2] though detailed examination[1] shows that the stereospecificity of substitution is slightly lower (94–95% retention, 4–5% conversion to the other diastereoisomer). Resolution of the racemic *threo*-acetate produced from optically active 1-[14]C-*threo*-toluene-*p*-sulphonate confirms that the inverted product is completely rearranged by phenyl migration,[3] in contrast with results in the 1,2,2-triphenylethyl system (see Paragraph 7.3.3).

Interruption of the acetolysis of the *threo*-toluene-*p*-sulphonate after 70% reaction has been shown to give unchanged toluene-*p*-sulphonate ester which is 93% racemic, the recovered ester in the *erythro*-case being optically pure. The racemization prior to solvolysis is due to ion-pair return. This is shown by interrupting the acetolysis of 3-phenyl-2-butyl *p*-bromobenzenesulphonate, carried out in the presence of a ten-fold excess of lithium toluene-*p*-sulphonate, before completion. It is found that racemic *threo*-toluene-*p*-sulphonate is recovered from *threo* starting material, and optically pure *erythro*-toluene-*p*-sulphonate from *erythro* starting material, but together with about forty times as much of the corresponding *p*-bromobenzenesulphonate esters. Since recombination of free ions cannot account for the predominance of *p*-bromobenzenesulphonate, the intermediate carbonium ion must be present as part of an ion pair. Moreover the absence of a "special" salt effect of lithium perchlorate (Paragraph 5.3.3) indicates that recombination occurs from intimate ion pairs.[4]

The occurrence of racemization *during* the actual solvolysis has been demonstrated in the formolysis of *threo*-3-phenyl-2-butyl toluene-*p*-sulphonate

---

[1] Cram, 1952a.
[2] Cram, 1949.
[3] W. B. Smith and Showalter, 1965.
[4] Winstein, Clippinger *et al.*, 1954.

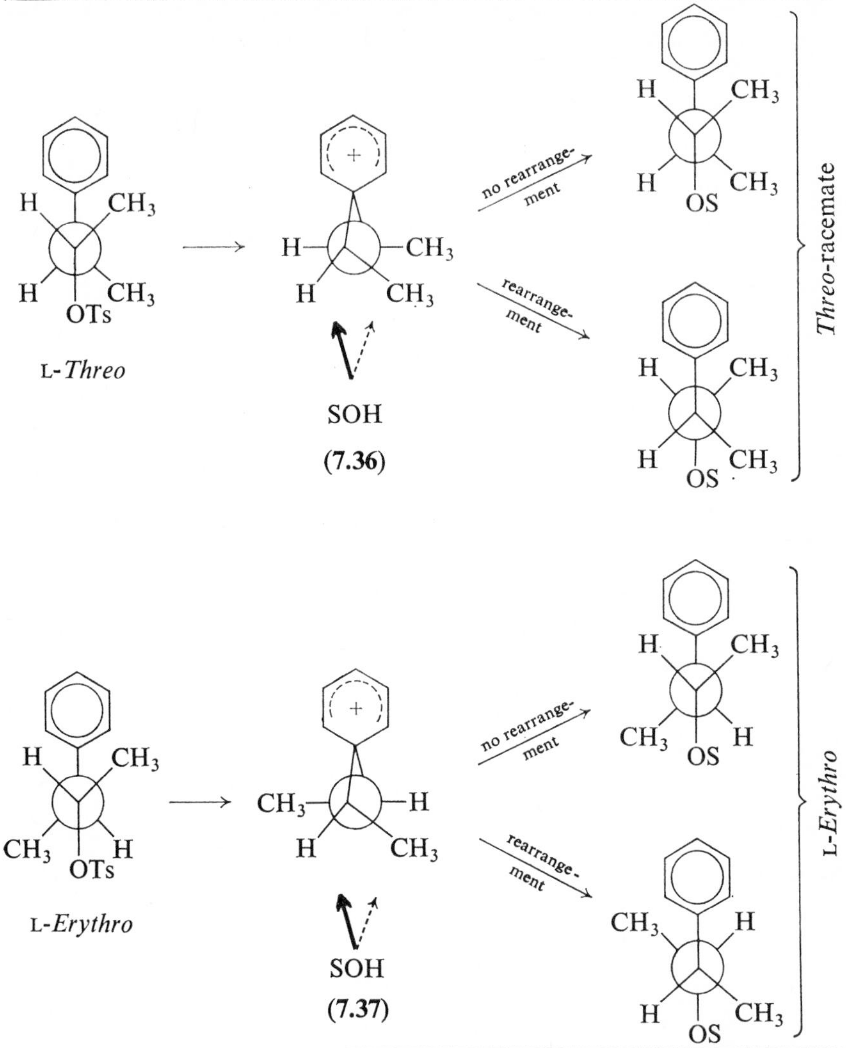

FIG. 7.5. The steric course of unimolecular solvolysis of the 3-phenyl-2-butyl toluene-*p*-sulphonates.

by the isolation of unchanged ester which is only 18% racemic after 60% reaction. The complete racemization of the *threo*-product must therefore largely arise during the solvolysis.

These stereochemical studies on solvolysis products thus provide strong evidence for some configuration-holding interaction between the 3-phenyl group and C(2) in this system. Reaction through the symmetrical bridged ion offers a simple explanation.

It has, however, been pointed out that equilibration of the rearranged and unrearranged open ions which is more rapid than rotation about the C(2)–C(3) bond could lead to the same result.[1] The required values for the ratio of velocity constant of phenyl migration to that for rotation about the central carbon–carbon bond are not impossibly large.[2] Again, it must be admitted that the stereochemical investigations discussed above lead to the conclusion that the structures of the olefins formed in the concurrent unimolecular elimination are best accounted for by mechanisms involving open carbonium ions.[3]

Accordingly, kinetic evidence could be decisive, especially since the 3-phenyl-2-butyl system is one in which rearranged and unrearranged open ions are identical (cf. p. 235).[4] The relevant data are given in Table 7.3, 2-butyl toluene-*p*-sulphonate being used as the reference compound.

Table 7.3. *Titrimetric rate constants for solvolysis of* 3-phenyl-2-butyl toluene-p-sulphonate[a]

	$10^5 k$ (sec^{-1})	
Compound	Acetolysis (49·6°)	Formolysis (25°)
2-Butyl	0·43	5·07
threo-3-Phenyl-2-butyl	0·24	22·8
erythro-3-Phenyl-2-butyl	0·27	28·0

[a] From a more extensive compilation of Brown, Morgan and Chloupek, 1965.

It has been argued that the rate constants for acetolysis of the 3-phenyl-2-butyl esters need correction for the inductive effect of the phenyl group (by a factor of ten), for internal return (by a factor of five),[5] and for a certain amount of steric hindrance to solvation not present in the reference compound.[6] The estimated rate enhancement due to bridging on this basis is a factor of 66. However, this estimate neglects the possibility of internal return in the reference compound. Such an objection does not apply in formolysis, for which ion-pair return is of much less importance. With allowance for the inductive effect this would indicate that bridging brings about a 40-fold increase in reaction rate, though this figure may be somewhat too large because of the neglect of a certain degree of steric acceleration. The kinetic results thus support though not strongly, the proposal of bridged carbonium-ion formation in formolysis: in acetolysis the rate enhancement is too small to be convincing evidence in favour of bridging.[7]

[1] H. C. Brown, Morgan and Chloupek, 1965.
[2] Collins, Benjamin and Lietzke, 1965.
[3] Cram, 1952b.
[4] Schleyer, 1964b.
[5] Winstein and Schreiber, 1952a; W. B. Smith and Showalter, 1964.
[6] Cram, 1956; Cram, 1964.
[7] See, however, Jensen and Ouellette, 1963.

With SbF_5-FSO_3H, 3-phenyl-2-butyl toluene-p-sulphonate forms a stable solution of a carbonium ion. The NMR spectrum is not consistent with a bridged formulation but corresponds to the 2-phenyl-2-butyl cation.[1] Though suggestive, this result is not strictly relevant to the solvolytic studies referred to earlier since the nature of the solvent may affect the importance of intra-molecular charge dispersal.

Other β-phenylethyl systems. For these systems care must be exercised in assessing kinetic results for "unsymmetrical" compounds, i.e. those in which the rearranged and unrearranged carbon skeletons are different, especially when internal return occurs. Thus, for example, the rate of acetolysis of 2-phenyl-1-propyl p-bromobenzenesulphonate (**7.38**) increases continuously during the course of the reaction, consistent with some internal return to the

$$CH_3.CH.CH_2OBs \qquad\qquad CH_3.CHOBs.CH_2$$
$$(\textbf{7.38}) \qquad\qquad\qquad (\textbf{7.39})$$

more reactive secondary ester (**7.39**).[2] Moreover, genuine rate enhancements could be attributable to direct formation of a rearranged unbridged ion.

It is obvious that additional β-substituents having lone-pair electrons could compete with the phenyl group in promoting ionization of the β-phenylethyl system at the α-carbon atom. We shall restrict ourselves here to discussing the effects of introducing methyl and phenyl substituents at the α- and β-carbon atoms. Effects similar to those found in cases of bridging by neighbouring lone-pair electrons are to be expected. Some kinetic results are presented in Table 7.4.

Phenyl bridging is not thought to be of major importance in acetolysis of β-phenylethyl and 1-phenyl-2-propyl toluene-p-sulphonates. Thus, in the latter case, substitution occurs with inversion and racemization. However, when formic acid is the solvent, retention of configuration at the α-carbon atom predominates.[3] Rearrangement studies using ^{14}C-labelling indicate some 11 % reaction through a bridged intermediate in the acetolysis of β-phenylethyl toluene-p-sulphonate.[4] In formic acid the corresponding figure is about 90 %. The kinetic results bear out the conclusions reached on the basis of other criteria of bridging: little or no enhancement of the acetolysis rate is indicated.

Introduction of methyl groups on the β-carbon atom of β-phenylethyl toluene-p-sulphonate gives substantial rate enhancements even without adjustment for polar influences. The effect is much reduced by a methyl substituent

[1] Olah, Pittman *et al.*, 1966b; Brookhart, Anet *et al.*, 1966.
[2] Winstein and Schreiber, 1952b.
[3] Winstein, Brown *et al.*, 1952.
[4] Lee, Slater and Spinks, 1957; Lee, Tkachuk and Slater, 1959.

Table 7.4. *Rate constants* (sec^{-1}) *for acetolysis of compounds of the type* $PhCR^1R^2 . CR^3R^4OTs$ (k_{Ph}) *and* $HCR^1R^2 . CR^3R^4OTs$ (k_H) *at* $49.6°$[a]

R^1	H	H	H	H	CH_3	CH_3	Ph	Ph	Ph
R^2	H	H	CH_3	CH_3	CH_3	CH_3	H	H	Ph
R^3	H	H	H	H	H	H	H	H	H
R^4	H	CH_3	H	CH_3	H	CH_3	H	CH_3	H
$10^8 k_{Ph}$	1·6	58·5	3·1	$\begin{cases}240T^b\\270E\end{cases}$	99	15,500	11·5	390	1680
$10^8 k_H$	4·3	215	0·3	430	1	1280	1·6	58·5	11·5
k_{Ph}/k_H	0·37	0·27	10	$\begin{cases}0\cdot55T\\0\cdot63E\end{cases}$	99	12	7·2	6·7	146
k_{Ph}/k_{Ph}^{calc} [c]	—	2·2	—	$\begin{cases}3\cdot5T\\4\cdot0E\end{cases}$	—	94	—	57	—

[a] Winstein, Morse et al., 1952a.
[b] T, *threo*; E, *erythro*.
[c] Streitwieser, 1956b: k_{Ph}^{calc} estimated assuming that bridged ions are not formed.

on the α-carbon atom. The pattern of behaviour is therefore very similar to that observed in bridging by neighbouring groups having lone-pair electrons. Phenyl bridging would thus seem to be important here.

Somewhat surprisingly, the presence of a second β-phenyl substituent leads to only modest rate enhancements. With triphenylethyl toluene-p-sulphonate the observed effect is doubtless caused at least in part by the release of steric strain due to compression among the phenyl groups in the starting material. Moreover, since only rearranged products are found, direct formation of the 1,2,2-triphenylethyl cation cannot be ruled out, the structure **7.40** approximating to that of the transition state rather than of an intermediate. Support

$$\text{Ph}_2\text{C}\text{———}\text{CH}_2$$
$$\text{OTs}^-$$

(7.40)

for this argument comes from the inclusion of points for triphenylethyl systems in a fairly good linear free energy correlation between rates of acetolysis of substituted β-phenylethyl sulphonate esters (PhCR^{1}R^2.CHR^{3}OBs) and rates of sodium borohydride reduction of the corresponding carbonyl compounds (PhCR^{1}R^2.CO.R^3).[1] Since the rate of the reduction seems to be dependent mainly on the change in steric compressions between the groups attached to the carbonyl carbon atom as the hybridization state of the latter changes from sp^2 to sp^3 and not at all on phenyl-bridging, solvolyses in which such bridging is important should evince marked deviations from the correlation. The argument is weakened by the fact that the regression line is not adequately defined by points for solvolyses in which bridging is certainly unimportant.[2]

Stereochemical studies along lines similar to those described for the 3-phenyl-2-butyl system have been extended to a range of β-phenylethyl compounds having a variety of alkyl substituents on the α- and β-carbon atoms. It has been concluded[3] that a phenyl-bridged ion is formed as the first intermediate from a β-phenylethyl sulphonate ester if (i) the β-carbon atom carries one or two alkyl or aryl substituents in addition to the potentially bridging phenyl group, (ii) the α-carbon atom carries not more than one alkyl substituent, and (iii) there are no aryl substituents on the α-carbon atom. These

---

[1] H. C. Brown, 1962; H. C. Brown, Bernheimer and Morgan, 1965.

[2] Capon and Rees, 1962; the same is true of a related investigation of the rates of borohydride reduction of bicyclo[2,2,1]heptanones and bicyclo[2,2,2]octanones and solvolysis of the corresponding toluene-p-sulphonates (H. C. Brown and Muzzio, 1966). However, 1-p-methoxyphenyl-2-propyl derivatives show substantial positive deviations from the correlation (H. C. Brown, Bernheimer $et\ al.$, 1967).

[3] Cram, 1956; Cram and Allinger, 1957.

requirements can be rationalized in terms of the polar effects of the α- and β-substituents on the stabilization of bridged and open carbonium ions. The steric effects of the substituents also influence the importance of bridging. Formation of ions such as **7.36** and **7.37** brings about eclipsing of substituent groups on the α- and β-carbon atoms. Knowledge of such interactions in simple aliphatic compounds suggests that *cis*-ions (e.g. **7.36**) have a higher energy content than the corresponding *trans*-ions (e.g. **7.37**). Since the transition states leading to these ions embody similar interactions, the *cis*-ion should be formed more slowly than the *trans*-ion. In agreement with this, the stereochemistry of the substitution products indicates that a greater proportion of acetolysis occurs through open carbonium ions in the case of *threo*-4-phenyl-3-hexyl toluene-*p*-sulphonate than with the *threo*-3-phenyl-2-butyl ester.[1] As eclipsing of ethyl groups introduces more strain than eclipsing of methyl groups, formation of the *cis*-phenonium ion from the former compound competes less well with reaction through open carbonium ions than in the case of the latter. However, an alternative interpretation in terms of rapidly interconverting unbridged ions is also possible (see p. 242).

Substituents in the phenyl bridge. The delocalization of the charge in phenyl-bridged carbonium ions, as formulated in structures **7.5–7.8**, indicates that the stability and rate of formation of such ions should be sensitive to substituents in the aromatic ring. In particular, electron-releasing substituents (especially when situated in the *o*- or *p*-positions), should promote bridged-ion formation. In agreement with these considerations, introduction of a *p*-methoxy substituent into 3-phenyl-2-butyl toluene-*p*-sulphonate gives a *titrimetric* rate constant for acetolysis 130 times greater than predicted for reaction through open carbonium ions (see Paragraph 5.3.3).[2] Moreover, a "special salt effect" of added lithium perchlorate is observed. Since this is not found in the unsubstituted compound, it would seem that the presence of the methoxyl group stabilizes the first carbonium ion-pair intermediate, enabling it to be transformed to a solvent-separated ion-pair before capture by the nucleophile.[3] A *p*-methoxy group even promotes bridging in the β-phenylethyl system as indicated by the NMR spectrum of the chloride in SbF_5-SO_2,[4] solvolysis rates,[5] and [14]C- scrambling.[6] The evidence for bridged-ion formation in these systems thus seems fairly conclusive.

Methoxy substituents in the *m*-position of β-phenyl groups generally have a rate-retarding influence.[7] In the *o*-position, anchimeric assistance by the lone-

[1] Cram and Abd Elhafez, 1953.

[2] Winstein, Brown *et al.*, 1952.

[3] Winstein and Robinson, 1958; Winstein, Clippinger *et al.*, 1954, 1956; Fainberg, Robinson and Winstein, 1956; Fainberg and Winstein, 1956b.

[4] Olah, Namanworth *et al.*, 1967.

[5] Winstein, Lindegren *et al.*, 1953; cf. H. C. Brown, Bernheimer *et al.*, 1967.

[6] Jenny and Winstein, 1958; see also, J. D. Roberts and Regan, 1953.

[7] Winstein and Heck, 1956.

pair electrons on the oxygen atom (MeO-5 participation) may compete with that due to the aryl group.[1]

The methanolysis of β-(4-hydroxyphenyl)ethyl bromide (7.41) in methanol containing methoxide ion is 10^6 times more rapid than that of the corresponding p-methoxy-compound.[2] The spirodienone 7.42 can be isolated and is clearly a reaction intermediate formed by anchimeric assistance to the cleavage of the carbon–bromine bond by the β-phenoxide substituent. Reaction of 7.42 with methanol is acid-catalysed. The conjugate acid and the dienone itself are thus close models for aryl-bridged carbonium ions.

OH

$CH_2 \cdot CH_2Br$

(7.41)

O

H_2C——CH_2

(7.42)

X

$(CH_3)_2C \cdot CH_2OBs$

(7.43)

Support for the generality of bridging by a β-situated substituted phenyl group is provided by kinetic results on the acetolysis of a series of m- and p-substituted neophyl p-bromobenzenesulphonates (7.43; X = m-OMe, m-Me, p-Br, p-CO_2Me, p-CHPh_2, p-OMe and p-Me].[3] Substituents have a marked effect on the reaction rate, which is satisfactorily correlated by Hammett substituent constants, σ, with the exception of the p-methoxy-compound which is solvolysed much more rapidly than predicted. While this result might be interpreted as indicating bridging only in the p-methoxy case, all the kinetic data can be correlated by use of σ^+-values, the reaction constant, ρ, then having a value of $-2 \cdot 96$ [cf. $-4 \cdot 54$ for the solvolysis of substituted t-cumyl halides used in defining the σ^+-values, and -3 for migratory aptitudes in the pinacol rearrangement (Paragraph 6.4.3)]. This suggests substantial direct conjugation between the p-substituents and the developing cationic centre in the solvolysis transition state, leading to an aryl-bridged intermediate or to the rearranged tertiary carbonium ion.

Aryl-bridging of necessity entails some loss of resonance stability in the bridging group. Compared with the phenyl group, the 9-anthryl group would lose relatively little. Thus 9-anthrylethyl toluene-p-sulphonate (7.44) shows substantial anchimeric acceleration, participation apparently being important even in quite nucleophilic solvents (e.g. 60 % dioxan–water) where bridged-ion formation is normally considered to be less likely.[4] In aqueous dioxan the product is the corresponding alcohol, but in the presence of sodium bicarbonate (kinetic control) the spiro-alcohol 7.45 can be isolated in 85 % yield.

[1] Heck, Corse et al., 1957.
[2] Winstein and Baird, 1957; Baird and Winstein, 1957, 1963.
[3] Heck and Winstein, 1957c.
[4] Eberson, Petrovich et al., 1965.

Even then, the simple substitution product must arise from a symmetrical intermediate, since deuterium-labelling at the α-carbon atom of **7.44** gives 9-anthrylethanol in which deuterium is equally divided between the α- and β-carbon atoms. The intermediate carbonium ion has been formulated as **7.46**.

CH$_2$.CH$_2$OTs

(7.44)   (7.45)   (7.46)

The protons attached to the three-membered ring show an unusually large chemical shift to low field in the NMR spectrum of solutions of the ion in SO$_2$-SbF$_5$.[1] This part of the structure may therefore be involved in the delocalization of the positive charge. For this reason the formula **7.46** has been drawn with four partial bonds to the 9-position of the anthracene nucleus.

Bridging of non-adjacent carbon atoms. Such bridging seems to be much less important than that described so far, its effects being recognizable only when the bridging group bears one or more methoxyl substituents.

For example, acetolysis and formolysis of 4-phenyl-1-butyl *p*-bromobenzenesulphonate shows no evidence of bridging, but the introduction of a *p*-methoxy group increases the rate of solvolysis slightly, with proportionate appearance of methoxytetralin in the product. The 2,4-dimethoxyphenyl ester **7.47** is formolysed about ten times and acetolysed four times more rapidly than the parent compound, and the entropy of activation is about -10 cal mole^{-1} deg^{-1}, close to the value thought to characterize solvolyses in which bridging is important.[2] The structure of the carbonium-ion intermediate is thought to be **7.48** and, consistent with this, a considerable proportion of the product is found to be the tetralin **7.49**. Some support for this interpretation

OCH$_3$ OCH$_3$ OCH$_3$

OCH$_3$ OCH$_3$ OCH$_3$
CH$_2$.CH$_2$.CH$_2$.CH$_2$OBs

(7.47)   (7.48)   (7.49)

is provided by the very high rate of solvolysis of spirodienyl esters, such as **7.50**, compared with the corresponding compound with only one double bond.[3]

[1] Eberson and Winstein, 1965.
[2] Heck and Winstein, 1957b.
[3] Friedrich and Winstein, 1962.

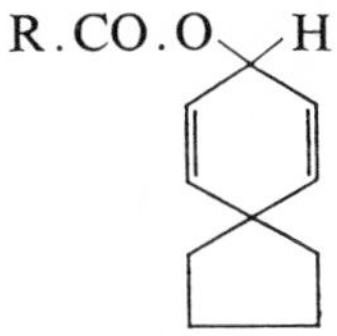

$$R.CO.O \diagdown H$$

(7.50)

Bridging of this type is much less important in secondary esters, e.g. 5-aryl-2-pentyl esters,[1] although the bicyclic product is obtained. Nor is it important in esters having longer methylene chains.[2] Participation with formation of a six-membered ring has been suggested in the solvolysis of 3,5-dimethoxyphenyl-1-butyl p-bromobenzenesulphonate[3] but the kinetic evidence in favour of this proposal is not strong.

Aryl-bridging in cyclic systems. Incorporation of the aryl substituent into a cyclic system imposes certain conformational restrictions which may make participation highly probable, because the aryl group and reaction centre are held together in suitable relative orientation, or may rule it out completely if achievement of the necessary stereochemistry is impossible.

In the cyclopentyl and cyclohexyl series, the available evidence[4] from the solvolysis of toluene-p-sulphonates apparently rules out anchimeric assistance to ionization by neighbouring *trans*-phenyl and -p-anisyl groups. This may be rationalized as due to angle strain involved in the bridged cyclopentyl cation **7.51** and due to the high energy involved in placing a phenyl substituent in an axial position in **7.52** so as to participate in the formation of the cyclohexyl cation. Other interpretations are possible.

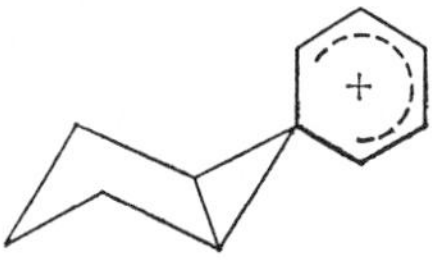

     (7.51) 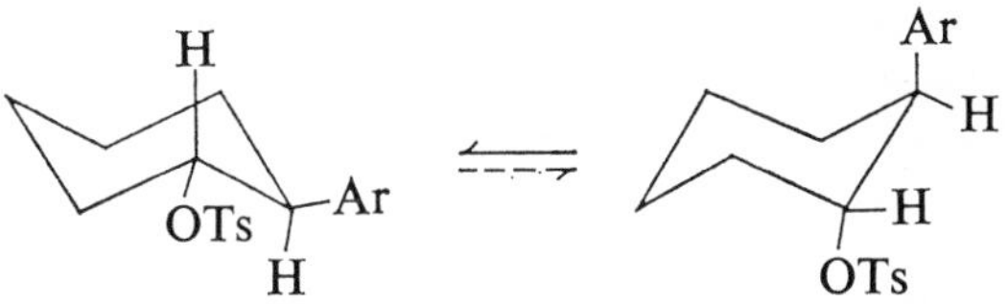   **(7.52)**

Even greater restrictions apply when the aromatic ring of the potential bridging group is fused to another ring. Kinetic evidence suggests the formation of bridged ion **7.54** from **7.53**[5] and of **7.56** in the solvolysis of the toluene-p-sulphonates **7.55** ($n = 5$–8)[6] but they are not produced in the deamination of

[1] Heck and Winstein, 1957a.

[2] Heck and Winstein, 1957a; Corey and Sauers, 1957.

[3] Heck and Winstein, 1957b.

[4] Summarized by H. C. Brown, Morgan and Chloupek, 1965; see, however, Sneen, Jenkins and Riddle, 1962.

[5] Huisgen, Rauenbusch *et al.*, 1964.

[6] Huisgen, Seidl and Wimmer, 1964; Huisgen and Seidl, 1964.

the corresponding amines.[1] Kinetic[2] and stereochemical evidence (substitution with racemization)[3] indicates that acetolysis of *exo*-2-benzonorbornenyl sulphonate esters (e.g. **7.57**) involves formation of the symmetrical bridged ion (**7.58**).[4] Kinetic and product evidence has also been advanced[5] for arylbridging in ring systems incorporating the *p*-phenylene group.[6]

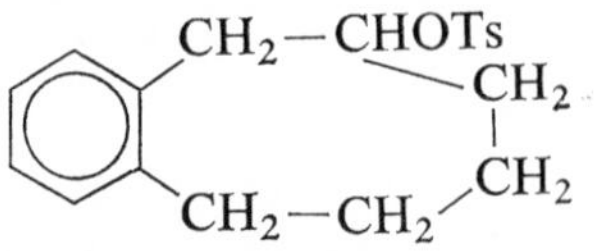

(7.53)

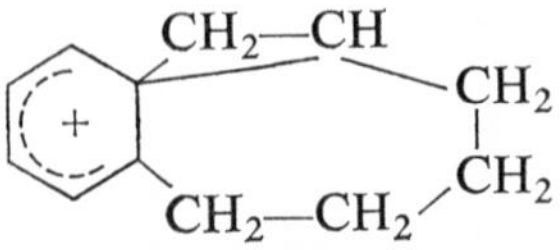

(7.54)

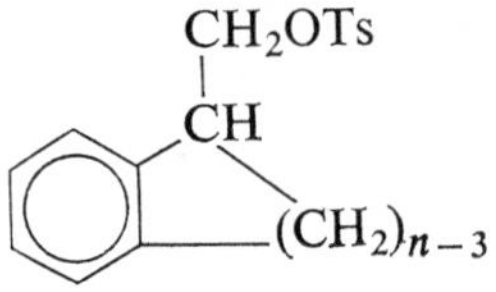

(7.55)

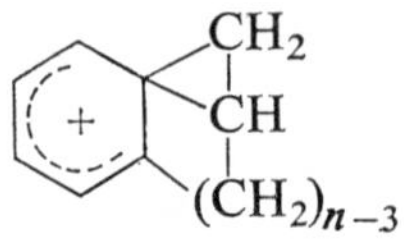

(7.56)

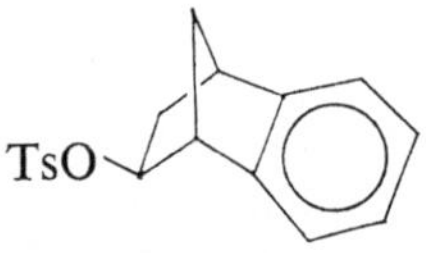

(7.57)

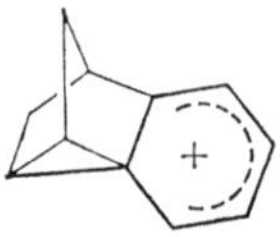

(7.58)

7.4.2 ALKENYL-BRIDGED IONS: HOMOALLYLIC CATIONS

Open chain systems. Considerable stability can be expected for carbonium ions in which there is a vinyl group attached to the β-carbon atom[7] which can interact with C_α to form a σ-type bond by p-π overlap (**7.59a**). Some discussion,

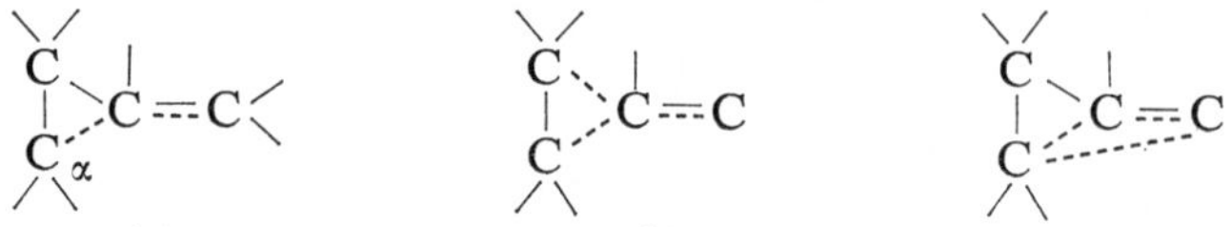

(a)   (b)   (c)

(7.59)

[1] Seidl, Huisgen and Hill, 1964.
[2] Schleyer, 1964b; Bartlett and Giddings, 1960; but see H. C. Brown and Tritle, 1966.
[3] Giddings and Dirlam, 1963.
[4] Cf. Cristol and Tanner, 1964.
[5] Cram and Goldstein, 1963.
[6] See also Cram and Singer, 1963.
[7] Simonetta and Winstein, 1954; Woods, Carboni and Roberts, 1956; Piccolini and Winstein, 1963.

based both on theoretical considerations[1] as well as experimental observation, has been concerned with the possibility that more extensive delocalization of electrons is involved, such as is shown in **7.59b** and **c** (cf. **7.46**). Since the system does not contain sufficient electrons for the formulation of two fused cyclopropane rings with electron-pair bonds, **7.59c** represents bridging in an electron-deficient system. There is thus some blurring of the border-line between electron-sufficient and electron-deficient bridged carbonium ions. There has been little examination of the possibility of bridging by carbon–carbon triple bonds.[2]

The but-3-enyl system is the simplest in which a homoallylic carbonium ion might be expected. There appears to be no participation by the β-vinyl substituent in solvolysis of the chloride in ethanol and aqueous ethanol,[3] evidence indicating that the but-3-enyl system is particularly prone to undergo bimolecular displacement.[4] Formolysis of but-3-enyl toluene-p-sulphonate is, however, 3·7 times faster than that of the butyl ester and is also less sensitive to lyate ion.[5] After allowance for but-3-enyl formate produced by bimolecular displacement, the reaction products are similar to those obtained from solvolytic reactions of cyclopropylmethyl and cyclobutyl compounds (see Paragraph 7.5.2), namely but-3-enyl formate (10%), which is the most stable thermodynamically,[6] cyclopropylmethyl (**7.60**) (45%) and cyclobutyl (**7.61**) (45%) formates. Moreover, starting from 1,1-dideuteriobut-3-enyl toluene-p-sulphonate, the deuterium label is randomly distributed among the methylene groups of **7.60** and **7.61**. Nitrous acid deamination of but-3-enylamine also gives ring-closed products and, starting from α-^{14}C-labelled amine, almost (but not quite) complete shuffling of the label among three of the four positions occurs.[7] This has been interpreted as evidence for rapid (but not instantaneous)

$$
\begin{array}{l}
CH_2 \\
\quad \diagdown \\
\quad\quad CH.CH_2.O.CO.H \\
\quad \diagup \\
CH_2
\end{array}
\qquad\qquad
\begin{array}{l}
CH_2—CH_2 \\
\;|\qquad\;\; | \\
CH_2—CH.O.CO.H
\end{array}
$$

$$
(\mathbf{7.60}) \qquad\qquad\qquad\qquad (\mathbf{7.61})
$$

$$
\begin{array}{l}
CH_2\text{---}CH_2 \\
\;|\qquad\;\; \| \\
CH_2—CH
\end{array}
\quad\rightleftharpoons\quad
\begin{array}{l}
CH_2—CH_2 \\
\;|\qquad\;\; | \\
CH_2\text{==}CH
\end{array}
$$

$$
(\mathbf{a}) \qquad\qquad\qquad (\mathbf{b})
$$

$$
(\mathbf{7.62})
$$

[1] Howden and Roberts, 1963.
[2] Peterson and Kamat, 1966.
[3] Streitwieser, 1956b.
[4] Bergstrom and Siegel, 1952.
[5] Servis and Roberts, 1964.
[6] J. D. Roberts and Mazur, 1951a.
[7] Renk and Roberts, 1961.

interconversion of unsymmetrical "bicyclobutonium" ions (e.g. **7.59c**) as shown in **7.62** (but see Paragraph 7.5.2).

Kinetic evidence for bridging by β-vinyl groups is more convincing when methyl and phenyl substituents are attached to the double bond. Some formolysis results are given in Table 7.5. In ethanol, methyl- or phenyl-substituted sulphonate esters, except 4-methylpent-3-enyl, are solvolysed more slowly

Table 7.5. *Relative rates of formolysis of methyl-substituted but-3-enyl toluene-p-sulphonates in* 10% *pyridine-formic acid at* 50°[a]

Compound	~~~OTs	~~~OTs	~~~OTs
k_{rel}	1·0	3·7	770
Principal product	—	HCO.O~▷ and □O.COH	▷◁ HCO.O

Compound	~~~OTs	~~~OTs	~~~OTs
k_{rel}	165	12	4500[b]
Principal product	▷◁ HCO.O	□—O.COH	—

[a] Servis and Roberts, 1965.
[b] For acetolysis relative to ethyl toluene-p-sulphonate, $k = 1200$; $\Delta S^{\ddagger} \sim -8$ cal mole^{-1} deg^{-1} (Rogan, 1962).

than their saturated analogues, confirming that the formolyses are indeed unimolecular. Substantial proportions of ring-closed products are formed, as has been known for some time.[1] Methyl substitution on the β-carbon in but-3-enyl sulphonate esters also leads to large anchimeric accelerations,[2] the general pattern of behaviour thus closely resembling that found in the case of β-phenylethyl compounds. Whether the interaction of the double bond with the cationic centre in these substituted but-3-enyl systems is homoallylic (**7.59a**) or involves more extensive electron delocalization is not known. In the reaction of 1,1-dideuterio-4-methylpent-3-enyl chloride with phenol to give the homochroman **7.63**, the deuterium label is distributed between the starred positions owing to rearrangement of the chloride by internal return.[3] This suggests that ionization of the chloride may involve a more symmetrical intermediate than **7.64**. This could be **7.65** or **7.66**.

[1] Bruylants and Dewael, 1928; Favorskaya and Fridman, 1945.
[2] Wilcox and Nealy, 1963; Bly and Swindell, 1965.
[3] Corbin, Hart and Wagner, 1962; Hart, Corbin et al., 1963.

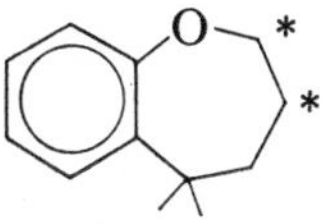

(7.63) 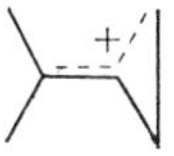 (7.64) 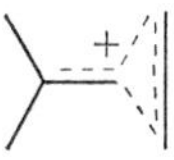 (7.65) 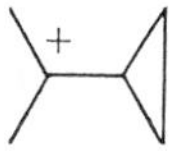 (7.66)

Participation in carbonium-ion formation by double bonds separated from the site of heterolysis by more than one saturated carbon atom is known, but the evidence for bridged-ion intermediates is not decisive. Thus, formolysis of 5-hexenyl p-nitrobenzenesulphonate is twice as rapid as formolysis of the saturated compound and gives 68 % of cyclohexyl formate.[1] A similar kinetic effect but less cyclic product is found in acetolysis.[2] These observations are probably explicable in terms of some participation leading to a cyclic ion. The 4-pentenyl and 6-heptenyl compounds show no rate enhancement and give no cyclic products. In the case of the decadienyl naphthalene-2-sulphonate esters 7.67 and 7.68, however, the stereochemistry of the ring fusion in the resultant bicyclic products is determined by the stereochemistry of the 5,6-double bond, viz. *trans* → *trans* ring fusion, *cis* → *cis* ring fusion.[3] This stereospecificity, which might be related to biological cyclization of polyisoprenoids,

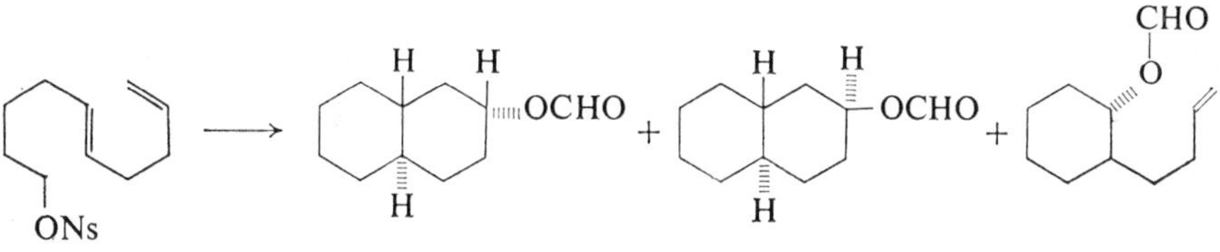

(7.67)

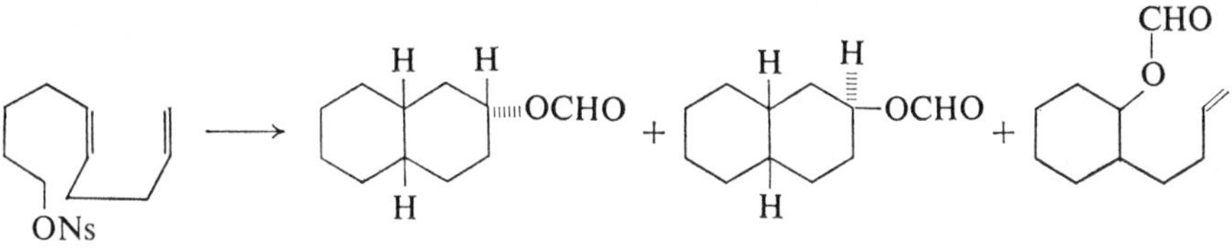

(7.68)

could be a result of conformational factors in the product-determining step of reactions of cyclic cations, but could also be explained in terms of reactions of the bridged ions 7.69 and 7.70.

Cyclic systems. The additional steric constraints found in cyclic systems compared with acyclic compounds can have the effect of either making bridging particularly favourable or rendering it impossible. It is not surprising that in cyclic systems the effects of bridging extend over a very wide range.

[1] Johnson, Bailey et al., 1964.
[2] Bartlett, Closson and Cogdell, 1965.
[3] Johnson, Bailey et al., 1964; Johnson and Crandall, 1964, 1965.

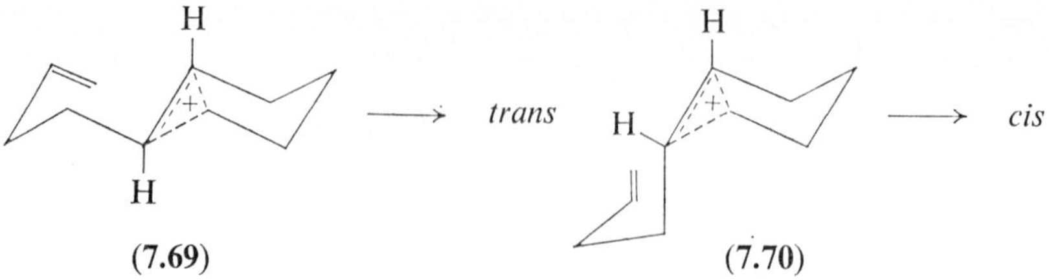

(7.69)   (7.70)

Cycloalkenylmethyl systems. In the transition state for solvolysis of diaryl-cyclopropenylmethyl toluene-*p*-sulphonates (7.71), the π-orbital of the double bond is orthogonal to the developing vacant *p*-orbital at the α-carbon atom. Participation by the double bond in the ionization is thus not possible. However, kinetic and product evidence indicates bridged-ion formation, and this would seem to involve bridging by the β-γ carbon–carbon single bond.[1]

Homoallylic interaction becomes more important in less strained carbocycles. Thus acetolysis at 70° of cyclopent-2-enylmethyl naphthalene-2-sulphonate (7.72) is ten times as fast as for the saturated analogue and gives a

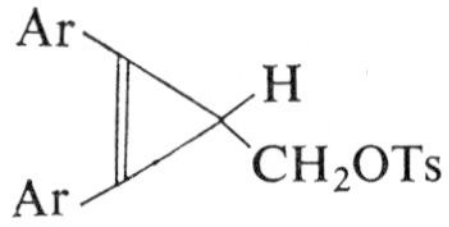

(7.71) 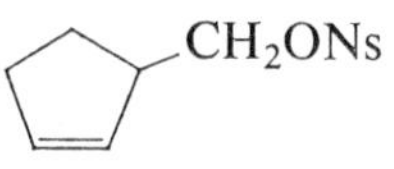   (7.72) 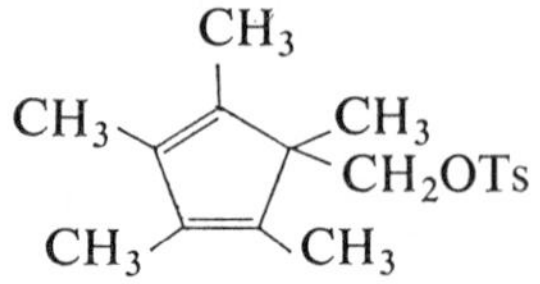   (7.73)

variety of products, some of which retain a cyclopropyl ring.[2] A much larger ($\sim 10^{10}$-fold) anchimeric acceleration is claimed for the cyclopentadienyl-methyl toluene-*p*-sulphonate 7.73,[3] the kinetically controlled product being the bicyclic diene 7.74 rather than the expected pentamethylbenzene. A number of formulations of the intermediate cation are possible (7.75a, b, c).

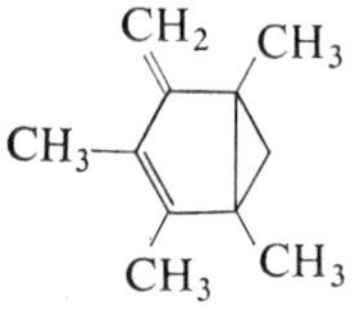

(7.74)   (7.75)

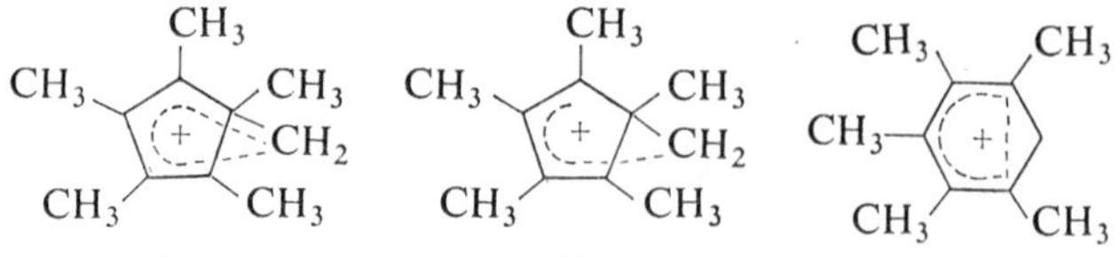

Somewhat similar ambiguities exist in the formulation of the ion formed in solvolysis of the dihydrobenzyl toluene-*p*-sulphonate 7.76 (R=OCH$_3$). Solvolysis is about 100 times more rapid than for the unsubstituted compound (7.76; R=H) and yields a cycloheptatriene derivative, unlike the parent

---

[1] Breslow, Lockhart and Small, 1962.
[2] Hanack and Schneider, 1964.
[3] Winstein and Battiste, 1960; de Vries, 1960.

compound.[1] The product, at least, can be rationalized in terms of initial formation of an intermediate ion of structure **7.77**.

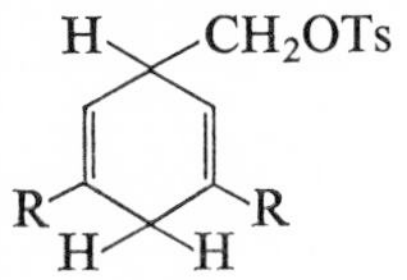

(7.76) 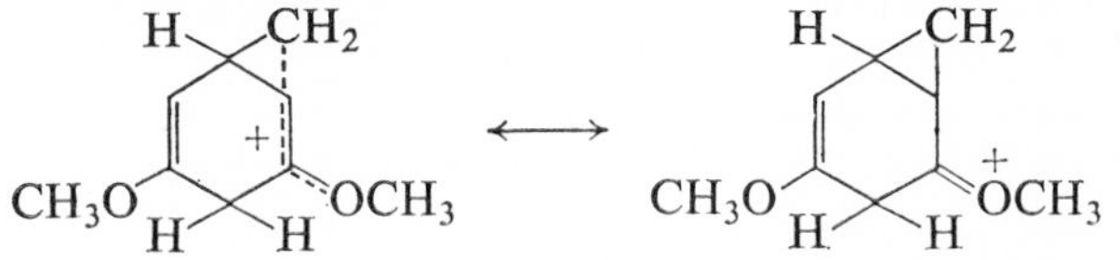　　　　　　　　　　　　　　(7.77)

There is much evidence that bridged ions are formed by interaction between carbon–carbon double bonds and carbonium centres in cycloalkenylmethyl compounds which are not homoallylic (e.g. **7.78**). Since such intermediates appear to be of the electron-deficient type and are more commonly formed from bicyclic compounds (e.g. **7.79**), discussion is deferred. (See Paragraphs 7.5.3 and 7.5.4.)

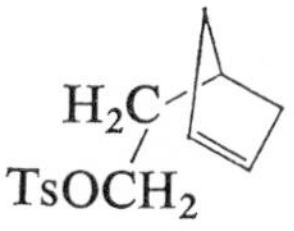

(7.78) 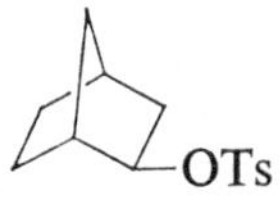　　　　　　　(7.79)

Cycloalkenyl systems. The possiblity of homoallylic resonance is further restricted when the double bond and the cationic centre are in the same ring. The smallest ring for which such interaction has been established is eight-membered. Thus cyclo-oct-3-enyl *p*-bromobenzenesulphonate (**7.80**) is aceto-lysed twice as rapidly as the cyclo-octyl ester, giving a mixture of acetates related to **7.80** and **7.81** in which the rearranged bicyclic one predominates.[2]

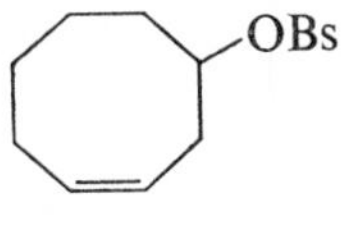

(7.80) 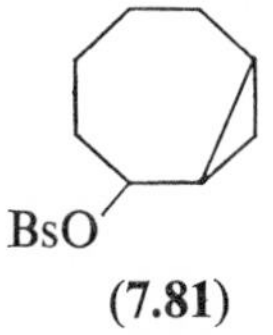　　　　　　　(7.81)

Anchimeric acceleration appears small because there is substantial steric acceleration of solvolysis of cyclo-octyl *p*-bromobenzenesulphonate[3] due to transannular compressions; these are much reduced in the unsaturated ester. The same intermediate may be involved in reactions of the bicyclic system **7.81**.[4]

[1] Chapman and Fitton, 1961, 1963; Nelson, Fassnacht and Piper, 1961.
[2] Cope and Peterson, 1959.
[3] H. C. Brown and Ham, 1956; see however, Szkrybalo, 1964.
[4] Cope, Moon and Peterson, 1962; Cope, Moon and Park, 1962.

The facility of transannular reactions in medium-sized rings[1] permits participation by more remote double bonds in carbonium-ion formation.[2] The evidence for bridged *intermediates* is not unequivocal. For example *cis*- and *trans*-5-cyclodecenyl *p*-nitrobenzoates (**7.82** and **7.83**) are solvolysed respectively 5 and 1500 times more rapidly than the corresponding saturated ester to give bicyclic (decalyl) products.[3] Moreover the reactions are stereo-specific, **7.82** giving *cis-cis*-decalyl alcohol (**7.86**; X = OH) whereas **7.83** gives the *trans-trans*-product (**7.87**; X = OH). While the intermediates could be the bridged ions **7.84** and **7.85**, the stereospecificity could arise by conformational control of the transannular reaction and subsequent reaction of the *cis*- and *trans*-decalyl cations with solvent, since deamination of the corresponding bicyclic amines (**7.86** and **7.87**; X = NH$_2$) occurs with retention of configuration.[4]

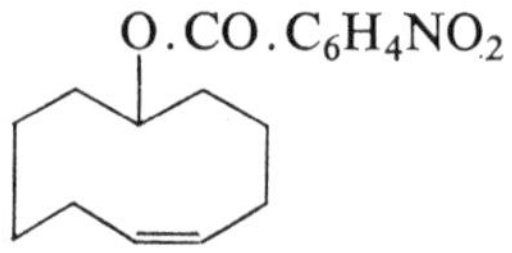

O.CO.C$_6$H$_4$NO$_2$

O.CO.C$_6$H$_4$NO$_2$

(7.82)

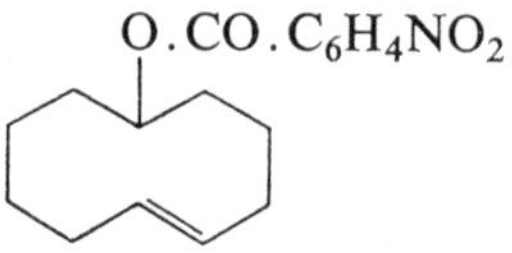

(7.83)

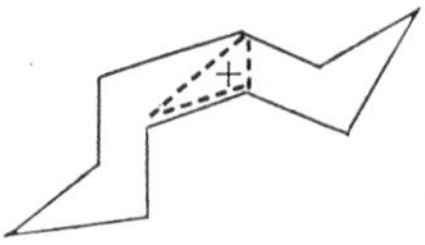

(7.84)

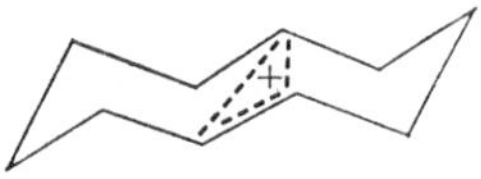

(7.85)

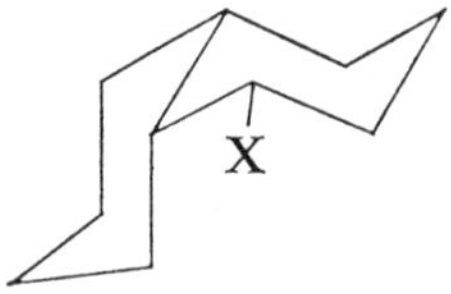

X

(7.86)

X

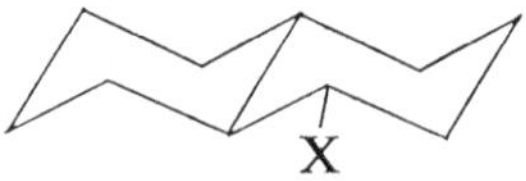

(7.87)

Bicyclo[2,2,1]*heptyl and related systems.* The importance of geometrical considerations in determining whether bridging occurs in homoallylic systems is well illustrated by this series. Thus, while *endo*-2-norbornenyl derivatives (**7.88**; X = O.SO$_2$Ar, Cl) show no evidence of anchimeric acceleration in solvolysis, the corresponding *exo*-derivatives (**7.89**) react much more rapidly

[1] Prelog and Traynham, 1963; Cope, Martin and McKervey, 1966.
[2] E.g., Cope and Peterson, 1959; Cope, Grisar, and Peterson, 1960.
[3] Goering and Closson, 1961; see also Goering, Espy and Closson, 1959; Goering, Olson and Espy, 1956.
[4] W. G. Dauben, Tweit and Mannerskantz, 1954.

(see Table 7.1).[1] The principal reaction product from both stereoisomers is the nortricyclyl compound **7.90** accompanied by some *exo*-norbornenyl product in proportion decreasing with decreasing nucleophilic activity of the solvent.[2] This variation is due to interconversion of 2-norbornenyl and nortricyclyl derivatives prior to solvolysis. While these results may be simply rationalized in terms of formation of the homoallylic cation **7.91**, the observation that **7.88** and **7.89** ($X = O.SO_2.C_6H_4Br$ and NH_2) labelled with ^{14}C in the 2,3-positions undergo carbonium-ion reactions with 30–48 % rearrangement of the label requires for its explanation a more complex series of intermediates. Slow equilibration of **7.91** and **7.92** in competition with solvent attack seems probable (contrast with **7.58**).[2] Solvolysis of nortricyclyl compounds is also anchimerically assisted[3] and probably proceeds through similar intermediates.[4] Analogous intermediates can explain the course of electrophilic addition (e.g. of bromine) to norborna-2,5-diene.[5]

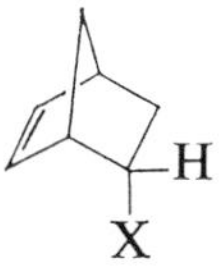

(7.88) 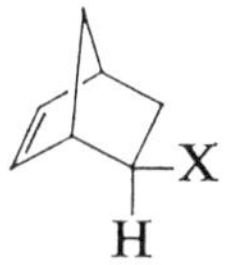　　　　　　(7.89) 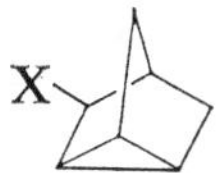　　　　　　(7.90)

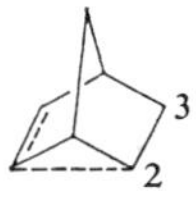

(7.91) 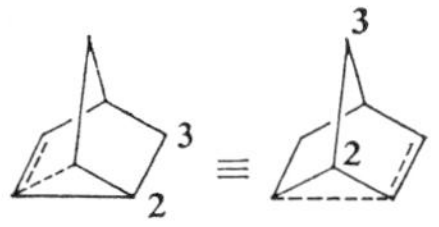　　　　　　(7.92)

The stereochemical requirements for bridging by a double bond at C_β is further emphasized by the results of Table 7.6. The 7-isopropylidene group is conveniently situated for anchimeric assistance to ionization of the *endo*- but not the *exo*-esters by p-π overlap. This is borne out by the much larger rate ratios observed for the *endo*-pairs, where anchimeric acceleration does not occur in the reference compounds (see Paragraph 7.5.3), compared with the *exo*-pairs. Moreover, the 7-isopropylidene-*endo*-esters solvolyse without rearrangement, unlike the *exo*-esters for which other types of bridging not involving the isopropylidene group are possible.

[1] Schleyer, 1964a,b; Winstein, Walborsky and Schreiber, 1950; J. D. Roberts, Bennett and Armstrong, 1950; J. D. Roberts and Bennett, 1954.
[2] J. D. Roberts, Lee and Saunders, 1955; but see Cristol, Morrill and Sanchez, 1966.
[3] Schleyer, 1964b.
[4] Winstein, Walborsky and Schreiber, 1950; see also: Richey and Buckley, 1963; Story and Fahrenholtz, 1964a,b, 1966.
[5] Winstein and Shatavsky, 1956a,b.

Reference compound	k_r	Compound	k	k/k_r
 (structure, OTs)	$2 \cdot 36 \times 10^{-5}$	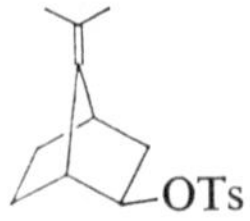 (structure, OTs)	$1 \cdot 76 \times 10^{-4}$	7·5
 (structure, OTs)	$8 \cdot 4 \times 10^{-8}$	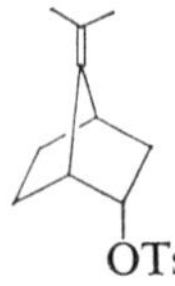 (structure, OTs)	$2 \cdot 26 \times 10^{-5}$	270
 (structure, OTs)	$1 \cdot 5 \times 10^{-5}$	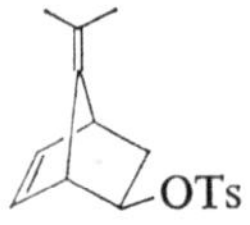 (structure, OTs)	$6 \cdot 27 \times 10^{-5}$	4·2
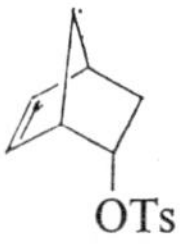 (structure, OTs)	2×10^{-9}	 (structure, OTs)	$3 \cdot 7 \times 10^{-6}$	1850

[a] DePuy, Ogawa and McDaniel, 1961; see also van Tamelen and Judd, 1958.

Even more spectacular kinetic effects are found in the 7-norbornenyl series. Some results are given in Table 7.7. The relative rates compared with that for 7-norbornyl toluene-p-sulphonate are somewhat misleading owing to certain steric peculiarities of the reference compound unconnected with bridged carbonium-ion formation:[1] Schleyer's[2] estimates (Table 7.1) of the degree of anchimeric acceleration are preferable. Clearly, the enhancement of the rate of acetolysis is dependent upon the position of the double bond relative to the leaving group. The large enhancement in the case of **7.95** is attributable to stabilization of the incipient positive charge on C(7) by the π-orbital of the double bond, favourably situated to interact from the side opposite to the leaving group.[3] This interaction, leading to the intermediate ion **7.99**, also

Table 7.6. *Rate constants* (sec^{-1}) *for acetolysis at 25° of* exo- *and* endo-7-isopropyli-
dene-2-norbornenyl toluene-p-sulphonates[a]

[1] Schleyer and Nicholas, 1961; Winstein and Kosower, 1959.
[2] Schleyer, 1964b.
[3] For similar observations on enols with structures related to **7.95**, see Gassman and Marshall, 1966a; Lumb and Whitham, 1966.

explains the exclusive production of solvolysis product of retained configuration[1] and is consistent with the NMR spectrum of stable solutions of the ion in SO_2-FSO_3H.[2] Simple MO calculations[3] suggest that **7.99** may be of similar stability to the allyl cation (cf. Paragraph 5.2.6). It is to be noted that in these compounds the p-π interaction (e.g. in **7.99**) is symmetrical, unlike that envisaged for simpler homoallylic systems. Similar p-π overlap in the *transition state* for ionization of the *syn*-isomer (**7.94**) is not possible and, significantly, the reaction is not only much slower than for **7.95** but also yields the rearranged product **7.100**. Since the acetolysis of **7.94** seems to be substantially accelerated, the allylic ion **7.101**, formed by participation of the *anti*-C_β–C_γ σ-bond electrons, has been suggested as the intermediate.

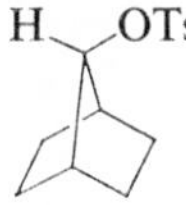

(7.93) 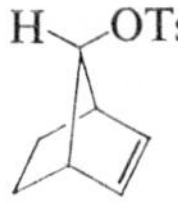   (7.94) 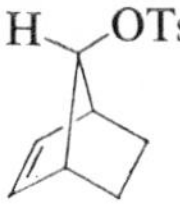   (7.95) 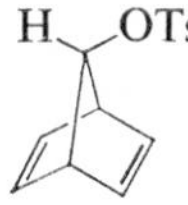   (7.96) 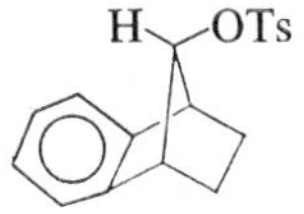   (7.97)

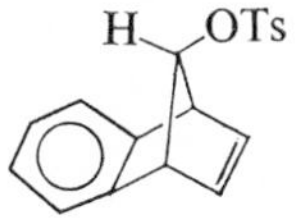

(7.98) 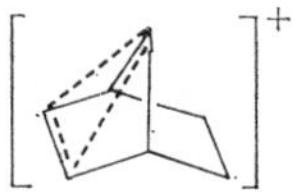   (7.99) 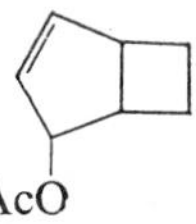   (7.100) 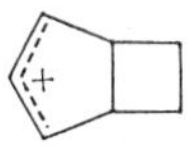   (7.101)

Table 7.7. *Relative rates of acetolysis* (25°) *of 7-norbornyl toluene-p-sulphonates*

Compound	(7.93)	(7.94)	(7.95)	(7.96)	(7.97)	(7.98)
Relative rate	1	$10^{3\cdot7}$	$10^{11\cdot3}$	10^{14}	$10^{5\cdot8}$	10^8
Reference		a	b	c	d	d
Anchimeric acceleration[e]	1	$10^{5\cdot6}$	$10^{12\cdot9}$	—	$10^{9\cdot1}$	—

[a] Winstein and Stafford, 1957.
[b] Winstein, Shatavsky et al., 1955.
[c] Winstein and Ordronneau, 1960.
[d] Bartlett and Giddings, 1960.
[e] Schleyer, 1964b.

In the carbonium ion formed from **7.96**, interactions similar to those in **7.99** are possible. Further structures, involving more extensive delocalization of the positive charge, are also conceivable (e.g. **102a, b, c**) but only by using anti-bonding orbitals. The examination of the stable tetrafluoroborate salt in liquid sulphur dioxide at $-10°$ indicates that the pairs of protons on C(2)

[1] Winstein, Lewin and Pande, 1963; see also Diaz, Brookhart and Winstein, 1966; Brookhart, Diaz and Winstein, 1966.
[2] Brookhart, Diaz and Winstein, 1966; Richey and Lustgarten, 1966.
[3] Woods, Carboni and Roberts, 1956.

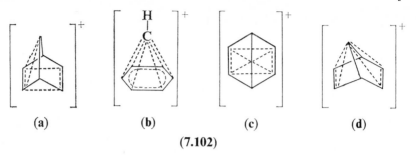

(a)   (b)   (c)   (d)

(7.102)

and C(3) and on C(5) and C(6) have different chemical shifts and are coupled
not only with the bridgehead protons but also with the proton on C(7). This
would fit the unsymmetrical structure **7.102d**[1] which is also supported by a
theoretical treatment.[2] An alternative formulation of the ion in terms of rapidly
equilibrating structures (e.g. **7.103a, b**) might, however, better explain[3] the
rather small chemical shift of the proton resonance at C(7)($\delta = -3\cdot48$ p.p.m.)
and the isolation of the tricyclic hydrocarbons **7.104** and **7.105** from solvolysis
of norbornadienyl chloride in the presence of sodium borohydride.[4] Measurements of the temperature dependence of the NMR spectrum should resolve
the ambiguity.

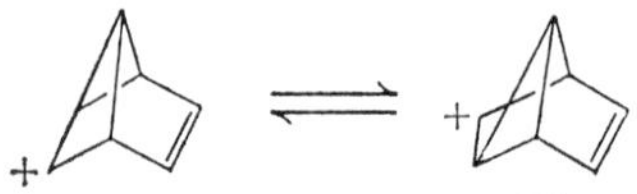

(a)   (b)

(7.103)

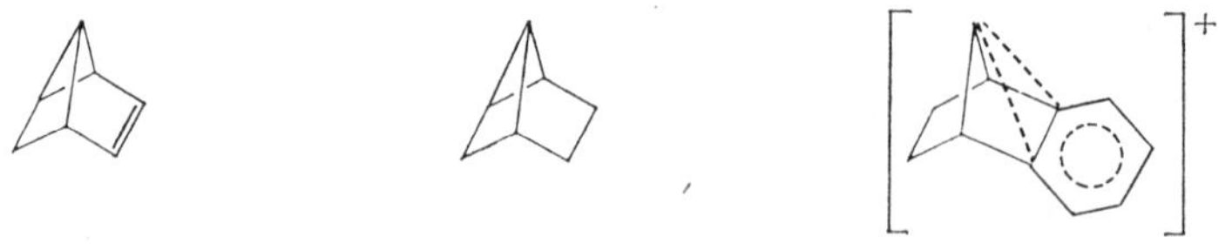

(7.104)   (7.105)   (7.106)

When the double bond of *anti*-7-norbornenyl arenesulphonates is incorporated in a benzene ring as in **7.97**, its ability to promote ionization at C(7) is
considerably diminished, though still substantial. While a structure (**7.106**)
analogous to **7.99** can be written for the intermediate cation, it is evident that
the benzene resonance would be partly lost (cf. **7.58**), offsetting to some
extent the reduction in energy due to p-π overlap. There is some evidence for a

[1] Story, Snyder *et al.*, 1963; Story and Saunders, 1962, 1960.
[2] Hoffmann, 1964a,b.
[3] Deno, 1964a.
[4] H. C. Brown and Bell, 1962, 1963; but see Brookhart, Diaz and Winstein, 1966.

degree of direct conjugation between substituents in the benzene ring and
C(7).[1]

Bicyclo[2,2,2] and [3,2,1]octenyl systems show broadly similar effects to
those found in bicyclo[2,2,1]heptenyl compounds. Thus (+)-*endo*-2-bicyclo-
[2,2,2]oct-5-enyl toluene-*p*-sulphonate (**7.107**) undergoes anchimerically

(7.107)   (7.108)   (7.109)   (7.110)   (7.111)

assisted solvolysis[2] giving mainly the rearranged acetate **7.109** which is racemic. This indicates reaction through the rearranged allylic cation **7.110**
without participation of the double bond. Anchimeric assistance is considerably greater in the case of the *exo*-toluene-*p*-sulphonate **7.108**,[3] and the
product is largely the tricyclic acetate **7.111**, suggesting reaction *via* **7.112**.

(7.112)   (7.113)   (7.114)

The formation of a small amount of the rearranged acetate **7.113** may
indicate some incursion of ions with the more delocalized structure **7.114**.
Solvolysis at 25° of *anti*-8-bicyclo[3,2,1]oct-2-enyl toluene-*p*-sulphonate
(**7.115**) is $2 \cdot 6 \times 10^5$ times faster than the *syn*-ester (**7.116**) (cf. the 7-norbornenyl
analogues).[4] The molecular dimensions preclude a symmetrical p-π interaction
in the intermediate ion, which can be formulated as **7.117**.

(7.115)   (7.116)   (7.117)

Cholesteryl and related systems. We have seen how the anchimeric acceleration of solvolysis, with retention of configuration, in cholesteryl compounds
(e.g. **7.32**) led to the first suggestion of homoallylic cations (Paragraph 7.2.2).
With the leaving group in the 3α-position (see **7.118**) participation by the

[1] Tanida, 1963; Tanida, Tsuji and Ishitobi, 1964; Tanida and Ishitobi, 1966.
[2] Goering and Sloan, 1961b; Goering and Towns, 1963; Schleyer, 1964b.
[3] LeBel and Huber, 1963.
[4] LeBel and Spurlock, 1964.

10

double bond in the ionization is not possible, the solvolysis is much slower than for the 3β-compound and the product is the 3,5-diene.[1]

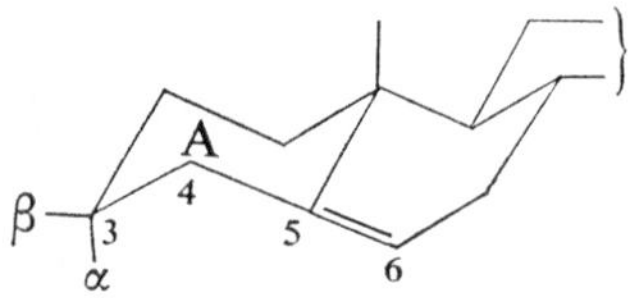

(7.118) 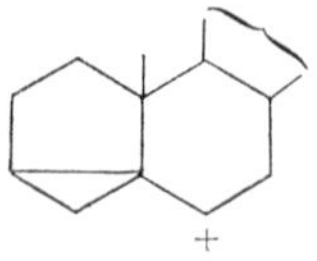   (7.119) 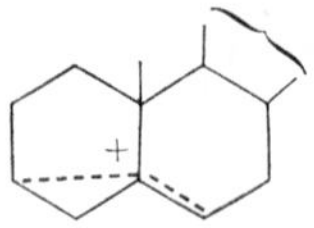   (7.120)

The intermediate cation in the solvolysis of cholesteryl compounds could be represented as the 3,5-cyclocholestan-6-yl cation (**7.119**), the structure **7.120** approximating to the transition state for its formation. The bridged representation is usually preferred because of the rapidity of ionization of i-cholesteryl compounds (e.g. **7.121**) and the formation of products by attack on both C(3) and C(6),[2] Alternative interpretations are possible.[3]

The introduction of methyl substituents into the 4-position of the cholesteryl group has similar effects to the introduction of a β-methyl group into the but-3-enyl system (Table 7.5). Again a more delocalized ion (**7.122**, analogous to **7.65**) seems to be favoured by the methyl substitution. Accordingly

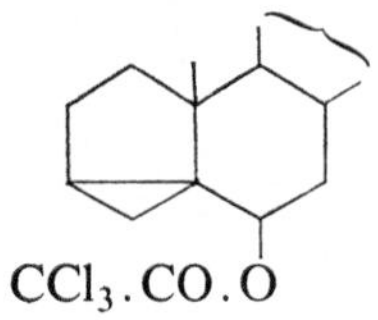

CCl$_3$.CO.O   R$_\beta$ R$_\alpha$ H   CH$_3$

(7.121) 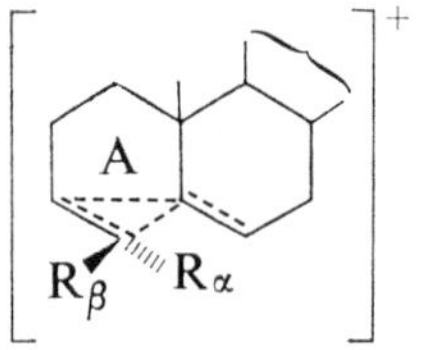   (7.122) 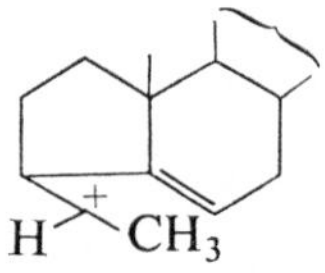   (7.123)

4α-methylcholesteryl sulphonate esters are acetolysed some twenty times more rapidly than the parent compound,[4] presumably because of the increased importance of the valence-bond structure **7.123** to the mesomeric ion (**7.122**; R$_\alpha$=CH$_3$, R$_\beta$=H). Introduction of a 4β-methyl substituent has a very much smaller effect, attributable to distortion of ring A, due to 1,3-diaxial methyl interaction, and consequently less favourable juxtaposition of C(3) and the double bond.[5] The importance of delocalization like that in **7.122** in the intermediate for the solvolysis of simple cholesteryl compounds is unknown,

---

[1] King and Bigelow, 1952; Shoppee and Williams, 1955.

[2] Winstein and Adams, 1948; Winstein and Schlesinger, 1948; Kosower and Winstein, 1956.

[3] Winstein and Kosower, 1959.

[4] Julia, Lavaux et al., 1964; De Sousa and Moriarty, 1965.

[5] Vandenheuvel, Moriarty and Wallis, 1962; de Sousa and Moriarty, 1965; see also: Vandenheuvel and Wallis, 1962; Shoppee and Johnston, 1962.

though it may be significant that ionization of **7.124** yields the same mixture of products as the cholesteryl ester.[1]

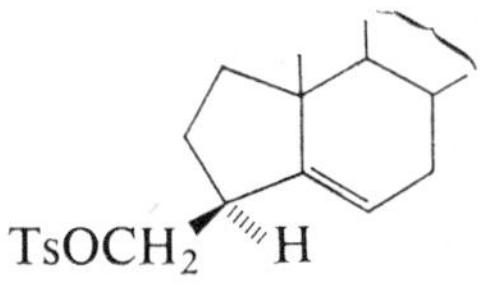

TsOCH₂   H
(7.124)

7.5 Electron-deficient Bridged Carbonium Ions

7.5.1 ALKYL- AND HYDROGEN-BRIDGING IN ACYCLIC SYSTEMS

Some of the earliest suggestions of bridged carbonium ions referred, without much real evidence, to bridging by alkyl groups.[2] Even now the evidence is sparse. Ionization potentials indicate that C—C bond electrons are less tightly bound than C—H bond electrons, which suggests that alkyl bridging should be more important than hydrogen bridging.[3]

Application of the simple kinetic criterion of bridged-ion formation does not provide convincing evidence. For example, acetolysis of neopentyl toluene-p-sulphonate occurs at a rate almost identical with that of the ethyl ester, even though steric hindrance to solvent participation (solvation and/or nucleophilic attack leading to bimolecular substitution) is quite large in the former compound.[4] The high rate, unexpected on this basis, might be attributable to formation of the ion **7.125**, but such an explanation neglects the rate-enhancing inductive effect of the β-methyl substituents[5] and the possibility of steric acceleration (cf. the agreement between the observed and calculated rate constants for 3,3-dimethyl-2-butyl toluene-p-sulphonate in Table 7.1). In cases

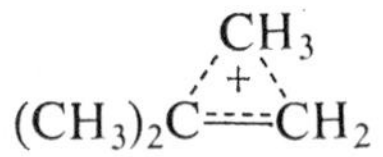

$$(CH_3)_2\overset{CH_3}{\overset{+}{C}}{=}\!=\!{=}CH_2$$

(7.125)

$$CH_3 . CHR . CHX . CH_3$$

(7.126)

where hydrogen-bridged carbonium ions are thought (see below) to be formed during solvolyses, titrimetric rate constants do not appear to be unusually large. Thus 3-methyl-2-butyl p-bromobenzenesulphonate (**7.126**; R = CH₃, X = p-BrC₆H₄.SO₃) undergoes solvolysis little faster than predicted by the

---

[1] Whitham, 1961; Whitham and Wickramasinghe, 1964.
[2] Watson, 1939; Eyring, Hulburt and Harman, 1943.
[3] Walsh, 1947.
[4] Winstein and Marshall, 1952; see also Dostrovsky and Hughes, 1946; McElrath, Fritz *et al.*, 1960.
[5] Nordlander, Jindal *et al.*, 1966.

Taft-Ingold equation[1] or by Schleyer's procedure (Table 7.1). In the case of *erythro*- and *threo*-3-cyclohexyl-2-butyl toluene-*p*-sulphonates (**7.126**; $R = C_6H_{11}$, $X = p\text{-}CH_3 . C_6H_4SO_3$), solvolysis rates are respectively twenty-five and six times greater than for the 2-butyl ester.[2] At least part of these rate accelerations seems attributable to steric acceleration.

In the case of hydrogen-bridging a further kinetic method of investigation is available. The isotope effect of replacing the hydrogen of the CHR-group in **7.126** ($R = CH_3$ or C_6H_{11}) by deuterium is to reduce the rate of solvolysis by a factor of about 2.[1,2] This is a much larger effect than normal for β-deuterium substitution (see Paragraph 4.2.7) and has been attributed to the participation of the β-hydrogen in the ionization. Support for this explanation is provided by the observation that the magnitude of β-deuterium-isotope effects is markedly dependent on the dihedral angle between the β-C—H(D) and C—X bonds,[3] being greatest when the angle is 180° and least for a dihedral angle of 90°. Large deuterium-isotope effects have also been observed in the solvolysis of 4-t-butylcyclohexyl *p*-bromobenzenesulphonates which are conformationally fixed.[4] For the *cis*-compound (**7.127**) introduction of an axial β-deuterium gives $k_H/k_D = 1\cdot436$ in 50% aqueous ethanol at 35°; equatorial β-deuterium gives $k_H/k_D = 1\cdot096$. Furthermore, while the effect of two equatorial β-deuterium atoms can be predicted from the effect of one, two axial β-deuterium atoms lead to a greater rate reduction than expected. These results suggest stabilization of the transition state of ionization and of the inter-

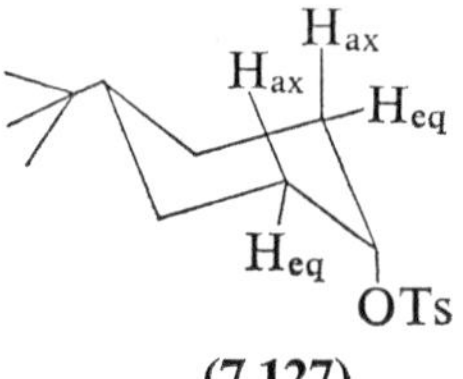

(7.127)

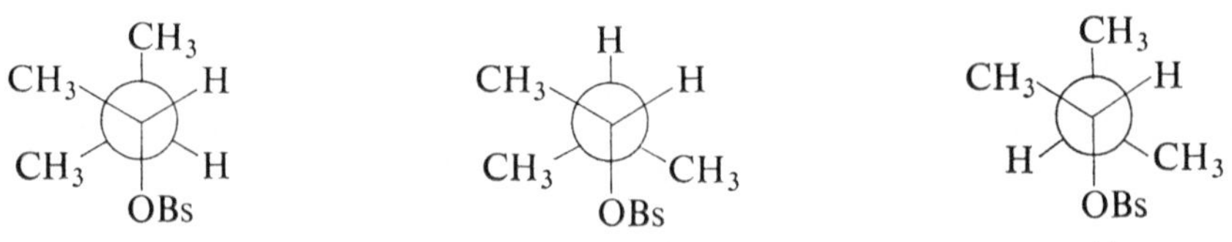

(a)   (b)   (c)

(7.128)

[1] Winstein and Takahashi, 1958.
[2] Cram and Tadanier, 1959.
[3] Shiner and Humphrey, 1963; Shiner and Jewett, 1964.
[4] Shiner and Jewett, 1965a,b.

mediate carbonium ion by hyperconjugation. Such a stabilizing influence is conceptually akin to bridging, and a substantial proportion of the 15% yield of substitution products is rearranged or of retained configuration.[1]

In the case of 3-methyl-2-butyl p-bromobenzenesulphonate, shown in its three possible conformations in **7.128**, the absence of observable anchimeric acceleration may be attributable to the necessity for rotation about the central C—C bond in order to transform the most populated conformation (**7.128c**) into a conformation (**7.128b**) in which hydrogen participation can occur. The energy difference between rotamers would offset the lowering of the energy barrier for ionization due to bridging. This might offer a general explanation of the absence of marked kinetic effects due to bridging by relatively small groups (e.g. H or CH_3) but cannot be a factor in determining the rate of solvolysis of **7.127**. Moreover, it is not immediately apparent why methyl bridging is not important in solvolysis of **7.128**, since a *trans*-methyl-bridged ion could arise directly from the most stable conformer.

Stereochemical evidence of hydrogen and alkyl bridging is not convincing. In the solvolysis of 3-cyclohexyl-2-butyl toluene-p-sulphonate, the (minor) products of substitution with and without migration of hydrogen are **7.129** and **7.126** ($R = C_6H_{11}$, $X = OH$). Surprisingly, the rearranged product shows predominant retention of configuration at the migration origin, while the 3-cyclohexyl-2-butanol is formed with predominant inversion at C(2). If a hydrogen-bridged carbonium ion were the only intermediate this would require solvent attack from the direction of the bridge, a conclusion which contrasts sharply with those reached from stereochemical studies in other systems.

$$C_6H_{11} \diagdown$$
$$\phantom{C_6H_{11}}C.CH_2.CH_3$$
$$CH_3 \diagup$$
$$OH$$

(7.129)

Studies of isotopic redistribution in nitrous acid deamination provide evidence of a somewhat different type of bridged ion. Early investigations[2] of ^{14}C-rearrangement in compounds of the type $R.CH_2.^{14}CH_2.NH_2$ seemed best explained in terms of interconversion of unbridged carbonium ions, since the amount of rearrangement bore no consistent relationship to the expected bridging ability of the group $R(H, CH_3, ArCH_2)$. Careful examination of the deamination of 1-labelled n-propylamine, which yields n-propyl alcohol, i-propyl alcohol, propene and a little cyclopropane, indicates 3–4% rearrangement of the label in the n-propyl alcohol fraction to C(2) and C(3) to nearly, but not quite, the same extent.[3] This result rules out the possibility of 1,3-hydride

---

[1] Winstein and Holness, 1955b.

[2] J. D. Roberts and Yancey, 1952; J. D. Roberts and Halmann, 1953; A. W. Fort and Roberts, 1956.

[3] Lee and Kruger, 1965; cf. Reutov and Shatkina, 1962.

shifts[1] in the n-propyl cation, and, when taken in conjunction with deuterium and tritium labelling experiments,[2] the occurrence of successive 1,2-hydride shifts. The findings can be satisfactorily accounted for if some 5 % of n-propanol arises from so-called protonated cyclopropane intermediates, first detected in mass-spectrometric studies (see Section 7.6), which undergo interconversion (7.130a, b, c).[3] The methyl-bridged ion 7.131 could be a precursor. The mechanism involving protonated cyclopropane intermediates (7.130) also accounts satisfactorily for the formation of appreciable quantities of cyclopropane in the deamination of n-propylamine.[4] Protonated cyclopropanes also provide a satisfactory interpretation of the acid-catalysed ring-opening of cyclopropane[5] and may be involved in the reaction of n-propoxide and related alkoxide ions with dihalocarbenes[6] (p. 52).

$$
\begin{array}{cccc}
\text{(a)} & \text{(b)} & \text{(c)} & \\
\underset{\text{(7.130)}}{} & & & \text{(7.131)}
\end{array}
$$

7.5.2 THE CYCLOPROPYLMETHYL-CYCLOBUTYL AND RELATED PROBLEMS

The rates of solvolysis of cyclopropylmethyl chloride and benzenesulphonate in absolute or aqueous ethanol are unusually high compared with other primary alkyl (including but-3-enyl) derivatives.[7] For example, the benzenesulphonate undergoes ethanolysis some 500 times more rapidly than the ethyl ester. Cyclopropylmethyl chloride shows internal return to cyclobutyl and but-3-enyl chlorides during acetolysis.[8] The rearranged chlorides are stable under the reaction conditions and are therefore not precursors of the rearranged acetates which accompany cyclopropylmethyl acetate in the reaction product.

[1] Karabatsos and Orzech, 1962; Reutov and Shatkina, 1962.

[2] Lee, Kruger and Wong, 1965; Karabatsos, Orzech and Meyerson, 1965.

[3] Cf. Skell and Starer, 1960; Silver, 1960.

[4] Aboderin and Baird, 1964. On this basis, protonated cyclopropanes are much less important in the deamination of n-butylamine, isobutylamine and neopentylamine (Skell and Starer, 1960; Silver, 1960; Bayless, Mendicino and Friedman, 1965; Hsi and Meyerson, 1966; Karabatsos, Mount et al., 1966).

[5] Baird and Aboderin, 1963, 1964a; for related work on opening of cyclopropane rings in reactions involving carbonium ions, see LaLonde and Forney, 1963; LaLonde and Tobias, 1963, 1964; LaLonde and Batelka, 1964; Corey and Atkinson, 1964; DePuy, Schnack et al. ,1965; Schleyer, Van Dine et al., 1966; Deno and Lincoln, 1966.

[6] Skell and Starer, 1962; Skell and Maxwell, 1962.

[7] J. D. Roberts and Mazur, 1951a; Bergstrom and Siegel, 1952.

[8] J. D. Roberts and Mazur, 1951a; Caserio, Graham and Roberts, 1961.

An almost identical mixture of cyclopropylmethyl, cyclobutyl and but-3-enyl derivatives is obtained in nitrous acid deamination of cyclopropylmethylamine and cyclobutylamine.[1] The rate of acetolysis of cyclobutyl toluene-p-sulphonate[2] is also unusually rapid and considerable anchimeric acceleration is indicated.[3] Again a mixture of cyclobutyl, cyclopropylmethyl and but-3-enyl derivatives is formed. But-3-enyl toluene-p-sulphonate gives a similar mixture (see Paragraph 7.4.2.) All these facts at first sight strongly suggest bridging.

Nitrous acid deamination of cyclopropylmethylamine-1-^{14}C gives products with the activity distributed as shown in **7.132**.[3] The label is nearly, but not quite, statistically distributed among the three methylenes. On treatment with Lucas's reagent (aqueous $HCl/ZnCl_2$) (equilibrating conditions) cyclopropylmethanol-1-^{14}C is converted to but-3-enyl chloride in which the label is statistically distributed (cf. **7.132c**). A similar pattern of results is observed using deuterium labels on C(1).[4]

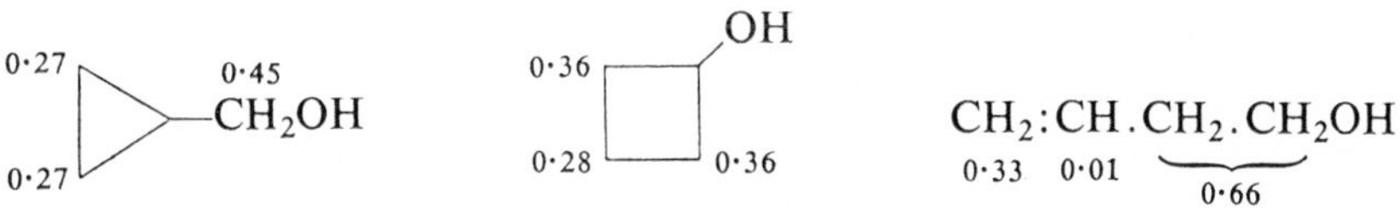

$$\begin{array}{ccc} \text{(a, 48\%)} & \text{(b, 47\%)} & \text{(c, 5\%)} \end{array}$$

(7.132)

The results of labelling experiments are explicable in terms of unbridged carbonium ions, the interconversion of which is more rapid than their reaction with the solvent, though not so rapid that, under conditions of kinetic control, the label is statistically distributed. J. D. Roberts and his co-workers, bearing in mind the rapid rate of solvolysis of cyclopropylmethyl and cyclobutyl derivatives, prefer to formulate the intermediates as bridged ions (**7.133**, Figure 7.6). These ions are considered to be rapidly interconvertible, the reaction involving change in nuclear positions. However, the interconversions are not instantaneous since this would have the same consequence as the formation of a single, highly symmetrical bridged ion (**7.134**). This hypothesis seems to account for the results of both the kinetic and isotopic labelling experiments.

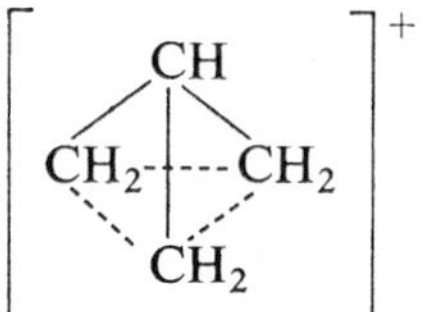

(7.134)

[1] J. D. Roberts and Mazur, 1951a.
[2] J. D. Roberts and Chambers, 1951; H. C. Brown and Ham, 1956.
[3] Mazur, White *et al.*, 1959; J. D. Roberts and Mazur, 1951b.
[4] Caserio, Graham and Roberts, 1961.

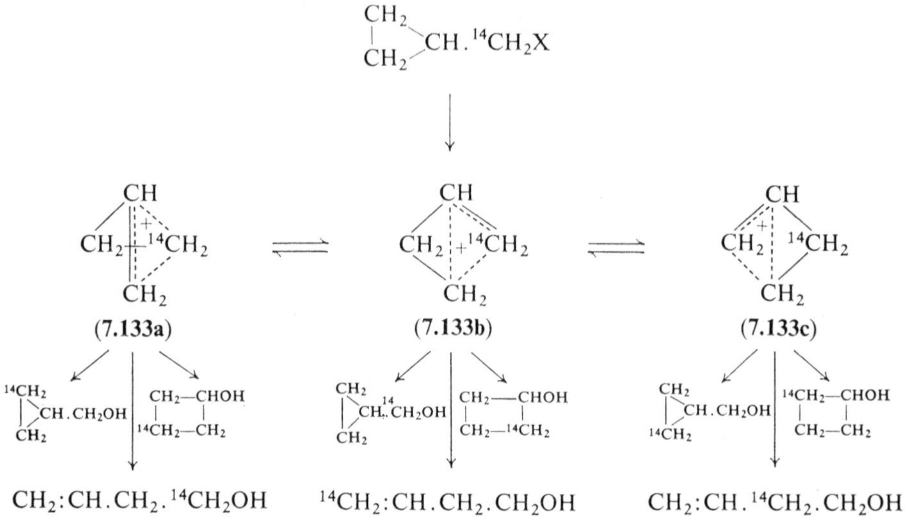

$$
\begin{array}{c}
CH_2 \\
| \quad \diagdown \\
CH_2 \diagup CH.^{14}CH_2X
\end{array}
$$

$$\downarrow$$

$$
\begin{array}{ccc}
CH & CH & CH \\
\diagup\vdots\diagdown & \diagup\vdots\diagdown & \diagup\vdots\diagdown \\
CH_2 \!\!\overset{+}{\underset{}{|}}\!\!^{14}CH_2 & CH_2\,\overset{+}{|}\,^{14}CH_2 & CH_2\,|\,^{14}CH_2 \\
\diagdown\vdots\diagup & \diagdown\vdots\diagup & \diagdown\vdots\diagup \\
CH_2 & CH_2 & CH_2 \\
(7.133a) & (7.133b) & (7.133c)
\end{array}
$$

$$
\begin{array}{ccc}
^{14}CH_2 \quad CH_2\!\!-\!\!CHOH & CH_2 \quad CH_2\!\!-\!\!CHOH & CH_2 \quad ^{14}CH_2\!\!-\!\!CHOH \\
|\diagup CH.CH_2OH \;\;|\quad| & \diagup^{14}CH.CH_2OH \;\;|\quad| & \diagup CH.CH_2OH \;\;|\quad| \\
CH_2 \qquad\quad ^{14}CH_2\!\!-\!\!CH_2 & CH_2 \qquad\quad CH_2\!\!-\!\!^{14}CH_2 & ^{14}CH_2 \qquad\quad CH_2\!\!-\!\!CH_2
\end{array}
$$

$$CH_2\!:\!CH.CH_2.^{14}CH_2OH \qquad ^{14}CH_2\!:\!CH.CH_2.CH_2OH \qquad CH_2\!:\!CH.^{14}CH_2.CH_2OH$$

FIG. 7.6. Rearrangement during carbonium ion reactions of cyclopropylmethyl-1-^{14}C derivatives (according to J. D. Roberts).

Angle strain in the three-membered ring could provide the driving force for bridging on ionization of cyclopropylmethyl compounds,[1] and, indeed, there is a progressive return to solvolysis rates typical of simple primary alkyl derivatives in the series cyclopropylmethyl, cyclobutylmethyl,[2] cyclopentylmethyl and cyclohexylmethyl.[3] But cyclopropyl groups seem capable of increasing rates of carbonium ion formation at an adjacent carbon atom even when rearrangements are not involved[4] (Section 4.3), the effect of each additional cyclopropyl group being roughly the same (Table 7.8, Column 1). This could arise by overlap of the vacant p-orbital on the central carbon atom with the bent orbitals of the two $\alpha\beta$-carbon–carbon bonds of each three-membered ring,[5] in keeping with what is known about the stereochemistry of these ions and the marked deshielding of all the ring protons in their NMR-spectrum (Paragraph 2.3.1). The unbridged representation of the cyclopropylmethyl cation, which on this basis is equivalent to **7.59b**, appears best to describe the intermediate in these reactions.

Deuterium and phenyl substituents in the cyclopropyl ring have only a small effect on the rate of solvolysis of cyclopropylmethyl derivatives (Table 7.8). The small effect of the phenyl groups may be related to their small effect

[1] Wilcox and Mesirov, 1962; Winstein and Kosower, 1959.
[2] Wilt and Roberts, 1962b; Winstein and Marshall, 1952; Winstein and Holness, 1955a.
[3] Felkin and Le Ny, 1957; see also W. G. Dauben and Rogan, 1956.
[4] Hart and Sandri, 1959; Hart and Law, 1962, 1964.
[5] See Breslow, 1963, for an alternative view.

Table 7.8. *Substituent effects on relative solvolysis rates of cyclopropylmethyl derivatives*

Solvent / X⁻	1 — 80% Dioxan–water (w/w) (60°) p-NO₂.C₆H₄.CO₂⁻	2 — Acetic acid (20°) C₆H₅.SO₃⁻	3 — 90% Dioxan–water (v/v) (25°) β-C₁₀H₇.SO₃⁻	4 — 60% Acetone–water (v/v) (65°) p-NO₂.C₆H₄.CO₂⁻
	(i-Pr)₃CX 1/240	△ H / CH₂X (1)	△ H / CH₂X (1)	—
	△ H / CX(i-Pr)₂ (1)	△ H / CD₂X 0.77	△ CH₃ / CH₂X 40[a]	△ H / CHX.CH₃ (1)
	(△)₂CX(i-Pr) 950[b]	△ D / CH₂X 0.87	△ Ph / CH₂X 1·3[c]	△ H / CHX.Ph 179
	(△)₃CX 1,030,000[b]	△ CD₂/CD₂ H / CH₂X 1·02	Ph–△ H / CH₂X *cis* 0·62 *trans* 2·19	△ H / CHX.p-Tol 2140
Ref.	d	e	f	g

[a] From halide solvolysis in aqueous ethanol (Cox, Caserio *et al.*, 1961; see, however, D. D. Roberts, 1964; Schleyer and Van Dine, 1966).

[b] Comparison through hydrolysis of the benzoate in 95% dioxan–water at 25°.

[c] Solvent: acetic acid (Wilt and Roberts, 1962a). For values in other solvents, see D. D. Roberts, 1965.

[d] Hart and Sandri, 1959; Hart and Law, 1962, 1964.

[e] Borčić, Nikoletić and Sunko, 1962.

[f] Sneen, Lewandowski *et al.*, 1961.

[g] Sneen and Baron, 1961.

10*

on the stability of cyclopropenyl cations, although other conclusions might be drawn[1]. The extent to which rearrangements occur is also reduced by substitution.[2] The most substantial substituent effects in Table 7.8 are found in 1-aryl substituted derivatives (Column 4) for which the transition state and intermediate carbonium ion are less likely to be bridged. The results of kinetic[3] and stereochemical[4] investigations of solvolytic reactions of methyl-substituted cyclopropylmethyl derivatives seem best accommodated by structure **7.59b**.[5]

A further manifestation of the unusual behaviour of compounds containing three-membered rings appears in reactions of bicyclo[3,1,0]hexyl derivatives. *cis*-3-Bicyclo[3,1,0]hexyl toluene-*p*-sulphonate (**7.135**; R=H, X=OTs) undergoes acetolysis some nine times more rapidly than the *trans*-isomer, shows a "special salt effect", and yields the *cis*-acetate almost exclusively. In contrast the *trans*-toluene-*p*-sulphonate is converted to a mixture of *cis*-acetate and olefin (2:1).[6] More significantly, however, while acetolysis of 3-deuterio-*trans*-toluene-*p*-sulphonate gives *cis*-acetate which is still deuteriated only at C(3), the product from 3-deuterio-**7.135** has the isotopic label distributed equally between C(3) and the two bridgehead carbon atoms.[7] Similar scrambling occurs if the *cis*-toluene-*p*-sulphonate is labelled at the

(7.135)   (7.136)

bridgehead positions. These observations can be satisfactorily interpreted in terms of the symmetrical, so-called trishomocyclopropenyl cation (**7.136**; R=H),[8] which is regarded by Winstein as the first member of a series of "homoaromatic "compounds.[9]

However, structure **7.136** is *not* compatible with the observation that *cis*-3-deuteriobicyclo[3,1,0]hexylamine (**7.135**; R=H, X=NH$_2$) undergoes deamination to give a mixture of *cis*- and *trans*-3-alcohols with little scrambling of the label, together with *cis*- and *trans*-2-alcohols.[10] Also acetolysis of **7.135**

[1] Sneen, Lewandowski *et al.*, 1961.

[2] Cox, Caserio *et al.*, 1961; Silver, Caserio *et al.*, 1961.

[3] Schleyer and Van Dine, 1966.

[4] Vogel and Roberts, 1966; Richey and Richey, 1966.

[5] See also, Birladeanu, Hanafusa *et al.*, 1966.

[6] Winstein, Sonnenberg and de Vries, 1959; Winstein and Sonnenberg, 1961a.

[7] Winstein, Sonnenberg and de Vries, 1959; Winstein and Sonnenberg, 1961b.

[8] For a review, see Winstein, Friedrich *et al.*, 1966.

[9] Winstein, 1959; but see also, Boikess and Winstein, 1963; Radlick and Winstein, 1963; Untch, 1963.

[10] Corey and Dawson, 1963.

($R = C_6H_5$, $X = OTs$) is slower than that of the unsubstituted compound and yields a mixture of the rearranged acetate **7.137** and the related olefins **7.138** and **7.139**.[1] While this is unexpected if **7.136** ($R = Ph$) is the intermediate, the apparent instability of the unrearranged acetate **7.135** ($R = Ph$, $X = OAc$) reduces the significance of the structure of the products. Nevertheless, intermediates of lower symmetry than **7.136** ($R = H$) (e.g. **7.140**) which could even be unbridged, and which undergo interconversion more rapidly than they react with solvent, could explain the toluene-*p*-sulphonate solvolyses. Clearly further investigation is necessary.[2]

(7.137)   (7.138)   (7.139)

(7.140)

7.5.3 BICYCLO[2,2,1]HEPTYL AND RELATED SYSTEMS

This represents one of the most intensively studied groups of compounds. The skeletal rearrangements of the bicyclic monoterpenoids, all of which are alkylated bicycloheptyl compounds, have long been known and interpreted in terms of Wagner-Meerwein reactions involving unbridged carbonium ions (see Section 6.4). More recently, evidence has accumulated which seems to require that the carbonium ions involved are bridged. Because this evidence is less equivocal in the case of non-terpenoid compounds, and because monoterpenoid rearrangements have been extensively reviewed recently in terms of the structures of the intermediate carbonium ions,[3] we shall concentrate our attention on rather simpler bicycloheptyl compounds, beginning with the simplest bicyclo[2,2,1]heptyl system, norbornyl.

Norbornyl compounds. Some relative rates of solvolysis of *exo*- (**7.141**) and *endo*-2-norbornyl (**7.142**) compounds are given in Table 7.9.[4]

Estimation of the extent of anchimeric acceleration directly from solvolysis rates is difficult since the values depend markedly on the reference compound

[1] Corey and Uda, 1963.

[2] Further work on compounds incorporating three-membered rings may be found in: Norin, 1964; Sauers, 1962; Wiberg and Wenzinger, 1965; Colter and Musso, 1965; Gassman and Zalar, 1966; Applequist and Landgrebe, 1964.

[3] de Mayo, 1959; Berson, 1963.

[4] For mass-spectrometric evidence, see DeJongh and Shrader, 1966.

Table 7.9. *Relative rates* (k_{rel}) *of solvolysis of 2-norbornyl derivatives*[a]

	k_{rel}				$k_{rel}^{obs}/k_{rel}^{calc}$
Leaving group	p-Br·C$_6$H$_4$·SO$_3^-$		Cl$^-$	Hg	p-CH$_3$·C$_6$H$_4$·SO$_3^-$
Solvent	CH$_3$CO$_2$H	CH$_3$OH	80% C$_2$H$_5$OH/H$_2$O	CH$_3$CO$_2$H	CH$_3$CO$_2$H
Temperature (°C)	25	25	85	25	50
Cyclopentyl	32·4	(1)	—	—	1
Cyclohexyl	(1)	—	—	(1)	(1)
endo-2-Norbornyl	1·5	1/113	(1)	1/43	2·5
exo-2-Norbornyl	516	3·9	70	112	2000
Reference	b	c	d	e	f

[a] Values in parentheses are reference points for the columns in which they appear.
[b] Winstein, Morse et al., 1952.
[c] H. C. Brown, Chloupek and Rei, 1964b.
[d] J. D. Roberts and Bennett, 1954.
[e] Winstein, Vogelfanger et al., 1962.
[f] Schleyer, 1964a,b.

used, the leaving group and the solvent. Significantly, however, Schleyer's[1] method of calculating acetolysis rates gives good agreement (within 0·4 log unit) for cyclopentyl and endo-norbornyl toluene-p-sulphonates but indicates a 2000-fold acceleration in the case of the exo-ester. Values of $\Delta S^{\ddagger}$ for

(7.141)   (7.142)   (7.143)

solvolysis of the exo- and endo-chlorides are the same; the rate difference arises from different values of $\Delta H^{\ddagger}$ and therefore decreases as the temperature increases.[2] The volume of activation ($\Delta V^{\ddagger}$) in the solvolysis of the exo-p-bromobenzenesulphonate (14·3 cm^{3}mole^{-1}) is significantly lower than that for the endo- and cyclopentyl-esters (17·7 and 17·8 cm^{3}mole^{-1}). This has been taken to imply less electrostriction of the solvent by the transition complex from **7.141** owing to a more diffuse charge.[3]

Other relevant experimental facts concerning these systems are product compositions. Solvolysis of both exo- and endo-2-norbornyl derivatives leads almost exclusively to exo-2-norbornyl substitution products.[4] There is no evidence of exo–endo interconversion prior to solvolysis.[5] Significantly, the small amount of elimination product is almost entirely nortricyclene (**7.143**).[6]

Optically active exo- or endo-2-norbornyl p-bromobenzenesulphonates yield racemic exo-solvolysis product.[7] Internal return results in some racemization of the exo-ester before solvolysis, but this alone could not account for the complete[6] loss of optical activity.[8] Clearly, a symmetrical intermediate is involved.

These results are explicable, according to one view, if the symmetrical bridged ion **7.144** is the intermediate in the solvolysis of exo-2-norbornyl derivatives, the stereochemistry of the reactant being such that bridging can occur in the transition state of ionization. In the endo-isomers it is geometrically impossible for the ejection of the leaving group to be assisted by the incipient

[1] Schleyer, 1964a.

[2] Lee and Wong, 1964, 1965.

[3] le Noble and Yates, 1965.

[4] Winstein and Trifan, 1949; Winstein, Clippinger et al., 1965; Goering and Schewene, 1965.

[5] Winstein and Trifan, 1952a.

[6] Winstein, Clippinger et al., 1965.

[7] Winstein and Trifan, 1949, 1952a,b.

[8] Winstein and Trifan, 1952b.

bridging by C(6) in the transition state: bridging by C(7) is also unlikely since it would produce substantial angle strain in the transition state. A large solvolysis rate for the *exo-* relative to the *endo-*isomer should therefore constitute *prima facie* evidence for bridging during the ionization of the *exo-*compounds. In agreement with this explanation, anchimeric assistance is not observed in the *endo-*series, although the reaction product suggests that the bridged ion is involved later. The methylene bridge, by shielding the rear side of C(1) and C(2), restricts attack by solvent molecules to the front side with resultant formation of *exo-*product. Moreover, reaction at C(1) and C(2) gives *exo-*products which are enantiomeric. It also seems significant that deuterium substitution at either of the 6-positions causes a much larger kinetic isotope effect on the solvolysis rate of **7.141** (X = *p*-bromobenzenesulphonate) than on that of the corresponding *endo-*ester.[1]

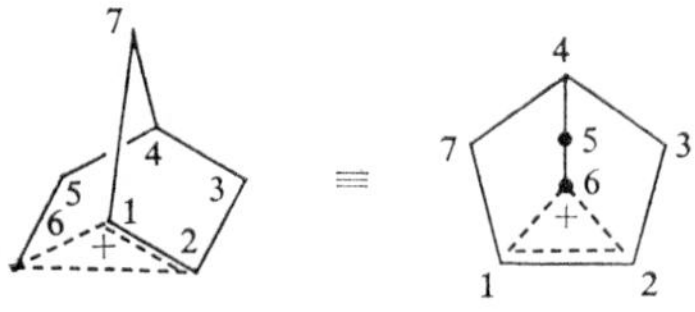

(7.144) 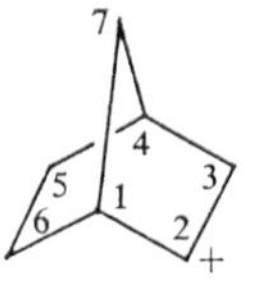   (7.145) 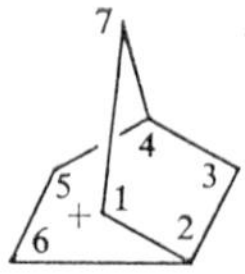   (7.146) 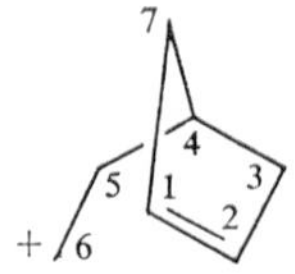   (7.147)

Structures **7.145**—**7.147** may be regarded as limiting forms of **7.144**.[1] Of these, **7.145** and **7.146** are interrelated through a 1,2-shift, and thus also related to the rearranged and unrearranged products. This is confirmed by the observation that *exo-*2-norbornyl *p*-bromobenzenesulphonate, labelled with ^{14}C at C(2) and C(3), gives on acetolysis *exo-*2-norbornyl acetate in which part of the label is distributed to C(1) and C(7).[2] In addition, some 15% of the label appears at C(5) and C(6). While this might be thought to require the participation of a more symmetrical intermediate ion (**7.148**),[3] the fact that

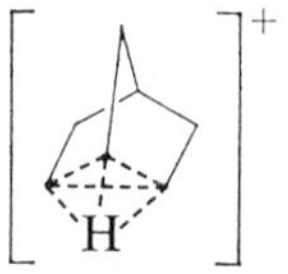

(7.148) 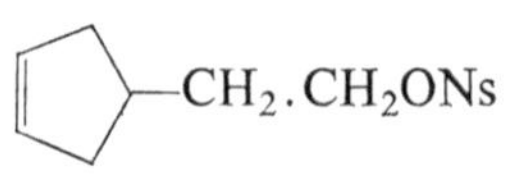   (7.149)

the proportion of label appearing at C(5) and C(6) decreases with increasing nucleophilic activity of the solvent suggests that a 6,2-hydride shift competes with solvent attack on the first-formed norbornyl cation. This conclusion is supported by work on monoterpenoids, in which the 6,2-hydride shift leads to the

[1] Murr, Nickon, *et al.*, 1967; Jerkunica, Borčić and Sunko, 1967.
[2] J. D. Roberts and Lee, 1951; J. D. Roberts, Lee and Saunders, 1954.
[3] Berson and Grubb, 1965.

formation of a different product[1] and by NMR examination of stable solutions of the 2-norbornyl cation which reveals the occurrence of rapid 6,2-shifts.[2]

Inclusion of **7.147** among the limiting structures of the norbornyl cation is suggested by the fact that 2-cyclopent-3-enylethyl p-nitrobenzenesulphonate (**7.149**) is solvolysed much more rapidly than its saturated analogue and yields *exo*-2-norbornyl products.[3] This indicates anchimeric assistance to ionization by the π-electrons of the double bond, sometimes referred to as the π-route to bridged bicyclic cations (in contrast to the σ-route just described).[4]

An alternative explanation of the rearrangements occurring during solvolysis of 2-norbornyl compounds is that the unbridged ion **7.145** is formed first and interconverts with the rearranged ion **7.146** at a rate which is much more rapid than reaction of either cation with the solvent.[5] [The rapid equilibration of **7.145** and **7.146** has even been suggested to inhibit approach of solvent molecules to the rear side of C(1) and C(2) (sometimes referred to as the "windshield wiper effect") with resultant formation of *exo*-substitution product exclusively.[6]] Such an explanation can probably be discounted for the following reasons:

1. If the ionization of *exo*-2-norbornyl compounds gives an unbridged ion, then the rate of solvolysis should not be accelerated. The much faster solvolysis of the *exo*- compared with the *endo*-compound must then be ascribed to the unexpectedly low reactivity of the latter. This low reactivity has been attributed to steric *hindrance* to separation of an *endo*-leaving group (see p. 233).[7] However, there seems to be little other evidence to support this suggestion for members of the *endo*-2-norbornyl series such as *endo*-2-norbornyl toluene-*p*-sulphonate.

2. Optically active *exo*-2-norbornyl esters yield *exo*-product which is > 99·95 % racemic, so that, assuming reaction *via* unbridged intermediates, the rate of conversion of the first-formed unbridged ion (**7.145**) to the rearranged ion (**7.146**) must be more than 2000 times faster than its reaction with the solvent. The latter reaction is estimated to have a rate constant of 10^9 to 10^{10} sec^{-1}, and thus the rate constant for equilibration must be close to 10^{13} sec^{-1}, the value predicted by absolute rate theory for a reaction having zero free

---

[1] E.g. W. Hückel and Volkmann, 1963.

[2] Schleyer, Watts *et al.*, 1964; Saunders, Schleyer and Olah, 1964; Fraenkel, Ralph and Kim, 1965; see also Lee and Lam, 1966a.

[3] Bartlett and Bank, 1961, Bartlett, Bank *et al.*, 1965.

[4] Winstein and Carter, 1961; see also Le Ny, 1960; Lawton, 1961, Goering and Sloan, 1961a,b; Bartlett and Sargent, 1965; Bartlett, Trahanovsky *et al.*, 1965; Gream and Wege, 1964; Lee and Lam, 1966b.

[5] Winstein and Trifan, 1952b; J. D. Roberts, Lee and Saunders, 1954; H. C. Brown, 1966.

[6] H. C. Brown, 1962. Torsional (eclipsing) effects about the C(1)—C(2) bond in the transition state for reaction of the carbonium ion may also play a part in favouring the *exo*-product (Schleyer, 1967a,b).

[7] H. C. Brown, 1962; H. C. Brown, Chloupek and Rei, 1964c.

energy of activation.[1] Attempts to trap an unbridged 2-norbornyl cation by reaction with an ambident leaving group (Figure 7.7) both gave racemic product indicating that stepwise rearrangement, if it occurs, takes place much more rapidly than re-orientation and collapse of the ion pair.[2] The NMR spectrum of the 2-norbornyl cation in SbF_5–SO_2–SO_2F_2 shows that the protons on C(1) and C(2) [and on C(6)] are equivalent at least down to temperatures of $-120°$.[3] These NMR experiments therefore do not conflict with the conclusion that interconversion of **7.145** and **7.146** is without activation energy, i.e., that these structures are merely limiting forms of a single intermediate ion.

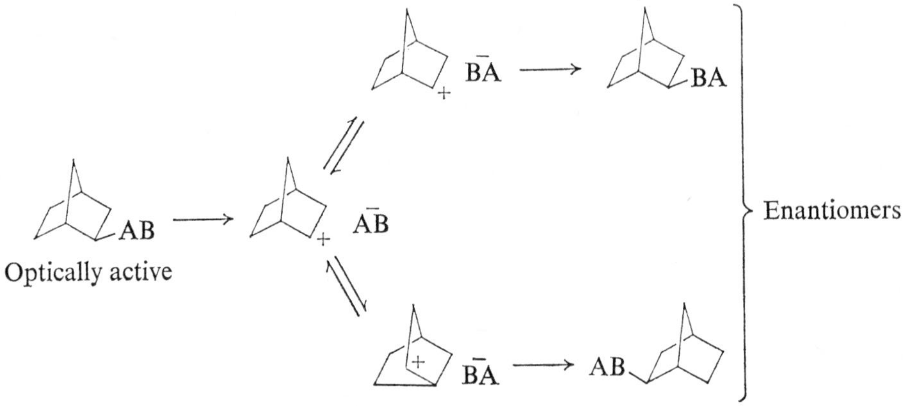

FIG. 7.7. Reaction of ambident nucleophiles with unbridged norbornyl cations.

$$(AB = m\text{–}SO_3^-.C_6H_4.CO_2^-,[4] \text{ or } p\text{–}CF_3.C_6H_4.CO.S^-.[5])$$

3. Finally, nitrous acid deamination of the 2-norbornylamines (**7.141** and **7.142**; $X = NH_2$) gives substitution products containing small amounts of *endo*-material, the proportion depending upon the stereochemistry of the starting material. Moreover, there is considerable retention of optical activity, particularly in the *endo*-product.[6] This behaviour, under circumstances where bridged-ion formation is probably less important, contrasts sharply with that observed in other solvolytic reactions.

[1] Winstein, 1965; Bunton and O'Connor, 1965.
[2] Corey, Casanova *et al.*, 1963; S. G. Smith and Petrovich, 1964, 1965.
[3] M. Saunders, Schleyer and Olah, 1964.
[4] Corey, Casanova *et al.*, 1963.
[5] S. G. Smith and Petrovich, 1964. 1965,
[6] Berson and Remanick, 1964; Berson and Ben Efraim, 1959; Corey, Casanova *et al.*, 1963; see also Corey and Casanova, 1963.

In the norbornyl series, then, a bridged structure for the intermediate ion seems probable on the basis of present evidence (cf. below).

Substituted norbornyl compounds. With the exception of certain terpenoids, carbonium-ion reactions of substituted norbornyl compounds have received much less intensive study than the parent bicyclic system. Accordingly, the interpretation of experimental observations is difficult and to some extent determined by personal preference.

The introduction of a methyl or phenyl group in the 2-*endo*-position of *exo*-2-norbornyl chloride increases the rate of ethanolysis by several orders of magnitude.[1] This effect resembles that of α-substitution in cyclopentyl chloride. The *exo–endo* rate ratio for the bicyclic tertiary chlorides is similar to that for 2-norbornyl chloride itself.[2] On the other hand, introduction of a methyl or aryl group at the (bridgehead) 1-position of *exo*-2-norbornyl chloride or *endo*-2-methyl-*exo*-2-norbornyl chloride has a relatively small effect on the solvolysis rate,[3] which is again similar to the effects of analogous structural changes in the cyclopentyl series.[4] It can therefore be argued that the carbonium ions involved in all these reactions are unbridged, the large effect of 2-substituents and small effect of 1-substituents indicating that the positive charge is localized on C(2).[5]

If this view is accepted, the large *exo–endo* rate ratios and predominant *exo*-substitution[6] observed in solvolyses of bicyclo[2,2,1]heptyl compounds are no longer valid criteria of bridging, even in unsubstituted norbornyl derivatives. However, it can be argued that the kinetic similarities between 2-substituted and unsubstituted 2-norbornyl sulphonate esters (or chlorides) arise by coincidence.[7] *endo*-Groups attached to C(2) and C(6) are compressed in tertiary *exo*-2-norbornyl derivatives, and this compression would increase on forming a bridged transition state but would decrease on ionization without bridging. The large rate of solvolysis of, for example, *endo*-2-methyl-*exo*-2-norbornyl toluene-*p*-sulphonate compared with that of its epimer would then be attributed to steric acceleration rather than bridging. This postulate requires the thermodynamic stability of the former compound to be less than that of the epimer. There is no direct evidence on this point. (The corresponding alcohols show little difference in stability.[8]) On the other hand, there is some support

[1] H. C. Brown, Chloupek and Rei, 1964a,b; H. C. Brown and Rei, 1964b.

[2] H. C. Brown and Rei, 1964a.

[3] Schleyer and Kleinfelter, 1960; H. C. Brown and Bell, 1964a; H. C. Brown and Rei, 1964a.

[4] H. C. Brown and Ham, 1956; H. C. Brown, Morgan and Chloupek, 1965.

[5] H. C. Brown, 1966. Other pertinent results are reported by H. C. Brown and Takeuchi, 1966; H. C. Brown and Liu, 1967. For the many counter-arguments, see especially Winstein, 1965; Dewar and Marchand, 1965.

[6] H. C. Brown and Bell, 1964b; Bell and Brown, 1964; Colter, Friedrich *et al.*, 1965.

[7] Sargent, 1966.

[8] Rei and Brown, 1966.

for the idea of steric hindrance of formation of a bridged transition state (although this refers to a secondary toluene-*p*-sulphonate): 6,6-dimethyl substitution retards the solvolysis not only of *endo*-2-norbornyl toluene-*p*-sulphonate (which is due to steric hindrance to the departure of the leaving group) but also of the *exo*-toluene-*p*-sulphonate.[1]

Exclusive 2,3- and 1,6-*exo*-hydride shifts in carbonium ions formed from certain methyl- and phenyl-substituted 2-norbornyl derivatives seem to be best interpreted in terms of bridged ions,[2] but alternative steric explanations have also been advanced.[3]

Again, the major problem in many discussions is the estimation of solvolysis rates in the absence of anchimeric assistance. Especially for tertiary systems, where Schleyer's procedure is inapplicable, the choice of an appropriate reference compound is critical. Thus the rapid rates observed in the solvolysis of a number of terpenoid compounds may arise at least in part from steric acceleration.[4]

One may expect that α-substituent groups that are capable of dispersing a positive charge would generally make bridging less important relative to the formation of unbridged ions. The demonstration, by spectroscopic and other methods, that treatment of **7.150** with acid yields a rapidly interconverting

(7.150)

pair of unbridged ions[5] (Paragraph 2.3.1) supports this.[6] The extent to which unbridged ions are involved in the reactions of other substituted norbornyl derivatives requires further study. Examination of the influence of destabilizing substituents[7] may prove fruitful.

[1] Schleyer, Donaldson and Watts, 1965; see also Berson, McRowe and Bergman, 1966, and p. 233.

[2] Berson, Bergman *et al.*, 1965; Berson, Hammons *et al.*, 1965; Collins, Cheema *et al.*, 1965; Benjamin and Collins, 1966; Benjamin, Ponder and Collins, 1966.

[3] H. C. Brown, 1966; Schleyer, 1967a.

[4] H. C. Brown and Chloupek, 1963; Beltramé, Bunton *et al.*, 1964; see, however, Bunton and O'Connor, 1965.

[5] Schleyer, Kleinfelter and Richey, 1963; but see Sargent, 1966.

[6] Cf. Bartlett, Webster *et al.*, 1959; Bartlett, Dills and Richey, 1960.

[7] Gassman and Marshall, 1965, 1966b.

7.5.4 OTHER SATURATED BICYCLIC SYSTEMS

Kinetic evidence for formation of bridged ions in saturated bicyclic systems other than [2,2,1]heptyl and [3,1,0]hexyl is sparse. Stereochemical observations are thus correspondingly more important, though some of the stereospecificity observed may be explicable without recourse to the postulation of bridged intermediates.

Estimates[1] of the anchimeric acceleration in the acetolysis of a number of bicyclic toluene-*p*-sulphonates are given in Table 7.10, together with the proportion of the product in which substitution occurs with retention of configuration.

The kinetic evidence for bridging in the acetolysis of 7.154 (X=H, Y= OTs) and 7.155 is scarcely convincing, yet these reactions show the highest proportions of substitution with retention. Even in cases where substantial rate accelerations are detectable, mixtures of products are obtained, and the stereochemistry of some products cannot be explained in terms of the likely bridged carbonium ion (e.g. the formation of 7.158 in 14% yield from 7.152 *via* 7.157). In some instances, ionization directly to the rearranged unbridged

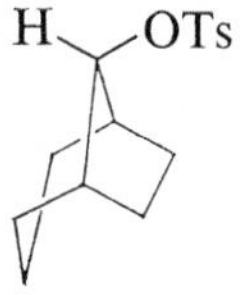

(7.151) 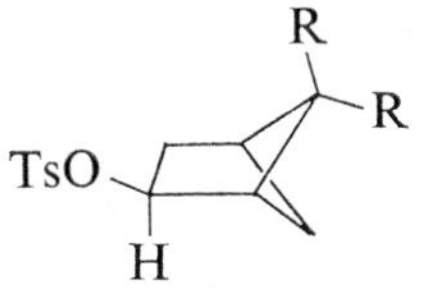   (7.152) 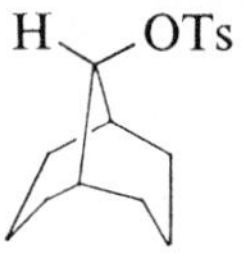   (7.153)

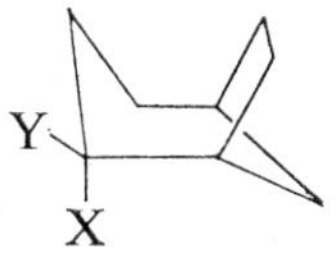

(7.154) 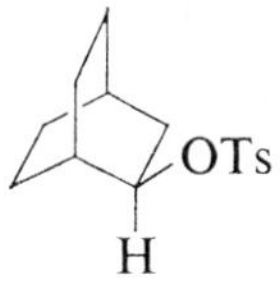   (7.155) 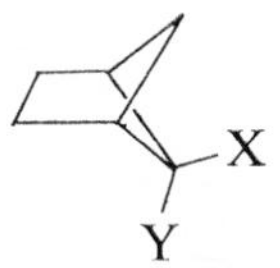   (7.156)

Exo: X=OTs; Y= H
Endo: X=H; Y= OTs

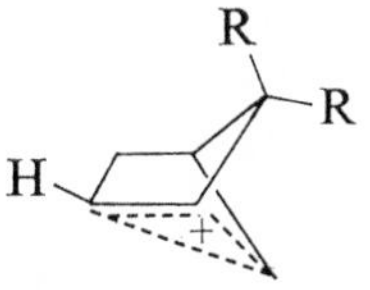

(7.157) 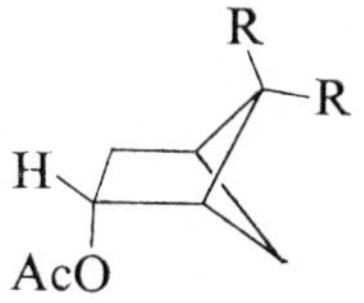   (7.158)

[1] Schleyer, 1964b.

Table 7.10. *Estimated^d anchimeric acceleration in acetolysis at 25° of some saturated bicyclic toluene-p-sulphonates*

Compound	$\log(k_{obs}/k_{calc})$	% Retention	Ref.
exo-8-Bicyclo[3,2,1]octyl (**7.151**)	4·2^a	0	*e*
2-Bicyclo[2,1,1]hexyl (**7.152**; R = H)	2·9^b	56^c	*d, f*
9-Bicyclo[3,3,1]nonyl (**7.153**)	1·5	5	*e*
Axial-2-bicyclo[3,2,1]octyl (**7.154**; X = OTs, Y = H)	1·2	~30	*g*
Equatorial-2-bicyclo[3,2,1]octyl (**7.154**; X = H, Y = OTs)	0·4	100	*g*
2-Bicyclo[2,2,2]octyl (**7.155**)	0·9	~60	*g*

^{a} For the *endo*-compound, $\log(k_{obs}/k_{calc})$ is 0·1.
^{b} For 5-bicyclo[2,1,1]hexyl toluene-*p*-sulphonates (**7.156**), $k_{endo}/k_{exo} = 3 \times 10^6$, suggesting bridging analogous to that in solvolysis of the cyclobutyl ester (Wiberg and Fenoglio, 1963).
^{c} Refers to 5,5-dimethyl-2-bicyclo[2,1,1]hexyl toluene-*p*-sulphonate (**7.152**; R = CH₃).
^{d} Schleyer, 1964b.
^{e} Foote and Woodward, 1964.
^{f} Meinwald, Gassman and Hurst, 1962; Meinwald and Gassman, 1963.
^{g} Walborsky, Baum and Youssef, 1961; Goering and Sloan, 1961a,b.

carbonium ion may occur.[1] The isomeric 2-bicyclo-octyl cations, obtainable by a variety of routes,[2] show a particularly complex pattern of behaviour, which in some cases seems to require interconversion of unbridged and bridged forms of the same ion at rates comparable to that of nucleophilic attack by solvent.[3]

7.6 Bridged Carbonium Ions in the Gas Phase

Thus far we have dealt with evidence for the formation of bridged carbonium ions in solution, that is to say solvated ions. In the absence of solvent, which, by interacting with positive charge, tends to reduce the charge delocalization within the carbonium ion, bridging should be more important. Moreover, generation of gas-phase carbonium ions by electron impact produces highly energetic species for which unusual structures become more probable.

As discussed in Paragraph 4.2.4, certain gas-phase eliminations from alkyl halides are thought to involve formation of carbonium ion–halide ion pairs. Rearrangement of the carbon skeleton accompanies elimination in some cases.

[1] Winstein, Gadient *et al.*, 1958.
[2] Le Ny, 1960; Goering and Sloan, 1961a,b; Winstein and Carter, 1961; Walborsky, Baum and Youssef, 1961; Berson and Reynolds-Warnhoff, 1962, 1964; Berson and Willner, 1962, 1964; Berson and Poonian, 1966.
[3] Berson and Reynolds-Warnhoff, 1962, 1964; Berson and Willner, 1962, 1964.

For example, the pyrolysis of neopentyl chloride at 450° yields a mixture of isomeric pentenes as the major product, indicating methyl migration during the reaction.[1] This is not, of course, evidence of the formation of bridged intermediates. However, elimination from bornyl and isobornyl chlorides at 350°, giving mixtures of camphene, tricyclene and bornene of which the first two compounds constitute 70–80%, takes place at rates which are in the ratio 1:10.[2] This rate ratio is of the same order of magnitude as the ratio predicted by extrapolation of the rates of solvolysis of the chlorides or racemization of the corresponding alcohols in solution to 350°. This seems to indicate anchimeric acceleration of the gas-phase elimination from isobornyl chloride, giving the bridged ion **7.159** (see, however, p. 278). Bridged ions may also be involved in certain eliminations which are accompanied by rearrangement when alcohols are passed over "non-acidic" alumina at high temperature.[3]

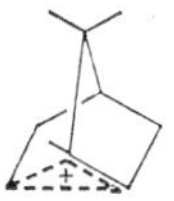

(**7.159**)

In Paragraph 7.5.1, evidence concerning the formation of cationated cyclopropanes in certain reactions in solution was discussed. The possibility of the existence of such species was based on mass spectrometric observations as follows:[4]

1. In the mass spectrum of t-butylbenzene a metastable peak is found at $m/e = 69.6$ indicating the occurrence of the process:

$$C_6H_5.\overset{+}{C}(CH_3)_2 \;\rightarrow\; C_7H_7^+ + C_2H_4.$$

Using t-butylbenzene-α-^{13}C, the ratio of intensities of the peaks of $m/e = 91:m/e = 92$ was 2:1, indicating that the aliphatic carbon atoms become equivalent during the decomposition. The overall fragmentation may be represented:

$$C_6H_5.^{13}C(CH_3)_3 + e^- \;\rightarrow\; C_6H_5.^{13}\overset{+}{C}(CH_3)_2 + CH_3\cdot + 2e^-$$

$$C_6H_5.^{13}\overset{+}{C}(CH_3)_2 \;\rightarrow\; \begin{bmatrix} C_6H_5^+ \\ ^{13}CH_2\!\!-\!\!CH_2 \\ \diagdown\diagup \\ CH_2 \end{bmatrix} \;\rightarrow\; \begin{matrix} C_7H_7^+ \;+\; C_6^{13}CH_7^+ \;+C_2H_4 \\ (m/e = 91)\;\;(m/e = 92) \end{matrix}$$

(**7.160**)

[1] Maccoll and Swinbourne, 1960, 1964.
[2] Maccoll and Bicknell, 1962.
[3] Herling and Pines, 1963.
[4] Rylander and Meyerson, 1956.

The occurrence of certain peaks and their relative intensities in the mass spectra of related compounds can be satisfactorily interpreted in terms of species analogous to **7.160**.

2. An ion $C_3H_7^+$ which has an ionization potential differing from that of the isopropyl cation by almost 0·5 eV appears in the mass spectra of both n- and iso-alkanes.

3. 2-Deuteriated propane and n- and iso-butane show peaks in their mass spectra corresponding to the formation of CH_2D^+. This result and observation 2 are explicable if protonated cyclopropane is formed during the fragmentations in question.

Cyclopropane rings bear some similarity to carbon–carbon double bonds, and it is not unreasonable to formulate cationated cyclopropanes as analogues of π-complexes (**7.161**).

$$R^+$$
$$CH_2\!\!-\!\!CH_2$$
$$\diagdown\diagup$$
$$CH_2$$

(7.161)

$$H$$
$$CH_2\overset{+}{\cdots}CH_2$$
$$\diagdown\diagup$$
$$CH_2$$

(7.162)

Extended Hückel calculations[1] (see Paragraph 5.2.6) predict that the more stable structure for protonated cyclopropane would be **7.162**. Rapid rearrangement among the three equivalent structures for **7.162** would be required for such a species to account for the isotopic scrambling in observations 1 and 3.

7.7 Conclusion

From the foregoing account, it will be evident that the study of bridged carbonium ions is a lively field for experimentation, speculation and controversy. As for all studies of reaction mechanism, the conclusions to be drawn represent a balance of probabilities, a balance which can be swung in one direction or the other by the results of new experiments. In some cases the balance of probabilities suggests that a particular carbonium ion is best represented by a bridged structure. In others the situation is more delicately balanced and further investigation seems necessary. In carbonium-ion chemistry as a whole, the majority of observations seem to be satisfactorily interpretable without the postulation of bridged structures. Generalizations are particularly hazardous in the field of bridged carbonium ions at the present time and one probably cannot even assume that the importance of bridging in the carbonium ion formed from a given reactant under different conditions is always the same. Each system needs to be considered individually.

[1] Hoffmann, 1964b.

8 | RELATED SPECIES

8.1 Acylium Ions

8.1.1 NOMENCLATURE

There appears to be no agreed nomenclature for ions of the general formula $R.CO^+$. Acylium ions, acyl cations, oxocarbonium ions and acylonium ions are names that have all been used at various times. We shall adopt a system of nomenclature analogous to that used for carbonium ions in the rest of the book. Thus we shall employ acylium ion as the generic term and use the term acyl cation to specify a particular structure, e.g. benzoyl cation, $C_6H_5.CO^+$, acetyl cation, $CH_3.CO^+$.

8.1.2 STABLE ACYLIUM IONS: PHYSICAL EVIDENCE

Conductivity. Acyl halides and Lewis acids (e.g. $CH_3.CO.F\text{-}BF_3$, $C_6H_5.CO.Cl\text{-}SbCl_5$) form complexes which, in liquid sulphur dioxide at low temperatures, have conductivities of similar magnitude to typical inorganic electrolytes, such as potassium iodide,[1] and which can be formulated as acylium salts (i.e. $CH_3.CO^+BF_4^-$, $C_6H_5.CO^+SbCl_6^-$). Acetic anhydride has a small but significant conductivity[2] which may be due to self-ionization:[3]

$$(CH_3.CO)_2O \rightleftharpoons CH_3.CO^+ + CH_3.CO_2^-.$$

Indeed, acetyl chloride can be titrated conductimetrically with metal acetates in acetic anhydride, indicating that the acyl halide is a Lewis acid in this solvent system.[4]

---

[1] Seel, 1943a,b.

[2] N. F. Hall and Voge, 1933.

[3] Mackenzie and Winter, 1948a.

[4] Jander, Rüsberg and Schmidt, 1948; but see E. A. Evans, Huston and Norris, 1952.

Cryoscopy in sulphuric acid. Some of the first evidence suggesting the stable existence of acylium ions came from cryoscopic measurements on carboxylic acids in sulphuric acid analogous to those which indicated carbonium ion formation from alcohols (Section 2.4). A selection of results for substituted benzoic acids and some related compounds is given in Table 8.1.

Table 8.1. *ν-Values from cryoscopic measurements on substituted benzoic acids and related compounds,* ⟨○⟩—CO.X, *in sulphuric acid*

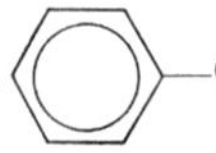

X	Substituent					ν	Ref.
	2	3	4	5	6		
OH	H	H	H	H	H	2·0	a
	CH$_3$	H	CH$_3$	H	CH$_3$	4·0	a
	CH$_3$	H	H	H	CH$_3$	2·9–3·5	a
	CH$_3$	Br	CH$_3$	Br	CH$_3$	2·0–2·6	a
	CH$_3$	CH$_3$	H	CH$_3$	CH$_3$	4·01	b
	CH$_3$	CH$_3$	CH$_3$	CH$_3$	CH$_3$	4·02	b
	CH$_3$	H	H	H	NO$_2$	<2	a
	Br	OCH$_3$	OCH$_3$	OCH$_3$	Br	<2	a
	CH$_3$	H	CO$_2$H	H	CH$_3$	>2	b
OCH$_3$	CH$_3$	H	CH$_3$	H	CH$_3$	5	c
Cl	CH$_3$	H	CH$_3$	H	CH$_3$	5	d
O.CO.C$_6$H$_5$	H	H	H	H	H	4	e

[a] Treffers and Hammett, 1937.
[b] Newman and Deno, 1951b.
[c] Newman, Kuivila and Garrett, 1945.
[d] Gillespie and Robinson, 1964, 1965b.
[e] Gillespie, 1950b.

Simple protonation of carboxylic acids is indicated by $\nu = 2$, but, when $\nu = 4$ *immediately after dissolution* of the organic acid, formation of acylium ions according to the equation,

$$R.CO.OH + 2H_2SO_4 \rightleftharpoons R.CO^+ + H_3O^+ + 2HSO_4^- \qquad (8.1)$$

is indicated. Intermediate values indicate incomplete conversion to the acyl cation. Evidently two *ortho*-substituents in the phenyl group are necessary for acylium ion formation presumably because they destabilize the protonated carboxylic acid with respect to the derived acylium ion by steric inhibition of resonance. However, acylium ion formation is only promoted by electron-releasing substituents. The last three entries in Table 8.1 also indicate conversion to the corresponding acylium ion.

Absorption spectroscopy. The common spectroscopic techniques, electronic, infrared, and NMR, have all been employed.

Acetyl and propionyl cations, generated from the corresponding carboxylic acids in 33 % oleum, show no maxima in the ultraviolet above 215 mμ.[1] Aroyl cations under the same conditions show fairly intense absorption (usually two maxima) in the aryl-conjugated region (250–350 mμ) and this can be used to study the equilibrium between the acylium ion and protonated carboxylic acid.[2]

Infrared spectroscopy provides important information concerning the formation of acylium ions and about the nature of the bonding in them.[3] Spectra of complexes formed by acyl halides and Lewis acids in the solid or liquid states and in solution can be readily obtained: the investigation of acyl cations in concentrated sulphuric acid by infrared spectroscopy is much more difficult experimentally.[4] Representative data for complexes of acyl halides and Lewis acids in the solid state are recorded in Table 8.2.

Although there is some dependence of the spectrum on the physical state of the complex[5] two types of interaction can be distinguished:

(i) Complexes in which the carbonyl absorption of the acyl halide is moved to lower frequencies (~ 1550 cm^{-1}), similar to that observed in complexes formed by ketones and Lewis acids, indicating an oxonium structure of type **8.1**. This has been confirmed by X-ray analysis[6] in one case.

(ii) Complexes in which the carbonyl absorption is replaced by one at higher frequencies (2200–2300 cm^{-1}) accompanied by absorption characteristic of the symmetrical anion derived from the Lewis acid. These are thought to be acylium (e.g. **8.2**) salts. X-ray crystallography of the $CH_3 \cdot CO \cdot F\text{-}SbF_5$ complex confirms that it is acetyl hexafluoroantimonate.[7]

The triple-bond character of the carbon–oxygen link is responsible for the high-frequency absorption [cf. carbon monoxide,[8] 2181 cm^{-1}; ketene,[9] 2151 cm^{-1}; and benzenediazonium ion,[10] 2280 cm^{-1} ($N \equiv N$)]. However, free aliphatic acylium ions may have somewhat lower carbon–oxygen absorption frequencies than those in Table 8.2. Thus the only high-frequency absorption

[1] Olah, Pittman *et al.*, 1966.
[2] Schubert, Donohue and Gardner, 1954; see also, Newman and Deno, 1951b; Schubert, Zahler and Robins, 1955; Schubert, Robins and Craven, 1959.
[3] E.g. Cooke, Susz and Herschmann, 1954.
[4] Oulevey and Susz, 1965.
[5] Cook, 1959; Cassimatis, Gagnaux and Susz, 1960.
[6] Rasmussen and Broch, 1965.
[7] Boer, 1966.
[8] Susz and Wuhrmann, 1957a.
[9] Arendale and Fletcher, 1957.
[10] Whetsel, Hawkins and Johnson, 1956.

Table 8.2. *Infrared frequencies in the range 1500–2300 cm⁻¹ for acyl halides and their solid complexes with Lewis acids*

Acyl halide	Lewis acid	Frequencies (cm⁻¹)		Ref.
$CH_3.CO.F$	—		1848(vs)	a
	BF_3	1560(w), 1619(m),	2299(vs)	a
	PF_5	1558(w), 1620(m),	2297(vs)	a
	SbF_5	1554(w), 1621(m),	2294(vs)	a
$CH_3.CO.Cl$	—	1800(vs)		a
	$AlCl_3$	1560, 1639	2200(sh), 2305	b
	$SbCl_5$	1587(w), 1709(m)	2283	a
$CH_3.CH_2.CO.F$	—	1848(vs)		c
	SbF_5	1554(w), 1621(w),	2290(vs)	c
$(CH_3)_2CH.CO.F$	—	1848(vs)		c
	SbF_5	1585(m)	2270(vs)	c
$(CH_3)_3C.CO.F$	—	1823(vs)		c
	SbF_5	1570(m),	2260(vs)	c
$C_6H_5.CO.F$	—	1812(vs)		c
	SbF_5	1531(m)	2212(vs)	c
$C_6H_5.CO.Cl$	—	1736(vs), 1776(vs)		c
	$SbCl_5$	1575(vs), 1656(vs)	2215(vw)	c
	$AlCl_3$	1560(vs), 1665(vs)		b
$2\text{-}CH_3.C_6H_4.CO.Cl$	—	1730(vs), 1770(vs)		b
	$TiCl_4$	1505, 1602		b
	$AlCl_3$	1525, 1602	2200	b
$2,6\text{-}(CH_3)_2C_6H_3.CO.Cl$	—	1780(vs)		b
	$AlCl_3$		2190(vs)	b
$2,4,6\text{-}(CH_3)_3C_6H_2.CO.Cl$	—	1785(vs)		b
	$AlCl_3$		2190(vs)	b

(s = strong, m = medium, w = weak, v = very, sh = shoulder)

[a] Olah, Kuhn et al., 1962.
[b] Susz and Cassimatis, 1961; see also, Susz and Wuhrmann, 1957b, Cassimatis, Gagnaux and Susz, 1960.
[c] Olah, Tolgyesi et al., 1963.

of the complex of acetyl chloride and gallium chloride in nitrobenzene solution[1] is at 2200 cm^{-1} whereas, in solid complexes, only a shoulder on a peak at about 2300 cm^{-1} appears at this frequency.

(8.1)   (a)   (b)   (c)
                                                                  (8.2)

NMR spectroscopy is also applicable to the study of acylium ion formation under a variety of conditions. For example, the chemical shift [in p.p.m. from internal $\overset{+}{N}(CH_3)_4$] of the methyl protons of acetic acid in the solvent system H_2O-H_2SO_4-SO_3 becomes more negative as the acidity increases and indicates three stable species, acetic acid ($\delta = -2 \cdot 0$ p.p.m.), protonated acetic acid ($\delta = -2 \cdot 67$ p.p.m.) and acetyl cation ($\delta = -3 \cdot 93$ p.p.m.).[2] The technique can be used to estimate rate and equilibrium constants for formation of acylium ions.[3] The ^{1}H- and ^{19}F-spectra of the complexes formed between acyl fluorides and antimony pentafluoride or boron trifluoride also indicate the formation of acylium ions.[4] For example, the ^{1}H-spectrum of the 1:1 complex of acetyl fluoride and antimony pentafluoride in sulphur dioxide solution shows two singlet resonances of unequal intensity at lower field than the proton resonance of acetyl fluoride itself (which is a doublet owing to ^{1}H–^{19}F spin–spin coupling). The low-field resonance ($\delta = -4 \cdot 08$ p.p.m. from $(CH_3)_4Si$) has been assigned to the acetyl cation. The other ($\delta = -2 \cdot 94$ p.p.m.), which predominates in solutions of the complex in hydrogen fluoride, may be due to acetyl hexa-fluoroantimonate ion pairs, although a highly polarized complex analogous to **8.1** cannot be ruled out completely.

8.1.3 ACYLIUM IONS AS REACTION INTERMEDIATES

Having shown that there is a substantial body of evidence for the formation of stable acylium ions under certain conditions, we now consider the extent to which such species are involved as transient intermediates in organic reactions. For the most part, the reactions in question are nucleophilic substitutions at a carbonyl carbon atom: $Y + R.CO.X \rightarrow R.CO.Y + X$. Two mechanisms (A

[1] Cook, 1962.
[2] Deno, Pittman and Wisotsky, 1964.
[3] Hogeveen, 1967.
[4] Olah, Kuhn *et al.*, 1962, 1964; Olah, Tolgyesi *et al.*, 1963; Olah, Moffatt *et al.*, 1964; Olah and Comisarow, 1966b.

and B) may be formulated, both of which are two-step and involve formation of a short-lived intermediate:

A: Acylium ion formation

$$R.CO.X \rightleftharpoons R.CO^+ + X \xrightarrow{\text{Y}} R.CO.Y$$

B: Carbonyl addition

$$R.CO.X + Y \rightleftharpoons R.\overset{\displaystyle O^-}{\underset{\displaystyle Y}{C}}{-}X \rightarrow R.CO.Y + X$$

(Inessential charges have been omitted).

A third possibility, a one-step displacement of X by Y, is generally regarded as improbable.[1] Both mechanisms A and B are amenable to catalysis by Brönsted and Lewis acids, though A requires the basic site in R.CO.X to be on X while B requires the basic site to be the carbonyl oxygen atom. Distinction between the two mechanisms depends to some extent on the nature of the attacking nucleophile and the subsequent discussion will be divided accordingly.

Substitution by nucleophiles having non-bonded electrons. This group of reactions embraces esterification, ester hydrolysis and solvolysis of acyl halides and related compounds. Since very reactive nucleophiles are involved, the mechanistic problem is, in principle, soluble by kinetic means since the slow step of both reactions should be the formation of the intermediate, and in one case the attacking nucleophile is involved whereas in the other it is not. In most reactions, however, Y is a solvent molecule and the observable kinetic form does not differentiate between the two mechanisms. Instead, less direct procedures, analogous to ones employed in similar studies of alkyl compounds, are employed (Table 8.3).

Presumptive evidence for acylium ion formation in acid-catalysed ester hydrolysis (Mechanism $A_{Ac}1$) is the ready hydrolysis of methyl mesitoate when its solution in concentrated sulphuric acid is poured on to ice, which contrasts with its resistance to hydrolysis under milder acidic conditions.[2] This is supported by the acidity dependence $(k_{obs} \propto h_0^{1.2})$,[3] the approximately zero value of $\Delta S^\ddagger$, and the absence of oxygen exchange in aqueous media.[4] Rate constants for the hydrolysis of 4-substituted-2,6-dimethylbenzoate esters correlate with

[1] Bunnett, 1959.
[2] Treffers and Hammett, 1937; for analogous observations on esterification, see Newman and Deno, 1951b; H. A. Smith and Smith, 1948; Newman, Craig and Garrett, 1949; M. E. Hill, 1960.
[3] Chmiel and Long, 1956.
[4] Bender, Ladenheim and Chen, 1961.

Table 8.3. *Criteria for the differentiation of acylium ion formation (A) and carbonyl addition (B) as mechanisms of substitution of acyl derivatives, R.CO.X*

Test	Observed effect	
	A	B
1. Substituent effects: Increasing electron repulsion	Increased reaction rate	Decreased reaction rate usually
Steric hindrance at C=O	Little effect	Large rate decrease
2. Change in solvent polarity	Large effect	Small effect
3. $\Delta H^{\ddagger}$ and $\Delta S^{\ddagger}$	Larger than for B	Smaller than for A
4. Added powerful nucleophile, Z	Much R.CO.Z but little effect on reaction rate	Much R.CO.Z with proportionate effect on rate
5. Change in acidity of aqueous reaction medium[a]	$k_{obs} \propto h_0$	$k_{obs} \propto [\overset{+}{H_3O}]$
6. Presence of $H_2^{18}O$ in solvent	No incorporation of ^{18}O in R.CO.X	^{18}O-Incorporation in R.CO.X[b]

[a] Not a reliable criterion by itself.
[b] Only if the protonated tetrahedral intermediate reverts to reactants more rapidly than it yields the products.

$\sigma^+(\rho = -3\cdot2)$.[1] For less sterically hindered esters, special reaction conditions (e.g. 99% H_2SO_4) are necessary to suppress the normal $A_{Ac}2$ mechanism of hydrolysis.[2] Acylium ion formation from substituted benzamides can also be detected this way.[3]

The effect of substituent groups on the rate of solvolysis of aroyl halides (Table 8.4) suggests that the intermediate formation of aroyl cations occurs only in very polar media (those near the bottom of the table). Confirmatory evidence comes from the substituent effect on $\Delta H^{\neq}$ and $\Delta S^{\neq}$,[4] the solvent effect on the rate and on the activation parameters for solvolysis[5] (see Table 8.4) and by trapping the intermediate benzoyl cation in the solvolysis of benzoyl chloride using anilines.[6] The detection of the mesitoyl cation in the solvolysis of mesitoyl chloride is made difficult[7] by the occurrence of a hydroxide-ion catalysed reaction in which oxygen exchange occurs.[8] In neutral or acid solution, however, rate constants correlate with $\sigma^+(\rho = -3\cdot8)$ and oxygen exchange is absent, indicating acylium ion formation under these conditions.[8]

The acidity dependence of the rate of hydrolysis of acetic mesitoic anhydride, in conjunction with the observation that $\Delta S^{\neq}$ is close to zero and mesitoyl–oxygen fission occurs, indicates that reaction is by way of the mesitoyl cation.[9] For aliphatic carboxylic acid chlorides[10] and anhydrides[11,12] the experimental evidence is complicated by large electrolyte effects. Attack by acetyl cations has been proposed as the mechanism for the Thiele acetylation of quinones by mixtures of acetic anhydride and mineral acid.[13]

Aromatic acylation: substitution of acyl derivatives by aromatic nucleophiles.[14] The overall reaction may be represented by Equation 8.2:

$$R.CO.X + ArH \rightarrow R.CO.Ar + H^+ + X^- \qquad (8.2)$$

and, when catalysed by metal halides, is usually referred to as Friedel-Crafts acylation. The effect of substituents in benzene on the rate of *m*- and *p*-benzoylation using benzoyl chloride-aluminium chloride in ethylene chloride solvent

[1] Bender and Chen, 1963b.
[2] Leisten, 1956; Kershaw and Leisten, 1960.
[3] Duffy and Leisten, 1960a,b; see also Ladenheim and Bender, 1960.
[4] D. A. Brown and Hudson, 1953b.
[5] Archer and Hudson, 1950; Gold, Hilton and Jefferson, 1954.
[6] Gold, Hilton and Jefferson, 1954.
[7] Cf. D. A. Brown and Hudson, 1953b; Bunton, Lewis and Llewellyn, 1954; Bunton and Lewis, 1956; see also H. K. Hall, 1955.
[8] Bender and Chen, 1963a.
[9] Bunton and Perry, 1960.
[10] Howald, 1962.
[11] Gold and Hilton, 1955.
[12] Bunton and Fendler, 1965.
[13] Mackenzie and Winter, 1948b,c.
[14] For a review, see Jensen and Goldman, 1965.

Table 8.4. *Relative rates of solvolysis at 25° of* p-$X.C_6H_4.CO.Cl$

Solvent		NO_2	Br	Cl	H	CH_3	CH_3O	Ref.
EtOH/Et$_2$O	(40/60 v/v)	32	2·5	2·1	1·0	0·47	0·25	a
EtOH		21·6	2·1	1·9	1·0	0·70	0·81	b
H$_2$O/Me$_2$CO	(5/95 w/v)	35	3·2	—	1·0	0·55	0·60	c
	(50/50 v/v)	11·5	0·92	0·85	1·0	2·9	~30	d
H$_2$O/HCO$_2$H	(1/99 v/v)	Very slow	0·086	—	1·0	6·6	Very fast	e

[a] Branch and Nixon, 1936.
[b] Norris and Young, 1935.
[c] D. A. Brown and Hudson, 1953a.
[d] Hudson and Wardill, 1950.
[e] Crunden and Hudson, 1956.

correlates well with their σ^+-values ($\rho = -9 \cdot 1$).[1] The results fit the Selectivity Relation (Paragraph 6.3.2) and indicate that the acylating species is an electrophile of fairly low reactivity[2] and considerable bulk. The latter property is indicated by the occurrence of little or no o-substitution in alkylbenzenes.[3] The problem is to decide the structure of the electrophile.

It has long been recognized that aromatic acylation can be formulated in terms of attack on the aromatic compound either by an acylium ion or by the related oxonium complex. The kinetic form of the reaction usually involves a function F of the catalyst concentration, i.e.

$$v = k[\text{ArH}][\text{R.CO.X}]F([\text{Catalyst}]) \qquad (8.3)$$

for catalysts which are weak electron acceptors.[4] It becomes

$$v = k[\text{ArH}].[\text{Complex}] \qquad (8.4)$$

for catalysts powerful enough to complex the acylating agent completely.[5] This rules out attack by a *free* acyl cation[6] but does not distinguish between the oxonium complex and an acylium ion pair as the electrophile. Spectroscopic studies (Paragraph 8.1.2) are suggestive in some cases, but alone are not sufficient proof, since the active electrophile could be present in sub-spectroscopic concentration. The observation of halogen exchange between an acyl halide and metal halide catalyst during acylation[7] is similarly inconclusive, though acylation by a system in which such exchange does not occur (e.g. COCl_2-AlCl_3)[8] is evidence for attack by the oxonium complex. However, important evidence that the electrophile can be regarded as an acylium ion-pair is the relative invariance of the reactivity and isomer distribution in the acylation of toluene by a variety of combinations of acylating agent and catalyst (Table 8.5). Thus, while it is clear that a single mechanism is unlikely to apply under all conditions,[9] most of the evidence is interpretable in terms of rate-determining attack by a small, equilibrium concentration of acylium-ion pair on the aromatic compound.[10] Further investigation is clearly desirable.

Other reactions. The formation of acylium ions in decarbonylation reactions and their reversible decomposition into carbonium ions and carbon monoxide

[1] H. C. Brown and Marino, 1959b, 1962.

[2] H. C. Brown and Jensen, 1958b; H. C. Brown and Marino, 1959a,b, 1962.

[3] H. C. Brown, Marino and Stock, 1959; H. C. Brown and Marino, 1959b; Olah, Moffatt *et al.*, 1964; Olah, Kuhn *et al.*, 1964.

[4] E.g. H. C. Brown and Young, 1957; Jensen and Brown, 1958.

[5] Jensen, Marino and Brown, 1959; H. C. Brown, Marino and Stock, 1959.

[6] H. C. Brown and Jensen, 1958a.

[7] Fairbrother, 1937, 1941; Baddeley and Voss, 1954; Oulevey and Susz, 1961.

[8] Huston, 1956; Huston and Lang, 1957; Olah and Olah, 1965.

[9] Satchell, 1961b; Olah, Kuhn *et al.*, 1964.

[10] A fairly small kinetic isotope effect is observed under certain circumstances in displacing deuterium from the aromatic compound (Olah, Kuhn *et al.*, 1964; Jensen and Goldman, 1965).

Table 8.5. *Isomer percentages in the acylation of toluene at 25°*

Acylating agent	Catalyst	Solvent	Rel. rate $(C_6H_6=1)$	Products			Ref.
				o	m	p	
$CH_3.CO.F$	SbF_5	CH_3NO_2	125	1·4	0·9	97·7	a
$CH_3.CO.Cl$	$SbCl_5$	CH_3NO_2	121	0·8	0·9	98·3	b
$CH_3.CO.Cl$	$AlCl_3$	CH_3NO_2	134	1·2	1·3	97·5	b
$CH_3.CO.Cl$	$AlCl_3$	$CH_2Cl.CH_2Cl$	128	1·2	1·3	97·5	c
$CH_3.CO.Br$	$AlBr_3$	CH_3NO_2	136	0·8	1·5	97·7	b
$(CH_3.CO)_2O$	$SbCl_5$	CH_3NO_2	—	1·3	1·0	97·6	b
$Ph.CO.Cl$	$AlCl_3$	$Ph.CO.Cl$	110	9·3	1·5	89·3	d
$Ph.CO.Cl$	$AlCl_3$	$CH_2Cl.CH_2Cl$	117	8·4	1·4	90·2	c
$Ph.CO.Cl$	$\{ GaCl_3,FeCl_3$ $SbCl_5,SbCl_4 \}$ $Ph.CO.Cl$		—	9·1 ± 0·5	90·9 ± 0·5		d

[a] Olah, Kuhn *et al.*, 1964.
[b] Olah, Moffatt *et al.*, 1964.
[c] H. C. Brown and Marino, 1959a,b.
[d] H. C. Brown and Jensen, 1958b; Jensen and Brown, 1958.

11

have already been discussed (Paragraph 3.1.2). An alternative reaction of acylium ions is rearrangement to give an α-ketocarbonium ion (e.g. **8.5**). Thus pivaloyl chloride (**8.3**) on treatment with aluminium chloride in the presence of a hydride ion donor (isopentane) gives methyl isopropyl ketone (**8.6**).[1] Presumably a 1,2-shift of a methyl group competes with loss of carbon

$$(CH_3)_3C.CO.Cl \quad (CH_3)_3\overset{+}{C}.CO \quad (CH_3)_2\overset{+}{C}.CO.CH_3$$
$$\textbf{(8.3)} \qquad\qquad \textbf{(8.4)} \qquad\qquad \textbf{(8.5)}$$

$$(CH_3)_2CH.CO.CH_3$$
$$\textbf{(8.6)}$$

monoxide from the trimethylacetyl cation (**8.4**). A similar rearrangement of **8.7** to **8.8** may be one of the steps in the formation of ethyl isopropyl ketone (**8.9**, 17%) as well as the expected α-methylvaleric acid (**8.10**, 5%) when n-pentane is treated with carbon monoxide and aluminium chloride.[2]

$$CH_3.CH_2.CH.CH_2.CH_3 \qquad CH_3.CH_2.CO.\overset{+}{C}H.CH_2.CH_3$$
$$\qquad\quad |$$
$$\qquad\quad CO$$
$$\qquad\quad +$$
$$\qquad\textbf{(8.7)} \qquad\qquad\qquad\qquad \textbf{(8.8)}$$

$$CH_3.CH_2.CO.CH(CH_3)_2 \qquad CH_3.CH_2.CH_2.CH.CH_3$$
$$\qquad\qquad\qquad\qquad\qquad\qquad\qquad |$$
$$\qquad\qquad\qquad\qquad\qquad\qquad\quad CO.OH$$
$$\qquad\textbf{(8.9)} \qquad\qquad\qquad\qquad\quad \textbf{(8.10)}$$

8.2 Other Species with Reactive Centres on Carbon

8.2.1 CARBENES[3]

The term carbene describes an organic species which contains a divalent carbon atom bearing two non-bonded electrons (**8.11**). This "electronic sextet" makes carbenes formally similar to carbonium ions. However, carbenes may exist in one of two electronic states having different multiplicities: in the higher-energy singlet state, the non-bonded electrons occupy the same orbital and have opposite spins, and in the triplet state the electrons occupy different orbitals and have parallel spins.[4] In the triplet state, the unpaired electrons are expected to control the behaviour of the carbene, which should thus bear

[1] Balaban and Nenitzescu, 1959.
[2] Balaban and Nenitzescu, 1960.
[3] For a comprehensive review, see Kirmse, 1964.
[4] For a review, see Gaspar and Hammond, 1964; but see also DeMore and Benson, 1964.

little resemblance to that of carbonium ions. Singlet carbenes, which possess one vacant and one doubly occupied carbon orbital, can be likened to both carbonium ions and carbanions. Their overall behaviour is thus expected to depend to a large extent on the polar nature of the attached atoms or groups, electron-repelling substituents promoting carbanion character and electron-attracting substituents carbonium ion character.

$$R_2C:$$

(8.11)

Formation of carbenes. The carbene $RR'C:$ is formally related to the carbonium ion $RR'C^+H$ as a base is to its conjugate acid. Though evidence in support of such an interconversion has been advanced,[1] alternative interpretations are possible.[2] The commonest methods of formation of carbenes can be represented generally as

$$\overset{\backslash}{\underset{/}{C}}.X \rightarrow \overset{\backslash}{\underset{/}{C}}:+X^- \quad (X = \text{halogen or } N_2^+) \quad\quad (8.5)$$

analogous to carbonium ion formation by heterolysis. The reaction can be brought about thermally or by photolysis. Except in some photosensitized reactions, the carbene formed is initially in the singlet state. Its subsequent chemical behaviour depends on the rapidity of its reactions in the singlet state compared with spin inversion which forms the triplet. As we are here concerned with the analogy between carbonium ions and carbenes we shall concentrate attention on the reactions of carbenes in the singlet state.

Reactions of singlet carbenes. Insertion. The reaction

$$R_2C: \; + \; \overset{\backslash}{\underset{/}{C}}{-}X \longrightarrow \overset{\backslash}{\underset{/}{C}}.CR_2X \quad (X = H, \; C{\overset{/}{\underset{\backslash}{}}}, \text{ halogen})$$

is the most characteristic reaction of carbenes. For singlet carbenes, there is evidence that the reaction takes place in one step through a transition state like **8.12**. There appears to be no direct analogy in carbonium-ion chemistry, although carbonium-ion rearrangement might be regarded as an intramolecular insertion reaction (see below).

Addition to olefins. Another common reaction of carbenes is addition to olefins, forming cyclopropanes, and this, in the case of singlet carbenes,

[1] Wanzlick and Schikora, 1961; Lemal and Kawano, 1962; Kirmse, 1963.
[2] Lemal, Lovald and Kawano, 1964; Winberg, Carnahan *et al.*, 1965; Bethell, Whittaker and Callister, 1965.

appears to be stereospecific, e.g., *cis*-2-butene (**8.13**) gives a *cis*-1,2-dimethyl-cyclopropane (**8.14**). Accordingly the reaction has been formulated as a one-step addition by way of the transition state **8.15**, analogous to the "bromonium ion" intermediate (**8.16**) in electrophilic addition of bromine to olefins.

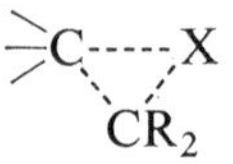

$$\begin{array}{ccc} \text{(8.12)} & \text{(8.13)} & \text{(8.14)} \end{array}$$

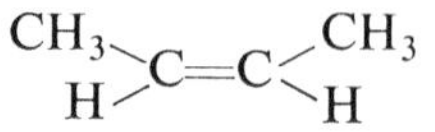

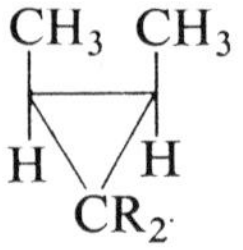

The analogy extends to the relative reactivity of olefins toward the two types of reagent (Table 8.6): the greater reactivity of the carbon–carbon double bonds

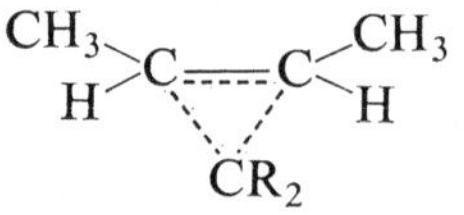

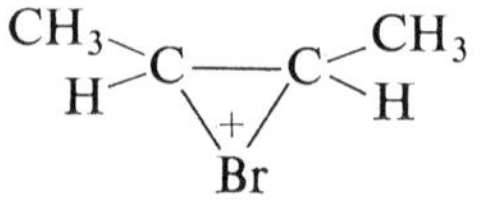

$$\begin{array}{cc} \text{(8.15)} & \text{(8.16)} \end{array}$$

with the larger number of attached methyl groups constitutes evidence that the carbenes involved behave as electrophiles. The formation of cyclopropanes from olefins is not, however, confined to carbenes: the same transformation can be achieved using α-halocarbanions[1] and certain organo-metallic reagents.[2] The precise nature of some of the reactive species in Table 8.6 is not completely specified.[3]

Reaction with non-bonded electron pairs. The rate-limiting step in the hydrolysis of chloroform can be represented:

$$CCl_3^- \longrightarrow :CCl_2 + Cl^- \qquad (8.7)$$

Added chloride ion reduces the observed reaction rate, an effect analogous to the mass-law effect of common ions in the unimolecular solvolysis of alkyl halides by way of carbonium ions.[4] Similar, but more pronounced, effects are observed when bromide or iodide ions are added,[5] and mixed haloforms can be isolated from the reaction mixture. These effects can be envisaged as arising from competition between nucleophiles for the carbene, reaction with halide ions re-forming the trihalocarbanion and reaction with water giving the hydrolysis products. The relative rate constants for the reactions of a number of nucleophiles with dichloromethylene are given in Table 8.7. Values correlate

[1] W. T. Miller and Whalen, 1964; Hoeg, Lusk and Crumbliss, 1965.
[2] Simmons and Smith, 1958; Blanchard and Simmons, 1964; Simmons, Blanchard and Smith, 1964; Hoberg, 1962.
[3] Closs and Moss, 1964.
[4] Hine and Dowell, 1954.
[5] Hine and Dowell, 1954; Hine, Butterworth and Langford, 1958.

Table 8.6. *Relative reactivities of carbenes and bromine towards olefins*

Carbene	:CCl$_2$	:CBr$_2$		:CHCl	:CHPh		Br$_2$
Source	A	A		A	B	C	—
Isobutene	1·00	1·00	1·00	1·00	1·00	1·00	1·00
trans-2-Butene	—	—	—	0·45	1·10	0·59	—
cis-2-Butene	—	—	—	0·91	2·02	1·83	—
Trimethylethylene	2·95	1·99	3·2	1·78	3·6	2·0	1·9
Tetramethylethylene	6·77	1·86	3·5	2·80	—	—	2·5
Ref.	a	a	b	c	d	d	b

A = base-induced α-elimination of HX at −20° to 0°.
B = photolysis of the corresponding diazoalkane at −10°.
C = lithium alkyl-induced α-elimination of Br$_2$ at −10°.

[a] Doering and Henderson, 1958.
[b] Skell and Garner, 1956.
[c] Closs and Schwartz, 1960; Closs and Closs, 1963.
[d] Closs and Moss, 1964.

well with nucleophilic activities (n) obtained from rates of bimolecular displacement of bromide ion from methyl bromide (Paragraph 6.2.2).

Table 8.7. *Relative reactivities k_x of nucleophiles (X^-) towards dichloromethylene in water at $35°^a$ ($k_{water} = 1$)*

X^-	Concentration (M)	k_x/k_{water}	n
Cl	0·08	56·8 ⎫	
Cl	0·16	61·1 ⎬	3·04
Cl	0·20	79·9 ⎭	
Br	0·08	164 ⎫	
Br	0·20	158 ⎭	3·89
I	0·08	480 ⎫	
I	0·16	532 ⎭	5·04
OH	—	229	4·20

[a] Hine and Dowell, 1954.

The results of Table 8.7 also suggest that dichloromethylene reacts with water by co-ordination to the non-bonded electrons on the oxygen atom. A similar conclusion can be reached for the reaction of diphenylmethylene with water from the absence of a deuterium isotope effect on the product-forming steps in the thermal decomposition of diphenyldiazomethane in the presence of water and deuterium oxide.[1] Such reactions are evidently analogous to carbonium-ion reactions.

Reaction of dichlorocarbene with phenoxide ion yields *o*- and *p*-hydroxy-benzaldehydes, indicating an initial process analogous to electrophilic attack by a carbonium ion on an aromatic compound.[2] With alkoxides, however, dihalomethylenes suffer displacement of halide ion (Paragraph 3.1.2).

Rearrangement. The most important reaction in this category is the Wolff rearrangement of diazoketones to ketenes:

$$R.CO.CN_2R' \rightarrow O:C:CRR' + N_2 \qquad (8.8)$$

The reaction can be brought about by photolysis, thermolysis or reaction with silver oxide or benzoate, all in the presence of a hydroxy- or amino-compound to trap the ketene as a stable product. The reaction is usually formulated as initial formation of a carbene, $R.CO.\ddot{C}R'$, followed by migration of the group R to the divalent centre. The available evidence is not very convincing, however: while the two-step mechanism seems probable in the photolytic and

[1] Bethell, Whittaker and Callister, 1965.
[2] Hine and Van der Veen, 1959.

thermal rearrangement,[1] the mechanism of the "catalysed" reactions is yet to be studied in detail. Moreover arguments can be advanced in favour of a synchronous loss of nitrogen from and migration of R to the diazo-carbon atom.[2]

Rearrangement occurs in carbenes not containing a keto-group, and, in favourable cases, this type of shift can compete with the Wolff rearrangement.[3] Relative migratory aptitudes of substituted phenyl groups can be simply evaluated from the ratios of products in, for example, the thermal decomposition of 2,2,2-triaryldiazoethanes.[4] Some values are given in Table 8.8. The small effect of the polar nature of the substituent on the migratory aptitude is similar to that observed for a carbonium ion of similar structure obtained by nitrous acid deamination. This suggests that the carbene is an intermediate of very high energy, though the driving force for rearrangement in this particular case may be largely relief of steric compression in the triarylmethyl group.

8.2.2 RADICAL CATIONS

The species formed by removal of an electron from an electrically neutral organic molecule has, of necessity, one unpaired electron and carries a positive charge. When the positive charge resides on carbon, the radical cation is formally analogous in some ways to a carbonium ion.

Formation of radical cations in the gas phase by electron impact and their subsequent fragmentation into neutral and positively charged entities is a feature of mass spectrometry.[5] This aspect of the subject will not be pursued here. In solution, radical cations are less commonly observed. Radical cations are most readily formed from molecules possessing relatively weakly bound electrons. π-Electrons are much more readily removed from hydrocarbons than σ-electrons. Electron removal from simple aromatic hydrocarbons (e.g. benzene, naphthalene) is not known, but polycyclic hydrocarbons yield the corresponding radical cation (e.g. from anthracene one obtains the cation shown in one of its valence-bond structures in **8.17**).

(**8.17**)   (**8.18**)   (**8.19**)

[1] Franzen, 1957.

[2] Kaplan and Meloy, 1966.

[3] E.g. Baddeley, Holt and Kenner, 1949; Horner and Spietschka, 1952; Franzen, 1957; Newman and Arkell, 1959.

[4] Sargeant and Shechter, 1964.

[5] For reviews, see Reed, 1962; McLafferty, 1963.

Table 8.8. *Migratory aptitudes of substituted phenyl groups in the thermal decomposition of 1-aryl-2-diazo-1,1-diphenylethanes and in certain carbonium-ion reactions*

Substituent	Migratory aptitude		
	$ArCPh_2.\ddot{C}H$	$ArCHPh.CH_2^+$	$ArCHPh.CH_2^+$
$p\text{-}OCH_3$	1·67	21·2	1·44
$p\text{-}CH_3$	1·36	1·98	0·89
$o\text{-}CH_3$	4·00	0·82	—
H	(1·00)	(1·00)	(1·00)
$p\text{-}Cl$	1·15	—	—
$p\text{-}NO_2$	0·60	—	—
Source	$ArCPh_2.CHN_2(90°)$	$ArCHPh.CH_2OH/P_2O_5$ (refluxing xylene)	$ArCHPh.CH_2NH_2/HNO_2$ (70–80°)
Ref.	a	b	c

[a] Sargeant and Shechter, 1964.
[b] Benjamin and Collins, 1953; Burr and Ciereszko, 1952.
[c] Ciereszko and Burr, 1952.

In solution, radical cation formation requires an electron acceptor. Iodine and bromine can fulfil this function.[1] Aluminium chloride, which forms a weak "π-complex" with benzene,[2] removes an electron from polynuclear aromatic hydrocarbons such as anthracene and perylene (**8.18**).[3] Other metal halides behave similarly.[4] This behaviour explains the detection of radicals in Friedel-Crafts reaction mixtures containing benzene, chloroform or benzyl chloride, and aluminium chloride, since some anthracene is formed.[5] Simple electron transfer does not occur, at least in some cases; for example, perylene behaves as a weak 1:1 electrolyte in antimony trichloride solution, but the radical cation, evidenced by its colour and ESR-spectrum, appears only on admission of oxygen.[6]

Radical cations are formed from polycyclic aromatic hydrocarbons on addition of the solid to concentrated sulphuric acid. There is evidence that protonation of the aromatic compound is the first step[7] in the reaction and, indeed, protonation is the only reaction if the hydrocarbon is added in solution in an inert solvent (see Paragraph 2.3.3). The reaction has accordingly been formulated:[8]

$$\left.\begin{aligned}
A + H_2SO_4 &\rightleftharpoons AH^+ + HSO_4^- \\
AH^+ + A &\rightarrow AH\cdot + A^{+\cdot} \\
AH\cdot + 2H_2SO_4 &\rightarrow A^+ + 2H_2O + SO_2 + HSO_4^-
\end{aligned}\right\} \qquad (8.9)$$

In some cases other oxidizing agents must be present.[9] Hexamethylbenzene in sulphuric acid yields the corresponding cation radical on irradiation.[10] Without irradiation, hexamethylbenzene gives a different stable cation radical, believed to be **8.19**.[11] This underlines the importance of obtaining direct evidence concerning the structure of cation radicals in systems where other rapid chemical processes can occur.

Radical cations can be detected when aromatic hydrocarbons are adsorbed on certain activated silica-alumina catalysts.[12] The catalytic activity of such materials, in, for example, the "cracking" of hydrocarbons may be related to this.

[1] E.g. Danyluk and Schneider, 1962; Singer and Kommandeur, 1961; Buck Lupinski and Oosterhoff, 1958.

[2] H. C. Brown and Wallace, 1953a.

[3] Rooney and Pink, 1961b; Forbes and Sullivan, 1966.

[4] Weissman, de Boer and Conradi, 1957; Kinoshita, 1962.

[5] Adams and Nicksic, 1962; Banks, Farnell et al., 1964.

[6] J. R. Atkinson, Jones and Baughan, 1964.

[7] Kon and Blois, 1958.

[8] Carrington, Dravnieks and Symons, 1959.

[9] Aalbersberg, Gaaf and Mackor, 1961.

[10] Hulme and Symons, 1965; see also, Aalbersberg, Hoijtink et al., 1959.

[11] Hulme and Symons, 1966.

[12] Rooney and Pink, 1961a; Scott, Flockhart and Pink, 1964; Flockhart, Scott and Pink, 1966.

11*

Relatively little is known about the chemical reactions of organic radical cations, the chief interest in these species up till now being centred on their ESR spectra.[1] Both carbonium-ion and radical behaviour is expected. Radical cations formed from vinylic compounds seem capable of initiating polymerization involving both radical and cationic propagation, though dimerization of radical centres probably quickly terminates the former.[2] Proton transfer seems to be the first step in the decay of the hexamethylbenzene cation radical, $C_6(CH_3)_6^+$, and this is followed by dimerization of the product pentamethylbenzyl radical.[3]

8.3 Hetero-atom Analogues

8.3.1 INTRODUCTION

This Section deals briefly with analogues of carbonium ions in which the positive charge is associated with an atom (other than carbon) which has more low-lying orbitals than pairs of electrons to fill them. Boron analogues have already been mentioned in Section 1.2.

Inspection of Pauling's electronegativity values for elements close to carbon in the Periodic Classification (Table 8.9) suggests that nitrogen, oxygen,

Table 8.9. *Electronegativities (Pauling's scale) of some elements*

H 2·1						
Li 1·0	Be 1·5	B 2·0	C 2·5	N 3·0	O 3·5	F 4·0
Na 0·9	Mg 1·2	Al 1·5	Si 1·8	P 2·1	S 2·5	Cl 3·0
			Ge 1·8	As 2·0	Se 2·4	Br 2·8

fluorine and chlorine will be less capable of supporting a positive charge than carbon, but that silicon, phosphorus and sulphur, for example, should be better than carbon. However, evidence for these hetero-atom analogues of carbonium ions is rather sparse. This suggests that factors other than electronegativity are of greater importance in determining whether these cations are formed as stable entities or as reactive intermediates in chemical transformations. Two of these factors may well be the necessity of delocalizing the positive charge, especially by conjugation, and the absence of alternative, low-energy routes for chemical reactions. On both counts, organic derivatives of elements other than those of the first row of the Periodic Classification might not be expected to form carbonium ion analogues. However, systematic searches for such species may yet prove successful.

[1] For a review, see Symons, 1963.
[2] Bawn, Fitzsimmons and Ledwith, 1964; Tokura, Nagai and Sonoyama, 1965.
[3] Hulme and Symons, 1965.

8.3.2 SILICONIUM IONS

From the electronegativity values in Table 8.9, siliconium ions might be expected to be more stable than the corresponding carbonium ions. Electron-impact experiments indicate, however, that roughly the same amount of energy is required to produce t-butyl cations from t-butyl halides as to produce trimethylsilyl cations from trimethylsilyl halides in the gas phase.[1]

In solution, siliconium ions prove to be much more elusive than carbonium ions. Physical methods, such as conductivity, cryoscopy in sulphuric acid and electronic absorption spectroscopy, which provide such compelling evidence for the formation of stable carbonium ions, yield no evidence of formation of siliconium ions.[2] In particular, the presence of phenyl or p-dimethylamino-phenyl groups attached to silicon has no apparent stabilizing influence: thus the silicon analogue even of crystal violet is non-conducting. Triphenylchloro-derivatives of other Group IVB elements, germanium, tin and lead, are also non-electrolytes in polar organic solvents. Nucleophilic substitution at silicon usually occurs by bimolecular mechanisms. Unimolecular reactions of silyl compounds are rare, but there is some evidence of siliconium-ion formation. Thus the optically active silyl halide **8.20**, on treatment with bromide or iodide ion (but not the more basic fluoride ion) in chloroform solution, gives substitution product at a rate which is very much less than the rate of loss of optical activity and not very sensitive to the nature of the substituting agents.[3]

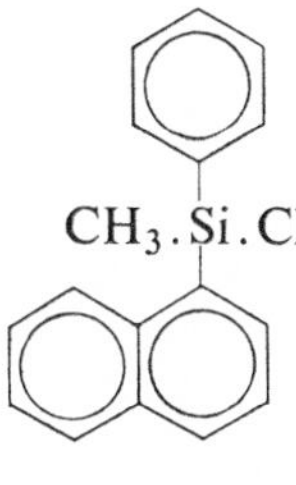

$$CH_3 . Si . Cl$$

(**8.20**)

Moreover, using radioactive chloride ion, the velocity constants for racemization (k_α) and chloride exchange (k_{ex}) are equal: racemization by successive bimolecular displacements requires that $k_\alpha = 2\ k_{ex}$. The rate of the reaction

$$(CH_3)_3Si . CH_2 . CH_2Cl \xrightarrow{ROH} (CH_3)_3Si . OR + CH_2 : CH_2 + HCl \quad (8.10)$$

displays a sensitivity to solvent polarity and an insensitivity to lyate ion similar to that of t-butyl chloride. These facts suggest that the trimethylsilyl

[1] Hess, Lampe and Sommer, 1964, 1965.
[2] For a review of such investigations, see Eaborn, 1959; Sommer, 1965.
[3] Sommer, Stark and Michael, 1964.

cation and ethylene are formed either synchronously with the departure of the chloride ion or by fragmentation of a slowly-formed primary carbonium ion.[1] There is evidence that the 1,2-shift,

$$(C_2H_5)_3Si.\overset{+}{C}H.CH_3 \rightarrow (C_2H_5)_2\overset{+}{S}i.CH(CH_3).CH_2.CH_3 \qquad (8.11)$$

competes with fragmentation in the formation of **8.22** from **8.21**,[2] although such a transformation need not involve formation of a siliconium ion.[3]

$$(CH_3.CH_2)_3Si.CHCl.CH_3 \qquad (CH_3.CH_2)_2SiCl.CH(CH_3)CH_2.CH_3$$
$$\textbf{(8.21)} \qquad\qquad\qquad\qquad \textbf{(8.22)}$$

8.3.3 OTHERS

Many well-known molecular rearrangements, e.g., the Beckmann, Curtius, Lossen, Schmidt and Baeyer-Villiger reactions, involve intramolecular migration of an alkyl or aryl group from carbon to nitrogen or oxygen in an analogous fashion to carbonium-ion rearrangements.[4] While analogies are drawn between these rearrangements and those of carbonium ions, direct evidence that an un-rearranged species bearing a positive charge on nitrogen (or oxygen) is formed prior to the 1,2-shift is lacking. Generally, the reactions are formulated with synchronous rearrangement and heterolysis giving a rearranged cation. Thus, for example, the stereospecific migration of the group *anti* to the hydroxyl in the Beckmann rearrangement (and, where appropriate, fragmentation) of oximes is generally regarded as ruling out a 1,2-shift in the carbonium ion analogue **8.23** and favouring reaction by way of a transition complex of structure **8.24**. In some cases **8.24** might be regarded as an intermediate.

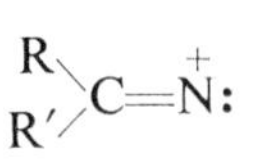

$$\overset{R}{\underset{R'}{\diagdown}}\overset{+}{C}=\overset{..}{N}: \qquad\qquad R'.\overset{\overset{R}{\diagup\diagdown}}{\overset{+}{C}{=\!=\!=}N} \qquad\qquad R\,R'N:$$
$$\textbf{(8.23)} \qquad\qquad\qquad \textbf{(8.24)} \qquad\qquad\qquad \textbf{(8.25)}$$

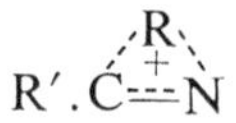

The nitrogen analogue of a carbonium ion **8.25** bears a formal similarity to a carbene. That this similarity may extend to chemical reactivity is suggested

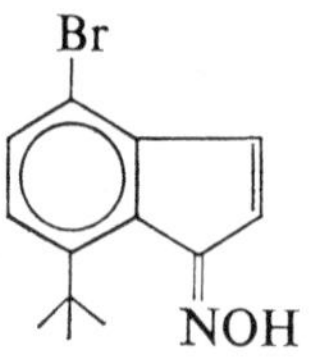

$$\textbf{(8.26)} \qquad\qquad \textbf{(8.27)} \qquad\qquad \textbf{(8.28)} \qquad\qquad \textbf{(8.29)}$$

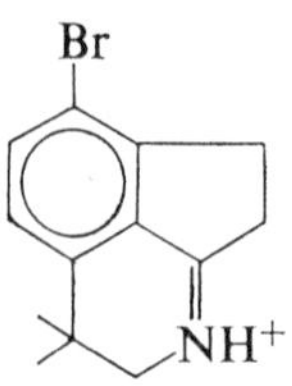

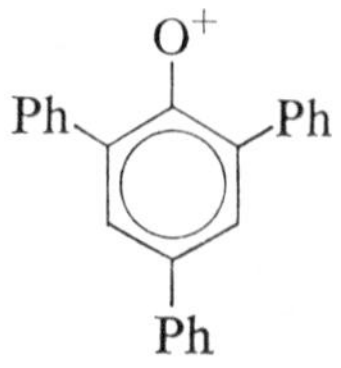

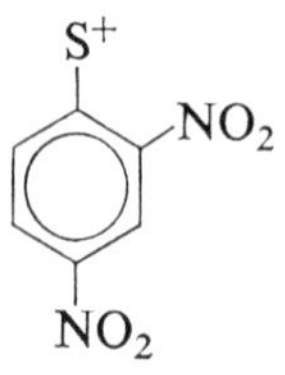

[1] Sommer and Baughman, 1961.
[2] Sommer, Bailey *et al.*, 1954.
[3] Brook, Pannell *et al.*, 1964.
[4] For a review, see P. A. S. Smith, 1963.

by the 70% conversion of the oxime **8.26** to **8.27** in which the oxime-nitrogen has apparently become inserted in a carbon–hydrogen bond of the adjacent t-butyl group.[1] Clearly further investigation is necessary.

The oxygen analogue (**8.28**) of a benzyl cation, prepared as the tetrafluoroborate from the corresponding phenoxy-radical, is reported to be stable.[2]

For heavier elements of Groups V and VI, positive-ion formation is anticipated to be less likely, by analogy with silicon, notwithstanding the decreased electronegativity. Evidence has been adduced for the formation of sulphenium ions such as **8.29**,[3] but re-examination, particularly of the cryoscopic results, seems desirable.

[1] Lansbury, Colson and Mancuso, 1964; Lansbury and Mancuso, 1966.
[2] Dimroth, Umbach and Thomas, 1967.
[3] For a review of the evidence, see Kharasch, 1961.

APPENDIX: A BIBLIOGRAPHY OF
CARBONIUM-ION CHEMISTRY

The ramifications of carbonium-ion chemistry are wide and its literature is vast. One of the aims of the present volume has been to define more clearly than hitherto the shape of the subject, so that individual contributions and further developments may be seen in perspective. Inevitably, the production of a book short enough to enable this shape to be appreciated necessitated the abridging of arguments and the omission of detail. This Appendix is intended as a guide to supplementary reading.

There is no substitute for the reading of original publications. However, the enormous number wholly or in part concerned with aspects of carbonium-ion chemistry, the wider implications of the subject and the controversies which have arisen (and continue to arise) make it desirable for the uninitiated to approach original contributions by way of specialized review articles. The list below has been compiled with an eye to present-day needs rather than to its being comprehensive. While most reviews are from the present decade, a few older articles are included because they contain comprehensive statements of points of view of historical interest. The list is divided up according to the chapters of the present volume to which the reviews correspond. Some more general reviews are also listed.

The literature of carbonium-ion chemistry continues to expand rapidly. "Current awareness" of developments is a problem in all fields of chemistry, not least that concerned with carbonium ions. The ultimate solution, scrutiny of a large fraction of the world's chemical journals month by month, is impossible in the finite time and with the limited library facilities usually available to the practising chemist. Even the regular perusal of *Chemical Abstracts* as a rapid method of keeping abreast of published research is becoming increasingly impracticable to all save the narrow specialist, though computer techniques are beginning to ameliorate the situation. A compromise solution, which is far from perfect since it inevitably relies on the selection by individuals of published papers, is the use of annual digests of the literature. For carbonium-ion chemistry such annual accounts are to be found in *Annual Reports on the Progress of Chemistry* (of the Chemical Society) and *Annual Review of Physical Chemistry*. A recent innovation, which promises to be of great value, is the projected annual series of volumes beginning with "Organic Reaction Mechanisms, 1965", by B. Capon, M. J. Perkins and C. W. Rees (Wiley, New York, 1966). These regular compilations and also that of N. C. Deno (*Prog. Phys. Org. Chem.*, 1964, **2**, 129) give an outline of results and conclusions, usually with a minimal amount of comment and evaluation.

Reviews of Carbonium-ion Chemistry

A. Books and articles covering several aspects of the subject

L. P. Hammett, "Physical Organic Chemistry." McGraw-Hill, New York, 1940.[a]

C. K. Ingold, "Structure and Mechanism in Organic Chemistry". Cornell Univ. Press, Ithaca, N.Y. and Bell, London, 1953.[a]

J. E. Leffler, "The Reactive Intermediates of Organic Chemistry". Interscience, New York, 1956, Chapters V–VIII.

C. A. Bunton, "Nucleophilic Substitution at a Saturated Carbon Atom". Elsevier, Amsterdam, 1963.

P. B. D. de la Mare and R. Bolton, "Electrophilic Additions to Unsaturated Systems". Elsevier, Amsterdam, 1966.

P. de Mayo (Ed.) "Molecular Rearrangements". Wiley, New York, 1963.

G. A. Olah (Ed.) "The Friedel-Crafts and Related Reactions". Wiley, New York, 1963–5 (4 vols.).

A. Streitwieser, "Solvolytic Displacement Reactions". McGraw-Hill, New York, 1962.[b]

E. R. Thornton, "Solvolysis Mechanisms". Ronald Press Co., New York, 1964.

D. Bethell and V. Gold, *Quart. Rev.* 1958, **12**, 173.

N. C. Deno, *Prog. Phys. Org. Chem.* 1964, **2**, 129; *Chem. Eng. News* 1964, **42**, (No. 40) 88.

W. Hückel, *Nova Acta Leopoldina* (*Neue Folge*), 1966, **30**, No. 174.

G. M. Kramer, *Adv. Petrol. Chem.*, 1964, **9**, 232.

---

[a] A more general text book which has had a profound influence on the development of the subject.

[b] This book consists of the review by A. Streitwieser *Chem. Rev.*, 1956, **56**, 571, and an appendix covering developments up to 1963.

B. Specialized reviews

Chapter 1

The analogy between carbonium carbon and boron:
    H. C. Longuet-Higgins, *Quart. Rev.* 1957, **11,** 121.

Chapter 2

Spectroscopic methods of studying carbonium ions (NMR, infrared, ultraviolet):
    G. A. Olah and C. U. Pittman, *Adv. Phys. Org. Chem.* 1966, **4,** 305.

Mass spectrometry:
    R. I. Reed, "Ion Production by Electron Impact". Academic Press, London, 1962.
    C. A. McDowell (Ed.), "Mass Spectrometry". McGraw-Hill, New York, 1963.
    F. W. McLafferty (Ed.), "Mass Spectrometry of Organic Molecules". Academic Press, New York, 1963.
    R. I. Reed (Ed.), "Mass Spectrometry". Academic Press, London, 1965.

Cryoscopy in sulphuric acid:
    R. J. Gillespie and J. A. Leisten, *Quart. Rev.* 1954, **8,** 40.

Conductance:
    N. N. Lichtin, *Prog. Phys. Org. Chem.* 1963, **1,** 75.

Chapter 3

Alkyl-oxygen fission in the reactions of esters:
    A. G. Davies and J. Kenyon, *Quart. Rev.* 1955, **9,** 203.

Formation of carbonium ions from diazoalkanes:
    R. A. More O'Ferrall, *Adv. Phys. Org. Chem.* 1967, **5,** 331.

Fragmentation reactions:
    C. A. Grob in "Theoretical Organic Chemistry. The Kekulé Symposium". Butterworths, London, 1959, p. 114.
    C. A. Grob, *Bull. Soc. Chim. France*, 1960, 1360.
    C. A. Grob, *Gazzetta*, 1962, **92,** 902.

Protonation of olefins:
    M. J. S. Dewar and R. C. Fahey, *Angew. Chem.* 1964, **76,** 320 (Internat. Ed. **3,** 245).

Chapter 4

Energetics of carbonium-ion formation:
    F. H. Field and J. L. Franklin, "Electron Impact Phenomena". Academic Press, New York, 1957.
    R. R. Bernecker and F. A. Long, *J. Phys. Chem.*, 1961, **65,** 1565.
    A. G. Harrison in "Mass Spectrometry of Organic Molecules", Ed. F. W. McLafferty. Academic Press, New York, 1963, p. 207.
    F. P. Lossing in "Mass Spectrometry", Ed. C. A. McDowell. McGraw-Hill, New York, 1963, p. 442.
    A. Streitwieser, *Prog. Phys. Org. Chem.* 1963, **1,** 1.
    D. W. Turner, *Adv. Phys. Org. Chem.*, 1966, **4,** 31.

Tabulations of data:

  T. L. Cottrell, "The Strengths of Chemical Bonds". Butterworths, London, 2nd Ed., 1958.

  V. I. Vedeneyev, L. V. Gurvich, V. N. Kondrat'yev, V. A. Medvedev and Ye. L. Frankevich, "Bond Energies, Ionization Potentials and Electron Affinities". Arnold, London, 1966 (Russian original published in 1962).

Protonation equilibria of hydrocarbons:

  E. M. Arnett, *Prog. Phys. Org. Chem.* 1963, **1**, 223.

  H.-H. Perkampus and E. Baumgarten, *Angew. Chem.* 1964, **76**, 965 (Internat. Ed. **3**, 776).

  H.-H. Perkampus, *Adv. Phys. Org. Chem.* 1966, **4**, 195.

Linear free energy relations:

  R. W. Taft, in "Steric Effects in Organic Chemistry", Ed. M. S. Newman. Wiley, New York, 1956, Chapter 13.

  L. M. Stock and H. C. Brown, *Adv. Phys. Org. Chem.* 1963, **1**, 35.

  C. D. Ritchie and W. F. Sager, *Prog. Phys. Org. Chem.* 1964, **2**, 323.

Heterolytic reactions in the gas phase:

  A. Maccoll in "Theoretical Organic Chemistry, The Kekulé Symposium". Butterworths, London, 1959, p. 230.

  A. Maccoll in "The Transition State". Chem. Soc. Spec. Publ. No. 16, 1962, p. 159.

  A. Maccoll, *Adv. Phys. Org. Chem.* 1965, **3**, 91.

Aromatic hydrogen isotope exchange:

  V. Gold in "Friedel-Crafts and Related Reactions", Ed. G. A. Olah, Vol. II. Wiley, New York, 1964, p. 1253.

Cyclopropenyl cations:

  A. Krebs, *Angew. Chem.* 1965, **77**, 10 (Internat. Ed., **4**, 10).

Cycloheptatrienyl cations:

  T. Nozoe, *Prog. Org. Chem.* 1961, **5**, 132.

Chapter 5

Molecular orbital calculations:

  A. Streitwieser, "Molecular Orbital Theory for Organic Chemists". Wiley, New York, 1962.

Ion association:

  S. Winstein, XVth Congress of Pure and Applied Chemistry, *Experientia*, Supplementum II, 1955, p. 137.

  Y. Pocker, *Prog. Reaction Kinetics*, 1962, **1**, 215.

  S. Winstein, A. F. Diaz, B. R. Appel and R. Baker in "Organic Reaction Mechanisms". Chem. Soc. Spec. Publ. No. 19, 1965, p. 109.

  M. Szwarc, *Makromol. Chem.* 1965, **89**, 44.

Chapter 6

Reactions of allylic cations:

  R. H. DeWolfe and W. G. Young, *Chem. Rev.* 1956, **56**, 753.

  H. L. Goering, *Record Chem. Prog.* 1960, **21**, 109.

P. B. D. de la Mare in "Molecular Rearrangements", Ed. P. de Mayo. Wiley, New York, 1963, p. 27.

R. H. DeWolfe and W. G. Young in "The Chemistry of Alkenes", Ed. S. Patai. Wiley, New York, 1964, p. 681.

Deamination:

J. H. Ridd, *Quart. Rev.* 1961, **15,** 418.

H. Zollinger, "Azo and Diazo Chemistry". Interscience, New York, 1961, Chapter 6.

Aromatic alkylation:

G. A. Olah (Ed.), "Friedel-Crafts and Related Reactions". Wiley, New York, 1963, Vols. I and II.

R. O. C. Norman and R. Taylor "Electrophilic Substitution in Benzenoid Compounds". Elsevier, Amsterdam, 1965.

Cationic polymerization:

P. H. Plesch (Ed.) "The Chemistry of Cationic Polymerization". Pergamon Press, Oxford, 1963.

B. L. Erusalimskii, *Uspekhi Khim.* 1963, **32,** 1458 (*Russ. Chem. Rev.*, 1963, **32,** 651).

D. C. Pepper in "Friedel-Crafts and Related Reactions", Ed. G. A. Olah. Wiley, New York, 1964, Vol. II p. 1293.

J. P. Kennedy and A. W. Langer, *Fortschr. Hochpolym.-Forsch.* 1964, **3,** 508.

L. S. Bresler, *Uspekhi Khim.*, 1965, **34,** 895 (*Russ. Chem. Rev.*, 1965, **34,** 366).

Elimination and fragmentation reactions (see also Chapter 3):

D. V. Banthorpe, "Elimination Reactions". Elsevier, Amsterdam, 1963.

W. H. Saunders in "The Chemistry of Alkenes", Ed. S. Patai. Wiley, New York, 1964, p. 149.

Rearrangements:

F. C. Whitmore, *Chem. Eng. News*, 1948, **26,** 668.

G. W. Wheland, "Advanced Organic Chemistry". Wiley, New York, 2nd Ed., 1957, Chapters 12 and 13.

P. de Mayo (Ed.), "Molecular Rearrangements". Wiley, New York, 1963, Chapters by Y. Pocker, J. A. Berson and R. Breslow especially.

W. Gerrard and H. R. Hudson, *Chem. Rev.* 1965, **65,** 697.

Pinacol rearrangement:

C. J. Collins, *Quart. Rev.* 1960, **14,** 357.

Intermolecular hydride transfer reactions:

N. C. Deno, H. J. Peterson and G. S. Saines, *Chem. Rev.* 1960, **60,** 7.

D. N. Kursanov and Z. N. Parnes, *Uspekhi Khim.* 1961, **30,** 1381 (*Russ. Chem. Rev.* 1961, **30,** 598).

Chapter 7

Neighbouring-group participation:

B. Capon, *Quart. Rev.* 1964, **18,** 45.

Bridged carbonium ions in solution:

J. A. Berson in "Molecular Rearrangements", Ed. P. de Mayo. Wiley, New York, 1963, p. 111.

D. J. Cram, *J. Amer. Chem. Soc.* 1964, **86**, 3767.

M. J. S. Dewar and A. P. Marchand, *Ann. Rev. Phys. Chem.* 1965, **16**, 321.

P. D. Bartlett, "Non-classical Ions. Reprints and Commentary". Benjamin, New York, 1965.

B. Capon, M. J. Perkins and C. W. Rees, "Organic Reaction Mechanisms, 1965". Wiley, New York, 1966, p. 1.

G. D. Sargent, *Quart. Rev.* 1966, **20**, 301.

G. E. Gream, *Rev. Pure Appl. Chem.* 1966, **16**, 25.

Arguments against bridged carbonium ions:

H. C. Brown in "The Transition State". Chem. Soc. Spec. Publ. No. 16, 1962, p. 140.

W. Hückel, *J. prakt. Chem.* 1965, **28**, 27.

H. C. Brown, *Chem. Brit.* 1966, 199.

Bridged ions in the gas phase:

A. Maccoll in "The Transition State". Chem. Soc. Spec. Publ. No. 16, 1962, p. 159.

Chapter 8

Acylium ions:

J. E. Leffler, "The Reactive Intermediates of Organic Chemistry". Interscience, New York, 1956, p. 131.

G. A. Olah (Ed.), "The Friedel-Crafts and Related Reactions", Volume III, Wiley, New York, 1965. (Especially contributions by F. R. Jensen and G. Goldman and by A. Balaban and C. D. Nenitzescu.)

P. F. G. Praill, "Acylation Reactions". Pergamon Press, Oxford, 1963.

Carbenes:

J. Hine, "Divalent Carbon". Ronald Press Co., New York, 1964.

W. Kirmse, "Carbene Chemistry". Academic Press, New York, 1964.

A. Ledwith, R. I. C. Lecture Series, 1964, No. 5.

Radical Cations:

M. C. R. Symons, *Adv. Phys. Org. Chem.* 1963, **1**, 283.

Hetero-analogues:

C. Eaborn, "Organosilicon Compounds". Butterworths, London, 1959.

L. H. Sommer, "Stereochemistry, Mechanism and Silicon". McGraw-Hill, New York, 1965.

J. E. Leffler, "The Reactive Intermediates of Organic Chemistry". Interscience. New York, 1956, Chapter VIII.

P. A. S. Smith in "Molecular Rearrangements", Ed. P. de Mayo. Wiley, New York, 1963, p. 457.

N. Kharasch in "Organic Sulphur Compounds", Vol. 1. Pergamon Press, Oxford, 1961, p. 375.

References

Aalbersberg, W. I., Gaaf, J. and Mackor, E. L. (1961). *J. Chem. Soc.* 905.

Aalbersberg, W. I., Hoijtink, G. J., Mackor, E. L. and Weijland, W. P. (1959). *J. Chem. Soc.* 3055.

Aboderin, A. A. and Baird, R. L. (1964). *J. Amer. Chem. Soc.* **86,** 2300.

Adams, J. Q. and Nicksic, S. W. (1962). *J. Amer. Chem. Soc.* **84,** 4355.

Adkins, H. (1943). In "Organic Chemistry", 2nd Ed. (H. Gilman, ed.), p. 1066ff. Wiley, New York.

Airs, R. S., Balfe, M. P. and Kenyon, J. (1942). *J. Chem. Soc.* 18.

Aitken, I. M. and Reid, D. H. (1956). *J. Chem. Soc.* 3487.

Albery, W. J. and Bell, R. P. (1961). *Trans. Faraday Soc.* **57,** 1942.

Aléonard, S. (1958). *Bull. Soc. Chim. France.* 827.

Allen, R. H. and Yats, L. D. (1961). *J. Amer. Chem. Soc.* **83,** 2799.

Anderson, C. B., Friedrich, E. C. and Winstein, S. (1963). *Tetrahedron Letters.* 2037.

Applequist, D. E. and Landgrebe, J. A. (1964). *J. Amer. Chem. Soc.* **86,** 1543.

Archer, B. L. and Hudson, R. F. (1950). *J. Chem. Soc.* 3259.

Arcus, C. L. and Kenyon, J. (1938). *J. Chem. Soc.* 1912.

Arcus, C. L. and Smith, J. W. (1939), *J. Chem. Soc.* 1748.

Arendale, W. F. and Fletcher, W. H. (1957). *J. Chem. Phys.* **26,** 793.

Arndt, F. and Lorenz, L. (1930). *Ber.* **63,** 3121.

Arnett, E. M. (1963). *Prog. Phys. Org. Chem.* **1,** 223.

Arnett, E. M., Bentrude, W. G. and Duggleby, P. M. (1965). *J. Amer. Chem. Soc.* **87,** 2048.

Arnett, E. M., Bentrude, W. G., Burke, J. J. and Duggleby, P. M. (1965). *J. Amer. Chem. Soc.* **87,** 1541.

Arnett, E. M. and Burke, J. J. (1966). *J. Amer. Chem. Soc.* **88,** 2340.

Arnett, E. M. and Bushick, R. D. (1964). *J. Amer. Chem. Soc.* **86,** 1564.

Arnett, E. M., Duggleby, P. M. and Burke, J. J. (1963). *J. Amer. Chem. Soc.* **85,** 1350.

Arnett, E. M. and McKelvey, D. R. (1965). *J. Amer. Chem. Soc.* **87,** 1393.

Arnett, E. M., Wu, C. Y., Anderson, J. N. and Bushick, R. D. (1962). *J. Amer. Chem. Soc.* **84,** 1674.

Atkinson, G. and Kor, S. K. (1965). *J. Phys. Chem.* **69,** 128.

Atkinson, J. R., Jones, T. P. and Baughan, E. C. (1964). *J. Chem. Soc.* 5808.

Ausloos, P. and Lias, S. G. (1965). *Disc. Faraday Soc.* **39,** 36

Bachmann, W. E. and Ferguson, J. W. (1934). *J. Amer. Chem. Soc.* **56,** 2081.

Bachmann, W. E. and Sternberger, H. R. (1934). *J. Amer. Chem. Soc.* **56,** 170.

Baddeley, G., Holt, G. and Kenner, J. (1949). *Nature,* **163,** 766.

Baddeley, G., Holt, G. and Voss, D. (1952). *J. Chem. Soc.* 100.

Baddeley, G. and Nield, P. G. (1954). *J. Chem. Soc.* 4684.

Baddeley, G. and Voss, D. (1954). *J. Chem. Soc.* 418.

Baeyer, A. (1905). *Ber.* **38,** 569.

Baeyer, A. and Villiger, V. (1902). *Ber.* **35,** 1189.

Bailey, T. H., Fox, J. R., Jackson, E., Kohnstam, G. and Queen, A. (1966). *Chem. Comm.* 122.

Baird, R. L. and Aboderin, A. A. (1963). *Tetrahedron Letters.* 235.

Baird, R. L. and Aboderin, A. A. (1964). *J. Amer. Chem. Soc.* **86,** 252.

Baird, R. L. and Winstein, S. (1957). *J. Amer. Chem. Soc.* **79,** 4238.

Baird, R. L. and Winstein, S. (1963). *J. Amer. Chem. Soc.* **85,** 567.

Balaban, A. T. and Nenitzescu, C. D. (1959). *Annalen,* **625,** 66.

Balaban, A. T. and Nenitzescu, C. D. (1960). *Tetrahedron,* **10,** 55.

Banks, R. E., Farnell, L. F., Haszeldine, R. N., Preston, P. N. and Sutcliffe, L. H. (1964). *Proc. Chem. Soc.* 396.

Banthorpe, D. V. (1963). "Elimination Reactions". Elsevier, Amsterdam.

Bartlett, P. D. (1951). *Bull. Soc. Chim. France,* **18,** C100.

Bartlett, P. D. (1965). "Non-Classical Ions. Reprints and Commentary". Benjamin, New York.

Bartlett, P. D. and Bank, S. (1961). *J. Amer. Chem. Soc.* **83,** 2591.

Bartlett, P. D., Bank, S., Crawford, R. J. and Schmid, G. H. (1965). *J. Amer. Chem. Soc.* **87,** 1288.

Bartlett, P. D. and Brown, R. F. (1940). *J. Amer. Chem. Soc.* **62,** 2927.

Bartlett, P. D., Closson, W.D. and Cogdell, T. J. (1965). *J. Amer. Chem. Soc.* **87,** 1308.

Bartlett, P. D., Condon, F. E. and Schneider, A. (1944). *J. Amer. Chem. Soc.* **66,** 1531.

Bartlett, P. D., Dills, C. E. and Richey, H. G. (1960). *J. Amer. Chem. Soc.* **82,** 5414.

Bartlett, P. D. and Giddings, W. P. (1960). *J. Amer. Chem. Soc.* **82,** 1240.

Bartlett, P. D. and Knox, L. H. (1939). *J. Amer. Chem. Soc.* **61,** 3184.

Bartlett, P. D. and McCollum, J. D. (1956). *J. Amer. Chem. Soc.* **78,** 1441.

Bartlett, P. D. and Rüchardt, C. (1960). *J. Amer. Chem. Soc.* **82,** 1756.

Bartlett, P. D. and Sargent, G. D. (1965). *J. Amer. Chem. Soc.* **87,** 1297.

Bartlett, P. D. and Stiles, M. (1955). *J. Amer. Chem. Soc.* **77,** 2806.

Bartlett, P. D., Trahanovsky, W. S., Bolon, D. A. and Schmid, G. H. (1965). *J. Amer. Chem. Soc.* **87,** 1314.

Bartlett, P. D., Webster, E. R., Dills, C. E. and Richey, H. G. (1959). *Annalen,* **623,** 217.

Barton, D. H. R. (1949). *J. Chem. Soc.* 2174.

Bateman, L. C., Church, M. G., Hughes, E. D., Ingold, C. K. and Taher, N. A. (1940). *J. Chem. Soc.* 979.

Bateman, L. C., Cooper, K. A., Hughes, E. D. and Ingold, C. K. (1940). *J. Chem. Soc.* 925.

Bateman, L. C. and Hughes, E. D. (1940). *J. Chem. Soc.* 945.

Bateman, L. C., Hughes, E. D. and Ingold, C. K. (1940). *J. Chem. Soc.* 974.

Battiste, M. A. (1961). *J. Amer. Chem. Soc.* **83**, 4101.

Batts, B. D. and Gold, V. (1964). *J. Chem. Soc.* 4284.

Bauge, K., Smith, J. W. and Wassermann, A. (1962). *J. Chem. Soc.* 864.

Bawn, C. E. H., Bell, R. M., Fitzsimmons, C. and Ledwith, A. (1965). *Polymer*, **6**, 661.

Bawn, C. E. H., Fitzsimmons, C. and Ledwith, A. (1964). *Proc. Chem. Soc.* 391.

Bawn, C. E. H. and Ledwith, A. (1962). *Quart. Rev.* **16**, 361.

Bayles, J. W., Cotter, J. L. and Evans, A. G. (1955). *J. Chem. Soc.* 3104.

Bayles, J. W., Evans, A. G. and Jones, J. R. (1955). *J. Chem. Soc.* 206.

Bayles, J. W., Evans, A. G. and Jones, J. R. (1957). *J. Chem. Soc.* 1020.

Bayless, J. H., Friedman, L., Smith, J. A., Cook, F. B. and Shechter, H. (1965). *J. Amer. Chem. Soc.* **87**, 661.

Bayless, J. H., Mendicino, F. D. and Friedman, L. (1965). *J. Amer. Chem. Soc.* **87**, 5790.

Bell, H. M. and Brown, H. C. (1964). *J. Amer. Chem. Soc.* **86**, 5007.

Bell, H. M. and Brown, H. C. (1966). *J. Amer. Chem. Soc.* **88**, 1473.

Beltramé, P., Bunton, C. A., Dunlop, A. and Whittaker, D. (1964). *J. Chem. Soc.* 658.

Bender, M. L. and Buist, G. J. (1958). *J. Amer. Chem. Soc.* **80**, 4304.

Bender, M. L. and Chen, M. C. (1963a). *J. Amer. Chem. Soc.* **85**, 30.

Bender, M. L. and Chen, M. C. (1963b). *J. Amer. Chem. Soc.* **85**, 37.

Bender, M. L., Ladenheim, H. and Chen, M. C. (1961). *J. Amer. Chem. Soc.* **83**, 123.

Benjamin, B. M. and Collins, C. J. (1953). *J. Amer. Chem. Soc.* **75**, 402.

Benjamin, B. M. and Collins, C. J. (1956a). *J. Amer. Chem. Soc.* **78**, 4329.

Benjamin, B. M. and Collins, C. J. (1956b). *J. Amer. Chem. Soc.* **78**, 4952.

Benjamin, B. M. and Collins, C. J. (1961). *J. Amer. Chem. Soc.* **83**, 3662.

Benjamin, B. M. and Collins, C. J. (1966). *J. Amer. Chem. Soc.* **88**, 1556.

Benjamin, B. M., Ponder, B. W. and Collins, C. J. (1966). *J. Amer. Chem. Soc.* **88**, 1558.

Benjamin, B. M., Schaeffer, H. J. and Collins, C. J. (1957). *J. Amer. Chem. Soc.* **79**, 6160.

Benjamin, B. M., Wilder, P. and Collins, C. J. (1961). *J. Amer. Chem. Soc.* **83**, 3654.

Bensley, B. and Kohnstam, G. (1955). *J. Chem. Soc.* 3408.

Benson, F. R. and Ritter, J. J. (1949). *J. Amer. Chem. Soc.* **71**, 4128.

Benson, S. W. (1958). *J. Amer. Chem. Soc.* **80**, 5151.

Bentley, A. and Evans, A. G. (1952a). *Research*, **5**, 535.

Bentley, A. and Evans, A. G. (1952b). *J. Chem. Soc.* 3468.

Bentley, A., Evans, A. G. and Halpern, J. (1951). *Trans. Faraday Soc.* **47**, 711.

Berenblum, I. (1945). *Nature*, **156**, 601.

Bergmann, E. and Polanyi, M. (1933). *Naturwiss*, **21**, 378.

Bergmann, E., Polanyi, M. and Szabo, A. L. (1936). *Trans. Faraday Soc.* **32**, 843.

Bergstrom, C. G. and Siegel, S. (1952). *J. Amer. Chem. Soc.* **74**, 145, 254.

Bernecker, R. R. and Long, F. A. (1961). *J. Phys. Chem.* **65**, 1565.

Berry, R. S., Dehl, R. and Vaughan, W. R. (1961). *J. Chem. Phys.* **34**, 1460.

Berson, J. A. (1960). *Tetrahedron Letters*, No. 16, 17 (Errata, ibid., No. 23, 38).

Berson, J. A. (1963). In "Molecular Rearrangements" (P. de Mayo, ed.), p. 111. Interscience, New York.

Berson, J. A. and Ben-Efraim, D. A. (1959). *J. Amer. Chem. Soc.* **81,** 4094.

Berson, J. A., Bergman, R. G., Hammons, J. H. and McRowe, A. W. (1965). *J. Amer. Chem. Soc.* **87,** 3246.

Berson, J. A. and Grubb, P. W. (1965). *J. Amer. Chem. Soc.* **87,** 4016.

Berson, J. A., Hammons, J. H., McRowe, A. W., Bergman, R. G., Remanick, A. and Houston, D. (1965). *J. Amer. Chem. Soc.* **87,** 3248.

Berson, J. A., McRowe, A. W. and Bergman, R. G. (1966). *J. Amer. Chem. Soc.* **88,** 1067.

Berson, J. A. and Poonian, M. S. (1966). *J. Amer. Chem. Soc.* **88,** 170.

Berson, J. A. and Remanick, A. (1964). *J. Amer. Chem. Soc.* **86,** 1749.

Berson, J. A. and Reynolds-Warnhoff, P. (1962). *J. Amer. Chem. Soc.* **84,** 682.

Berson, J. A. and Reynolds-Warnhoff, P. (1964). *J. Amer. Chem. Soc.* **86,** 595.

Berson, J. A. and Willner, D. (1962). *J. Amer. Chem. Soc.* **84,** 675.

Berson, J. A. and Willner, D. (1964). *J. Amer. Chem. Soc.* **86,** 609.

Berti, G. (1957). *J. Org. Chem.* **22,** 230.

Bertoli, V. and Plesch, P. H. (1966). *Chem. Comm.* 625.

Bethell, D. and Callister, J. D. (1963a), *J. Chem. Soc.* 3801.

Bethell, D. and Callister, J. D. (1963b). *J. Chem. Soc.* 3808.

Bethell, D. and Gold, V. (1958a). *J. Chem. Soc.* 1905.

Bethell, D. and Gold, V. (1958b). *J. Chem. Soc.* 1930.

Bethell, D. and Gold, V. (1958c). *Quart. Rev.* **12,** 173.

Bethell, D., Gold, V. and Riley, T. (1959). *J. Chem. Soc.* 3134.

Bethell, D. and Howard, R. D. (1966). *Chem. Comm.* 94.

Bethell, D., Whittaker, D. and Callister, J. D. (1965). *J. Chem. Soc.* 2466.

Bicknell, R. C. and Maccoll, A. (1961). *Chem. and Ind.* 1912.

Bicknell, R. C. and Maccoll, A. (1965). Unpublished observations, quoted by Maccoll, 1965.

Biddulph, R. H., Plesch, P. H. and Rutherford, P. P. (1965). *J. Chem. Soc.* 275.

Birchall, T., Bourns, A. N., Gillespie, R. J. and Smith, P. J. (1964). *Canad. J. Chem.* **42,** 1433.

Birchall, T. and Gillespie, R. J. (1964). *Canad. J. Chem.* **42,** 502.

Birladeanu, L., Hanafusa, T., Johnson, B. and Winstein, S. (1966). *J. Amer. Chem. Soc.* **88,** 2316.

Bistrzycki, A. and Herbst, C. (1901). *Ber.* **34,** 3073.

Bistrzycki, A. and Reintke, E. (1905). *Ber.* **38,** 839.

Bjerrum, N. (1926). *Kgl. Danske Videnskab. Selskab. Math.-fys. Medd.* (9) **7,** 1.

Blanchard, E. P. and Simmons, H. E. (1964). *J. Amer. Chem. Soc.* **86,** 1337.

Blandamer, M. J., Gough, T. E. and Symons, M. C. R. (1966). *Trans. Faraday Soc.* **62,** 286.

Bly, R. S. and Swindell, R. T. (1965). *J. Org. Chem.* **30,** 10.

Bodendorf, K. and Böhme, H. (1935). *Annalen,* **516,** 1.

Boer, F. P. (1966). *J. Amer. Chem. Soc.* **88,** 1572.

Boikess, R. S. and Winstein, S. (1963). *J. Amer. Chem. Soc.* **85,** 343.

Bonin, M. A., Busler, W. R. and Williams, F. (1965). *J. Amer. Chem. Soc.* **87.** 199.

Bonner, W. A. and Collins, C. J. (1953). *J. Amer. Chem. Soc.* **75,** 5372.

Bonner, W. A. and Collins, C. J. (1955). *J. Amer. Chem. Soc.* **77,** 99.

Bonner, W. A. and Collins, C. J. (1956). *J. Amer. Chem. Soc.* **78,** 5587.

Bonthrone, W. and Reid, D. H. (1966). *J. Chem. Soc. (B),* 91.

Boozer, C. E. and Lewis, E. S. (1954). *J. Amer. Chem. Soc.* **76,** 794.

Borčić, S., Nikoletić, M. and Sunko, D. E. (1962). *J. Amer. Chem. Soc.* **84,** 1615.

Borkowski, R. P. and Ausloos, P. (1964). *J. Chem. Phys.* **40,** 1128.

Boyd, R. H. (1963). *J. Amer. Chem. Soc.* **85,** 1555.

Boyd, R. H., Taft, R. W., Wolf, A. P. and Christman, D. R. (1960). *J. Amer. Chem. Soc.* **82,** 4729.

Branch, G. E. K. and Nixon, A. C. (1936). *J. Amer. Chem. Soc.* **58,** 2499.

Braun, J. von and Friehmelt, E. (1933). *Ber.* **66,** 684.

Bresler, L. S. (1963). *Uspekhi Khim.* **34,** 895 (*Russ. Chem. Rev.,* **34,** 366).

Breslow, R. (1963). In "Molecular Rearrangements" (P. de Mayo, ed.), p. 270. Interscience, New York.

Breslow, R. (1965). *Chem. Eng. News,* **43** (No. 26), 90.

Breslow, R., Bahary, W. and Reinmuth, W. (1961). *J. Amer. Chem. Soc.* **83,** 1763.

Breslow, R. and Chang, H. W. (1961). *J. Amer. Chem. Soc.* **83,** 2367.

Breslow, R., Chang, H. W. and Yager, W. A. (1963). *J. Amer. Chem. Soc.* **85,** 2033.

Breslow, R., Chang, H. W., Hill, R. and Wasserman, E. (1967). *J. Amer. Chem. Soc.* **89,** 1112.

Breslow, R., Haynie, R. and Mirra, J. (1959). *J. Amer. Chem. Soc.* **81,** 247.

Breslow, R., Hill, R. and Wasserman, E. (1964). *J. Amer. Chem. Soc.* **86,** 5349.

Breslow, R. and Höver, H. (1960). *J. Amer. Chem. Soc.* **82,** 2644.

Breslow, R., Höver, H. and Chang, H. W. (1962). *J. Amer. Chem. Soc.* **84,** 3168.

Breslow, R., Lockhart, J. and Chang, H. W. (1961). *J. Amer. Chem. Soc.* **83,** 2375.

Breslow, R., Lockhart, J. and Small, A. (1962). *J. Amer. Chem. Soc.* **84,** 2793.

Breslow, R. and Peterson, R. (1960). *J. Amer. Chem. Soc.* **82,** 4426.

Brickstock, A. and Pople, J. A. (1954). *Trans. Faraday Soc.* **50,** 901.

Brook, A. G., Pannell, K. H., Legrow, G. E. and Sheeto, J. J. (1964). *J. Organometallic Chem.* **2,** 491.

Brookhart, M., Anet, F. A. L. and Winstein, S. (1966). *J. Amer. Chem. Soc.* **88,** 5657.

Brookhart, M., Anet, F. A. L., Cram, D. J. and Winstein, S. (1966). *J. Amer. Chem. Soc.* **88,** 5659.

Brookhart, M., Diaz, A. F. and Winstein, S. (1966). *J. Amer. Chem. Soc.* **88,** 3135.

Brouwer, D. M. and Mackor, E. L. (1964). *Proc. Chem. Soc.* 147.

Brouwer, D. M., MacLean, C. and Mackor, E. L. (1965). *Disc. Faraday Soc.* **39,** 121.

Brown, D. A. and Hudson, R. F. (1953a). *J. Chem. Soc.* 883.

Brown, D. A. and Hudson, R. F. (1953b). *J. Chem. Soc.* 3352.

Brown, F., Davies, T. D., Dostrovsky, I., Evans, O. J. and Hughes, E. D. (1951). *Nature,* **167,** 987.

Brown, F., Hughes, E. D., Ingold, C. K. and Smith, J. F. (1951). *Nature,* **168,** 65.

Brown, G. R. and Pepper, D. C. (1963). *J. Chem. Soc.* 5930.

Brown, G. R. and Pepper, D. C. (1965). *Polymer,* **6,** 497.

Brown, H. C. (1962). In "The Transition State", p. 152.   Chem. Soc. Spec. Publ. No. 16.

Brown, H. C. (1966). *Chem. Brit.* 199.

Brown, H. C. (1967). *Chem. Eng. News* **45** (No. 7), 86.

Brown, H. C. and Bell, H. M. (1962). *J. Org. Chem.* **27,** 1928.

Brown, H. C. and Bell, H. M. (1963). *J. Amer. Chem. Soc.* **85,** 2324.

Brown, H. C. and Bell, H. M. (1964a). *J. Amer. Chem. Soc.* **86,** 5003.

Brown, H. C. and Bell, H. M. (1964b). *J. Amer. Chem. Soc.* **86,** 5006.

Brown, H. C., Bernheimer, R. and Morgan, K. J. (1965). *J. Amer. Chem. Soc.* **87,** 1280.

Brown, H. C., Bernheimer, R., Kim, C. J. and Scheppele, S. E. (1967). *J. Amer. Chem. Soc.* **89,** 370.

Brown, H. C. and Bolto, B. A. (1959). *J. Amer. Chem. Soc.* **81,** 3320.

Brown, H. C. and Brady, J. D. (1949). *J. Amer. Chem. Soc.* **71,** 3573.

Brown, H. C. and Brady, J. D. (1952). *J. Amer. Chem. Soc.* **74,** 3570.

Brown, H. C. and Chloupek, F. J. (1963). *J. Amer. Chem. Soc.* **85,** 2322.

Brown, H. C., Chloupek, F. J. and Rei, M.-H. (1964a). *J. Amer. Chem. Soc.* **86,** 1246.

Brown, H. C., Chloupek, F. J. and Rei, M.-H. (1964b). *J. Amer. Chem. Soc.* **86,** 1247.

Brown, H. C., Chloupek, F. J. and Rei, M.-H. (1964c). *J. Amer. Chem. Soc.* **86,** 1248.

Brown, H. C. and Cleveland, J. D. (1966). *J. Amer. Chem. Soc.* **88,** 2051.

Brown, H. C. and Fletcher, R. S. (1949). *J. Amer. Chem. Soc.* **71,** 1845.

Brown, H. C. and Fletcher, R. S. (1950). *J. Amer. Chem. Soc.* **72,** 1223.

Brown, H. C. and Grayson, M. (1953). *J. Amer. Chem. Soc.* **75,** 6285.

Brown, H. C. and Ham, G. (1956). *J. Amer. Chem. Soc.* **78,** 2735.

Brown, H. C. and Jensen, F. R. (1958a). *J. Amer. Chem. Soc.* **80,** 2291.

Brown, H. C. and Jensen, F. R. (1958b). *J. Amer. Chem. Soc.* **80,** 2296.

Brown, H. C. and Jungk, H. (1956). *J. Amer. Chem. Soc.* **78,** 2182.

Brown, H. C. and Liu, K.-T. (1967). *J. Amer. Chem. Soc.* **89,** 466.

Brown, H. C. and Marino, G. (1959a). *J. Amer. Chem. Soc.* **81,** 3308.

Brown, H. C. and Marino, G. (1959b). *J. Amer. Chem. Soc.* **81,** 5611.

Brown, H. C. and Marino, G. (1962). *J. Amer. Chem. Soc.* **84,** 1658.

Brown, H. C., Marino, G. and Stock, L. M. (1959). *J. Amer. Chem. Soc.* **81,** 3310.

Brown, H. C., Morgan, K. J. and Chloupek, F. J. (1965). *J. Amer. Chem. Soc.* **87,** 2137.

Brown, H. C. and Moritani, I. (1955). *J. Amer. Chem. Soc.* **77,** 3623.

Brown, H. C. and Muzzio, J. (1966). *J. Amer. Chem. Soc.* **88,** 2811.

Brown, H. C. and Nakagawa, M. (1955a). *J. Amer. Chem. Soc.* **77,** 3610.

Brown, H. C. and Nakagawa, M. (1955b). *J. Amer. Chem. Soc.* **77,** 3614.

Brown, H. C. and Nelson, K. L. (1953). *J. Amer. Chem. Soc.* **75,** 6292.

Brown, H. C. and Neyens, A. H. (1962a). *J. Amer. Chem. Soc.* **84,** 1233.

Brown, H. C. and Neyens, A. H. (1962b). *J. Amer. Chem. Soc.* **84,** 1655.

Brown, H. C. and Okamoto, Y. (1955). *J. Amer. Chem. Soc.* **77,** 3619.

Brown, H. C. and Okamoto, Y. (1957). *J. Amer. Chem. Soc.* **79,** 1913.

Brown, H. C. and Pearsall, H. W. (1951). *J. Amer. Chem. Soc.* **73,** 4681.

Brown, H. C. and Pearsall, H. W. (1952). *J. Amer. Chem. Soc.* **74,** 191.

Brown, H. C. and Rei, M.-H. (1964a). *J. Amer. Chem. Soc.* **86,** 5004.

Brown, H. C. and Rei, M.-H. (1964b). *J. Amer. Chem. Soc.* **86,** 5008.

Brown, H. C., Rothberg, I., Schleyer, P. R., Donaldson, M. M. and Harper, J. J. (1966). *Proc. Nat. Acad. Sci.* **56**, 1653.

Brown, H. C. and Smoot, C. R. (1956). *J. Amer. Chem. Soc.* **78**, 6255.

Brown, H. C. and Stern, A. (1950). *J. Amer. Chem. Soc.* **72**, 5068.

Brown, H. C. and Takeuchi, K. (1966). *J. Amer. Chem. Soc.* **88**, 5336.

Brown, H. C. and Tritle, G. L. (1966). *J. Amer. Chem. Soc.* **88**, 1320.

Brown, H. C. and Wallace, W. J. (1953a). *J. Amer. Chem. Soc.* **75**, 6265.

Brown, H. C. and Wallace, W. J. (1953b). *J. Amer. Chem. Soc.* **75**, 6268.

Brown, H. C. and Young, H. L. (1957). *J. Org. Chem.* **22**, 724.

Brown, R. F. (1952). *J. Amer. Chem. Soc.* **74**, 428.

Brown, R. F. (1954). *J. Amer. Chem. Soc.* **76**, 1279.

Brown, R. F., Nordmann, J. B. and Madoff, M. (1952). *J. Amer. Chem. Soc.* **74**, 432.

Brown, W. G., Widiger, A. H. and Letang, N. J. (1939). *J. Amer. Chem. Soc.* **61**, 2597.

Bruylants, P. and Dewael, A. (1928). *Bull. Sci. Acad. Roy. Belg.* (v)**14**, 140, *Chem. Abs.* **22**, 3883.

Bryan, R. F. (1964). *J. Amer. Chem. Soc.* **86**, 733.

Buck, H. M., Lupinski, J. H. and Oosterhoff, L. J. (1958). *Mol. Phys.* **1**, 196.

Bunnett, J. F. (1959). In "Theoretical Organic Chemistry. The Kekulé Symposium", p. 144. Butterworths, London.

Bunton, C. A. (1963). "Nucleophilic Substitution at Saturated Carbon", Elsevier, Amsterdam.

Bunton, C. A., Comyns, A. E. and Wood, J. L. (1951). *Research*, **4**, 383.

Bunton, C. A. and Fendler, J. H. (1965). *J. Org. Chem.* **30**, 1365.

Bunton, C. A., Greenstreet, C. H., Hughes, E. D. and Ingold, C. K. (1954a). *J. Chem. Soc.* 642.

Bunton, C. A., Greenstreet, C. H., Hughes, E. D. and Ingold, C. K. (1945b). *J. Chem. Soc.* 647.

Bunton, C. A., Hughes, E. D., Ingold, C. K. and Meigh, D. F. (1950). *Nature*, **166**, 679.

Bunton, C. A., Konasiewicz, A. and Llewellyn, D. R. (1955). *J. Chem. Soc.* 604.

Bunton, C. A. and Lewis, T. A. (1956). *Chem. and Ind.* 180.

Bunton, C. A., Lewis, T. A. and Llewellyn, D. R. (1954). *Chem. and Ind.* 1154.

Bunton, C. A. and O'Connor, C. (1965). *Chem. and Ind.* 1182.

Bunton, C. A. and Perry, S. G. (1960). *J. Chem. Soc.* 3070.

Burr, J. G. (1953). *J. Amer. Chem. Soc.* **75**, 5008.

Burr, J. G. (1954). *Chem. and Ind.* 850.

Burr, J. G. and Ciereszko, L. S. (1952). *J. Amer. Chem. Soc.* **74**, 5426.

Burwell, R. L. and Archer, S. (1942). *J. Amer. Chem. Soc.* **64**, 1032.

Burwell, R. L., Elkin, L. M. and Shields, A. D. (1952). *J. Amer. Chem. Soc.* **74**, 4570.

Bywater, S. and Worsfold, D. J. (1966). *Canad. J. Chem.* **44**, 1671.

Cacace, F., Ciranni, G. and Guarino, A. (1966). *J. Amer. Chem. Soc.* **88**, 2903.

Cannell, L. G. and Taft, R. W. (1956). *J. Amer. Chem. Soc.* **78**, 5812.

Capon, B. (1964). *Quart. Rev.* **18**, 45.

Capon, B., Perkins, M. J. and Rees, C. W. (1966). "Organic Reaction Mechanisms. 1965", p. 1. Wiley, New York.

Capon, B. and Rees, C. W. (1962). *Ann. Rep.* **59**, 207.

Carrington, A., Dravnieks, F. and Symons, M. C. R. (1959). *J. Chem. Soc.* 947.

Caserio, M. C., Graham, W. H. and Roberts, J. D. (1960). *Tetrahedron*, **11**, 171.

Cassimatis, D., Gagnaux, P. and Susz, B.-P. (1960). *Helv. Chim. Acta.* **43**, 424.

Cast, J. and Stevens, T. S. (1953). *J. Chem. Soc.* 4180.

Catchpole, A. G., Hughes, E. D. and Ingold, C. K. (1948). *J. Chem. Soc.* 8.

Challis, B. C. and Long, F. A. (1963). *J. Amer. Chem. Soc.* **85**, 2524.

Chapman, O. L. and Fitton, P. (1961). *J. Amer. Chem. Soc.* **83**, 1005.

Chapman, O. L. and Fitton, P. (1963). *J. Amer. Chem. Soc.* **85**, 41.

Chmiel, C. T. and Long, F. A. (1956). *J. Amer. Chem. Soc.* **78**, 3326.

Choi, S. U. and Brown, H. C. (1959). *J. Amer. Chem. Soc.* **81**, 3315.

Christol, H., Laurent, A. and Mousseron, M. (1961). *Bull. Soc. Chim. France*, 2313, 2319.

Christol, H., Laurent, A. and Solladie, G. (1963). *Bull. Soc. Chim. France*, 877.

Chu, T. L. and Weissman, S. I. (1954). *J. Chem. Phys.* **22**, 21.

Church, M. G., Hughes, E. D. and Ingold, C. K. (1940). *J. Chem. Soc.* 966.

Ciereszko, L. S. and Burr, J. G. (1952). *J. Amer. Chem. Soc.* **74**, 5431.

Cigén, R. (1958). *Acta. Chem. Scand.* **12**, 1456.

Cigén, R. (1960). *Acta. Chem. Scand.* **14**, 979.

Cigén, R. (1961a). *Acta. Chem. Scand.* **15**, 1892.

Cigén, R. (1961b). *Acta. Chem. Scand.* **15**, 1905.

Cigén, R. and Ekström, C.-G. (1963a). *Acta. Chem. Scand.* **17**, 1189.

Cigén, R. and Ekström, C.-G. (1963b), *Acta. Chem. Scand.* **17**, 1843.

Cigén, R. and Ekström, C.-G. (1963c). *Acta. Chem. Scand.* **17**, 2083.

Cigén, R. and Ekström, C.-G. (1964). *Acta. Chem. Scand.* **18**, 157.

Clarke, G. A. and Taft, R. W. (1962a). *J. Amer. Chem. Soc.* **84**, 2292.

Clarke, G. A. and Taft, R. W. (1962b). *J. Amer. Chem. Soc.* **84**, 2295.

Clifford, A. F., Beachell, H. C. and Jack, W. M. (1957). *J. Inorg. Nucl. Chem.* **5**, 57.

Closs, G. L. and Closs, L. E. (1963). *J. Amer. Chem. Soc.* **85**, 99.

Closs, G. L. and Moss, R. A. (1964). *J. Amer. Chem. Soc.* **86**, 4042.

Closs, G. L. and Schwartz, G. M. (1960). *J. Amer. Chem. Soc.* **82**, 5729.

Cocivera, M. and Winstein, S. (1963). *J. Amer. Chem. Soc.* **85**, 1702.

Coe, J. S. and Gold, V. (1960). *J. Chem. Soc.* 4940.

Cohen, S. G. and Schneider, A. (1941). *J. Amer. Chem. Soc.* **63**, 3382.

Colapietro, J. and Long, F. A. (1960). *Chem. and Ind.* 1056.

Collins, C. J. (1955). *J. Amer. Chem. Soc.* **77**, 5517.

Collins, C. J. (1960). *Quart. Rev.* **14**, 357.

Collins, C. J. and Benjamin, B. M. (1963). *J. Amer. Chem. Soc.* **85**, 2519.

Collins, C. J., Benjamin, B. M. and Lietzke, M. H. (1965). *Annalen*, **687**, 150.

Collins, C. J. and Bonner, W. A. (1955). *J. Amer. Chem. Soc.* **77**, 92.

Collins, C. J., Bonner, W. A. and Lester, C. T. (1959). *J. Amer. Chem. Soc.* **81**, 466.

Collins, C. J. and Bowman, N. S. (1959). *J. Amer. Chem. Soc.* **81**, 3614.

Collins, C. J., Cheema, Z. K., Werth, R. and Benjamin, B. M. (1964). *J. Amer. Chem. Soc.* **86**, 4913.

Collins, C. J., Christie, J. B. and Raaen, V. F. (1961). *J. Amer. Chem. Soc.* **83**, 4267.

Collins, C. J., Ciereszko, L. S. and Burr, J. G. (1953). *J. Amer. Chem. Soc.* **75**, 405.

Collins, C. J., Rainey, W. T., Smith, W. B. and Kaye, I. A. (1959). *J. Amer. Chem. Soc.* **81**, 460.

Collins, C. J., Staum, M. M. and Benjamin, B. M. (1962). *J. Org. Chem.* **27**, 3525.

Colpa, J. P., MacLean, C. and Mackor, E. L. (1963). *Tetrahedron*, **19,** Suppl. 2, 65.

Colter, A. K., Friedrich, E. C., Holness, N. J. and Winstein, S. (1965). *J. Amer. Chem. Soc.* **87,** 378.

Colter, A. K. and Musso, R. C. (1965). *J. Org. Chem.* **30,** 2462.

Colter, A. K., Schuster, I. I. and Kurland, R. J. (1965). *J. Amer. Chem. Soc.* **87.** 2278.

Colter, A. K., Wang, S. S., Megerle, G. M. and Ossip, P. S. (1964). *J. Amer. Chem. Soc.* **86,** 3106.

Conant, J. B. and Chow, B. F. (1933). *J. Amer. Chem. Soc.* **55,** 3752.

Conant, J. B., Kirner, W. R. and Hussey, R. E. (1925). *J. Amer. Chem. Soc.* **47,** 488.

Conant, J. B., Small, L. F. and Taylor, B. S. (1925). *J. Amer. Chem. Soc.* **47,** 1959.

Conant, J. B. and Werner, T. H. (1930). *J. Amer. Chem. Soc.* **52,** 4436.

Conrow, K. (1959). *J. Amer. Chem. Soc.* **81,** 5461.

Conrow, K. (1961). *J. Amer. Chem. Soc.* **83,** 2343.

Cook, D. (1959). *Canad. J. Chem.* **37,** 48.

Cook, D. (1962). *Canad. J. Chem.* **40,** 480.

Cook, D. (1963). *Canad. J. Chem.* **41,** 522.

Cooke, I., Susz, B.-P. and Herschmann, C. (1954). *Helv. Chim. Acta.* **37,** 1280.

Cooper, K. A. and Hughes, E. D. (1937). *J. Chem. Soc.* 1183.

Cooper, K. A., Hughes, E. D., Ingold, C. K. and MacNulty, B. J. (1948). *J. Chem. Soc.* 2038.

Cope, A. C., Grisar, J. M. and Peterson, P. E. (1960). *J. Amer. Chem. Soc.* **82,** 4299.

Cope, A. C., Martin, M. M. and McKervey, M. A. (1966). *Quart. Rev.* **20,** 119.

Cope, A. C., Moon, S. and Park, C. H. (1962). *J. Amer. Chem. Soc.* **84,** 4850.

Cope, A. C., Moon, S. and Peterson, P. E. (1962). *J. Amer. Chem. Soc.* **84,** 1935.

Cope, A. C. and Peterson, P. E. (1959). *J. Amer. Chem. Soc.* **81,** 1643.

Corbin, J. L., Hart, H. and Wagner, C. R. (1962). *J. Amer. Chem. Soc.* **84,** 1740.

Corey, E. J. and Atkinson, R. F. (1964). *J. Org. Chem.* **29,** 3703.

Corey, E. J., Bauld, N. L., LaLonde, R. T., Casanova, J. and Kaiser, E. T. (1960). *J. Amer. Chem. Soc.* **82,** 2645.

Corey, E. J. and Casanova, J. (1963). *J. Amer. Chem. Soc.* **85,** 165.

Corey, E. J., Casanova, J., Vatakencherry, P. A. and Winter, R. (1963). *J. Amer. Chem. Soc.* **85,** 169.

Corey, E. J. and Dawson, R. L. (1963). *J. Amer. Chem. Soc.* **85,** 1782.

Corey, E. J. and Sauers, C. K. (1957). *J. Amer. Chem. Soc.* **79,** 248.

Corey, E. J. and Uda, H. (1963). *J. Amer. Chem. Soc.* **85,** 1788.

Cotter, J. L. and Evans, A. G. (1959). *J. Chem. Soc.* 2988.

Cottrell, T. L. (1958). "The Strengths of Chemical Bonds", 2nd Ed. Butterworths, London.

Cowdrey, W. A., Hughes, E. D., Ingold, C. K., Masterman, S. and Scott, A. D. (1937) *J. Chem. Soc.* 1252.

Cox, E. F., Caserio, M. C., Silver, M. S. and Roberts, J. D. (1961). *J. Amer. Chem. Soc.* **83,** 2719.

Craig, R. A., Garrett, A. B. and Newman, M. S. (1950). *J. Amer. Chem. Soc.* **72,** 163.

Cram, D. J. (1949). *J. Amer. Chem. Soc.* **71,** 3863.

Cram, D. J. (1952a). *J. Amer. Chem. Soc.* **74,** 2129.

Cram, D. J. (1952b). *J. Amer. Chem. Soc.* **74,** 2137.

Cram, D. J. (1956). In "Steric Effects in Organic Chemistry" (M. S. Newman, ed.), Chapter 5. Wiley, New York.

Cram, D. J. (1960). *J. Chem. Educ.* **37,** 317.

Cram, D. J. (1964). *J. Amer. Chem. Soc.* **86,** 3767.

Cram, D. J. (1965). "Fundamentals of Carbanion Chemistry", Chapter 2. Academic Press, New York.

Cram, D. J. and Abd Elhafez, F. A. (1953). *J. Amer. Chem. Soc.* **75,** 3189.

Cram, D. J. and Allinger, J. (1957). *J. Amer. Chem. Soc.* **79,** 2858.

Cram, D. J. and Goldstein, M. (1963). *J. Amer. Chem. Soc.* **85,** 1063.

Cram, D. J. and Kopecky, K. R. (1959). *J. Amer. Chem. Soc.* **81,** 2748.

Cram, D. J. and McCarty, J. E. (1957). *J. Amer. Chem. Soc.* **79,** 2866.

Cram, D. J. and Sahyun, M. R. V. (1963). *J. Amer. Chem. Soc.* **85,** 1257.

Cram, D. J. and Singer, L. A. (1963). *J. Amer. Chem. Soc.* **85,** 1075.

Cram, D. J. and Tadanier, J. (1959). *J. Amer. Chem. Soc.* **81,** 2737.

Cristol, S. J., Morrill, T. C. and Sanchez, R. A. (1966). *J. Amer. Chem. Soc.* **88,** 3087.

Cristol, S. J. and Tanner, D. D. (1964). *J. Amer. Chem. Soc.* **86,** 3122.

Crunden, E. W. and Hudson, R. F. (1956). *J. Chem. Soc.* 501.

Cundall, R. B. (1963). In "The Chemistry of Cationic Polymerisation" (P. H. Plesch, ed.), Chapter 15. Pergamon, Oxford.

Cupas, C. A., Comisarow, M. B. and Olah, G. A. (1966). *J. Amer. Chem. Soc.* **88,** 361.

Curtin, D. Y. and Crew, M. C. (1955). *J. Amer. Chem. Soc.* **77,** 354.

Curtin, D. Y., Harris, E. E. and Meislich, E. K. (1952). *J. Amer. Chem. Soc.* **74,** 2901.

Curtin, D. Y. and Meislich, E. K. (1952a). *J. Amer. Chem. Soc.* **74,** 5518.

Curtin, D. Y. and Meislich, E. K. (1952b). *J. Amer. Chem. Soc.* **74,** 5905.

Curtin, D. Y. and Pollak, P. I. (1951). *J. Amer. Chem. Soc.* **73,** 992.

Dallinga, G., Smit, P. J. and Mackor, E. L. (1958). In "Steric Effects in Conjugated Systems" (G. W. Gray, ed.), p. 158. Butterworths, London.

Dallinga, G., Verrijn Stuart, A. A., Smit, P. J. and Mackor, E. L. (1957). *Z. Elektrochem.* **61,** 1019.

Danyluk, S. S. and Schneider, W. G. (1960). *J. Amer. Chem. Soc.* **82,** 997.

Danyluk, S. S. and Schneider, W. G. (1962). *Canad. J. Chem.* **40,** 1884.

Darwish, D. and Preston, E. A. (1964). *Tetrahedron Letters.* 113.

Dauben, H. J. and Bertelli, D. J. (1961a). *J. Amer. Chem. Soc.* **83,** 497.

Dauben, H. J. and Bertelli, D. J. (1961b). *J. Amer. Chem. Soc.* **83,** 4657.

Dauben, H. J., Gadecki, F. A., Harmon, K. M. and Pearson, D. L. (1957). *J. Amer. Chem. Soc.* **79,** 4557.

Dauben, H. J. and Honnen, L. R. (1958). *J. Amer. Chem. Soc.* **80,** 5570.

Dauben, H. J. and McDonough, L. M. (1962). 142nd A.C.S. Meeting, Atlantic City, Abstracts, p. 55Q.

Dauben, W. G. and Rogan J. B. (1956) quoted by A. Streitwieser, 1956b.

Dauben, W. G., Tweit, R. C. and Mannerskantz, C. (1954). *J. Amer. Chem. Soc.* **76,** 4420.

Davies, A. G. and Kenyon, J. (1955). *Quart. Rev.* **9,** 203.

Davis, R. E., Grosse, D., and Ohno, A. (1967). *Tetrahedron* **23,** 1029.

Dehl, R., Vaughan, W. R. and Berry, R. S. (1959). *J. Org. Chem.* **24,** 1616.

DeJongh, D. C. and Shrader, S. R. (1966). *J. Amer. Chem. Soc.* **88,** 3881.

de la Mare, P. B. D. (1963). In "Molecular Rearrangements" (P. de Mayo, ed.), Chapter 2. Interscience, New York.

de la Mare, P. B. D. and Bolton, R. (1966). "Electrophilic Additions to Unsaturated Systems". Elsevier, Amsterdam.

de Mayo, P. (1959). "The Mono- and Sesquiterpenoids" (The Chemistry of Natural Products, Vol. 2). Interscience, New York.

de Mayo, P. (1963). "Molecular Rearrangements". Wiley, New York.

DeMore, W. B. and Benson, S. W. (1964). *Adv. in Photochem.* **2**, 219.

Deno, N. C. (1964a). *Prog. Phys. Org. Chem.* **2**, 129.

Deno, N. C. (1964b), *Chem. Eng. News*, **42**, (No. 40), 88.

Deno, N. C. (1964c). In "Survey of Progress in Chemistry" (A. F. Scott, ed.), Vol. 2, p. 155. Academic Press, New York.

Deno, N. C., Berkheimer, H. E., Evans, W. L. and Peterson, H. J. (1959). *J. Amer. Chem.* Soc. **81**, 2344, 6535.

Deno, N. C., Bollinger, J., Friedman, N., Hafer, K., Hodge, J. D. and Houser, J. J. (1963). *J. Amer. Chem. Soc.* **85**, 2998.

Deno, N. C., Edwards, T. and Perizzolo, C. (1957). *J. Amer. Chem. Soc.* **79**, 2108.

Deno, N. C. and Evans, W. L. (1957). *J. Amer. Chem. Soc.* **79**, 5804.

Deno, N. C., Friedman, N. and Mockus, J. (1964). *J. Amer. Chem. Soc.* **86**, 5676.

Deno, N. C., Friedman, N., Hodge, J. D., MacKay, F. P. and Saines, G. (1962). *J. Amer. Chem. Soc.* **84**, 4713.

Deno, N. C., Friedman, N., Hodge, J. D. and Houser, J. J. (1963). *J. Amer. Chem. Soc.* **85**, 2995.

Deno, N. C., Groves, P. T. and Saines, G. (1959). *J. Amer. Chem. Soc.* **81**, 5790.

Deno, N. C., Groves, P. T., Jaruzelski, J. J. and Lugasch, M. N. (1960). *J. Amer. Chem. Soc.* **82**, 4719.

Deno, N. C., Jaruzelski, J. J. and Schriesheim, A. (1955). *J. Amer. Chem. Soc.* **77**, 3044.

Deno, N. C., Kish, F. A. and Peterson, H. J. (1965). *J. Amer. Chem. Soc.* **87**, 2157.

Deno, N. C. and Lincoln, D. N. (1966). *J. Amer. Chem. Soc.* **88**, 5357.

Deno, N. C., Liu, J. S., Turner, J. O., Lincoln, D. N. and Fruit, R. E. (1965). *J. Amer. Chem. Soc.* **87**, 3000.

Deno, N. C., Peterson, H. J. and Saines, G. S. (1960). *Chem. Rev.* **60**, 7.

Deno, N. C. and Pittman, C. U. (1964). *J. Amer. Chem. Soc.* **86**, 1871.

Deno, N. C., Pittman, C. U. and Turner, J. O. (1965). *J. Amer. Chem. Soc.* **87**, 2153.

Deno, N. C., Pittman, C. U. and Wisotsky, M. J. (1964). *J. Amer. Chem. Soc.* **86**, 4370.

Deno, N. C., Richey, H. G., Hodge, J. D. and Wisotsky, M. J. (1962a). *J. Amer. Chem. Soc.* **84**, 1498.

Deno, N. C., Richey, H. G., Liu, J. S., Hodge, J. D., Houser, J. J. and Wisotsky, M. J. (1962b). *J. Amer. Chem. Soc.* **84**, 2016.

Deno, N. C., Richey, H. G., Friedman, N., Hodge, J. D., Houser, J. J. and Pittman, C. U. (1963). *J. Amer. Chem. Soc.* **85**, 2991.

Deno, N. C., Richey, H. G., Liu, J. S., Lincoln, D. N. and Turner, J. O. (1965). *J. Amer. Chem. Soc.* **87**, 4533.

Deno, N. C. and Sacher, E. (1965). *J. Amer. Chem. Soc.* **87**, 5120.

Deno, N. C., Saines, G. and Spangler, M. (1962). *J. Amer. Chem. Soc.* **84**, 3295.

Deno, N. C. and Schriesheim, A. (1955). *J. Amer. Chem. Soc.* **77**, 3051.

DePuy, C. H. and King, R. W. (1960). *Chem. Rev.* **60**, 431.

DePuy, C. H., Ogawa, I. A. and McDaniel, J. C. (1961). *J. Amer. Chem. Soc.* **83,** 1668.

DePuy, C. H., Schnack, L. G., Hausser, J. W. and Wiedemann, W. (1965). *J. Amer. Chem. Soc.* **87,** 4006.

Dermer, O. C. and Billmeier, R. A. (1942). *J. Amer. Chem. Soc.* **64,** 464.

de Sousa, R. M. and Moriarty, R. M. (1965). *J. Org. Chem.* **30,** 1509.

de Vries, L. (1960). *J. Amer. Chem. Soc.* **82,** 5242.

Dewar, M. J. S. (1952). *J. Amer. Chem. Soc.* **74,** 3345.

Dewar, M. J. S. (1962). "Hyperconjugation". Ronald Press, New York.

Dewar, M. J. S. (1963). *Tetrahedron,* **19,** Suppl. 2, 89.

Dewar, M. J. S. and Fahey, R. C. (1963a). *J. Amer. Chem. Soc.* **85,** 2245.

Dewar, M. J. S. and Fahey, R. C. (1963b). *J. Amer. Chem. Soc.* **85,** 2248.

Dewar, M. J. S. and Fahey, R. C. (1963c). *J. Amer. Chem. Soc.* **85,** 3645.

Dewar, M. J. S. and Fahey, R. C. (1964). *Angew. Chem.* **76,** 320 (Internat. Ed. **3,** 245).

Dewar, M. J. S. and Ganellin, C. R. (1959). *J. Chem. Soc.* 2438.

Dewar, M. J. S. and Marchand, A. P. (1965). *Ann. Rev. Phys. Chem.* **16,** 321.

Dewar, M. J. S. and Sampson, R. J. (1956). *J. Chem. Soc.* 2789.

Dewar, M. J. S. and Sampson, R. J. (1957). *J. Chem. Soc.* 2946, 2952.

DeWolfe, R. H. and Young, W. G. (1956). *Chem. Rev.* **56,** 753.

DeWolfe, R. H. and Young, W. G. (1964). In "The Chemistry of Alkenes" (S. Patai, ed.), p. 681. Interscience, New York.

Diaz, A. F., Brookhart, M. and Winstein, S. (1966). *J. Amer. Chem. Soc.* **88,** 3133.

Diaz, A. F. and Winstein, S. (1966). *J. Amer. Chem. Soc.* **88,** 1318.

Diffenbach, R. A., Sano, K. and Taft, R. W. (1966). *J. Amer. Chem. Soc.* **88,** 4747.

Dilthey, W. and Dinklage, R. (1929). *Ber.* **62,** 1834.

Dimroth, K., Umbach, W. and Thomas, H. (1967). *Chem. Ber.* **100,** 132.

Doering, W. E. and Aschner, T. C. (1949). *J. Amer. Chem. Soc.* **71,** 838.

Doering, W. E. and Aschner, T. C. (1953). *J. Amer. Chem. Soc.* **75,** 393.

Doering, W. E. and Henderson, W. A. (1958). *J. Amer. Chem. Soc.* **80,** 5274.

Doering, W. E. and Knox, L. H. (1954). *J. Amer. Chem. Soc.* **76,** 3203.

Doering, W. E. and Krauch, H. (1956). *Angew. Chem.* **68,** 661.

Doering, W. E., Levitz, M., Sayigh, A., Sprecher, M. and Whelan, W. P. (1953), *J. Amer. Chem. Soc.* **75,** 1008.

Doering, W. E., Saunders, M., Boyton, H. G., Earhart, H. W., Wadley, E. F., Edwards, W. R. and Laber, G. (1958). *Tetrahedron,* **4,** 178.

Doering, W. E., Streitwieser, A. and Friedman, L. (1956) quoted by Streitwieser, 1956b.

Doering, W. E. and Zeiss, H. H. (1953). *J. Amer. Chem. Soc.* **75,** 4733.

Dostrovsky, I. and Hughes, E. D. (1946). *J. Chem. Soc.* 157, 161, 164, 166, 169, 171.

Dostrovsky, I., Hughes, E. D. and Ingold, C. K. (1946). *J. Chem. Soc.* 173.

Duffy, J. A. and Leisten, J. A. (1960a). *J. Chem. Soc.* 545.

Duffy, J. A. and Leisten, J. A. (1960b). *J. Chem. Soc.* 853.

Dunn, G. E. and Prysiazniuk, R. (1961). *Canad. J. Chem.* **39,** 285.

Dunphy, J. F. and Marvel, C. S. (1960). *J. Polymer Sci.* **47,** 1.

Eaborn, C. (1959). "Organosilicon Compounds". Butterworths, London.

Eaborn, C. and Taylor, R. (1961). *J. Chem. Soc.* 247, 1012.

Eberson, L., Petrovich, J. P., Baird, R. L., Dyckes, D. and Winstein, S. (1965). *J. Amer. Chem. Soc.* **87,** 3504.

Eberson, L. and Winstein, S. (1965). *J. Amer. Chem. Soc.* **87,** 3506.

Edwards, J. O. (1954). *J. Amer. Chem. Soc.* **76,** 1540.

Edwards, J. O. (1956). *J. Amer. Chem. Soc.* **78,** 1819.

Edwards, J. O. and Pearson, R. G. (1962). *J. Amer. Chem. Soc.* **84,** 16.

Ehrenson, S. (1961). *J. Amer. Chem. Soc.* **83,** 4493.

Ehrenson, S. (1962). *J. Amer. Chem. Soc.* **84,** 2681.

Ehret, A. and Winstein, S. (1966). *J. Amer. Chem. Soc.* **88,** 2048.

Eigen, M. (1957). *Disc. Faraday Soc.* **24,** 25.

Eigen, M. and Tamm, K. (1962). *Z. Elektrochem.* **66,** 107.

Elder, F. A., Giese, C., Steiner, B. and Inghram, M. (1962). *J. Chem. Phys.* **36,** 3292.

Emovon, E. U. (1963). *J. Chem. Soc.* 1246.

Épple, G. V., Odintsova, V. P. and Éntelis, S. G. (1962). *Izvest. Akad. Nauk. S.S.S.R. (Otdel. khim. Nauk).* 1365 (*Bull. Acad. Sci. U.S.S.R.* 1282).

Eriks, K. and Koh, L. L. (1963). Petroleum Research Fund Report No. 8, p. 5.

Erusalimskii, B. L. (1963). *Uspekhi Khim.* **32,** 1458 (*Russ. Chem. Rev.* **32,** 651).

Evans, A. G. (1946). *Trans. Faraday Soc.* **42.** 719.

Evans, A. G. (1951). *J. Appl. Chem.* **1,** 240.

Evans, A. G. and Hamann, S. D. (1951). *Trans. Faraday Soc.* **47,** 25.

Evans, A. G., Jones, J. A. G. and Osborne, G. O. (1954). *Trans. Faraday Soc.* **50,** 16, 470.

Evans, A. G., McEwan, I. H., Price, A. and Thomas, J. H. (1955). *J. Chem. Soc.* 3098.

Evans, A. G., Price, A. and Thomas, J. H. (1954). *Trans. Faraday Soc.* **50,** 568.

Evans, A. G., Price, A. and Thomas, J. H. (1955). *Trans. Faraday Soc.* **51,** 481.

Evans, A. G., Price, A. and Thomas, J. H. (1956). *Trans. Faraday Soc.* **52,** 332.

Evans, E. A., Huston, J. L. and Norris, T. H. (1952). *J. Amer. Chem. Soc.* **74,** 4985.

Eyring, H., Hulburt, H. M. and Harman, R. A. (1943). *Ind. Eng. Chem.* **35,** 511.

Fainberg, A. H., Robinson, G. C. and Winstein, S. (1956). *J. Amer. Chem. Soc.* **78,** 2777.

Fainberg, A. H. and Winstein, S. (1956a). *J. Amer. Chem. Soc.* **78,** 2763.

Fainberg, A. H. and Winstein, S. (1956b). *J. Amer. Chem. Soc.* **78,** 2770.

Fainberg, A. H. and Winstein, S. (1956c). *J. Amer. Chem. Soc.* **78,** 2780.

Fairbrother, F. (1937). *J. Chem. Soc.* 503.

Fairbrother, F. (1941). *J. Chem. Soc.* 293.

Fairbrother, F. and Wright, B. (1949). *J. Chem. Soc.* 1058.

Farnum, D. G. (1964). *J. Amer. Chem. Soc.* **86,** 934.

Farnum, D. G. and Burr, M. (1960). *J. Amer. Chem. Soc.* **82,** 2651.

Farnum, D. G. and Webster, B. (1963). *J. Amer. Chem. Soc.* **85,** 3502.

Fava, A., Iliceto, A., Ceccon, A. and Koch, P. (1965). *J. Amer. Chem. Soc.* **87,** 1045.

Favorskaya, T. A. and Fridman, S. A. (1945). *J. Gen. Chem. U.S.S.R.* **15,** 421.

Featherstone, W., Jackson, E. and Kohnstam, G. (1963). *Proc. Chem. Soc.* 175.

Feldman, M. and Winstein, S. (1961). *J. Amer. Chem. Soc.* **83,** 3338.

Felkin, H. and Le Ny, G. (1957). *Bull. Soc. Chim. France,* 1169.

Field, F. H. and Franklin, J. L. (1957). "Electron Impact Phenomena and the Properties of Gaseous Ions". Academic Press, New York.

Field, F. H. and Lampe, F. W. (1958). *J. Amer. Chem. Soc.* **80,** 5583.

Filler, R., Wang, C.-S., McKinney, M. A. and Miller, F. N. (1967). *J. Amer. Chem. Soc.* **89**, 1026.

Finch, A. C. M. and Symons, M. C. R. (1965). *J. Chem. Soc.* 378.

Fischer, E. O. and Fischer, R. D. (1960). *Angew. Chem.* **72**, 919.

Flockhart, B. D., Scott, J. A. N. and Pink, R. C. (1966). *Trans. Faraday Soc.* **62**, 730.

Flurry, R. L. and Lykos, P. G. (1963). *J. Amer. Chem. Soc.* **85**, 1033.

Foote, C. S. (1964). *J. Amer. Chem. Soc.* **86**, 1853.

Foote, C. S. and Woodward, R. B. (1964). *Tetrahedron*, **20**, 687.

Forbes, W. F. and Sullivan, P. D. (1966). *J. Amer. Chem. Soc.* **88**, 2862.

Fort, A. W. and Roberts, J. D. (1956). *J. Amer. Chem. Soc.* **78**, 584.

Fort, R. C. and Schleyer, P. R. (1964a). *Chem. Rev.* **64**, 277.

Fort, R. C. and Schleyer, P. R. (1964b). *J. Amer. Chem. Soc.* **86**, 4194.

Fox, J. R. and Kohnstam, G. (1964). *Proc. Chem. Soc.* 115.

Fraenkel, G., Carter, R. E., McLachlan, A. and Richards, J. H. (1960). *J. Amer. Chem. Soc.* **82**, 5846.

Fraenkel, G., Ralph, P. D. and Kim, J. P. (1965). *Canad. J. Chem.* **43**, 674.

Franklin, J. L. (1952). *Trans. Faraday Soc.* **48**, 443.

Franklin, J. L. and Field, F. H. (1953). *J. Chem. Phys.* **21**, 550.

Franklin, J. L. and Lumpkin, H. E. (1951). *J. Chem. Phys.* **19**, 1073.

Franzen, V. (1957). *Annalen*, **602**, 199.

Fredenhagen, K. and Dahmlos, J. (1929). *Z. anorg. Chem.* **178**, 272.

Freedman, H. H. and Frantz, A. M. (1962). *J. Amer. Chem. Soc.* **84**, 4165.

Freedman, H. H. and Young, A. E. (1964). *J. Amer. Chem. Soc.* **86**, 734.

Freedman, H. H., Young, A. E. and Sandel, V. R. (1964). *J. Amer. Chem. Soc.* **86**, 4722.

Friedrich, E. C. and Winstein, S. (1962). *Tetrahedron Letters*, 475.

Frisone, G. J. and Thornton, E. R. (1964). *J. Amer. Chem. Soc.* **86**, 1900.

Gandini, A. and Plesch, P. H. (1964). *Proc. Chem. Soc.* 240.

Gandini, A. and Plesch, P. H. (1965a). *J. Polymer Sci.* **B3**, 127.

Gandini, A. and Plesch, P. H. (1965b). *J. Chem. Soc.* 4826.

Gandini, A. and Plesch, P. H. (1965c). *J. Chem. Soc.* 6019.

Gaspar, P. P. and Hammond, G. S. (1964). In "Carbene Chemistry" (W. Kirmse, ed.), Chapter 12. Academic Press, New York.

Gassman, P. G. and Marshall, J. L. (1965). *J. Amer. Chem. Soc.* **87**, 4648.

Gassman, P. G. and Marshall, J. L. (1966a). *J. Amer. Chem. Soc.* **88**, 2599.

Gassman, P. G. and Marshall, J. L. (1966b). *J. Amer. Chem. Soc.* **88**, 2822.

Gassman, P. G. and Zalar, F. V. (1966). *J. Amer. Chem. Soc.* **88**, 2252.

Gerrard, W. and Hudson, H. R. (1965). *Chem. Rev.* **65**, 697.

Giddings, W. P. and Dirlam, J. (1963). *J. Amer. Chem. Soc.* **85**, 3900.

Gillespie, R. J. (1950a). *J. Chem. Soc.* 2542.

Gillespie, R. J. (1950b). *J. Chem. Soc.* 2997.

Gillespie, R. J. (1963). In "Friedel-Crafts and Related Reactions", Vol. 1 (G. A. Olah, ed.), p. 169. Interscience, New York.

Gillespie, R. J. and Leisten, J. A. (1954). *Quart. Rev.* **8**, 40.

Gillespie, R. J. and Robinson, E. A. (1964). *J. Amer. Chem. Soc.* **86**, 5676.

Gillespie, R. J. and Robinson, E. A. (1965a). In "Non-aqueous Solvent Systems" (T. C. Waddington, ed.). Academic Press, London.

12

Gillespie, R. J. and Robinson, E. A. (1965b). *J. Amer. Chem. Soc.* **87**, 2428.
Gillespie, R. J. and Wasif, S. (1953a). *J. Chem. Soc.* 209.
Gillespie, R. J. and Wasif, S. (1953b). *J. Chem. Soc.* 221.
Gleave, J. L., Hughes, E. D. and Ingold, C. K. (1935). *J. Chem. Soc.* 236.
Gleicher, G. J. and Schleyer, P. R. (1967). *J. Amer. Chem. Soc.* **89**, 582.
Goering, H. L. (1960). *Record Chem. Prog.* **21**, 109.
Goering, H. L. and Closson, W. D. (1961). *J. Amer. Chem. Soc.* **83**, 3511.
Goering, H. L., Doi, J. T. and McMichael, K. D. (1964). *J. Amer. Chem. Soc.* **86**, 1951.
Goering, H. L., Espy, H. H. and Closson, W. D. (1959). *J. Amer. Chem. Soc.* **81**, 329.
Goering, H. L. and Levy, J. F. (1962). *J. Amer. Chem. Soc.* **84**, 3853.
Goering, H. L. and Levy, J. F. (1964). *J. Amer. Chem. Soc.* **86**, 120.
Goering, H. L., Olson, A. C. and Espy, H. H. (1956). *J. Amer. Chem. Soc.* **78**, 5371.
Goering, H. L., Pombo, M. M. and McMichael, K. D. (1963). *J. Amer. Chem. Soc.* **85**, 965.
Goering, H. L. and Schewene, C. B. (1965). *J. Amer. Chem. Soc.* **87**, 3516.
Goering, H. L. and Sloan, M. F. (1961a). *J. Amer. Chem. Soc.* **83**, 1397.
Goering, H. L. and Sloan, M. F. (1961b). *J. Amer. Chem. Soc.* **83**, 1992.
Goering, H. L. and Towns, D. L. (1963). *J. Amer. Chem. Soc.* **85**, 2295.
Gold, V. (1955). *J. Chem. Soc.* 1263.
Gold, V. (1956a). *J. Chem. Soc.* 3944.
Gold, V. (1956b). *J. Chem. Soc.* 4633.
Gold, V. (1964). In "Friedel-Crafts and Related Reactions", Vol. 2. (G. A. Olah, ed.), p. 1253. Interscience, New York.
Gold, V. and Hawes, B. W. V. (1951). *J. Chem. Soc.* 2102.
Gold, V., Hawes, B. W. V. and Tye, F. L. (1952). *J. Chem. Soc.* 2167.
Gold, V. and Hilton, J. (1955), *J. Chem. Soc.* 843.
Gold, V., Hilton, J. and Jefferson, E. G. (1954). *J. Chem. Soc.* 2756.
Gold, V. and Kessick, M. A. (1965a). *J. Chem. Soc.* 6718.
Gold, V. and Kessick, M. A. (1965b). *Discuss. Farady Soc.* **39**, 84.
Gold, V. and Riley, T. (1960). *J. Chem. Soc.* 2973.
Gold, V. and Riley, T. (1962). *J. Chem. Soc.* 4183.
Gold, V. and Satchell, R. S. (1963a). *J. Chem. Soc.* 1930.
Gold, V. and Satchell, R. S. (1963b). *J. Chem. Soc.* 1938.
Gold, V. and Tye, F. L. (1952a). *J. Chem. Soc.* 2172.
Gold, V. and Tye, F. L. (1952b). *J. Chem. Soc.* 2181.
Gold, V. and Tye, F. L. (1952c). *J. Chem. Soc.* 2184.
Gold, V. and Waterman, D. C. A. (1967). *Chem. Comm.* 40.
Goldfinger, G. and Kane, T. (1948). *J. Polymer Sci.* **3**, 462.
Goldschmidt, S. and Christmann, F. (1925). *Annalen*, **442**, 246.
Golomb, D. (1959a). *J. Chem. Soc.* 1327.
Golomb, D. (1959b). *J. Chem. Soc.* 1334.
Gomberg, M. (1902a). *Ber.* **35**, 1822.
Gomberg, M. (1902b). *Ber.* **35**, 2397.
Gomberg, M. and Cone, L. H. (1909). *Annalen*, **370**, 142.
Gomberg, M. and Sullivan, F. W. (1922). *J. Amer. Chem. Soc.* **44**, 1810.
Gomes de Mesquita, A. H., MacGillavry, C. H. and Eriks, K. (1965). *Acta Cryst.* **18**, 437.

Grace, J. A. and Symons, M. C. R. (1959). *J. Chem. Soc.* 958.

Grant, G. H. and Hinshelwood, C. N. (1933). *J. Chem. Soc.* 258.

Gream, G. E. (1966). *Rev. Pure Appl. Chem.* **16,** 25.

Gream, G. E. and Wege, D. (1964). *Tetrahedron Letters*, 535.

Greensfelder, B. S. (1955). In "The Chemistry of Petroleum Hydrocarbons", Vol. 2 (B. T. Brooks, C. E. Boord, S. S. Kurtz and L. Schmerling, ed.), Chapter 27. Reinhold, New York.

Greenwood, H. H. and McWeeny, R. (1966). *Adv. Phys. Org. Chem.* **4,** 73.

Griffiths, T. R. and Symons, M. C. R. (1960). *Mol. Phys.* **3,** 90.

Grinter, R. and Mason, S. F. (1964a). *Trans. Faraday Soc.* **60,** 882.

Grinter, R. and Mason, S. F. (1964b). *Trans. Faraday Soc.* **60,** 889.

Grob, C. A. (1959). In "Theoretical Organic Chemistry. The Kekulé Symposium", p. 114. Butterworths, London.

Grob, C. A. (1960). *Bull. Soc. Chim. France*, 1360.

Grob, C. A. (1962), *Gazzetta*, **92,** 902.

Grob, C. A., Hoegerle, R. M. and Ohta, M. (1962). *Helv. Chim. Acta*, **45,** 1823.

Grob, C. A. and Jenny, F. A. (1960). *Tetrahedron Letters*, No. **23,** 25.

Grob, C. A., Ostermayer, F. and Raudenbusch, W. (1962). *Helv. Chim. Acta*. **45,** 1672.

Grob, C. A., Schwarz, W. and Fischer, H. P. (1964). *Helv. Chim. Acta*. **47,** 1385.

Grosse, A. V. and Ipatieff, V. N. (1943). *J. Org. Chem.* **8,** 438.

Grubb, H. M. and Meyerson, S. (1963). In "Mass Spectrometry of Organic Ions" (F. W. McLafferty, ed.), p. 453. Academic Press, New York.

Grunwald, E. (1954). *Analyt. Chem.* **26,** 1696.

Grunwald, E., Heller, A. and Klein, F. S. (1957). *J. Chem. Soc.* 2604.

Grunwald, E. and Winstein, S. (1948). *J. Amer. Chem. Soc.* **70,** 846.

Gustavson, G. (1878), quoted by G. Wagner, *Ber.* **11,** 1251.

Hafner, K. and Pelster, H. (1961). *Angew. Chem.* **73,** 342.

Hakka, L., Queen, A. and Robertson, R. E. (1965). *J. Amer. Chem. Soc.* **87,** 161.

Halevi, E. A. (1963). *Prog. Phys. Org. Chem.* **1,** 109.

Hall, H. K. (1955). *J. Amer. Chem. Soc.* **77,** 5993.

Hall, N. F. and Voge, H. H. (1933). *J. Amer. Chem. Soc.* **55,** 239.

Hammett, L. P. (1940), "Physical Organic Chemistry". McGraw-Hill, New York.

Hammett, L. P. (1935). *Chem. Rev.* **17,** 125.

Hammett, L. P. and Chapman, R. P. (1934). *J. Amer. Chem. Soc.* **56,** 1282.

Hammett, L. P. and Deyrup, A. J. (1933). *J. Amer. Chem. Soc.* **55,** 1900.

Hammett, L. P. and Lowenheim, F. A. (1934). *J. Amer. Chem. Soc.* **56,** 2620.

Hammond, G. S. (1955). *J. Amer. Chem. Soc.* **77,** 334.

Hanack, M. and Schneider, H. J. (1964). *Tetrahedron*, **20,** 1863.

Hanazaki, I., Hosoya, H. and Nagakura, S. (1963). *Bull. Chem. Soc. Japan*, **36,** 1673.

Hanazaki, I. and Nagakura, S. (1965). *Tetrahedron*, **21,** 2441.

Hanhart, W. and Ingold, C. K. (1927). *J. Chem. Soc.* 997.

Hanna, M. W. (1965). "Quantum Mechanics in Chemistry". Benjamin, New York.

Hantzsch, A. (1907). *Z. phys. Chem.* **61,** 257.

Hantzsch, A. (1908). *Z. phys. Chem.* **65,** 41.

Hantzsch, A. (1921). *Ber.* **54,** 2573.

Hantzsch, A. (1922). *Ber.* **55,** 953.

Hantzsch, A. and Meyer, K. H. (1910). *Ber.* **43,** 336.

Harden, G. D. and Maccoll, A. (1955). *J. Chem. Soc.* 2454.

Harmon, K. M., Alderman, S. D., Benker, K. E., Diestler, D. J. and Gebauer, P. A. (1965). *J. Amer. Chem. Soc.* **87,** 1700.

Harmon, K. M. and Cummings, F. E. (1962). *J. Amer. Chem. Soc.* **84,** 1751.

Harmon, K. M., Cummings, F. E., Davies, D. A. and Diestler, D. J. (1962a). *J. Amer. Chem. Soc.* **84,** 120.

Harmon, K. M., Cummings, F. E., Davies, D. A. and Diestler, D. J. (1962b). *J. Amer. Chem. Soc.* **84,** 3349.

Harmon, K. M. and Davis, S. (1962). *J. Amer. Chem. Soc.* **84,** 4359.

Harmon, K. M. and Harmon, A. B. (1961). *J. Amer. Chem. Soc.* **83,** 865.

Harmon, K. M., Harmon, A. B. and Cummings, F. E. (1962). *J. Amer. Chem. Soc.* **83,** 3912.

Harrison, A. G. (1963). In "Mass Spectrometry of Organic Ions" (F. W. McLafferty, ed.), p. 207. Academic Press, New York.

Harrison, A. G., Honnen, L. R., Dauben, H. J. and Lossing, F. P. (1960). *J. Amer. Chem. Soc.* **82,** 5593.

Harrison, A. G., Kebarle, P. and Lossing, F. P. (1961). *J. Amer. Chem. Soc.* **83,** 777.

Hart, H. and Cassis, F. A. (1954). *J. Amer. Chem. Soc.* **76,** 1634.

Hart, H., Corbin, J. L., Wagner, C. R. and Wu, C.-Y. (1963). *J. Amer. Chem. Soc.* **85,** 3269.

Hart, H. and Fish, R. W. (1958). *J. Amer. Chem. Soc.* **80,** 5894.

Hart, H. and Fish, R. W. (1960). *J. Amer. Chem. Soc.* **82,** 5419.

Hart, H. and Fish, R. W. (1961). *J. Amer. Chem. Soc.* **83,** 4460.

Hart, H. and Law, P. A. (1962). *J. Amer. Chem. Soc.* **84,** 2462.

Hart, H. and Law, P. A. (1964). *J. Amer. Chem. Soc.* **86,** 1957.

Hart, H. and Sandri, J. M. (1959). *J. Amer. Chem. Soc.* **81,** 320.

Hart, H., Spliethoff, W. L. and Eleuterio, H. S. (1954). *J. Amer. Chem. Soc.* **76,** 4547.

Hart, H., Sulzberg, T. and Rafos, R. R. (1963). *J. Amer. Chem. Soc.* **85,** 1800.

Hawdon, A. R., Hughes, E. D. and Ingold, C. K. (1952). *J. Chem. Soc.* 2499.

Hawthorne, M. F. (1956). *J. Org. Chem.* **21,** 363.

Hayes, M. J. and Pepper, D. C. (1961). *Proc. Roy. Soc.* **A263,** 63.

Heck, R., Corse, J., Grunwald, E. and Winstein, S. (1957). *J. Amer. Chem. Soc.* **79,** 3278.

Heck, R. and Winstein, S. (1957a). *J. Amer. Chem. Soc.* **79,** 3105.

Heck, R. and Winstein, S. (1957b). *J. Amer. Chem. Soc.* **79,** 3114.

Heck, R. and Winstein, S. (1957c). *J. Amer. Chem. Soc.* **79,** 3432.

Heilbronner, E. and Simonetta, M. (1952). *Helv. Chim. Acta.* **35,** 1049.

Herling, J. and Pines, H. (1963). *Chem. and Ind.* 984.

Herzberg, G. (1961). *Proc. Roy. Soc.* **A262,** 291.

Herzberg, G. and Shoosmith, J. (1956). *Canad. J. Phys.* **34,** 523.

Hess, G. G., Lampe, F. W. and Sommer, L. H. (1964). *J. Amer. Chem. Soc.* **86,** 3174.

Hess, G. G., Lampe, F. W. and Sommer, L. H. (1965). *J. Amer. Chem. Soc.* **87,** 5327.

Higashimura, T., Kanoh, N. and Okamura, S. (1966). *J. Macromol. Chem.* **1,** 109.

Hill, E. A. (1965). *Chem. and Ind.* 1696.

Hill, M. E. (1960). *J. Amer. Chem. Soc.* **82,** 2866.

Hine, J. (1962). "Physical Organic Chemistry", 2nd Ed. McGraw-Hill, New York.

Hine, J. (1964). "Divalent Carbon". Ronald Press, New York.

Hine, J., Butterworth, R. and Langford, P. B. (1958). *J. Amer. Chem. Soc.* **80**, 819.

Hine, J. and Dowell, A. M. (1954). *J. Amer. Chem. Soc.* **76**, 2688.

Hine, J. and van der Veen, J. M. (1959). *J. Amer. Chem. Soc.* **81**, 6446.

Hinman, R. L. and Lang, J. (1964). *J. Amer. Chem. Soc.* **86**, 3796.

Hoberg, H. (1962). *Annalen*, **656**, 1.

Hoeg, D. F., Lusk, D. I. and Crumbliss, A. L. (1965). *J. Amer. Chem. Soc.* **87**, 4147.

Hoffmann, R. (1963). *J. Chem. Phys.* **39**, 1397.

Hoffmann, R. (1964a). *J. Amer. Chem. Soc.* **86**, 1259.

Hoffmann, R. (1964b). *J. Chem. Phys.* **40**, 2480.

Hoffmann, R. and Olofson, R. A. (1966). *J. Amer. Chem. Soc.* **88**, 943.

Hofmann, J. E. and Schriesheim, A. (1962a). *J. Amer. Chem. Soc.* **84**, 953.

Hofmann, J. E. and Schriesheim, A. (1962b). *J. Amer. Chem. Soc.* **84**, 957.

Hogen-Esch, T. E. and Smid, J. (1966a). *J. Amer. Chem. Soc.* **88**, 307.

Hogen-Esch, T. E. and Smid, J. (1966b), *J. Amer. Chem. Soc.* **88**, 318.

Hogeveen, H. (1967). *Rec. Trav. Chim.* **86**, 289.

Horner, L. and Spietschka, E. (1952). *Chem. Ber.* **85**, 225.

Howald, R. A. (1962). *J. Org. Chem.* **27**, 2043.

Howden, M. E. H. and Roberts, J. D. (1963). *Tetrahedron*, **19**, Suppl. 2, 403.

Hückel, E. (1931). *Z. Physik*, **70**, 204.

Hückel, W. (1965). *J. prakt. Chem.* (4) **28**, 27.

Hückel, W. (1966). *Nova Acta Leopoldina (Neue Folge)*, **30**, No. 174.

Hückel, W. and Volkmann, D. (1963). *Annalen*, **664**, 31.

Hudson, R. F. (1962). *Chimia*, **16**, 173.

Hudson, R. F. and Saville, B. (1955). *J. Chem. Soc.* 4130.

Hudson, R. F. and Wardill, J. E. (1950). *J. Chem. Soc.* 1729.

Hughes, E. D. (1935a). *J. Chem. Soc.* 255.

Hughes, E. D. (1935b). *J. Amer. Chem. Soc.* **57**, 708.

Hughes, E. D. (1938). *Trans. Faraday Soc.* **34**, 202.

Hughes, E. D. (1941). *Trans. Faraday Soc.* **37**, 603.

Hughes, E. D. and Ingold, C. K. (1933a). *J. Chem. Soc.* 523.

Hughes, E. D. and Ingold, C. K. (1933b). *J. Chem. Soc.* 1571.

Hughes, E. D., Ingold, C. K. and Masterman, S. (1937). *J. Chem. Soc.* 1196.

Hughes, E. D., Ingold, C. K. and Patel, C. S. (1933). *J. Chem. Soc.* 526.

Hughes, E. D., Ingold, C. K. and Scott, A. D. (1937). *J. Chem. Soc.* 1201.

Hughes, E. D., Ingold, C. K. and Shapiro, U. G. (1937). *J. Chem. Soc.* 1277.

Hughes, E. D., Ingold, C. K. and Shiner, V. J. (1953). *J. Chem. Soc.* 3827.

Hughes, E. D., Ingold, C. K., Martin, R. J. L. and Meigh, D. F. (1950). *Nature*, **166**, 679.

Hughes, E. D., Ingold, C. K., Mok, S. F. and Pocker, Y. (1957a). *J. Chem. Soc.* 1238.

Hughes, E. D., Ingold, C. K., Mok, S. F., Patai, S. and Pocker, Y. (1957b). *J. Chem. Soc.* 1265.

Huisgen, R., Rauenbusch, E., Seidl, G. and Wimmer, I. (1964). *Annalen*, **671**, 41.

Huisgen, R. and Reimlinger, H. (1956a). *Annalen*, **599**, 161.

Huisgen, R. and Reimlinger, H. (1956b), *Annalen*, **599**, 183.

Huisgen, R. and Rüchardt, C. (1956a), *Annalen*, **601**, 1.

Huisgen, R. and Rüchardt, C. (1956b). *Annalen*, **601**, 21.
Huisgen, R. and Seidl, G. (1964). *Tetrahedron*, **20**, 231.
Huisgen, R., Seidl, G. and Wimmer, I. (1964). *Tetrahedron*, **20**, 623.
Hulett, J. R. (1964). *Quart. Rev.* **18**, 227.
Hulme, R. and Symons, M. C. R. (1965). *J. Chem. Soc.* 1120.
Hulme, R. and Symons, M. C. R. (1966). *J. Chem. Soc.* (*A*), 446.
Hunt, J. P. (1963). "Metal Ions in Aqueous Solution". Chapters 4 and 6. Benjamin, New York.
Huntsman, W. D. and Eggers, E. A. (1964). *J. Org. Chem.* **29**, 94.
Hurd, C. D. and Blunck, F. H. (1938). *J. Amer. Chem. Soc.* **60**, 2419.
Hush, N. S. and Pople, J. A. (1955). *Trans. Faraday Soc.* **51**, 600.
Huston, J. L. (1956). *J. Inorg. Nuclear Chem.* **2**, 128.
Huston, J. L. and Lang, C. E. (1957). *J. Inorg. Nuclear Chem.* **4**, 30.
Huyser, E. S. (1960). *J. Amer. Chem. Soc.* **82**, 394.
Hyne, J. B. (1960). *J. Amer. Chem. Soc.* **82**, 5129.
Hyne, J. B. (1963). *J. Amer. Chem. Soc.* **85**, 304.
Hyne, J. B., Golinkin, H. S. and Laidlaw, W. G. (1966). *J. Amer. Chem. Soc.* **88**, 2104.
Hyne, J. B. and Wills, R. (1963). *J. Amer. Chem. Soc.* **85**, 3650.
Hyne, J. B., Wills, R. and Wonkka, R. E. (1962). *J. Amer. Chem. Soc.* **84**, 2914.
Iliceto, A., Fava, A., Mazzucato, U. and Rossetto, O. (1961). *J. Amer. Chem. Soc.* **83**, 2729.
Ingold, C. K. (1930). *J. Chem. Soc.* 1032.
Ingold, C. K. (1957). *Proc. Chem. Soc.* 279.
Ingold, C. K. (1953). "Structure and Mechanism in Organic Chemistry". Cornell Univ. Press, Ithaca, N.Y. and Bell, London.
Ingold, C. K. and Rothstein, E. (1928). *J. Chem. Soc.* 1217.
Ipatieff, V. N., Pines, H. and Schmerling, L. (1940). *J. Org. Chem.* **5**, 253.
Jacquier, R. and Christol, H. (1957). *Bull. Soc. Chim. France*, 596, 600.
Jaffé, H. H. (1953). *Chem. Rev.* **53**, 191.
Jander, G., Rüsberg, E. and Schmidt, H. (1948). *Z. anorg. Chem.* **255**, 238.
Jennen, J. J. (1966). *Chimia*, **20**, 309.
Jenny, E. F. and Winstein, S. (1958). *Helv. Chim. Acta.* **41**, 807.
Jensen, F. R. and Brown, H. C. (1958). *J. Amer. Chem. Soc.* **80**, 3039.
Jensen, F. R. and Goldman, G. (1965). In "Friedel-Crafts and Related Reactions" (G. A. Olah, ed.), Vol. III, p. 1003. Wiley, New York.
Jensen, F. R., Marino, G. and Brown, H. C. (1959). *J. Amer. Chem. Soc.* **81**, 3303.
Jensen, F. R. and Ouellette, R. J. (1961), *J. Amer. Chem. Soc.* **83**, 4477.
Jensen, F. R. and Ouellette, R. J. (1963). *J. Amer. Chem. Soc.* **85**, 367.
Jenson, E. D. and Taft, R. W. (1964). *J. Amer. Chem. Soc.* **86**, 116.
Jerkunica, J. M., Borčić, S. and Sunko, D. E. (1967). *J. Amer. Chem. Soc.* **89**, 1732.
Johnson, W. S., Bailey, D. M., Owyang, R., Bell, R. A., Jacques, B. and Crandall, J. K. (1964). *J. Amer. Chem. Soc.* **86**, 1959.
Johnson, W. S. and Crandall, J. K. (1964). *J. Amer. Chem. Soc.* **86**, 2085.
Johnson, W. S. and Crandall, J. K. (1965). *J. Org. Chem.* **30**, 1785.
Jones, D. A. K. and Smith, G. G. (1964). *J. Org. Chem.* **29**, 3531.
Jones, L. W. and Wallis, E. S. (1926). *J. Amer. Chem. Soc.* **48**, 169.
Jordan, D. O. and Treloar, F. E. (1961). *J. Chem. Soc.* 734.

Jordan, N. W. and Elliott, I. W. (1962). *J. Org. Chem.* **27,** 1445.

Jorgenson, M. J. and Hartter, D. R. (1963). *J. Amer. Chem. Soc.* **85,** 878.

Julia, S., Lavaux, J. P., Pathak, S. R. and Whitham, G. H. (1964). *J. Chem. Soc.* 2633.

Jungk, H., Smoot, C. R. and Brown, H. C. (1956). *J. Amer. Chem. Soc.* **78,** 2185.

Jutz, C. and Voithenleitner, F. (1964). *Chem. Ber.* **97,** 29.

Kaplan, F. and Meloy, G. K. (1966). *J. Amer. Chem. Soc.* **88,** 950.

Karabatsos, G. J., Hsi, N. and Meyerson, S. (1966). *J. Amer. Chem. Soc.* **88,** 5649.

Karabatsos, G. J., Mount, R. A., Rickter, D. O. and Meyerson, S. (1966). *J. Amer. Chem. Soc.* **88,** 5651.

Karabatsos, G. J. and Orzech, C. E. (1962). *J. Amer. Chem. Soc.* **84,** 2838.

Karabatsos, G. J., Orzech, C. E. and Meyerson, S. (1965). *J. Amer. Chem. Soc.* **87,** 4394.

Karabatsos, G. J. and Vane, F. M. (1963). *J. Amer. Chem. Soc.* **85,** 729.

Karabatsos, G. J., Vane, F. M. and Meyerson, S. (1963). *J. Amer. Chem. Soc.* **85,** 733.

Karplus, M. (1959). *J. Chem. Phys.* **30,** 11.

Katz, T. J. and Gold, E. H. (1964). *J. Amer. Chem. Soc.* **86,** 1600.

Katz, T. J., Hall, J. R. and Neikam, W. C. (1962). *J. Amer. Chem. Soc.* **84,** 3199.

Kazanskii, K. S. and Éntelis, S. G. (1962). *Kinetika i Kataliz,* **3,** 36.

Keefer, R. M. and Andrews, L. J. (1962). *J. Amer. Chem. Soc.* **84,** 941.

Kehrmann, F. and Wentzel, F. (1901). *Ber.* **34,** 3815.

Keller, C. E. and Pettit, R. (1966). *J. Amer. Chem. Soc.* **88,** 604. 606.

Kendrick, L. W., Benjamin, B. M. and Collins, C. J. (1958). *J. Amer. Chem. Soc.* **80,** 4057.

Kennedy, J. P. (1964). *J. Polymer Sci.* **A2,** 5171.

Kennedy, J. P., Elliott, J. J. and Hudson, B. E. (1964). *Makromol. Chem.* **79,** 109.

Kennedy, J. P. and Langer, A. W. (1964). *Fortschr. Hochpolym.-Forsch.* **3,** 508.

Kennedy, J. P. and Thomas, R. M. (1962). *Makromol. Chem.* **53,** 28.

Kennedy, J. P. and Thomas, R. M. (1963). *Makromol. Chem.* **64,** 1.

Kenyon, J., Lipscomb, A. G. and Phillips, H. (1930). *J. Chem. Soc.* 415.

Kenyon, J. and Phillips, H. (1930). *Trans. Faraday Soc.* **26,** 451.

Kenyon, J. and Young, D. P. (1941). *J. Chem. Soc.* 263.

Kershaw, D. N. and Leisten, J. A. (1960). *Proc. Chem. Soc.*, 84.

Kharasch, N. (1961). "Organic Sulphur Compounds", Vol. I, Chapter 32. Pergamon, Oxford.

Kilpatrick, M. and Hyman, H. H. (1958). *J. Amer. Chem. Soc.* **80,** 77.

Kilpatrick, M. and Luborsky, F. E. (1953). *J. Amer. Chem. Soc.* **75,** 577.

King, L. C. and Bigelow, M. J. (1952). *J. Amer. Chem. Soc.* **74,** 6238.

Kinoshita, M. (1962). *Bull. Chem. Soc. Japan,* **35,** 1137.

Kirkwood, J. G. (1934). *J. Chem. Phys.* **2,** 351.

Kirkwood, J. G. (1939). *Chem. Rev.* **24,** 233.

Kirmse, W. (1963). *Annalen,* **666,** 9.

Kirmse, W. (1964). "Carbene Chemistry". Academic Press, New York.

Kitaigorodskii, A. I., Struchkov, Y. T., Khotsyanova, T. L., Vol'pin, M. E. and Kursanov, D. N. (1960). *Izvest. Akad. Nauk S.S.S.R. (Otdel. Khim. Nauk),* 45 (*Bull. Acad. Sci. U.S.S.R.* 32).

Kleinfelter, D. C., Trent, E. S., Mallory, J. E. and Dye, T. E. (1966). *J. Amer. Chem. Soc.* **88,** 5350.

Koch, H. and Haaf, W. (1958). *Annalen,* **618,** 251.

Koch, H. and Haaf, W. (1960). *Annalen*, **638**, 111, 122.

Kochi, J. K. (1962). *J. Amer. Chem. Soc.* **84**, 3271; *Tetrahedron*, 1962, **18**, 483.

Koehl, W. J. (1964). *J. Amer. Chem. Soc.* **86**, 4686.

Kohnstam, G. (1962). In "The Transition State", p. 179. Chem. Soc. Spec. Publ. No. 16.

Kohnstam, G. (1967). *Adv. Phys. Org. Chem.* **5**, 121.

Kon, H. and Blois, M. S. (1958). *J. Chem. Phys.* **28**, 743.

Kosower, E. M. (1956). *J. Amer. Chem. Soc.* **78**, 5700.

Kosower, E. M. (1958). *J. Amer. Chem. Soc.* **80**, 3253.

Kosower, E. M. (1964). *J. Org. Chem.* **29**, 956.

Kosower, E. M. (1965). *Prog. Phys. Org. Chem.* **3**, 81.

Kosower, E. M. and Winstein, S. (1956). *J. Amer. Chem. Soc.* **78**, 4347.

Kramer, G. M. (1964). *Adv. Petrol. Chem.* **9**, 232.

Krebs, A. (1965). *Angew. Chem.* **77**, 10 (Internat. Ed. **4**, 10).

Kresge, A. J., Barry, G. W., Charles, K. R. and Chiang, Y. (1962). *J. Amer. Chem. Soc.* **84**, 4343.

Kresge, A. J. and Chiang, Y. (1959). *J. Amer. Chem. Soc.* **81**, 5509.

Kresge, A. J. and Chiang, Y. (1961a). *Proc. Chem. Soc.* 81.

Kresge, A. J. and Chiang, Y. (1961b). *J. Amer. Chem. Soc.* **83**, 2877.

Kresge, A. J. and Chiang, Y. (1967). *J. Chem. Soc.* (*B*) 53.

Kresge, A. J., Hakka, L. E., Mylonakis, S. and Sato, Y. (1965). *Discuss. Faraday Soc.* **39**, 75.

Kresge, A. J., Lichtin, N. N., Rao, K. N. and Weston, R. E. (1965). *J. Amer. Chem. Soc.* **87**, 437.

Kresge, A. J., Rao, K. N. and Lichtin, N. N. (1961). *Chem. and Ind.* 53.

Kurland, R. J., Schuster, I. I. and Colter, A. K. (1965). *J. Amer. Chem. Soc.* **87**, 2279.

Kursanov, D. N. and Parnes, Z. N. (1961). *Uspekhi Khim.* **30**, 1381 (*Russ. Chem. Rev.*, **30**, 598).

Ladenheim, H. and Bender, M. L. (1960). *J. Amer. Chem. Soc.* **82**, 1895.

LaLonde, R. T. and Batelka, J. J. (1964). *Tetrahedron Letters*, 445.

LaLonde, R. T. and Forney, L. S. (1963). *J. Amer. Chem. Soc.* **85**, 3767.

LaLonde, R. T. and Tobias, M. A. (1963). *J. Amer. Chem. Soc.* **85**, 3771.

LaLonde, R. T. and Tobias, M. A. (1964). *J. Amer. Chem. Soc.* **86**, 4068.

Lane, J. F. and Wallis, E. S. (1941). *J. Amer. Chem. Soc.* **63**, 1674.

Lansbury, P. T., Colson, J. G. and Mancuso, N. R. (1964). *J. Amer. Chem. Soc.* **86**, 5225.

Lansbury, P. T. and Mancuso, N. R. (1966). *J. Amer. Chem. Soc.* **88**, 1205.

Latimer, W. M., Pitzer, K. S. and Slansky, C. M. (1939). *J. Chem. Phys.* **7**, 108.

Latimer, W. M. and Slansky, C. M. (1940). *J. Amer. Chem. Soc.* **62**, 2019.

Laurent, A. and Mison, P. (1962). *Bull. Soc. Chim. France*, 956.

Lawton, R. G. (1961). *J. Amer. Chem. Soc.* **83**, 2399.

LeBel, N. A. and Huber, J. E. (1963). *J. Amer. Chem. Soc.* **85**, 3193.

LeBel, N. A. and Spurlock, L. A. (1964). *Tetrahedron*, **20**, 215.

Ledwith, A. and Sambhi, M. (1965). *Chem. Comm.* 64.

Lee, C. C. and Kruger, J. E. (1965). *J. Amer. Chem. Soc.* **87**, 3986.

Lee, C. C., Kruger, J. E. and Wong, E. W. C. (1965). *J. Amer. Chem. Soc.* **87**, 3985.

Lee, C. C. and Lam, L. K. M. (1966a). *J. Amer. Chem. Soc.* **88**, 2831.

Lee, C. C. and Lam, L. K. M. (1966b). *J. Amer. Chem. Soc.* **88**, 2834.

Lee, C. C., Slater, G. P. and Spinks, J. W. T. (1957). *Canad. J. Chem.* **35**, 1417.

Lee, C. C. Tkachuk, R. and Slater, G. P. (1959). *Tetrahedron*, **7**, 206.

Lee, C. C. and Wong, E. W. C. (1964). *J. Amer. Chem. Soc.* **86**, 2752.

Lee, C. C. and Wong, E. W. C. (1965). *Canad. J. Chem.* **43**, 2254.

Leffek, K. T., Robertson, R. E. and Sugamori, S. (1965). *J. Amer. Chem. Soc.* **87**, 2097.

Leffler, J. E. (1956). "The Reactive Intermediates of Organic Chemistry", Ch. V–VIII. Interscience, New York.

Leffler, J. E. and Grunwald, E. (1963). "Rates and Equilibria of Organic Reactions". Wiley, New York.

Leftin, H. P. (1960). *J. Phys. Chem.* **64**, 1714.

Leftin, H. P. (1962), quoted by H. H. Jaffé and M. Orchin, "Theory and Applications of Ultraviolet Spectroscopy", p. 454. Wiley, New York.

Leisten, J. A. (1956). *J. Chem. Soc.* 1572.

Lemal, D. M. and Kawano, K. I. (1962). *J. Amer. Chem. Soc.* **84**, 1761.

Lemal, D. M., Lovald, R. A. and Kawano, K. I. (1964). *J. Amer. Chem. Soc.* **86**, 2518.

le Noble, W. J. and Yates, B. L. (1965). *J. Amer. Chem. Soc.* **87**, 3515.

Le Ny, G. (1960). *Compt. rend.* **251**, 1526.

Levy, A. A. and Wassermann, A. (1965). *J. Polymer Sci.* **A3**, 2703.

Lévy, H. A. and Brockway, L. O. (1937). *J. Amer. Chem. Soc.* **59**, 2085.

Lewis, E. S. (1958). *J. Amer. Chem. Soc.* **80**, 1371.

Lewis, E. S. (1959). *Tetrahedron*, **5**, 143.

Lewis, G. N., Magel, T. T. and Lipkin, D. (1942). *J. Amer. Chem. Soc.* **64**, 1774.

Ley, J. B. and Vernon, C. A. (1957). *J. Chem. Soc.* 2987.

Lichtin, N. N. (1963). *Prog. Phys. Org. Chem.* **1**, 75.

Lichtin, N. N., Lewis, E. S., Price, E. and Johnson, R. R. (1959). *J. Amer. Chem. Soc.* **81**, 4520.

Lieser, K. H. and Pfluger, C. E. (1960). *Chem. Ber.* **93**, 176.

Long, F. A., Pritchard, J. G. and Stafford, F. E. (1957). *J. Amer. Chem. Soc.* **79**, 2362.

Long, F. A. and Schulze, J. (1964). *J. Amer. Chem. Soc.* **86**, 327.

Longuet-Higgins, H. C. (1950). *J. Chem. Phys.* **18**, 265, 275, 283.

Longuet-Higgins, H. C. (1957). *Quart. Rev.* **11**, 121.

Longworth, W. R. and Mason, C. P. (1966). *J. Chem. Soc.* (*A*), 1164.

Longworth, W. R. and Plesch, P. H. (1958). *Proc. Chem. Soc.* 117.

Lossing, F. P. (1963). In "Mass Spectrometry" (C. A. McDowell, ed.), p. 442. McGraw-Hill, New York.

Lowen, A. M., Murray, M. A. and Williams, G. (1950). *J. Chem. Soc.* 3318.

Lowry, T. M. (1925). *Inst. Intern. Chim. Solvay. Conseil Chim.* (*Brussels*), 130.

Lumb, J. T. and Whitham, G. H. (1966) *Chem. Comm.* 400.

McCaulay, D. A., Higley, W. S. and Lien, A. P. (1956). *J. Amer. Chem. Soc.* **78**, 3009.

McCaulay, D. A. and Lien, A. P. (1951). *J. Amer. Chem. Soc.* **73**, 2013.

McCaulay, D. A. and Lien, A. P. (1952). *J. Amer. Chem. Soc.* **74**, 6246.

McCaulay, D. A., Shoemaker, B. H. and Lien, A. P. (1950). *Ind. Eng. Chem.* **42**, 2103.

Maccoll, A. (1959). In "Theoretical Organic Chemistry. The Kekulé Symposium", p. 230. Butterworths, London.

Maccoll, A. (1962). In "The Transition State", p. 158. *Chem. Soc. Spec. Publ.* No. 16.

12*

Maccoll, A. (1965). *Adv. Phys. Org. Chem.* **3**, 91.

Maccoll, A. and Bicknell, R. C. L. (1962), quoted by A. Maccoll, 1962.

Maccoll, A. and Swinbourne, E. S. (1960). *Proc. Chem. Soc.* 409.

Maccoll, A. and Swinbourne, E. S. (1964). *J. Chem. Soc.* 149.

Maccoll, A. and Thomas, P. J. (1955a). *Nature*, **176**, 392.

Maccoll, A. and Thomas, P. J. (1955b). *J. Chem. Soc.* 979.

Maccoll, A. and Thomas, P. J. (1955c). *J. Chem. Soc.* 2445.

McDowell, C. A. (1963). "Mass Spectrometry", McGraw-Hill, New York.

McElrath, E. N., Fritz, R. M., Brown, C., LeGall, C. Y. and Duke, R. B. (1960). *J. Org. Chem.* **25**, 2195.

Mackenzie, H. A. E. and Winter, E. R. S. (1948a). *Trans. Faraday Soc.* **44**, 159.

Mackenzie, H. A. E. and Winter, E. R. S. (1948b). *Trans. Faraday Soc.* **44**, 171.

Mackenzie, H. A. E. and Winter, E. R. S. (1948c). *Trans. Faraday Soc.* **44**, 243.

Mackor, E. L., Hofstra, A. and van der Waals, J. H. (1958a). *Trans. Faraday Soc.* **54**, 66.

Mackor, E. L., Hofstra, A. and van der Waals, J. H. (1958b). *Trans. Faraday Soc.* **54**, 186.

Mackor, E. L. and MacLean, C. (1964). *Pure Appl. Chem.* **8**, 393.

Mackor, E. L., Smit, P. J. and van der Waals, J. H. (1957). *Trans. Faraday Soc.* **53**, 1309.

McLafferty, F. W. (1963). "Mass Spectrometry of Organic Ions". Academic Press, New York.

MacLean, C. and Mackor, E. L. (1961). *Mol. Phys.* **4**, 241.

MacLean, C. and Mackor, E. L. (1962). *Disc. Faraday Soc.* **34**, 165.

MacLean, C., van der Waals, J. H. and Mackor, E. L. (1958). *Mol. Phys.* **1**, 247.

Mahler, J. E. and Pettit, R. (1962). *J. Amer. Chem. Soc.* **84**, 1511.

Malchick, S. P. and Hannan, R. B. (1959). *J. Amer. Chem. Soc.* **81**, 2119.

Martin, J. G. and Robertson, R. E. (1966). *J. Amer. Chem. Soc.* **88**, 5353.

Maskill, H., Southam, R. M. and Whiting, M. C. (1965). *Chem. Comm.* 496.

Mason, S. F. (1958). *J. Chem. Soc.* 808.

Mayo, F. R. and Lewis, F. M. (1944). *J. Amer. Chem. Soc.* **66**, 1594.

Mazur, R. H., White, W. N., Semenow, D. A., Lee, C. C., Silver, M. S. and Roberts, J. D. (1959). *J. Amer. Chem. Soc.* **81**, 4390.

Meerwein, H., Borner, P., Fuchs, O., Sasse, H. J., Schrodt, H. and Spille, J. (1956). *Chem. Ber.* **89**, 2060.

Meerwein, H., Delfs, D. and Morschel, H. (1960). *Angew. Chem.* **72**, 927.

Meerwein, H., Hammel, O., Serini, A. and Vorster, J. (1927). *Annalen*, **453**, 16.

Meerwein, H., Hederich, V., Morschel, H. and Wunderlich, K. (1960). *Annalen*, **635**, 1.

Meerwein, H., Laasch, P., Mersch, R. and Spille, J. (1956). *Chem. Ber.* **89**, 209.

Meerwein, H. and van Emster, K. (1922). *Ber.* **55**, 2500.

Meier, W., Meuche, D. and Heilbronner, E. (1962). *Helv. Chim. Acta.* **45**, 2628.

Meinwald, J. and Gassman, P. G. (1963). *J. Amer. Chem. Soc.* **85**, 57.

Meinwald, J., Gassman, P. G. and Hurst, J. J. (1962). *J. Amer. Chem. Soc.* **84**, 3722.

Melander, L. and Olsson, S. (1956). *Acta. Chem. Scand.* **10**, 879.

Melton, C. E. and Hamill, W. H. (1964). *J. Chem. Phys.* **41**, 3464.

Melton, C. E. and Joy, H. W. (1965). *J. Chem. Phys.* **42**, 1986.

Melville, H. W., Noble, B. and Watson, W. F. (1947). *J. Polymer Sci.* **2**, 229.

Meuche, D. and Heilbronner, E. (1962). *Helv. Chem. Acta.* **45**, 1965.

Meuche, D., Strauss, H. and Heilbronner, E. (1958). *Helv. Chim. Acta.* **41**, 57, 414.

Meyer, F. and Harrison, A. G. (1964). *J. Amer. Chem. Soc.* **86**, 4757.

Miller, V. A. (1947). *J. Amer. Chem. Soc.* **69**, 1764.

Miller, W. T. and Whalen, D. M. (1964). *J. Amer. Chem. Soc.* **86**, 2089.

Mills, J. A. (1953). *J. Chem. Soc.* 260.

Mislow, K. and Siegel, M. (1952). *J. Amer. Chem. Soc.* **74**, 1060.

Moelwyn-Hughes, E. A., Robertson, R. E. and Sugamori, S. (1965). *J. Chem. Soc.* 1965.

Möller, F. (1957). In Houben-Weyl, "Methoden der Organischen Chemie", 4th Ed., Vol. XI/1., p. 994. Stickstoffverbindungen II. Georg Thieme Verlag, Stuttgart.

Moodie, R. B., Connor, T. M. and Stewart, R. (1959). *Canad. Chem.* **37**, 1402.

More O'Ferrall, R. A. (1967). *Adv. Phys. Org. Chem.* **5**, 331.

Muetterties, E. L. (1957). *J. Amer. Chem. Soc.* **79**, 1004.

Muetterties, E. L. and Phillips, W. D. (1957). *J. Amer. Chem. Soc.* **79**, 2975.

Müller, E. and Huber-Emden, H. (1961). *Annalen*, **649**, 70.

Muller, N. and Mulliken, R. S. (1958). *J. Amer. Chem. Soc.* **80**, 3489.

Muller, N., Pickett, L. W. and Mulliken, R. S. (1954). *J. Amer. Chem. Soc.* **76**, 4770.

Mulliken, R. S. (1950). *J. Amer. Chem. Soc.* **72**, 600.

Mulliken, R. S. (1952a). *J. Amer. Chem. Soc.* **74**, 811.

Mulliken, R. S. (1952b). *J. Phys. Chem.* **56**, 801.

Murad, E. and Inghram, M. G. (1964). *J. Chem. Phys.* **40**, 3263.

Murr, B. L., Nickon, A., Swartz, T. D. and Werstiuk, N. H. (1967). *J. Amer. Chem. Soc.* **89**, 1730.

Murr, B. L. and Santiago, C. (1966). *J. Amer. Chem. Soc.* **88**, 1826.

Murray, M. A. and Williams, G. (1950). *J. Chem. Soc.* 3322.

Murray, R. W. and Kaplan, M. L. (1966). *J. Org. Chem.* **31**, 962.

Musher, J. I. (1962). *J. Chem. Phys.* **37**, 34.

Myhre, P. C. and Andersen, R. D. (1965). *Tetrahedron Letters*, 1497.

Naville, G., Strauss, H. and Heilbronner, E. (1960). *Helv. Chim. Acta.* **43**, 1221.

Necsoiu, I. and Nenitzescu, C. D. (1960). *Chem. and Ind.* 377.

Nelson, N. A., Fassnacht, J. H. and Piper, J. U. (1961). *J. Amer. Chem. Soc.* **83**, 206.

Nevell, T. P., de Salas, E. and Wilson, C. L. (1939). *J. Chem. Soc.* 1188.

Newman, M. S. and Arkell, A. (1959). *J. Org. Chem.* **24**, 385.

Newman, M. S., Craig, R. A. and Garrett, A. B. (1949). *J. Amer. Chem. Soc.* **71**, 869.

Newman, M. S. and Deno, N. C. (1951a). *J. Amer. Chem. Soc.* **73**, 3644.

Newman, M. S. and Deno, N. C. (1951b). *J. Amer. Chem. Soc.* **73**, 3651.

Newman, M. S., Kuivila, H. G. and Garrett, A. B. (1945). *J. Amer. Chem. Soc.* **67**, 704.

Ng, E. K. and Adam, F. C. (1964). *Canad. J. Chem.* **42**, 810.

Nordlander, J. E., Jindal, S. P., Schleyer, P. R., Fort, R. C., Harper, J. J. and Nicholas, R. D. (1966). *J. Amer. Chem. Soc.* **88**, 4475.

Norin, T. (1964). *Tetrahedron Letters*, 37.

Norman, R. O. C. and Taylor, R. (1965). "Electrophilic Substitution in Benzenoid Compounds". Elsevier, Amsterdam.

Norris, J. F. and Rubinstein, D. (1939). *J. Amer. Chem. Soc.* **61**, 1163.

Norris, J. F. and Sanders, W. W. (1901). *Am. Chem. J.* **25**, 54.

Norris, J. F. and Young, H. H. (1935). *J. Amer. Chem. Soc.* **57**, 1420.

Noyce, D. S. and Avarbock, H. S. (1962). *J. Amer. Chem. Soc.* **84**, 1644.

Noyce, D. S., King, P. A., Lane, C. A. and Reed, W. L. (1962). *J. Amer. Chem. Soc.* **84**, 1638.

Noyce, D. S., Matesich, M. A., Schiavelli, M. D. and Peterson, P. E. (1965). *J. Amer. Chem. Soc.* **87**, 2295.

Nozoe, T. (1961). *Prog. Org. Chem.* **5**, 132.

Oddo, G. and Scandola, E. (1909). *Gazzetta*, **39** (II), 1.

Ogg, R. A. and Polanyi, M. (1935). *Trans. Faraday Soc.* **31**, 604.

Okamoto, Y. and Brown, H. C. (1957). *J. Org. Chem.* **22**, 485.

Okamoto, Y., Inukai, T. and Brown, H. C. (1958). *J. Amer. Chem. Soc.* **80**, 4969.

Olah, G. A. (1963). "Friedel-Crafts and Related Reactions". Wiley, New York.

Olah, G. A. (1964). *J. Amer. Chem. Soc.* **86**, 932.

Olah, G. A. (1965a). In "Organic Reaction Mechanisms", p. 21. Chem. Soc. Spec. Publ., No. 19.

Olah, G. A. (1965b). *J. Amer. Chem. Soc.* **87**, 1103.

Olah, G. A., Baker, E. B. and Comisarow, M. B. (1964). *J. Amer. Chem. Soc.* **86**, 1265.

Olah, G. A., Baker, E. B., Evans, J. C., Tolgyesi, W. S., McIntyre, J. S. and Bastien, I. J. (1964). *J. Amer. Chem. Soc.* **86**, 1360.

Olah, G. A. and Comisarow, M. B. (1964). *J. Amer. Chem. Soc.* **86**, 5682.

Olah, G. A. and Comisarow, M. B. (1966a). *J. Amer. Chem. Soc.* **88**, 1818.

Olah, G. A. and Comisarow, M. B. (1966b). *J. Amer. Chem. Soc.* **88**, 3313, 4442.

Olah, G. A. and Comisarow, M. B. (1967). *J. Amer. Chem. Soc.* **89**, 1027.

Olah, G. A., Comisarow, M. B., Cupas, C. A. and Pittman, C. U. (1965). *J. Amer. Chem. Soc.* **87**, 2997.

Olah, G. A., Cupas, C. A. and Comisarow, M. B. (1966). *J. Amer. Chem. Soc.* **88**, 362.

Olah, G. A., Flood, S. H. and Moffatt, M. E. (1964a). *J. Amer. Chem. Soc.* **86**, 1060.

Olah, G. A., Flood, S. H. and Moffatt, M. E. (1964b). *J. Amer. Chem. Soc.* **86**, 1065.

Olah, G. A., Flood, S. H., Kuhn, S. J., Moffatt, M. E. and Overchuk, N. A. (1964). *J. Amer. Chem. Soc.* **86**, 1046.

Olah, G. A. and Friedman, N. (1966). *J. Amer. Chem. Soc.* **88**, 5330.

Olah, G. A., Friedman, N., Bollinger, J. M. and Lukas, J. (1966). *J. Amer. Chem. Soc.* **88**, 5328.

Olah, G. A. and Kuhn, S. J. (1958). *J. Amer. Chem. Soc.* **80**, 6535.

Olah, G. A., Kuhn, S. J. and Flood, S. H. (1962a). *J. Amer. Chem. Soc.* **84**, 1688.

Olah, G. A., Kuhn, S. J. and Flood, S. H. (1962b). *J. Amer. Chem. Soc.* **94**, 1695.

Olah, G. A., Kuhn, S. J. and Olah, J. A. (1957). *J. Chem. Soc.* 2174.

Olah, G. A., Kuhn, S. J. and Pavláth, A. (1956). *Nature*, **178**, 693.

Olah, G. A., Kuhn, S. J., Tolgyesi, W. S. and Baker, E. B. (1962). *J. Amer. Chem. Soc.* **84**, 2733.

Olah, G. A., Kuhn, S. J., Flood, S. H. and Hardie, B. A. (1964). *J. Amer. Chem. Soc.* **86**, 2203.

Olah, G. A. and Meyer, M. W. (1963). In "Friedel-Crafts and Related Reactions", Vol. I (G. A. Olah, ed.), p. 623. Interscience, New York.

Olah, G. A., Moffatt, M. E., Kuhn, S. J. and Hardie, B. A. (1964). *J. Amer. Chem. Soc.* **86**, 2198.

Olah, G. A. and Namanworth, E. (1966). *J. Amer. Chem. Soc.* **88**, 5327.

Olah, G. A., Namanworth, E., Comisarow, M. B. and Ramsey, B. (1967). *J. Amer. Chem. Soc.* **89**, 711.

Olah, G. A. and O'Brien, D. H. (1967). *J. Amer. Chem. Soc.* **89**, 1725.

Olah, G. A. and Olah, J. A. (1965). In "The Friedel-Crafts and Related Reactions", Vol. III (G. A. Olah, ed.), p. 1257. Interscience, New York.

Olah, G. A. and Overchuk, N. A. (1965). *J. Amer. Chem. Soc.* **87**, 5786.

Olah, G. A., Pavláth, A. and Olah, J. A. (1958). *J. Amer. Chem. Soc.* **80**, 6540.

Olah, G. A. and Pittman, C. U. (1965a). *J. Amer. Chem. Soc.* **87**, 3507.

Olah, G. A. and Pittman, C. U. (1965b). *J. Amer. Chem. Soc.* **87**, 3509.

Olah, G. A. and Pittman, C. U. (1966). *Adv. Phys. Org. Chem.* **4**, 305.

Olah, G. A., Pittman, C. U. and Sorensen, T. S. (1966). *J. Amer. Chem. Soc.* **88**, 2331.

Olah, G. A., Pittman, C. U., Waack, R. and Doran, M. (1966a). *J. Amer. Chem. Soc.* **88**, 1488.

Olah, G. A., Pittman, C. U., Namanworth, E. and Comisarow, M. B. (1966b). *J. Amer. Chem. Soc.* **88**, 5571.

Olah, G. A., Quinn, H. W. and Kuhn, S. J. (1960). *J. Amer. Chem. Soc.* **82**, 426.

Olah, G. A., Tolgyesi, W. S., Kuhn, S. J., Moffatt, M. E., Bastien, I. J. and Baker, E. B. (1963). *J. Amer. Chem. Soc.* **85**, 1328.

O'Reilly, D. E. and Leftin, H. P. (1960). *J. Phys. Chem.* **64**, 1555.

Otvos, J. W., Stevenson, D. P., Wagner, C. D. and Beeck, O. (1951). *J. Amer. Chem. Soc.* **73**, 5741.

Oulevey, G. and Susz, B.-P. (1961). *Helv. Chim. Acta.* **44**, 1425.

Oulevey, G. and Susz, B.-P. (1965). *Helv. Chim. Acta.* **48**, 630.

Overberger, C. G., Arond, L. H., Tanner, D., Taylor, J. J. and Alfrey, T. (1952). *J. Amer. Chem. Soc.* **74**, 4848.

Overberger, C. G. and Kamath, V. G. (1959). *J. Amer. Chem. Soc.* **81**, 2910.

Overberger, C. G., Tanner, D. and Pearce, E. M. (1958). *J. Amer. Chem. Soc.* **80**, 4566.

Parker, A. J. (1962). *Quart. Rev.* **16**, 163.

Patai, S. and Dayagi, S. (1962a). *J. Chem. Soc.* 716.

Patai, S. and Dayagi, S. (1962b). *J. Chem. Soc.* 726.

Patai, S., Dayagi, S. and Friedlander, R. (1962). *J. Chem. Soc.* 723.

Patai, S. and Israeli, Y. (1960). *J. Chem. Soc.* 2020.

Paul, M. A. and Long, F. A. (1957). *Chem. Rev.* **57**, 1.

Pauling, L. and Corey, R. B. (1951). *Proc. Nat. Acad. Sci.* **37**, 251.

Peach, M. E. and Waddington, T. C. (1962). *J. Chem. Soc.* 600.

Peach, M. E. and Waddington, T. C. (1965). In "Non-aqueous Solvent Systems" (T. C. Waddington, ed.). Academic Press, London.

Peacock, T. E. (1965). "Electronic Properties of Aromatic and Heterocyclic Molecules". Academic Press, London and New York.

Pearson, D. E., Baxter, J. F. and Martin, J. C. (1952). *J. Org. Chem.* **17**, 1511.

Pearson, R. G. (1963). *J. Amer. Chem. Soc.* **85**, 3533.

Pepper, D. C. (1964). In "Friedel-Crafts and Related Reactions", Vol. II (G. A. Olah, ed.), p. 1293. Interscience, New York.

Pepper, D. C. and Reilly, J. P. (1962). *J. Polymer Sci.*, **58**, 639.

Perkampus, H.-H. (1966). *Adv. Phys. Org. Chem.* **4**, 195.

Perkampus, H.-H. and Baumgarten, E. (1963). *Ber. Bunsenges. Phys. Chem.* **67**, 16.

Perkampus, H.-H. and Baumgarten, E. (1964a). *Ber. Bunsenges. Phys. Chem.* **68,** 70.
Perkampus, H.-H. and Baumgarten, E. (1964b). *Angew. Chem.* **76,** 965 (Internat. Ed. **3,** 776).
Peterson, P. E. and Kamat, R. J. (1966). *J. Amer. Chem. Soc.* **88,** 3152.
Pettit, R. (1956). *Chem. and Ind.* 1306.
Pfeiffer, P. (1927). "Organische Molekülverbindungen". Ferdinand Enke, Stuttgart.
Phillips, L. F. (1965). "Basic Quantum Chemistry". Wiley, New York.
Piccolini, R. J. and Winstein, S. (1963). *Tetrahedron,* **19,** suppl. 2, 423.
Pilar, F. L. (1958). *J. Chem. Phys.* **29,** 1119.
Pilar, F. L. (1959). *J. Chem. Phys.* **30,** 375.
Pincock, R. E., Grigat, E. and Bartlett, P. D. (1959). *J. Amer. Chem. Soc.* **81,** 6332.
Pines, H. and Arrigo, J. T. (1958). *J. Amer. Chem. Soc.* **80,** 4369.
Pittman, C. U. and Olah, G. A. (1965a). *J. Amer. Chem. Soc.* **87,** 2998.
Pittman, C. U. and Olah, G. A. (1965b). *J. Amer. Chem. Soc.* **87,** 5123.
Pittman, C. U. and Olah, G. A. (1965c). *J. Amer. Chem. Soc.* **87,** 5632.
Plattner, P. A. (1950). *Chimia,* **4,** 260.
Plattner, P. A., Fürst, A. and Marti, L. (1949). *Helv. Chim. Acta.* **32,** 2452.
Plattner, P. A., Heilbronner, E. and Weber, S. (1949). *Helv. Chim. Acta.* **32,** 574.
Plattner, P. A., Heilbronner, E. and Weber, S. (1950). *Helv. Chim. Acta.* **33,** 1663.
Plattner, P. A., Heilbronner, E. and Weber, S. (1952). *Helv. Chim. Acta.* **35,** 1036.
Plesch, P. H. (1963). "The Chemistry of Cationic Polymerisation". Pergamon Press, Oxford.
Pocker, Y. (1958). *J. Chem. Soc.* 240.
Pocker, Y. (1959). *Proc. Chem. Soc.* 386.
Pocker, Y. (1962). *Prog. Reaction Kinetics* **1,** 215.
Pollak, P. I. and Curtin, D. Y. (1950). *J. Amer. Chem. Soc.* **72,** 961.
Pople, J. A. (1957). *J. Phys. Chem.* **61,** 6.
Praill, P. F. G. (1963). "Acylation Reactions". Pergamon Press, Oxford.
Prelog, V. and Traynham, J. G. (1963). In "Molecular Rearrangements" (P. de Mayo, ed.), p. 593. Interscience, New York.
Price, C. C. (1941). *Chem. Rev.* **29,** 37.
Price, C. C. and Lund, M. (1940). *J. Amer. Chem. Soc.* **62,** 3105.
Price, E. and Lichtin, N. N. (1960). *Tetrahedron Letters,* No. 18, 10.
Pritchard, H. O. (1953). *Chem. Rev.* **52,** 529.
Pullmann, B., Mayot, M. and Berthier, G. (1950). *J. Chem. Phys.* **18,** 257.
Raaen, V. F. and Collins, C. J. (1958). *J. Amer. Chem. Soc.* **80,** 1409.
Raaen, V. F., Lietzke, M. H. and Collins, C. J. (1966). *J. Amer. Chem. Soc.* **88,** 369.
Radlick, P. and Winstein, S. (1963). *J. Amer. Chem. Soc.* **85,** 344.
Ramsey, B. G. and Taft, R. W. (1966). *J. Amer. Chem. Soc.* **88,** 3058.
Rasmussen, S. E. and Broch, N. C. (1965). *Chem. Comm.* 289.
Reed, R. I. (1962). "Ion Production by Electron Impact". Academic Press, London.
Reed, R. I. (1965). "Mass Spectrometry". Academic Press, London.
Rei, M.-H. and Brown, H. C. (1966). *J. Amer. Chem. Soc.* **88,** 5335.
Reichardt, C. (1965). *Angew. Chem.* **77,** 30 (Internat. Ed. **4,** 29).
Reid, D. H. (1965). *Quart. Rev.* **19,** 274.
Renk, E. and Roberts, J. D. (1961). *J. Amer. Chem. Soc.* **83,** 878.

Rennhard, H. H., Di Modica, G., Simon, W., Heilbronner, E. and Eschenmoser, A. (1957). *Helv. Chim. Acta.* **40,** 957.

Reutov, O. A. and Shatkina, T. N. (1962). *Tetrahedron,* **18,** 237.

Richey, H. G. and Buckley, N. C. (1963). *J. Amer. Chem. Soc.* **85,** 3057.

Richey, H. G. and Lustgarten, R. K. (1966). *J. Amer. Chem. Soc.* **88,** 3136.

Richey, H. G., Philips, J. C. and Rennick, L. E. (1965). *J. Amer. Chem. Soc.* **87,** 1381.

Richey, H. G., Rennick, L. E., Kushner, A. S., Richey, J. M. and Philips, J. C. (1965). *J. Amer. Chem. Soc.* **87,** 4017.

Richey, H. G. and Richey, J. M. (1966). *J. Amer. Chem. Soc.* **88,** 4971.

Ridd, J. H. (1961). *Quart. Rev.* **15,** 418.

Ritchie, C. D. and Sager, W. F. (1964). *Prog. Phys. Org. Chem.* **2,** 323.

Ritter, J. J. and Kalish, J. (1948). *J. Amer. Chem. Soc.* **70,** 4048.

Ritter, J. J. and Minieri, P. P. (1948). *J. Amer. Chem. Soc.* **70,** 4045.

Roberts, D. D. (1964). *J. Org. Chem.* **29,** 294.

Roberts, D. D. (1965). *J. Org. Chem.* **30,** 23.

Roberts, I. and Kimball, G. E. (1937). *J. Amer. Chem. Soc.* **59,** 947.

Roberts, J. D. and Bennett, W. (1954). *J. Amer. Chem. Soc.* **76,** 4623.

Roberts, J. D., Bennett, W. and Armstrong, R. (1950). *J. Amer. Chem. Soc.* **72,** 3329.

Roberts, J. D. and Chambers, V. C. (1951). *J. Amer. Chem. Soc.* **73,** 5034.

Roberts, J. D. and Halmann, M. (1953). *J. Amer. Chem. Soc.* **75,** 5759.

Roberts, J. D. and Lee, C. C. (1951). *J. Amer. Chem. Soc.* **73,** 5009.

Roberts, J. D., Lee, C. C. and Saunders, W. H. (1954). *J. Amer. Chem. Soc.* **76,** 4501.

Roberts, J. D., Lee, C. C. and Saunders, W. H. (1955). *J. Amer. Chem. Soc.* **77,** 3034.

Roberts, J. D. and Mazur, R. H. (1951a). *J. Amer. Chem. Soc.* **73,** 2509.

Roberts, J. D. and Mazur, R. H. (1951b). *J. Amer. Chem. Soc.* **73,** 3542.

Roberts, J. D. and Regan, C. M. (1953). *J. Amer. Chem. Soc.* **75,** 2069.

Roberts, J. D., Regan, C. M. and Allen, I. (1952). *J. Amer. Chem. Soc.* **74,** 3679.

Roberts, J. D. and Yancey, J. A. (1952). *J. Amer. Chem. Soc.* **74,** 5943.

Roberts, R. M., Baylis, E. K. and Fonken, G. J. (1963). *J. Amer. Chem. Soc.* **85,** 3454.

Roberts, R. M., Khalaf, A. A. and Greene, R. N. (1964). *J. Amer. Chem. Soc.* **86,** 2846.

Roberts, R. M. and Shiengthong, D. (1964). *J. Amer. Chem. Soc.* **86,** 2851.

Robertson, R. E. (1964). *Canad. J. Chem.* **42,** 1707.

Robinson, E. A. and Ciruna, J. A. (1964). *J. Amer. Chem. Soc.* **86,** 5677.

Rogan, J. B. (1962). *J. Org. Chem.* **27,** 3910.

Rooney, J. J. and Pink, R. C. (1961a). *Proc. Chem. Soc.* 70.

Rooney, J. J. and Pink, R. C. (1961b). *Proc. Chem. Soc.* 142.

Ropp, G. A. (1960). *J. Amer. Chem. Soc.* **82,** 842.

Rosenbaum, J. and Symons, M. C. R. (1960). *Mol. Phys.* **3,** 205.

Rosenberg, J. L. von, Mahler, J. E. and Pettit, R. (1962). *J. Amer. Chem. Soc.* **84,** 2842.

Rothstein, E. and Saville, R. W. (1949). *J. Chem. Soc.* 1946.

Rumpf, P. and Reynaud, R. (1964). *Bull. Soc. Chim. France,* 558.

Rylander, P. N. and Meyerson, S. (1956). *J. Amer. Chem. Soc.* **78,** 5799.

Sager, W. F. and Bradley, A. (1956). *J. Amer. Chem. Soc.* **78,** 1187.

Sandel, V. R. and Freedman, H. H. (1963). *J. Amer. Chem. Soc.* **85,** 2328.

Sargeant, P. B. and Shechter, H. (1964). *Tetrahedron Letters,* 3957.

Sargent, G. D. (1966). *Quart. Rev.* **20,** 301.

Satchell, D. P. N. (1961a). *J. Chem. Soc.* 1453, 3822.

Satchell, D. P. N. (1961b). *J. Chem. Soc.* 5404.

Sauers, R. R. (1962). *Tetrahedron Letters*, 1015.

Saunders, M., Schleyer, P. R. and Olah, G. A. (1964). *J. Amer. Chem. Soc.* **86**, 5680.

Saunders, W. H. (1964). In "The Chemistry of Alkenes" (S. Patai, ed.) p. 149. Wiley, New York.

Scatchard, G. (1939). *J. Chem. Phys.* **7**, 657.

Schaefer, T. and Schneider, W. G. (1963). *Canad. J. Chem.* **41**, 966.

Schaleger, L. L. and Long, F. A. (1963). *Adv. Phys. Org. Chem.* **1**, 1.

Schildknecht, C. E., Gross, S. T. and Zoss, A. O. (1949). *Ind. Eng. Chem.* **41**, 1998.

Schildknecht, C. E., Zoss, A. O. and McKinley, C. (1947). *Ind. Eng. Chem.* **39**, 180.

Schlenk, W. (1912). *Annalen*, **394**, 178.

Schlenk, W., Weickel, T. and Herzenstein, A. (1910). *Annalen*, **372**, 1.

Schlesinger, H. I. and Bunting, E. N. (1919). *J. Amer. Chem. Soc.* **41**, 1934.

Schleyer, P. R. (1964a). *J. Amer. Chem. Soc.* **86**, 1854.

Schleyer, P. R. (1964b). *J. Amer. Chem. Soc.* **86**, 1856.

Schleyer, P. R. (1967a). *J. Amer. Chem. Soc.* **89**, 699.

Schleyer, P. R. (1967b). *J. Amer. Chem. Soc.* **89**, 701.

Schleyer, P. R., Donaldson, M. M. and Watts, W. E. (1965). *J. Amer. Chem. Soc.* **87**, 375.

Schleyer, P. R., Fort, R. C. Watts, W. E., Comisarow, M. B. and Olah, G. A. (1964). *J. Amer. Chem. Soc.* **86**, 4195.

Schleyer, P. R. and Kleinfelter, D. C. (1960). 138th A.C.S. Meeting, Abstracts, p. 43P.

Schleyer, P. R., Kleinfelter, D. C. and Richey, H. G. (1963). *J. Amer. Chem. Soc.* **85**, 479.

Schleyer, P. R. and Nicholas, R. D. (1961). *J. Amer. Chem. Soc.* **83**, 182.

Schleyer, P. R. and Van Dine, G. W. (1966). *J. Amer. Chem. Soc.* **88**, 2321.

Schleyer, P. R., Van Dine, G. W., Schöllkopf, U. and Paust, J. (1966). *J. Amer. Chem. Soc.* **88**, 2868.

Schleyer, P. R., Watts, W. E., Fort, R. C., Comisarow, M. B. and Olah, G. A. (1964). *J. Amer. Chem. Soc.* **86**, 5679.

Schmerling, L. (1945). *J. Amer. Chem. Soc.* **67**, 1152.

Schmerling, L. and Meisinger, E. E. (1953). *J. Amer. Chem. Soc.* **75**, 6217.

Schmerling, L. and West, J. P. (1952). *J. Amer. Chem. Soc.* **74**, 3592.

Schmidlin, J. (1914). "Das Triphenylmethyl". Ferdinand Enke, Stuttgart.

Schrauzer, G. N. (1961). *J. Amer. Chem. Soc.* **83**, 2966.

Schubert, W. M., Donohue, J. and Gardner, J. D. (1954). *J. Amer. Chem. Soc.* **76**, 9.

Schubert, W. M. and Lamm, B. (1966). *J. Amer. Chem. Soc.* **88**, 120.

Schubert, W. M., Lamm, B. and Keeffe, J. R. (1964). *J. Amer. Chem. Soc.* **86**, 4727.

Schubert, W. M. and Quacchia, R. H. (1962). *J. Amer. Chem. Soc.* **84**, 3778.

Schubert, W. M. and Quacchia, R. H. (1963). *J. Amer. Chem. Soc.* **85**, 1278, 1284.

Schubert, W. M., Robins, J. and Craven, J. M. (1959). *J. Org. Chem.* **24**, 943.

Schubert, W. M., Zahler, R. E. and Robins, J. (1955). *J. Amer. Chem. Soc.* **77**, 2293.

Schug, J. C. and Deck, J. C. (1962). *J. Chem. Phys.* **37**, 2618.

Schulze, J. and Long, F. A. (1964). *J. Amer. Chem. Soc.* **86**, 331.

Scott, J. A. N., Flockhart, B. D. and Pink, R. C. (1964). *Proc. Chem. Soc.* 139.

Seel, F. (1943a), *Z. anorg. allg. Chem.* **250**, 331.

Seel, F. (1943b). *Z. anorg. allg. Chem.* **252,** 24.

Seidl, G., Huisgen, R. and Hill, J. H. M. (1964). *Tetrahedron,* **20,** 633.

Seiffert, W., Zimmermann, H. and Scheibe, G. (1962). *Angew. Chem.* **74,** 249 (Internat. Ed. **1,** 265).

Serres, C. and Fields, E. K. (1963). *J. Org. Chem.* **28,** 1624.

Servis, K. L. and Roberts, J. D. (1964). *J. Amer. Chem. Soc.* **86,** 3773.

Servis, K. L. and Roberts, J. D. (1965). *J. Amer. Chem. Soc.* **87,** 1331.

Sharman, S. H. (1962). *J. Amer. Chem. Soc.* **84,** 2951.

Sharp, D. W. A. (1958). *J. Chem. Soc.* 2558.

Sharp, D. W. A. and Sheppard, N. (1957). *J. Chem. Soc.* 674.

Sharpe, T. and Martin, J. C. (1966). *J. Amer. Chem. Soc.* **88,** 1815.

Shiner, V. J. (1953). *J. Amer. Chem. Soc.* **75,** 2925.

Shiner, V. J. and Humphrey, J. S. (1963). *J. Amer. Chem. Soc.* **85,** 2416.

Shiner, V. J. and Jewett, J. G. (1964). *J. Amer. Chem. Soc.* **86,** 945.

Shiner, V. J. and Jewett, J. G. (1965a). *J. Amer. Chem. Soc.* **87,** 1382.

Shiner, V. J. and Jewett, J. G. (1965b). *J. Amer. Chem. Soc.* **87,** 1383.

Shiner, V. J. and Verbanic, C. J. (1957). *J. Amer. Chem. Soc.* **79,** 373.

Shoppee, C. W. (1946). *J. Chem. Soc.* 1147.

Shoppee, C. W. and Johnston, G. A. R. (1962). *J. Chem. Soc.* 2684.

Shoppee, C. W. and Williams, D. F. (1955). *J. Chem. Soc.* 686.

Silver, M. S. (1960). *J. Amer. Chem. Soc.* **82,** 2971.

Silver, M. S. (1961a), *J. Amer. Chem. Soc.* **83,** 404.

Silver, M. S. (1961b). *J. Amer. Chem. Soc.* **83,** 3487.

Silver, M. S., Caserio, M. C., Rice, H. E. and Roberts, J. D. (1961). *J. Amer. Chem. Soc.* **83,** 3671.

Simmons, H. E., Blanchard, E. P. and Smith, R. D. (1964). *J. Amer. Chem. Soc.* **86,** 1347.

Simmons, H. E. and Smith, R. D. (1958). *J. Amer. Chem. Soc.* **80,** 5323.

Simonetta, M. and Heilbronner, E. (1964). *Theor. Chim. Acta,* **2,** 228.

Simonetta, M. and Winstein, S. (1954). *J. Amer. Chem. Soc.* **76,** 18.

Singer, L. S. and Kommandeur, J. (1961). *J. Chem. Phys.* **34,** 133.

Skell, P. S. and Garner, A. Y. (1956). *J. Amer. Chem. Soc.* **78,** 5430.

Skell, P. S. and Hall, W. L. (1963). *J. Amer. Chem. Soc.* **85,** 2851.

Skell, P. S. and Maxwell, R. J. (1962). *J. Amer. Chem. Soc.* **84,** 3963.

Skell, P. S. and Starer, I. (1959). *J. Amer. Chem. Soc.* **81,** 4117.

Skell, P. S. and Starer, I. (1960). *J. Amer. Chem. Soc.* **82,** 2971.

Skell, P. S. and Starer, I. (1962). *J. Amer. Chem. Soc.* **84,** 3962.

Skinner, H. A. (1953). In "Cationic Polymerization and Related Complexes" (P. H. Plesch, ed.), p. 28. Heffer, Cambridge.

Slansky, C. M. (1940). *J. Amer. Chem. Soc.* **62,** 2430.

Sleezer, P. D., Winstein, S. and Young, W. G. (1963). *J. Amer. Chem. Soc.* **85,** 1890.

Smith, G. G., Bagley, F. D. and Taylor, R. (1961). *J. Amer. Chem. Soc.* **83,** 3647.

Smith, G. G. and Brown, D. F. (1964). *Canad. J. Chem.* **42,** 294.

Smith, G. G. and Jones, D. A. K. (1963). *J. Org. Chem.* **28,** 3496.

Smith, G. G., Jones, D. A. K. and Brown, D. F. (1963). *J. Org. Chem.* **28,** 403.

Smith, G. G., Jones, D. A. K. and Taylor, R. (1963). *J. Org. Chem.* **28,** 3547.

Smith, H. A. and Smith, R. J. (1948). *J. Amer. Chem. Soc.* **70,** 2400.

Smith, P. A. S. (1963). In "Molecular Rearrangements" (P. de Mayo, ed.), Chapter 8. Interscience, New York.

Smith, S. G. (1962). *Tetrahedron Letters*, 979.

Smith, S. G., Fainberg, A. H. and Winstein, S. (1961). *J. Amer. Chem. Soc.* **83**, 618.

Smith, S. G. and Petrovitch, J. P. (1964). *Tetrahedron Letters*, 3363.

Smith, S. G. and Petrovich, J. P. (1965). *J. Org. Chem.* **30**, 2882.

Smith, W. B., Bowman, R. E. and Kmet, T. J. (1959). *J. Amer. Chem. Soc.* **81**, 997.

Smith, W. B. and Rao, P. S. (1961). *J. Org. Chem.* **26**, 254.

Smith, W. B. and Showalter, M. (1964). *J. Amer. Chem. Soc.* **86**, 4136.

Smoot, C. R. and Brown, H. C. (1956). *J. Amer. Chem. Soc.* **78**, 6245.

Sneen, R. A. and Baron, A. L. (1961). *J. Amer. Chem. Soc.* **83**, 614.

Sneen, R. A., Carter, J. V. and Kay, P. S. (1966). *J. Amer. Chem. Soc.* **88**, 2594.

Sneen, R. A., Jenkins, R. W. and Riddle, F. L. (1962). *J. Amer. Chem. Soc.* **84**, 1598.

Sneen, R. A. and Larsen, J. W. (1966). *J. Amer. Chem. Soc.* **88**, 2593.

Sneen, R. A., Lewandowski, K. M., Taha, I. A. I. and Smith, B. R. (1961). *J. Amer. Chem. Soc.* **83**, 4843.

Snell, A. H. and Pleasanton, F. (1958). *J. Phys. Chem.* **62**, 1377.

Sommer, L. H. (1965). "Stereochemistry, Mechanism and Silicon". McGraw-Hill, New York.

Sommer, L. H. and Baughman, G. A. (1961). *J. Amer. Chem. Soc.* **83**, 3346.

Sommer, L. H., Bailey, D. L., Gould, J. R. and Whitmore, F. C. (1954). *J. Amer. Chem. Soc.* **76**, 801.

Sommer, L. H., Stark, F. O. and Michael, K. W. (1964). *J. Amer. Chem. Soc.* **86**, 5683.

Sorensen, T. S. (1964). *Canad. J. Chem.* **42**, 2768.

Sorensen, T. S. (1965). *J. Amer. Chem. Soc.* **87**, 5075.

Steigman, J. and Hammett, L. P. (1937). *J. Amer. Chem. Soc.* **59**, 2536.

Stevenson, D. P., Wagner, C. D., Beeck, O. and Otvos, J. W. (1952). *J. Amer. Chem. Soc.* **74**, 3269.

Stewart, R. (1957). *Canad. J. Chem.* **35**, 766.

Stewart, R. and Yates, K. (1960). *J. Amer. Chem. Soc.* **82**, 4059.

Stiles, M. and Libbey, A. J. (1957). *J. Org. Chem.* **22**, 1243.

Stiles, M. and Mayer, R. P. (1959). *J. Amer. Chem. Soc.* **81**, 1497.

Stock, L. M. and Brown, H. C. (1963). *Adv. Phys. Org. Chem.* **1**, 35.

Stork, G. and Bersohn, M. (1960). *J. Amer. Chem. Soc.* **82**, 1261.

Story, P. R. and Fahrenholtz, S. R. (1964a). *J. Amer. Chem. Soc.* **86**, 527.

Story, P. R. and Fahrenholtz, S. R. (1964b). *J. Amer. Chem. Soc.* **86**, 1270.

Story, P. R. and Fahrenholtz, S. R. (1966). *J. Amer. Chem. Soc.* **88**, 374.

Story, P. R. and Saunders, M. (1960). *J. Amer. Chem. Soc.* **82**, 6199.

Story, P. R. and Saunders, M. (1962). *J. Amer. Chem. Soc.* **84**, 4876.

Story, P. R., Snyder, L. C., Douglass, D. C., Anderson, E. W. and Kornegay, R. L. (1963), *J. Amer. Chem. Soc.* **85**, 3630.

Stothers, J. B. and Bourns, A. N. (1960). *Canad. J. Chem.* **38**, 923.

Streitwieser, A. (1952). *J. Amer. Chem. Soc.* **74**, 5288.

Streitwieser, A. (1955). *J. Amer. Chem. Soc.* **77**, 1117.

Streitwieser, A. (1956a). *J. Amer. Chem. Soc.* **78**, 4935.

Streitwieser, A. (1956b). *Chem. Rev.* **56**, 571.

Streitwieser, A. (1957). *J. Org. Chem.* **22**, 861.

Streitwieser, A. (1961). "Molecular Orbital Theory for Organic Chemists". Wiley, New York.

Streitwieser, A. (1962). "Solvolytic Displacement Reactions". McGraw-Hill, New York.

Streitwieser, A. (1963). *Prog. Phys. Org. Chem.* **1**, 1.

Streitwieser, A. and Andreades, S. (1958). *J. Amer. Chem. Soc.* **80**, 6553.

Streitwieser, A., Brauman, J. I. and Bush, J. B. (1963). *Tetrahedron*, **19**, Suppl. 2, 379.

Streitwieser, A. and Coverdale, C. E. (1959). *J. Amer. Chem. Soc.* **81**, 4275.

Streitwieser, A. and Nair, P. M. (1959). *Tetrahedron*, **5**, 149.

Streitwieser, A. and Schaeffer, W. D. (1957a). *J. Amer. Chem. Soc.* **79**, 2888.

Streitwieser, A. and Schaeffer, W. D. (1957b). *J. Amer. Chem. Soc.* **79**, 6233.

Streitwieser, A. and Stang, P. J. (1965). *J. Amer. Chem. Soc.* **87**, 4953.

Streitwieser, A. and Walsh, T. D. (1963). *Tetrahedron Letters*, 27.

Streitwieser, A. and Walsh, T. D. (1965). *J. Amer. Chem. Soc.* **87**, 3686.

Sundaralingam, M. and Jensen, L. H. (1966). *J. Amer. Chem. Soc.* **88**, 198.

Susz, B.-P. and Cassimatis, D. (1961). *Helv. Chim. Acta*, **44**, 395.

Susz, B.-P. and Wuhrmann, J.-J. (1957a). *Helv. Chim. Acta*, **40**, 722.

Susz, B.-P. and Wuhrmann, J.-J. (1957b). *Helv. Chim. Acta*, **40**, 971.

Swain, C. G., Kaiser, L. E. and Knee, T. E. C.(1955). *J. Amer. Chem. Soc.* **77**, 4681.

Swain, C. G. and Kreevoy, M. M. (1955). *J. Amer. Chem. Soc.* **77**, 1122.

Swain, C. G. and Pegues, E. E. (1958). *J. Amer. Chem. Soc.* **80**, 812.

Swain, C. G. and Scott, C. B. (1953). *J. Amer. Chem. Soc.* **75**, 141.

Swain, C. G., Scott, C. B. and Lohmann, K. H. (1953). *J. Amer. Chem. Soc.* **75**, 136.

Swain, C. G. and Tsuchihashi, G.-I. (1962). *J. Amer. Chem. Soc.* **84**, 2021.

Symons, M. C. R. (1963). *Adv. Phys. Org. Chem.* **1**, 283.

Szkrybalo, W. (1964). Ph.D. Thesis, Wayne State University, quoted by E. L. Eliel, N. L. Allinger, S. J. Angyal and G. A. Morrison, "Conformational Analysis", p. 224. Interscience, New York.

Szwarc, M. (1950). *Chem. Rev.* **47**, 75.

Szwarc, M. (1965). *Makromol. Chem.* **89**, 44.

Taft, R. W. (1952). *J. Amer. Chem. Soc.* **74**, 3120.

Taft, R. W. (1953). *J. Amer. Chem. Soc.* **75**, 4231.

Taft, R. W. (1956). In "Steric Effect in Organic Chemistry" (M. S. Newman, ed.), Chapter 13. Wiley, New York.

Taft, R. W. (1960a). *J. Phys. Chem.* **64**, 1805.

Taft, R. W. (1960b). *J. Amer. Chem. Soc.* **82**, 2965.

Taft, R. W. (1961). *J. Amer. Chem. Soc.* **83**, 3350.

Taft, R. W. and McKeever, L. D. (1965). *J. Amer. Chem. Soc.* **87**, 2489.

Taft, R. W., Purlee, E. L., Riesz, P. and DeFazio, C. A. (1955). *J. Amer. Chem. Soc.* **77**, 1584.

Tanida, H. (1963). *J. Amer. Chem. Soc.* **85**, 1703.

Tanida, H. and Ishitobi, H. (1966). *J. Amer. Chem. Soc.* **88**, 3663.

Tanida, H., Tsuji, T. and Ishitobi, H. (1964). *J. Amer. Chem. Soc.* **86**, 4904.

Taylor, R., Smith, G. G. and Wetzel, W. H. (1962). *J. Amer. Chem. Soc.* **84**, 4817.

ter Borg, A. P., van Helden, R. and Bickel, A. F. (1962). *Rec. Trav. Chim.* **81**, 177.

Thomas, R. J. and Long, F. A. (1964). *J. Amer. Chem. Soc.* **86**, 4770.

Thomas, R. M., Sparks, W. J., Frolich, P. K., Otto, M. and Mueller-Cunradi, M. (1940). *J. Amer. Chem. Soc.* **62**, 276.

Thornton, E. R. (1964). "Solvolysis Mechanisms". Ronald Press, New York.

Tiffeneau, M. and Lévy, J. (1923). *Bull. Soc. Chim. France*, **33**, 758.

Tobey, S. W. and West, R. (1964). *J. Amer. Chem. Soc.* **86**, 1459.

Tobolsky, A. V. and Boudreau, R. J. (1961). *J. Polymer Sci.* **51**, S.53.

Tokura, N., Nagai, T. and Sonoyama, Y. (1965). *Tetrahedron Letters*, 1145.

Trahanovsky, W. S. (1965). *J. Org. Chem.* 1666.

Treffers, H. P. and Hammett, L. P. (1937). *J. Amer. Chem. Soc.* **59**, 1708.

Tuck, J. L. (1938). *Trans. Faraday Soc.* **34**, 222.

Turner, D. W. (1966). *Adv. Phys. Org. Chem.* **4**, 31.

Turner, R. B. (1950). *J. Amer. Chem. Soc.* **72**, 878.

Turner, R. B., Nettleton, D. E. and Perelman, M. (1958). *J. Amer. Chem. Soc.* **80**, 1430.

Untch, K. G. (1963). *J. Amer. Chem. Soc.* **85**, 345.

Valkanas, G. and Iconomou, N. (1963). *Helv. Chim. Acta*, **46**, 1089.

van Bekkum, H., Verkade, P. E. and Wepster, B. M. (1959). *Rec. Trav. Chim.* **78**, 815.

Vandenheuvel, W. J. A., Moriarty, R. M. and Wallis, E. S. (1962). *J. Org. Chem.* **27**, 725.

Vandenheuvel, W. J. A. and Wallis, E. S. (1962). *J. Org. Chem.* **27**, 1233.

van Helden, R., ter Borg, A. P. and Bickel, A. F. (1962). *Rec. Trav. Chim.* **81**, 599.

van Tamelen, E. E. and Judd, C. I. (1958). *J. Amer. Chem. Soc.* **80**, 6305.

Vedeneyev, V. I., Gurvich, L. V., Kondrat'yev, V. N., Medvedev, V. A. and Frank-evich, Ye. L. (1966). "Bond Energies, Ionization Potentials and Electron Affinities". Arnold, London.

Vernon, C. A. (1954). *J. Chem. Soc.* 423.

Veselý, K. (1961). *J. Polymer Sci.* **52**, 277.

Vogel, M. and Roberts, J. D. (1966). *J. Amer. Chem. Soc.* **88**, 2262.

Vol'pin, M. E., Koreshkov, Yu. D. and Kursanov, D. N. (1959). *Izvest. Akad. Nauk S.S.S.R.* (*Otdel. khim. Nauk*), 560 (*Bull. Acad. Sci. U.S.S.R. 535*).

Vol'pin, M. E., Zhdanov, S. I. and Kursanov, D. N. (1957). *Doklady Akad. Nauk S.S.S.R.*, **112**, 264.

Volz, H. and Volz de Lecea, M. J. (1964). *Tetrahedron Letters*, 1871.

Volz, H. and Volz de Lecea, M. J. (1966). *Tetrahedron Letters*, 4863.

Walborsky, H. M., Baum, M. E. and Youssef, A. A. (1961). *J. Amer. Chem. Soc.* **83**, 988.

Walden, P. (1902). *Ber.* **35**, 2018.

Walden, P. (1903). *Z. phys. Chem.* **43**, 443.

Wallis, E. S. and Dripps, R. D. (1933). *J. Amer. Chem. Soc.* **55**, 1701.

Wallis, E. S. and Nagel, S. C. (1931). *J. Amer. Chem. Soc.* **53**, 2787.

Walsh, A. D. (1947). *J. Chem. Soc.* 89.

Wanless, G. G. and Kennedy, J. P. (1965). *Polymer*, **6**, 111.

Wanzlick, H. W. and Schikora, E. (1961). *Chem. Ber.* **94**, 2389.

Ward, A. M. (1927a). *J. Chem. Soc.* 445.

Ward, A. M. (1927b). *J. Chem. Soc.* 2285.

Wassermann, A. (1954). *J. Chem. Soc.* 4329.

Wassermann, A. (1957). *Trans. Faraday Soc.* **53**, 1029.

Watson, H. B. (1939). *Ann. Rep.* **36,** 191.

Wawzonek, S., Berkey, R. A. and Thomson, D. (1956). *J. Electrochem. Soc.* **103,** 513.

Weaver, W. M. and Hutchison, J. D. (1964). *J. Amer. Chem. Soc.* **86,** 261.

Weiner, H. and Sneen, R. A. (1965a), *J. Amer. Chem. Soc.* **87,** 287.

Weiner, H. and Sneen, R. A. (1965b). *J. Amer. Chem. Soc.* **87,** 292.

Weissman, S. I., de Boer, E. and Conradi, J. J. (1957). *J. Chem. Phys.* **26,** 963.

West, R. and Kwitowski, P. T. (1966). *J. Amer. Chem. Soc.* **88,** 5280.

West, R., Sadô, A. and Tobey, S. W. (1966). *J. Amer. Chem. Soc.* **88,** 2488.

Westheimer, F. H. and Nicolaides, N. (1949). *J. Amer. Chem. Soc.* **71,** 25.

Westheimer, F. H. and Kharasch, M. S. (1946). *J. Amer. Chem. Soc.* **68,** 1871.

Whalley, E. (1964). *Adv. Phys. Org. Chem.* **2,** 93.

Wheland, G. W. (1934). *J. Chem. Phys.* **2,** 474.

Wheland, G. W. (1942). *J. Amer. Chem. Soc.* **64,** 900.

Wheland, G. W. (1957). "Advanced Organic Chemistry", 2nd Ed. Wiley, New York.

Whetsel, K. B., Hawkins, G. F. and Johnson, F. E. (1956). *J. Amer. Chem. Soc.* **78,** 3360.

White, W. N. and Fife, W. K. (1961). *J. Amer. Chem. Soc.* **83,** 3846.

Whitham, G. H. (1961). *Proc. Chem. Soc.* 422.

Whitham, G. H. and Wickramasinghe, J. A. F. (1964). *J. Chem. Soc.* 1655.

Whiting, M. C. (1966). *Chem. Brit.* 482.

Whitlock, H. W. (1962). *J. Amer. Chem. Soc.* **84,** 2807.

Whitmore, F. C. (1932). *J. Amer. Chem. Soc.* **54,** 3274.

Whitmore, F. C. (1948). *Chem. Eng. News,* **26,** 668.

Whitmore, F. C. and Stahly, E. E. (1933). *J. Amer. Chem. Soc.* **55,** 4153.

Whitmore, F. C. and Stahly, E. E. (1945). *J. Amer. Chem. Soc.* **67,** 2158.

Wiberg, K. B. (1965). In "Oxidation in Organic Chemistry" (K. B. Wiberg, ed.), Chapter 2. Academic Press, New York.

Wiberg, K. B. and Fenoglio, R. (1963). *Tetrahedron Letters,* 1273.

Wiberg, K. B. and Wenzinger, G. R. (1965). *J. Org. Chem.* **30,** 2278.

Wieland, H. and Dorrer, E. (1930). *Ber.* **63,** 404.

Wilcox, C. F. and Mesirov, M. E. (1962). *J. Amer. Chem. Soc.* **84,** 2757.

Wilcox, C. F. and Nealy D. L. (1963). *J. Org. Chem.* **28,** 3454.

Wilt, J. W. and Piszkiewicz, D. (1963). *Chem. and Ind.* 1761.

Wilt, J. W. and Roberts, D. D. (1962a). *J. Org. Chem.* **27,** 3430.

Wilt, J. W. and Roberts, D. D. (1962b). *J. Org. Chem.* **27,** 3434.

Winberg, H. E., Carnahan, J. E., Coffman, D. D. and Brown, M. (1965). *J. Amer. Chem. Soc.* **87,** 2055.

Winstein, S. (1939). *J. Amer. Chem. Soc.* **61,** 1635.

Winstein, S. (1951). *Bull. Soc. Chim. France,* C43.

Winstein, S. (1955). *Experientia,* Supplementum II, p. 137.

Winstein, S. (1959). *J. Amer. Chem. Soc.* **81,** 6524.

Winstein, S. (1965). *J. Amer. Chem. Soc.* **87,** 381.

Winstein, S. and Adams, R. (1948). *J. Amer. Chem. Soc.* **70,** 838.

Winstein, S. and Appel, B. R. (1964). *J. Amer. Chem. Soc.* **86,** 2718.

Winstein, S., Appel, B. R., Baker, R. and Diaz, A. F. (1965). In "Organic Reaction Mechanisms", p. 109. Chem. Soc. Spec. Publ., No. 19.

Winstein, S. and Baird, R. L. (1957), *J. Amer. Chem. Soc.* **79,** 756.

Winstein, S., Baker, R. and Smith, S. G. (1964). *J. Amer. Chem. Soc.* **86**, 2072.

Winstein, S. and Battiste, M. (1960). *J. Amer. Chem. Soc.* **82**, 5244.

Winstein, S., Brown, M., Schreiber, K. C. and Schlesinger, A. H. (1952). *J. Amer. Chem. Soc.* **74**, 1140.

Winstein, S. and Carter, P. (1961). *J. Amer. Chem. Soc.* **83**, 4485.

Winstein, S. and Clippinger, E. (1956). *J. Amer. Chem. Soc.* **78**, 2784.

Winstein, S., Clippinger, E., Fainberg, A. H., Heck, R. and Robinson, G. C. (1956). *J. Amer. Chem. Soc.* **78**, 328.

Winstein, S., Clippinger, E., Howe, R. and Vogelfanger, E. (1965). *J. Amer. Chem. Soc.* **87**, 376.

Winstein, S., Clippinger, E., Fainberg, A. H. and Robinson, G. C. (1954). *J. Amer. Chem. Soc.* **76**, 2597.

Winstein, S. and Fainberg, A. H. (1957). *J. Amer. Chem. Soc.* **79**, 5937.

Winstein, S., Friedrich, E. C. and Smith, S. G. (1964). *J. Amer. Chem. Soc.* **86**, 305.

Winstein, S., Friedrich, E. C., Baker, R. and Lin, Y.-i. (1966). *Tetrahedron*, **22**, Suppl. 8, 621.

Winstein, S., Gadient, F., Stafford, E. T. and Klinedinst, P. E. (1958). *J. Amer. Chem. Soc.* **80**, 5895.

Winstein, S., Gall, J. S., Hojo, M. and Smith, S. G. (1960). *J. Amer. Chem. Soc.* **82**, 1010.

Winstein, S. and Grunwald, E. (1946). *J. Amer. Chem. Soc.* **68**, 536.

Winstein, S. and Grunwald, E. (1948). *J. Amer. Chem. Soc.* **70**, 828.

Winstein, S., Grunwald, E. and Ingraham, L. L. (1948). *J. Amer. Chem. Soc.* **70**, 821.

Winstein, S., Grunwald, E. and Jones, H. W. (1951). *J. Amer. Chem. Soc.* **73**, 2700.

Winstein, S., Grunwald, E., Buckles, R. E. and Hanson, C. (1948). *J. Amer. Chem. Soc.* **70**, 816.

Winstein, S. and Heck, R. (1956). *J. Amer. Chem. Soc.* **78**, 4801.

Winstein, S., Hess, H. V. and Buckles, R. E. (1942). *J. Amer. Chem. Soc.* **64**, 2796.

Winstein, S., Hojo, M. and Smith, S. G. (1960). *Tetrahedron Letters*, No. 22, 12.

Winstein, S. and Holness, N. J. (1955a), *J. Amer. Chem. Soc.* **77**, 3054.

Winstein, S. and Holness, N. J. (1955b). *J. Amer. Chem. Soc.* **77**, 5562.

Winstein, S., Kaesz, H. D., Kreiter, C. G. and Friedrich, E. C. (1965). *J. Amer. Chem. Soc.* **87**, 3267.

Winstein, S., Klinedinst, P. E. and Clippinger, E. (1961). *J. Amer. Chem. Soc.* **83**, 4986.

Winstein, S., Klinedinst, P. E. and Robinson, G. C. (1961). *J. Amer. Chem. Soc.* **83**, 885.

Winstein, S. and Kosower, E. M. (1959). *J. Amer. Chem. Soc.* **81**, 4399.

Winstein, S., Lewin, A. H. and Pande, K. C. (1963). *J. Amer. Chem. Soc.* **85**, 2324.

Winstein, S., Lindegren, C. R., Marshall, H. and Ingraham, L. L. (1953). *J. Amer. Chem. Soc.* **75**, 147.

Winstein, S. and Lucas, H. J. (1939). *J. Amer. Chem. Soc.* **61**, 1576, 2845.

Winstein, S. and Marshall, H. (1952). *J. Amer. Chem. Soc.* **74**, 1120.

Winstein, S., Morse, B. K., Grunwald, E., Schreiber, K. C. and Corse, J. (1952a). *J. Amer. Chem. Soc.* **74**, 1113.

Winstein, S., Morse, B. K., Grunwald, E., Jones, H. W., Corse, J., Trifan, D. and Marshall, H. (1952b). *J. Amer. Chem. Soc.* **74**, 1127.

Winstein, S. and Ordronneau, C. (1960). *J. Amer. Chem. Soc.* **82**, 2084.

Winstein, S. and Robinson, G. C. (1958). *J. Amer. Chem. Soc.* **80**, 169.

Winstein, S. and Schlesinger, A. H. (1948). *J. Amer. Chem. Soc.* **70**, 3528.

Winstein, S. and Schreiber, K. C. (1952a). *J. Amer. Chem. Soc.* **74**, 2165.

Winstein, S. and Schreiber, K. C. (1952b). *J. Amer. Chem. Soc.* **74**, 2171.

Winstein, S. and Shatavsky, M. (1956a). *Chem. and Ind.* 56.

Winstein, S. and Shatavsky, M. (1956b). *J. Amer. Chem. Soc.* **78**, 592.

Winstein, S., Shatavsky, M., Norton, C. and Woodward, R. B. (1955). *J. Amer. Chem. Soc.* **77**, 4183.

Winstein, S., Smith, S. G. and Darwish, D. (1959). *J. Amer. Chem. Soc.* **81**, 5511.

Winstein, S. and Sonnenberg, J. (1961a). *J. Amer. Chem. Soc.* **83**, 3235.

Winstein, S. and Sonnenberg, J. (1961b). *J. Amer. Chem. Soc.* **83**, 3244.

Winstein, S., Sonnenberg, J. and De Vries, L. (1959). *J. Amer. Chem. Soc.* **81**, 6523.

Winstein, S. and Stafford, E. T. (1957). *J. Amer. Chem. Soc.* **79**, 505.

Winstein, S. and Takahashi, J. (1958). *Tetrahedron*, **2**, 316.

Winstein, S. and Trifan, D. (1949). *J. Amer. Chem. Soc.* **71**, 2953.

Winstein, S. and Trifan, D. (1952a). *J. Amer. Chem. Soc.* **74**, 1147.

Winstein, S. and Trifan, D. (1952b). *J. Amer. Chem. Soc.* **74**, 1154.

Winstein, S., Vogelfanger, E., Pande, K. C. and Ebel, H. F. (1962). *J. Amer. Chem. Soc.* **84**, 4993.

Winstein, S., Walborsky, H. M. and Schreiber, K. C. (1950). *J. Amer. Chem. Soc.* **72**, 5795.

Witschonke, C. R. and Kraus, C. A. (1947). *J. Amer. Chem. Soc.* **69**, 2472.

Woods, W. G., Carboni, R. A. and Roberts, J. D. (1956). *J. Amer. Chem. Soc.* **78**, 5653.

Young, A. E., Sandel, V. R. and Freedman, H. H. (1966). *J. Amer. Chem. Soc.* **88**, 4532.

Young, W. G. and Franklin, J. S. (1966). *J. Amer. Chem. Soc.* **88**, 785.

Young, W. G., Sharman, S. H. and Winstein, S. (1960). *J. Amer. Chem. Soc.* **82**, 1376.

Young, W. G., Winstein, S. and Goering, H. L. (1951). *J. Amer. Chem. Soc.* **73**, 1958.

Zahradník, R. and Michl, J. (1965). *Coll. Czech. Chem. Comm.* **30**, 520.

Zhdanov, S. I. (1958). *Z. phys. Chem. (Leipzig)*, Sonderheft, 235.

Zhdanov, S. I. and Frumkin, A. N. (1958). *Doklady Akad. Nauk S.S.S.R.* **122**, 412.

Ziegler, K. and Wollschitt, H. (1930). *Annalen*, **479**, 90.

Zimmerman, H. E. and Zweig, A. (1961). *J. Amer. Chem. Soc.* **83**, 1196.

Zollinger, H. (1961). "Azo and Diazo Chemistry". Interscience, New York.

Zuman, P., Chodkowski, J., Potěšilová, H. and Šantavý, F. (1958). *Nature*, **182**, 1535.

AUTHOR INDEX

Numbers in italic refer to the page on which a reference is listed in the section at the end of the text.

A

Aalbersberg, W. I., 301, *312*
Abd Elhafez, F. A., 246, *321*
Aboderin, A. A., 266, *312*, *313*
Adam, F. C., 22, 25, *335*
Adams, J. Q., 301, *312*
Adams, R., 230, 262, *345*
Adkins, H., 215, *312*
Airs, R. S., 177, *312*
Aitken, I. M., 125, *312*
Albery, W. J., 167, *312*
Alderman, S. D., 159, *328*
Aléonard, S., 29, *312*
Alfrey, T., 192, *337*
Allen, I., 167, *339*
Allen, R. H., 182, *312*
Allinger, J., 245, *321*
Andersen, R. D., 80, *335*
Anderson, C. B., 227, *312*
Anderson, E. W., 21, 116, 260, *342*
Anderson, J. N., 85, *313*
Andreades, S., 177, *343*
Andrews, L. J., 158, *331*
Anet, F. A. L., 21, 243, *316*
Appel, B. R., 158, 193, 309, *345*
Applequist, D. E., 271, *312*
Archer, B. L., 290, *312*
Archer, S., 181, *318*
Arcus, C. L., 177, *312*
Arendale, W. F., 285, *312*
Arkell, A., 299, *335*
Armstrong, R., 257, *339*
Arndt, F., 3, *312*
Arnett, E. M., 47, 75, 76, 77, 78, 81, 84, 85, 142, 147, 309, *312*, *313*

Arond, L. H., 192, *337*
Arrigo, J. T., 220, *338*
Aschner, T. C., 219, *323*
Atkinson, G., 152, *313*
Atkinson, J. R., 301, *313*
Atkinson, R. F., 266, *320*
Ausloos, P., 56, 57, 219, *313*, *316*
Avarbock, H. S., 97, *336*

B

Bachmann, W. E., 215, *313*
Baddeley, G., 180, 183, 219, 292, 299, *313*
Baeyer, A., 3, 7, *313*
Bagley, F. D., 103, *341*
Bahary, W., 31, *316*
Bailey, D. L., 304, *342*
Bailey, D. M., 253, *330*
Bailey, T. H., 37, 172, *313*
Baird, R. L., 247, 266, *312*, *313*, *323*, *345*
Baker, E. B., 16, 22, 23, 24, 25, 26, 49, 286, 287, *336*, *337*
Baker, R., 115, 158, 193, 270, 309, *345*, *346*
Balaban, A. T., 51, 294, 311, *313*
Balfe, M. P., 177, *312*
Bank, S., 275, *313*
Banks, R. E., 301, *313*
Banthorpe, D. V., 310, *313*
Baron, A. L., 269, *342*
Barry, G. W., 84, 114, *332*
Bartlett, P. D., 51, 90, 92, 94, 98, 208, 219, 220, 221, 250, 253, 259, 275, 278, 311, *313*, *338*
Barton, D. H. R., 102, *313*

Bastien, I. J., 16, 22, 23, 24, 25, 26, 49, 115, 286, 287, *336, 337*
Batelka, J. J., 266, *332*
Bateman, L. C., 38, 91, 149, 169, 171, *313, 314*
Battiste, M. A., 79, 254, *314, 346*
Batts, B. D., 105, *314*
Bauge, K., 115, *314*
Baughan, E. C., 301, *313*
Baughman, G. A., 304, *342*
Bauld, N. L., 58, *320*
Baum, M. E., 280, *344*
Baumgarten, E., 15, 86, 309, *337, 338*
Bawn, C. E. H., 159, 168, 190, 302, *314*
Baxter, J. F., 97, *337*
Bayles, J. W., 71, 72, 73, *314*
Bayless, J. H., 167, 266, *314*
Baylis, E. K., 183, 220, *339*
Beachell, H. C., 54, *319*
Beeck, O., 220, *337, 342,*
Bell, H. M., 219, 260, 277, *314, 317*
Bell, R. A., 253, *330*
Bell, R. M., 168, *314*
Bell, R. P., 167, *312*
Beltramé, P., 196, 278, *314*
Bender, M. L., 71, 288, 290, *314, 332*
Ben-Efraim, D. A., 276, *315*
Benjamin, B. M., 209, 213, 215, 217, 218, 237, 239, 242, 278, 300, *314, 319, 331*
Benker, K. E., 159, *328*
Bennett, W., 257, 272, *339*
Bensley, B., 172, *314*
Benson, F. R., 193, *314*
Benson, S. W., 124, 294, *314, 322*
Bentley, A., 72, *314*
Bentrude, W. G., 147, *312*
Berenblum, I., 124, *314*
Bergman, R. G., 278, *315*
Bergmann, E., 10, *314*
Bergstrom, C. G., 115, 251, 266, *314*
Berkey, R. A., 31, *345*
Berkheimer, H. E., 75, 77, 142, *322*
Bernecker, R. R., 62, 64, 308, *314*
Bernheimer, R., 245, 246, *317*
Berry, R. S., 16, 132, *314, 321*
Bersohn, M., 51, *342*
Berson, J. A., 210, 211, 235, 271, 274, 276, 278, 280, 310, *314, 315*
Bertelli, D. J., 58, 82, 111, 220, *321*
Berthier, G., 129, *338*
Berti, G., 79, *315*

Bertoli, V., 57, 189, *315*
Bethell, D., 80, 81, 98, 129, 158, 171, 180, 181, 183, 185, 193, 194, 295, 298, 307, *315*
Bickel, A. F., 112, 220, *343, 344*
Bicknell, R. C., 102, 281, *315, 334*
Biddulph, R. H., 188, *315*
Bigelow, M. J., 262, *331*
Billmeier, R. A., 49, *323*
Birchall, T., 16, 19, 53, 114, *315*
Birladeanu, L., 270, *315*
Bistrzycki, A., 52, *315*
Bjerrum, N., 150, *315*
Blanchard, E. P., 296, *315, 341*
Blandamer, M. J., 158, *315*
Blois, M. S., 301, *332*
Blunck, F. H., 104, *330*
Bly, R. S., 252, *315*
Bodendorf, K., 49, *315*
Boer, F. P., 285, *315*
Böhme, H., 49, *315*
Boikess, R. S., 270, *315*
Bollinger, J. M., 52, 83, 84, 113, *322, 336*
Bolon, D. A., 275, *313*
Bolto, B. A., 185, *317*
Bolton, R. 307, *322*
Bonin, M. A., 57, *315*
Bonner, W. A., 237, *315, 316, 319*
Bonthrone, W., 125, *316*
Boozer, C. E., 197, *316*
Borčić, S., 269, 274, *316, 330*
Borkowski, R. P., 219, *316*
Borner, P., 193, *334*
Boudreau, R. J., 191, *344*
Bourns, A. N., 71, 114, *315, 342*
Bowman, N. S., 213, *319*
Bowman, R. E., 208, *342*
Boyd, R. H., 53, 76, 81, 109, 176, *316*
Boyton, H. G., 56, 114, *323*
Bradley, A., 50, *339*
Brady, J. D., 55, 69, 85, 87, 184, *317*
Branch, G. E. K., 291, *316*
Brauman, J. I., 131, *343*
Braun, J. von, 208, *316*
Bresler, L. S., 310, *316*
Breslow, R., 21, 30, 31, 52, 78, 79, 80, 111, 112, 113, 254, 268, 310, *317*
Brickstock, A., 130, *316*
Broch, N. C., 285, *338*
Brockway, L. O., 4, *333*
Brook, A. G., 304, *316*

Brookhart, M., 21, 36, 211, 243, 259, 260, *316, 323*
Brouwer, D. M., 17, 18, 210, 213, *316*
Brown, C., 263, *334*
Brown, D. A., 290, 291, *316*
Brown, D. F., 103, *341*
Brown, F., 94, 229, *316*
Brown, G. R., 189, 191, *316*
Brown, H. C., 17, 55, 56, 69, 85, 86, 87, 94, 95, 96, 97, 98, 104, 180, 181, 182, 183, 184, 192, 197, 198, 199, 219, 223, 230, 233, 242, 245, 246, 249, 250, 255, 260, 267, 272, 275, 277, 278, 292, 293, 301, 309, 311, *314, 316, 317, 318, 319, 330, 331, 336, 338, 342*
Brown, M., 243, 246, 295, *345*
Brown, R. F., 208, *313, 318*
Brown, W. G., 55, *318*
Bruylants, P., 252, *318*
Bryan, R. F., 14, 113, *318*
Buck, H. M., 301, *318*
Buckles, R. E., 226, 227, *346*
Buckley, N. C., 257, *339*
Buist, G. J., 71, *314*
Bunnett, J. F., 288, *318*
Bunting, E. N., 29, *340*
Bunton, C. A., 35, 48, 171, 175, 176, 196, 276, 278, 290, 307, *314, 318*
Burke, J. J., 81, 147, *312*
Burr, J. G., 217, *318, 319*
Burr, M., 52, 300, *324*
Burwell, R. L., 181, *318*
Bush, J. B., 131, *343*
Bushick, R. D., 75, 76, 77, 78, 85, 142, *312, 313*
Busler, W. R., 57, *315*
Butterworth, R., 296, *329*
Bywater, S., 57, 189, *318*

C

Cacace, F., 47, *318*
Callister, J. D., 98, 193, 194, 295, 298, *315*
Cannell, L. G., 208, *318*
Capon, B., 225, 245, 307, 310, 311, *318*
Carboni, R. A., 135, 230, 250, 259, *347*
Carnahan, J. E., 295, *345*
Carrington, A., 301, *318*
Carter, J. V., 172, 174, *342*
Carter, P., 275, 280, *346*
Carter, R. E., 21, *325*
Casanova, J., 58, 276, *320*

Caserio, M. C., 115, 266, 267, 269, 270, *319, 320, 341*
Cassimatis, D., 285, 286, *319, 343*
Cassis, F. A., 54, 180, *328*
Cast, J., 193, *319*
Catchpole, A. G., 165, *319*
Ceccon, A., 153, 158, *324*
Challis, B. C., 105, *319*
Chambers, V. C., 267, *339*
Chang, H. W., 21, 30, 78, 79, 80, 84, 111, 112, 113, *316*
Chapman, O. L., 255, *319*
Chapman, R. P., 85, *327*
Charles, K. R., 84, 114, *332*
Cheema, Z. K., 278, *319*
Chen, M. C., 288, 290, *314*
Chiang, Y., 84, 105, 106, 109, 114, *332*
Chloupek, F. J., 223, 242, 249, 272, 275, 277, 278, *317*
Chmiel, C. T., 288, *319*
Chodkowski, J., 31, *347*
Choi, S. U., 185, *319*
Chow, B. F., 30, *320*
Christie, J. B., 237, *319*
Christman, D. R., 53, 176, *316*
Christmann, F., 58, 109, *326*
Christol, H., 193, *319, 330*
Chu, T. L., 25, 129, *319*
Church, M. G., 38, 149, 169, 171, *313, 319*
Ciereszko, L. S., 217, 300, *318, 319*
Cigén, R., 173, *319*
Ciranni, G., 47, *318*
Ciruna, J. A., 110, 113, *339*
Clarke, G. A., 150, *319*
Cleveland, J. D., 17, *317*
Clifford, A. F., 54, *319*
Clippinger, E., 154, 155, 156, 240, 246, 273, *346*
Closs, G. L., 296, 297, *319*
Closs, L. E., 297, *319*
Closson, W. D., 253, 256, *313, 326*
Cocivera, M., 195, 196, 200, *319*
Coe, J. S., 208, *319*
Coffman, D. D., 295, *345*
Cogdell, T. J., 253, *313*
Cohen, S. G., 48, *319*
Colapietro, J., 105, *319*
Collins, C. J., 209, 212, 213, 215, 217, 218, 237, 239, 242, 278, 300, 310, *314, 315, 316, 319, 331, 338*
Colpa, J. P., 132, 133, *320*

Colson, J. G., 305, *332*
Colter, A. K., 17, 159, 271, 277, *320, 332*
Comisarow, M. B., 20, 24, 54, 93, 110, 113, 114, 115, 231, 237, 243, 246, 275, 287, *321, 336, 337, 340*
Comyns, A. E., 48, *318*
Conant, J. B., 30, 47, 75, 92, *320*
Condon, F. E., 220, *313*
Cone, L. H., 50, *326*
Connor, T. M., 16, *335*
Conradi, J. J., 301, *345*
Conrow, K., 50, 52, 159, 202, 220, *320*
Cook, D., 49, 285, 287, *320*
Cook, F. B., 167, *314*
Cooke, I., 285, *320*
Cooper, K. A., 9, 43, 91, *314, 320*
Cope, A. C., 205, 255, 256, *320*
Corbin, J. L., 252, *320, 328*
Corey, E. J., 58, 128, 249, 276, *320*
Corey, R. B., 266, 270, 271, *337*
Corse, J., 244, 247, 272, *328, 346*
Cotter, J. L., 49, 71, 72, *314, 320*
Cottrell, T. L., 67, 309. *320*
Coverdale, C. E., 168, *343*
Cowdrey, W. A., 174, *320*
Cox, E. F., 115, 269, 270, *320*
Craig, R. A., 28, 53, 288, *320, 335*
Cram, D. J., 4, 21, 167, 190, 200, 215, 230, 232, 240, 242, 243, 245, 246, 250, 264, 311, *316, 320, 321*
Crandall, J. K., 253, *330*
Craven, J. M., 285, *340*
Crawford, R. J., 275, *313*
Crew, M. C., 217, *321*
Cristol, S. J., 250, 257, *321*
Crumbliss, A. L., 296, *329*
Crunden, E. W., 291, *321*
Cummings, F. E., 23, 49, 159, 220, *328*
Cundall, R. B., 191, 192, *321*
Cupas, C. A., 54, 110, *321, 336*
Curtin, D. Y., 215, 217, *321, 338*

D

Dahmlos, J., 68, *325*
Dallinga, G., 108, 125, *321*
Danyluk, S. S., 16, 301, *321*
Darwish, D., 149, 150, 153, *321, 347*
Dauben, H. J., 50, 58, 82, 111, 144, 220, 221, *321, 328*
Dauben, W. G., 256, 268, *321*

Davies, A. G., 308, *321*
Davies, D. A., 159, 220, *328*
Davies, T. D., 94, *316*
Davis, R. E., 233, *321*
Davis, S., 54, 159, 233, *328*
Dawson, R. L., 270, *320*
Dayagi, S., 186, *337*
De Boer, E., 301, *345*
Deck, J. C., 21, *340*
DeFazio, C. A., 146, *343*
Dehl, R., 16, 132, *314, 321*
DeJongh, D. C., 271, *321*
de la Mare, P. B. D., 178, 307, 310, *321*
Delfs, D., 168, *334*
de Mayo, P., 271, 307, 310, *322*
DeMore, W. B., 294, *322*
Deno, N. C., 7, 17, 19, 25, 26, 27, 28, 51, 53, 75, 77, 80, 81, 83, 84, 85, 97, 109, 110, 113, 114, 115, 116, 142, 194, 202, 219, 220, 221, 260, 266, 283, 285, 287, 288, 307, 310, *322, 335*
DePuy, C. H., 104, 258, 266, *322, 323*
Dermer, O. C., 49, *323*
de Salas, E., 8, 229, *335*
de Sousa, R. M., 262, *323*
de Vries, L., 254, 270, *323, 347*
Dewael, A., 252, *318*
Dewar, M. J. S., 52, 53, 102, 110, 126, 128, 129, 136, 158, 200, 222, 230, 277, 308, 311, *323*
DeWolfe, R. H., 165, 309, 310, *323*
Deyrup, A. J., 7, 28, *327*
Diaz, A. F., 36, 158, 193, 211, 259, 260, 309, *316, 323, 345*
Diestler, D. J., 159, 220, *328*
Diffenbach, R. A., 90, 172, *323*
Dills, C. E., 278, *313*
Dilthey, W., 3, *323*
Di Modica, G., 30, *339*
Dimroth, K., 305, *323*
Dinklage, R., 3, *323*
Dirlam, J., 250, *325*
Doering, W. E., 56, 79, 93, 111, 114, 140, 159, 177, 219, 297, *323*
Doi, J. T., 153, *326*
Donaldson, M. M., 233, 278, *318, 340*
Donohue, J., 285, *340*
Doran, M., 21, 25, 27, 189, *337*
Dorrer, E., 193, *345*
Dostrovsky, I., 11, 91, 94, 263, *316, 323*
Douglass, D. C., 21, 116, 260, *342*
Dowell, A. M., 296, 298, *329*

Dravnieks, F., 301, *318*
Dripps, R. D., 208, *344*
Duffy, J. A., 290, *323*
Duggleby, P. M., 147, *312*
Duke, R. B., 263, *334*
Dunlop, A., 196, 278, *314*
Dunn, G. E., 98, *323*
Dunphy, J. F., 191, 192, *323*
Dyckes, D., 247, *324*
Dye, T. E., 278, *331*

E

Eaborn, C., 107, 143, 303, 311, *323*
Earhart, H. W., 56, 114, *323*
Ebel, H. F., 47, 272, *347*
Eberson, L., 19, 114, 231, 247, 248, *323*
Edwards, J. O., 169, 170, *324*
Edwards, T., 194, *322*
Edwards, W. R., 114, *323*
Eggers, E. A., 221, *330*
Ehrenson, S., 129, *324*
Ehret, A., 156, *324*
Eigen, M., 138, 152, *324*
Ekström, C.-G., 173, *319*
Elder, F. A., 65, *324*
Eleuterio, H. S., 181, *328*
Elkin, L. M., 181, *318*
Elliott, I. W., 186, *331*
Elliott, J. J., 190, *331*
Emovon, E. U., 103, *324*
Éntelis, S. G., 78, 81, *324, 331*
Épple, G. V., 78, *324*
Eriks, K., 14, 71, 128, 129, 132, *324, 326*
Erusalimskii, B. L., 310, *324*
Eschenmoser, A., 30, *339*
Espy, H. H., 256, *326*
Evans, A. G., 28, 49, 71, 72, 73, 141, 143, *314, 324*
Evans, E. A., 283, *324*
Evans, J. C., 16, 22, 23, 24, 25, 26, 49, 115, *336*
Evans, O. J., 94, *316*
Evans, W. L., 75, 77, 97, 142, *322*
Eyring, H., 263, *324*

F

Fahey, R. C., 53, 102, 158, 200, 308, *323*
Fahrenholtz, S. R., 257, *342*

Fainberg, A. H., 145, 146, 147, 148, 154, 155, 156, 240, 246, *324, 342, 346*
Fairbrother, F., 72, 181, 292, *324*
Farnell, L. F., 301, *313*
Farnum, D. G., 21, 52, 53, 113, 132, *324*
Fassnacht, J. H., 255, *335*
Fava, A., 153, 158, *324, 330*
Favorskaya, T. A., 252, *324*
Featherstone, W., 147, *324*
Feldman, M., 159, *324*
Felkin, H., 268, *324*
Fendler, J. H., 290, *318*
Fenoglio, R., 280, *345*
Ferguson, J. W., 215, *313*
Field, F. H., 64, 93, 219, *324, 325*
Fields, E. K., 220, *341*
Fife, W. K., 98, *345*
Filler, R., 77, *325*
Finch, A. C. M., 26, *325*
Fischer, E. O., 58, *325*
Fischer, H. P., 93, *327*
Fischer, R. D., 58, *325*
Fish, R. W., 113, *328*
Fitton, P., 255, *319*
Fitzsimmons, C., 159, 168, 302, *314*
Fletcher, R. S., 94, 197, 198, *317*
Fletcher, W. H., 285, *312*
Flockhart, B. D., 301, *325, 340*
Flood, S. H., 180, 183, 184, 286, 287, 292, 293, *336*
Flurry, R. L., 129, *325*
Fonken, G. J., 183, 220, *339*
Foote, C. S., 233, 280, *325*
Forbes, W. F., 301, *325*
Forney, L. S., 266, *332*
Fort, A. W., 265, *325*
Fort, R. C., 93, 115, 263, 275, *325, 335, 340*
Fox, J. R., 37, 98, 172, *313, 325*
Fraenkel, G., 21, 275, *325*
Frankevich, Ye. L., 309, *344*
Franklin, J. L., 64, 93, 144, 308, *324, 325*
Franklin, J. S., 141, 178, *347*
Frantz, A. M., 113, *325*
Franzen, V., 299, *325*
Fredenhagen, K., 68, *325*
Freedman, H. H., 19, 71, 113, 132, *325, 339, 347*
Fridman, S. A., 252, *324*
Friedlander, R., 186, *337*
Friedman, L., 167, 177, 266, *314, 323*

Friedman, N., 19, 50, 51, 52, 83, 84, 110, 113, 114, *322, 336*
Friedrich, E. C., 116, 149, 152, 158, 227, 248, 270, 277, *312, 320, 325, 346*
Friehmelt, E., 208, *316*
Frisone, G. J., 109, *325*
Fritz, R. M., 263, *334*
Frolich, P. K., 189, *344*
Fruit, R. E., 115, *323*
Frumkin, A. N., 31, *347*
Fuchs, O., 193, *334*
Fürst, A., 85, *338*

G

Gaaf, J., 301, *312*
Gadecki, F. A., 50, 111, 220, *321*
Gadient, F., 280, *346*
Gagnaux, P., 285, 286, *319*
Gall, J. S., 153, *346*
Gandini, A., 53, 57, 189, *325*
Ganellin, C. R., 52, *323*
Gardner, J. D., 285, *340*
Garner, A. Y., 297, *341*
Garrett, A. B., 28, 53, 283, *320, 335*
Gaspar, P. P., 294, *325*
Gassman, P. G., 258, 271, 278, 280, *325, 334*
Gebauer, P. A., 159, *328*
Gerrard, W., 310, *325*
Giddings, W. P., 250, 259, *313, 325*
Giese, C., 65, *324*
Gillespie, R. J., 16, 19, 28, 29, 49, 53, 54, 110, 113, 114, 283, *315, 325, 326*
Gleave, J. L., 9, *326*
Gleicher, G. J., 93, *326*
Goering, H. L., 152, 153, 155, 156, 176, 256, 261, 273, 275, 280, *326, 347*
Gold, E. H., 21, 113, *331*
Gold, V., 26, 28, 47, 53, 55, 75, 80, 81, 85, 92, 94, 105, 109, 110, 111, 123, 124, 125, 129, 180, 181, 183, 185, 196, 208, 290, *314, 315, 319, 326*
Goldfinger, G., 191, *326*
Goldman, G., 290, 292, *330*
Goldschmidt, S., 58, *326*
Goldstein, M., 250, *321*
Golinkin, H. S., 147, *330*
Golomb, D., 149, 169, 171, 176, *326*
Gomberg, M., 3, 6, 7, 50, *326*
Gomes de Mesquita, A. H., 128, 129, 132, *326*

Gough, T. E., 158, *315*
Gould, J. R., 304, *342*
Grace, J. A., 26, *327*
Graham, W. H., 115, 266, 267, *319*
Grant, G. H., 9, *327*
Grayson, M., 56, 180, 182, *317*
Gream, G. E., 275, *327*
Greene, R. N., 183, 220, *339*
Greensfelder, B. S., 190, *327*
Greenstreet, C. H., 171, *318*
Greenwood, H. H., 120, *327*
Griffiths, T. R., 158, *327*
Grigat, E., 51, *338*
Grinter, R., 142, 219, 220, 221, *327*
Grisar, J. M., 256, *320*
Grob, C. A., 93, 202, 203, 204, *327*
Gross, S. T., 190, *340*
Grosse, A. V., 187, *327*
Grosse, D., 233, *321*
Groves, P. T., 77, 81, 83, 85, *322*
Grubb, H. M., 64, *327*
Grubb, P. W., 274, *315*
Grunwald, E., 92, 142, 148, 152, 170, 176, 226, 228, 229, 244, 247, 272, *327, 328, 346*
Guarino, A., 47, *318*
Gurvich, L. V., *344*
Gustavson, G., 181, *327*

H

Haaf, W., 51, *331, 332*
Hafer, K., 83, 113, *322*
Hafner, K., 84, 114, *327*
Hakka, L. E., 106, 109, *327, 332*
Halevi, E. A., 110, *327*
Hall, H. K., 290, *327*
Hall, J. R., 113, *331*
Hall, N. F., 283, *327*
Hall, W. L., 200, *341*
Halmann, M., 265, *339*
Halpern, J., 72, *314*
Ham, G., 255, 267, 277, *317*
Hamann, S. D., 143, *324*
Hamill, W. H., 65, *334*
Hammel, O., 8, *334*
Hammett, L. P., 7, 28, 29, 85, 96, 97, 167, 175, 176, 283, 288, *327, 342, 344*
Hammond, G. S., 89, 294, 307, *325, 327*
Hammons, J. H., 278, *315*
Hanack, M., 254, *327*
Hanafusa, T., 270, *315*

Hanazaki, I., 134, 189, *327*
Hanhart, W., 10, *327*
Hanna, M. W., 122, *327*
Hannan, R. B., 220, *334*
Hanson, C., 226, *346*
Hantzsch, A., 7, 28, *327, 328*
Harden, G. D., 101, *328*
Hardie, B. A., 292, 293, *336*
Harman, R. A., 263, *324*
Harmon, A. B., 49, *328*
Harmon, K. M., 23, 49, 50, 54, 111, 159, 220, *321, 328*
Harper, J. J., 233, 263, *318, 335*
Harris, E. E., 215, *321*
Harrison, A. G., 64, 98, 144, 308, *328, 335*
Hart, H., 17, 54, 111, 113, 115, 180, 181, 252, 268, 269, *320, 328*
Hartter, D. R., 76, 81, *331*
Haszeldine, R. N., 301, *313*
Hausser, J. W., 266, *323*
Hawdon, A. R., 151, 196, *328*
Hawes, B. W. V., 28, 47, 53, 75, *326*
Hawkins, G. F., 285, *345*
Hawthorne, M. F., 159, *328*
Hayes, M. J., 189, *328*
Haynie, R., 112, *316*
Heck, R., 154, 156, 217, 246, 247, 248, 249, *328, 346*
Hederich, V., 3, 48, 50, 219, 220, *334*
Heilbronner, E., 19, 25, 29, 30, 79, 81, 85, 111, 121, 125, 129, *328, 334, 335, 338, 339, 341*
Heller, A., 176, *327*
Henderson, W. A., 297, *323*
Herbst, C., 52, *315*
Herling, J., 281, *328*
Herschmann, C., 285, *320*
Herzberg, G., 65, *328*
Herzenstein, A., 30, *340*
Hess, G. G., 303, *328*
Hess, H. V., 227, *346*
Higashimura, T., 189, *328*
Higley, W. S., 54, *333*
Hill, E. A., 169, 172, *328*
Hill, J. H. M., 250, *341*
Hill, M. E., 288, *328*
Hill, R., 113, *316*
Hilton, J., 290, *326*
Hine, J., 206, 296, 298, 311, *329*
Hinman, R. L., 82, *329*
Hinshelwood, C. N., 9, *327*

Hoberg, H., 296, *329*
Hodge, J. D., 17, 19, 25, 26, 28, 51, 83, 84, 113, 114, *322*
Hoeg, D. F., 296, *329*
Hoegerle, R. M., 204, *327*
Hoffmann, R., 135, 178, 230, 260, 282, *329*
Hofmann, J. E., 212, 220, *329*
Hofstra, A., 55, 68, 85, 86, 87, 124, 125, 126, 129, *334*
Hogen-Esch, T. E., 158, *329*
Hogeveen, H., 287, *329*
Hoijtink, G. J., 301, *312*
Hojo, M., 149, 153, *346*
Holness, N. J., 265, 268, 277, *320, 346*
Holt, G., 180, 183, 299, *313*
Honnen, L. R., 58, 144, *321, 328*
Horner, L., 299, *329*
Hosoya, H., 134, *327*
Houser, J. J., 17, 19, 26, 28, 83, 84, 113, 114, *322*
Houston, D., 278, *315*
Höver, H., 21, 30, 52, 78, 79, 80, 111, 112, *316*
Howald, R. A., 290, *329*
Howard, R. D., 158, 171, *315*
Howden, M. E. H., 135, 230, 251, *329*
Howe, R., 273, *346*
Hsi, N., 266, *331*
Huber, J. E., 261, *332*
Huber-Emden, H., 168, *335*
Hückel, E., 111, 121, *329*
Hückel, W., 223, 230, 275, 307, 311, *329*
Hudson, B. E., 190, *331*
Hudson, H. R., 310, *325*
Hudson, R. F., 158, 169, 290, 291, *312, 316, 321, 329*
Hughes, E. D., 9, 10, 11, 32, 35, 38, 42, 43, 91, 94, 149, 151, 158, 165, 169, 171, 174, 175, 176, 195, 196, 197, 198, 229, 263, *313, 314, 316, 318, 319, 320, 323, 326, 328, 329*
Huisgen, R., 167, 168, 249, 250, *329, 330, 341*
Hulburt, H. M., 263, *324*
Hulett, J. R., 147, *330*
Hulme, R., 301, 302, *330*
Humphrey, J. S., 264, *341*
Hunt, J. P., 140, *330*
Huntsman, W. D., 221, *330*
Hurd, C. D., 104, *330*
Hurst, J. J., 280, *334*

Hush, N. S., 130, *330*
Hussey, R. E., 92, *320*
Huston, J. L., 283, 292, *324, 330*
Hutchison, J. D., 171, *345*
Huyser, E. S., 98, *330*
Hyman, H. H., 83, *331*
Hyne, J. B., 143, 147, *330*

I

Iconomou, N., 202, *344*
Iliceto, A., 153, 158, *324, 330*
Inghram, M. G., 65, *324, 335*
Ingold, C. K., 9, 10, 11, 32, 35, 38, 42, 43, 91, 99, 100, 102, 145, 149, 151, 158, 165, 166, 169, 171, 174, 175, 176, 182, 183, 196, 197, 198, 206, 229, 307, *313, 314, 316, 318, 319, 320, 323, 326, 327, 328, 329, 330*
Ingraham, L. L., 226, 228, 229, 246, *346*
Inukai, T., 95, 104, *336*
Ipatieff, V. N., 181, 187, *327, 330*
Ishitobi, H., 261, *342*
Israeli, Y., 98, *337*

J

Jack, W. M., 54, *319*
Jackson, E., 37, 147, 172, *313, 324*
Jacques, B., 253, *330*
Jacquier, R., 193, *330*
Jaffé, H. H., 96, *330*
Jander, G., 283, *330*
Jaruzelski, J. J., 75, 77, 81, *322*
Jefferson, E. G., 290, *326*
Jenkins, R. W., 249, *342*
Jennen, J. J., 3, *330*
Jenny, E. F., 152, 246, *330*
Jenny, F. A., 203, *327*
Jensen, F. R., 47, 91, 242, 290, 292, 293, *317, 330*
Jensen, L. H., 14, 128, 129, *343*
Jenson, E. D., 30, 31, 87, *330*
Jerkunica, J. M., 274, *330*
Jewett, J. G., 264, *341*
Jindal, S. P., 263, *335*
Johnson, B., 270, *315*
Johnson, F. E., 285, *345*
Johnson, R. R., 71, *333*

Johnson, W. S., 253, *330*
Johnston, G. A. R., 262, *341*
Jones, D. A. K., 103, *330, 341*
Jones, H. W., 92, 244, 272, *346*
Jones, J. A. G., 72, *324*
Jones, J. R., 72, 73, *314*
Jones, L. W., 208, *330*
Jones, T. P., 301, *313*
Jordan, D. O., 189, *330*
Jordan, N. W., 186, *331*
Jorgenson, M. J., 76, 81, *331*
Joy, H. W., 134, *334*
Judd, C. I., 258, *344*
Julia, S., 262, *331*
Junck, H., 180, 181, 182, *317, 331*
Jutz, C., 112, *331*

K

Kaesz, H. D., 116, *346*
Kaiser, E. T., 58, *320*
Kaiser, L. E., 39, *343*
Kalish, J., 193, *339*
Kamat, R. J., 251, *338*
Kamath, V. G., 191, *337*
Kane, T., 191, *326*
Kanoh, N., 189, *328*
Kaplan, F., 299, *331*
Kaplan, M. L., 159, *335*
Karabatsos, G. J., 212, 266, *331*
Karplus, M., 22, *331*
Katz, T. J., 21, 113, *331*
Kawano, K. I., 295, *333*
Kay, P. S., 172, 174, *342*
Kaye, I. A., 212, 218, *319*
Kazanskii, K. S., 81, *331*
Kebarle, P., 98, *328*
Keefer, R. M., 158, *331*
Keeffe, J. R., 53, 97, 109, *340*
Kehrmann, F., 7, *331*
Keller, C. E., 116, *331*
Kendrick, L. W., 213, *331*
Kennedy, J. P., 190, 310, *331, 344*
Kenner, J., 299, *313*
Kenyon, J., 174, 177, 208, 308, *312, 321, 331*
Kershaw, D. N., 290, *331*
Kessick, M. A., 53, 109, 196, *326*
Khalaf, A. A., 183, 220, *339*
Kharasch, M. S., 75, *345*
Kharasch, N., 305, *331*
Khotsyanova, T. L., 14, *331*

Kilpatrick, M., 68, 83, 86, 129, *331*
Kim, C. J., 245, 246, *317*
Kim, J. P., 275, *317, 325*
Kimball, G. E., 227, *339*
King, L. C., 262, *331*
King, P. A., 97, *336*
King, R. W., 104, *322*
Kinoshita, M., 301, *331*
Kirkwood, J. G., 147, 149, *331*
Kirmse, W., 294, 295, 311, *331*
Kirner, W. R., 92, *320*
Kish, F. A., 53, 109, *322*
Kitaigorodskii, A. I., 14, *331*
Klein, F. S., 176, *327*
Kleinfelter, D. C., 19, 277, 278, *331, 340*
Klinedinst, P. E., 156, 280, *346*
Kmet, T. J., 208, *342*
Knee, T. E. C., 39, *343*
Knox, L. H., 79, 92, 111, 159, *313, 323*
Koch, H., 51, *331, 332*
Koch, P., 153, 158, *324*
Kochi, J. K., 58, *332*
Koehl, W. J., 58, *332*
Koh, L. L., 14, 71, *324*
Kohnstam, G., 37, 39, 98, 147, 172, *313,
    314, 324, 325. 332*
Kommandeur, J., 301, *341*
Kon, H., 301, *332*
Konasiewicz, A., 176, *318*
Kondrat'yev, V. N., 309, *344*
Kopecky, K. R., 190, *321*
Kor, S. K., 152, *313*
Koreshkov, Yu. D., 112, *344*
Kornegay, R. L., 21, 116, 260, *342*
Kosower, E. M., 144, 145, 159, 258, 262,
    268, *332, 346*
Kramer, G. M., 307, *332*
Krauch, H., 159, *323*
Kraus, C. A., 49, *347*
Krebs, A., 309, *332*
Kreevoy, M. M., 158, *343*
Kreiter, C. G., 116, *346*
Kresge, A. J., 71, 82, 84, 105, 106, 109,
    114, *332*
Kruger, J. E., 265, 266, *332*
Kuhn, S. J., 23, 24, 55, 57, 115, 180, 182,
    183, 184, 286, 287, 292, 293, *336,
    337*
Kuivila, H. G., 283, *335*
Kurland, R. J., 17, *320, 332*
Kursanov, D. N., 14, 31, 112, 310, *331,
    332, 344*
13

Kushner, A. S., 115, *339*
Kwitowski, P. T., 113, *345*

L

Laasch, P., 193, *334*
Laber, G., 114, *323*
Ladenheim, H., 288, 290, *314, 332*
Laidlaw, W. G., 147, *330*
LaLonde, R. T., 58, 266, *320, 332*
Lam, L. K. M., 275, *332, 333*
Lamm, B., 53, 97, 109, *340*
Lampe, F. W., 219, 303, *324, 328*
Landgrebe, J. A., 271, *312*
Lane, C. A., 97, *336*
Lane, J. F., 208, *332*
Lang, C. E., 292, *330*
Lang, J., 82, *329*
Langer, A. W., 190, 310, *331*
Langford, P. B., 296, *329*
Lansbury, P. T., 305, *332*
Larsen, J. W., 38, *342*
Latimer, W. M., 141, *332*
Laurent, A., 193, *319, 332*
Lavaux, J. P., 262, *331*
Law, P. A., 17, 115, 269, *328*
Lawton, R. G., 275, *332*
LeBel, N. A., 261, *332*
Ledwith, A., 159, 168, 190, 302, 311,*314,
    332*
Lee, C. C., 115, 229, 235, 243, 257, 265,
    266, 267, 273, 274, 275, *332, 333,
    334, 339*
Leffek, K. T., 147, *333*
Leffler, J. E., 142, 170, 307, 311, *333*
Leftin, H. P., 16, 25, 51, *333, 337*
LeGall, C. Y., 263, *334*
Legrow, G. E., 304, *316*
Leisten, J. A., 28, 290, 308, *323, 325, 331,
    333*
Lemal, D. M., 295, *333*
le Noble, W. J., 273, *333*
Le Ny, G., 268, 275, 280, *324, 330*
Lester, C. T., 237, *319*
Letang, N. J., 55, *318*
Levitz, M., 93, *323*
Levy, A. A., 115, *333*
Lévy, H. A., 4, *333*
Lévy, J., 206, *344*
Levy, J. F., 153, 155, 156, 176, *326*
Lewandowski, K. M., 269, 270, *342*
Lewin, A. H., 259, *346*

Lewis, E. S., 71, 110, 171, 197, *316*, *333*
Lewis, F. M., 191, *334*
Lewis, G. N., 128, *333*
Lewis, T. A., 290, *318*
Ley, J. B., 208, *333*
Lias, S. G., 56, 57, *313*
Libbey, A. J., 79, *342*
Lichtin, N. N., 29, 50, 69, 70, 71, 308, *332*, *333*, *338*
Lien, A. P., 54, 68, 69, 85, 86, 87, 129, 183, *333*
Lieser, K. H., 180, *333*
Lietzke, M. H., 213, 242, *319*, *338*
Lin, Y.-i, 270, *346*
Lincoln, D. N., 83, 115, 116, 266, *322*
Lindegren, C. R., 226, 246, *346*
Lipkin, D., 128, *333*
Lipscomb, A. G., 174, *331*
Liu, J. S., 17, 26, 28, 83, 115, 116, *322*
Liu, K.-T., 277, *317*
Llewellyn, D. R., 176, 290, *318*
Lockhart, J., 78, 79, 111, 112, 254, *316*
Lohmann, K. H., 37, 170, 172, *343*
Long, F. A., 27, 39, 62, 64, 75, 81, 82, 83, 105, 106, 146, 288, 308, *314*, *319*, *330*, *337*, *340*, *343*
Longuet-Higgins, H. C., 127, 308, *333*
Longworth, W. R., 57, 70, *333*
Lorenz, L., 3, *312*
Lossing, F. P., 64, 65, 98, 144, 308, *328*, *333*
Lovald, R. A., 295, *333*
Lowen, A. M., 75, *333*
Lowenheim, F. A., 29, *327*
Lowry, T. M., 174, *333*
Luborsky, F. E., 68, 86, 129, *331*
Lucas, H. J., 227, *346*
Lugasch, M. N., 77, 81, *322*
Lukas, J., 52, *336*
Lumb, J. T., 258, *333*
Lumpkin, H. E., 144, *325*
Lund, M., 181, *338*
Lupinski, J. H., 301, *318*
Lusk, D. I., 296, *329*
Lustgarten, R. K., 259, *339*
Lykos, P. G., 129, *325*

M

McCarty, J. E., 215, *321*
McCaulay, D. A., 54, 68, 69, 85, 86, 87, 129, 183, *333*

Maccoll, A., 101, 102, 103, 104, 125, 281, 309, 311, 315, *328*, *333*, *334*
McCollum, J. D., 90, 171, 219, 220, 221, *313*
McDaniel, J. C., 258, *323*
McDonough, L. M., 221, *321*
McDowell, C. A., 64, 308, *334*
McElrath, E. N., 263, *334*
McEwan, I. H., 71, 72, *324*
MacGillavry, C. H., 14, 128, 129, 132, *326*
McIntyre, J. S., 16, 22, 23, 24, 25, 26, 49, 115, *336*
MacKay, F. P., 51, *322*
McKeever, L. D., 22, *343*
McKelvey, D. R., 147, *312*
Mackenzie, H. A. E., 283, 290, *334*
McKervey, M. A., 205, 256, *320*
McKinley, C., 190, *340*
McKinney, M. A., 77, *325*
Mackor, E. L., 16, 17, 18, 19, 21, 55, 68, 85, 86, 87, 108, 124, 126, 129, 132, 133, 210, 213, 301, *312*, *316*, *320*, *321*, *334*
McLachlan, A., 21, *325*
McLafferty, F. W., 13, 64, 299, 308, *334*
MacLean, C., 16, 17, 18, 19, 21, 55, 86, 132, 133, 210, 213, *316*, *320*, *334*
McMichael, K. D., 153, *326*
MacNulty, B. J., 43, *320*
McRowe, A. W., 278, *315*
McWeeny, R., 120, *327*
Madoff, M., 208, *318*
Magel, T. T., 128, *333*
Mahler, J. E., 58, 116, *334*, *339*
Malchick, S. P., 220, *334*
Mallory, J. E., 278, *331*
Mancuso, N. R., 305, *332*
Mannerskantz, C., 256, *321*
Marchand, A. P., 136, 222, 230, 277, 311, *323*
Marino, G., 292, 293, *317*, *330*
Marshall, H., 226, 244, 246, 263, 268, 272, *346*
Marshall, J. L., 258, 278, *325*
Marti, L., 85, *338*
Martin, J. C., 17, 97, *337*, *341*
Martin, J. G., 147, *334*
Martin, M. M., 205, 256, *320*, *321*
Martin, R. J. L., 175, *329*
Marvel, C. S., 191, 192, *323*
Maskill, H., 47, 167, *334*

Mason, C. P., 70, *333*
Mason, S. F., 137, 140, 219, 220, 221, *327, 334*
Masterman, S., 174, 175, *320, 329*
Matesich, M. A., 97, *336*
Maxwell, R. J., 266, *341*
Mayer, R. P., 213, 217, 218, *342*
Mayo, F. R., 191, *334*
Mayot, M., 129, *338*
Mazur, R. H., 115, 251, 266, 267, *334, 339*
Mazzucato, U., 158, *330*
Medvedev, V. A., 309, *344*
Meerwein, H., 3, 8, 48, 49, 50, 168, 193, 219, 220, *334*
Megerle, G. M., 159, *320*
Meier, W., 25, *334*
Meigh, D. F., 175, *318, 329*
Meinwald, J., 280, *334*
Meisinger, E. E., 187, *340*
Meislich, E. K., 215, *321*
Melander, L., 105, *334*
Meloy, G. K., 299, *331*
Melton, C. E., 65, 134, *334*
Melville, H. W., 191, *335*
Mendicino, F. D., 167, 266, *314*
Mersch, R., 193, *334*
Mesirov, M. E., 268, *345*
Meuche, D., 19, 25, 81, *334, 335*
Meyer, F., 64, *335*
Meyer, K. H., 7, *328*
Meyer, M. W., 13, *336*
Meyerson, S., 64, 212, 266, 281, *327, 331, 339*
Michael, K. W., 303, *342*
Michl, J., 125, *347*
Miller, F. N., 77, *325*
Miller, V. A., 187, *335*
Miller, W. T., 296, *335*
Mills, J. A., 168, *335*
Minieri, P. P., 193, *339*
Mirra, J., 112, *316*
Mislow, K., 208, *335*
Mison, P., 193, *332*
Mockus, J., 110, 113, *322*
Moelwyn-Hughes, E. A., 147, *335*
Moffatt, M. E., 23, 24, 115, 180, 183, 184, 286, 292, 293, *336, 337*
Mok, S. F., 158, *329*
Möller, F., 193, *335*
Moodie, R. B., 16, *335*
Moon, S., 255, *320*
More O'Ferrall, R. A., 308, *335*

Morgan, K. J., 223, 242, 245, 249. 277, *317*
Moriarty, R. M., 262, *323, 344*
Moritani, I., 198, *317*
Morrill, T. C., 257, *321*
Morschel, H., 3, 48, 50, 168, 219, 220, *334*
Morse, B. K., 244, 272, *346*
Moss, R. A., 296, 297, *319*
Mount, R. A., 266, *331*
Mousseron, M., 193, *319*
Mueller-Cunradi, M., 189, *344*
Muetterties, E. L., 54, *335*
Müller, E., 168, *335*
Muller, N., 129, 133, 134, *335*
Mulliken, R. S., 129, 133, 134, 159, *335*
Murad, E., 65, *335*
Murr, B. L., 174, 274, *335*
Murray, M. A., 75, *333, 335*
Murray, R. W., 159, *335*
Musher, J. I., 21, *335*
Musso, R. C., 271, *320*
Muzzio, J., 233, 245, *317*
Myhre, P. C., 80, *335*
Mylonakis, S., 106, *332*

N

Nagai, T., 302, *344*
Nagakura, S., 134, 189, *327*
Nagel, S. C., 208, *344*
Nair, P. M., 130, *343*
Nakagawa, M., 199, *317*
Namanworth, E., 16, 20, 47, 114, 231, 237, 243, 246, *337*
Naville, G., 79, *335*
Nealy, D. L., 252, *345*
Necsoiu, I., 51, *335*
Neikam, W. C., 113, *331*
Nelson, K. L., 183, *317*
Nelson, N. A., 255, *335*
Nenitzescu, C. D., 51, 294, 311, *313, 335*
Nettleton, D. E., 200, *344*
Nevell, T. P., 8, 229, *335*
Newman, M. S., 7, 28, 53, 283, 285, 288, 299, 309, *320, 335*
Neyens, A. H., 184, *317*
Ng, E. K., 22, 25, 129, *335*
Nicholas, R. D., 233, 258, 263, *335, 340*
Nickon, A., 274, *335*
Nicksic, S. W., 301, *312*
Nicolaides, N., 50, *345*

Nield, P. G., 219, *313*
Nikoletić, M., 269, *316*
Nixon, A. C., 291, *316*
Noble, B., 191, *335*
Nordlander, J. E., 263, *335*
Nordmann, J. B., 208, *318*
Norin, T., 271, *335*
Norman, R. O. C., 183, 310, *335*
Norris, J. F., 49, 161, 183, 291, *335, 336*
Norris, T. H., 7, 283, *324*
Norton, C., 259, *347*
Noyce, D. S., 97, *336*
Nozoe, T., 309, *336*

O

O'Brien, D. H., 168, *337*
O'Connor, C., 276, 278, *318*
Oddo, G., 7, 28, *336*
Odintsova, V. P., 78, *324*
Ogawa, I. A., 258, *323*
Ogg, R. A., 174, *336*
Ohno, A., 233, *321*
Ohta, M., 204, *327*
Okamoto, Y., 95, 104, 192, 198, *317, 336*
Okamura, S., 189, *328*
Olah, G. A., 13, 16, 17, 18, 20, 21, 22, 23, 24, 25, 26, 27, 47, 49, 50, 52, 54, 55, 57, 93, 110, 113, 114, 115, 168, 179, 180, 182, 183, 184, 189, 210, 213, 231, 237, 243, 246, 275, 276, 285, 286, 287, 292, 293, 307, 308, 310, 311, *321, 336, 337, 338, 340*
Olah, J. A., 50, 182, 292, *336, 337*
Olofson, R. A., 178, *329*
Olson, A. C., 256, *326*
Olsson, S., 105, *334*
Oosterhoff, L. J., 301, *318*
Ordronneau, C., 259, *347*
O'Reilly, D. E., 16, *337*
Orzech, C. E., 266, *331*
Osborne, G. O., 72, *324*
Ossip, P. S., 159, *320*
Ostermayer, F., 202, 203, 204, *327*
Otto, M., 189, *344*
Otvos, J. W., 220, *337, 342*
Ouellette, R. J., 47, 91, 242, *330*
Oulevey, G., 181, 285, 292, *337*
Overberger, C. G., 191, 192, *337*

Overchuk, N. A., 180, 183, 184, *336, 337*
Owyang, R., 253, *330*

P

Pande, K. C., 47, 259, 272, *346, 347*
Pannell, K. H., 304, *316*
Park, C. H., 255, *320*
Parker, A. J., 158, *337*
Parnes, Z. N., 310, *332*
Patai, S., 98, 158, 186, *329, 337*
Patel, C. S., 10, *329*
Pathak, S. R., 262, *331*
Paul, M. A., 27, 75, *337*
Pauling, L., 128, *337*
Paust, J., 266, *340*
Pavláth, A., 50, 55, *336, 337*
Peach, M. E., 54, *337*
Peacock, T. E., 122, *337*
Pearce, E. M., 192, *337*
Pearsall, H. W., 86, 180, *317*
Pearson, D. E., 97, *337*
Pearson, D. L., 50, 111, 220, *321*
Pearson, R. G., 169, *324, 337*
Pegues, E. E., 158, *343*
Pelster, H., 114, *327*
Pepper, D. C., 54, 56, 189, 191, 310, *316, 328, 337*
Perelman, M., 200, *344*
Perizzolo, C., 194, *322*
Perkampus, H.-H., 14, 15, 86, 125, 309, *337, 338*
Perkins, M. J., 307, 311, *318*
Perry, S. G., 290, *318*
Peterson, H. J., 53, 75, 77, 109, 142, 219, 310, *322*
Peterson, P. E., 97, 251, 255, 256, *320, 338, 336*
Peterson, R., 112, *316*
Petrovich, J. P., 247, 276, *323, 342*
Pettit, R., 58, 111, 116, *331, 334, 338, 339*
Pfeiffer, P., 13, *338*
Pfluger, C. E., 180, *333*
Philips, J. C., 115, *339*
Phillips, H., 174, *331*
Phillips, L. F., 122, *338*
Phillips, W. D., 54, *335*
Piccolini, R. J., 135, 230, 250, *338*
Pickett, L. W., 129, *335*
Pilar, F. L., 134, *338*
Pincock, R. E., 51, *338*

Pines, H., 181, 220, 281, *328*, *330*, *338*
Pink, R. C., 301, *325*, *339*, *340*
Piper, J. U., 255, *335*
Piszkiewicz, D., 112, 220, *345*
Pittman, C. U., 16, 17, 20, 21, 25, 26, 27, 54, 114, 115, 189, 237, 243, 285, 287, 308, *322*, *336*, *337*, *338*
Pitzer, K. S., 141, *332*
Plattner, P. A., 29, 55, 85, *338*
Pleasanton, F., 47, *342*
Plesch, P. H., 53, 56, 57, 179, 188, 189, 310, *315*, *325*, *333*, *338*
Pocker, Y., 72, 73, 158, 309, 310, *329*, *338*
Polanyi, M., 10, 174, *314*, *336*
Pollak, P. I., 215, *321*, *338*
Pombo, M. M., 153, *326*
Ponder, B. W., 278, *314*
Poonian, M. S., 210, 280, *315*
Pople, J. A., 130, *316*, *330*, *338*
Potešilová, H., 31, *347*
Praill, P. F. G., 311, *338*
Prelog, V., 205, 255, *338*
Preston, E. A., 153, *321*
Preston, P. N., 301, *313*
Price, A., 71, 72, *324*
Price, C. C., 56, 181, *338*
Price, E., 29, 71, *333*, *338*
Pritchard, H. O., 67, *338*
Pritchard, J. G., 146, *333*
Prysiazniuk, R., 98, *323*
Pullman, B., 129, *338*
Purlee, E. L., 146, *343*

Q

Quacchia, R. H., 84, 114, *340*
Queen, A., 37, 109, 172, *313*, *327*
Quinn, H. W., 57, *337*

R

Raaen, V. F., 213, 215, 218, 237, *319*, *338*
Radlick, P., 270, *338*
Rafos, R. R., 111, *328*
Rainey, W. T., 212, 218, *319*
Ralph, P. D., 275, *325*
Ramsey, B., 20, 114, 231, 246, *337*
Ramsey, B. G., 3, *338*
Rao, K. N., 71, *332*
Rao, P. S., 168, *342*
Rasmussen, S. E., 285, *338*

Raudenbusch, W., 202, 203, 204, *327*
Rauenbusch, E., 249, *329*
Reed, R. I., 308, *338*
Reed, W. L., 97, 299, *336*
Rees, C. W., 245, 307, 311, *318*
Regan, C. M., 167, 230, 246, *339*
Rei, M.-H., 272, 275, 277, *317*, *338*
Reichardt, C., 148, *338*
Reid, D. H., 124, 125, *312*, *316*, *338*
Reilly, J. P., 189, *337*
Reimlinger, H., 167, 168, *329*
Reinmuth, W., 31, *316*
Reintke, L., 52, *315*
Remanick, A., 276, 278, *315*
Renk, E., 251, *338*
Rennhard, H. H., 30, *339*
Rennick, L. E., 115, *339*
Reutov, O. A., 265, 266, *339*
Reynaud, R., 79, *339*
Reynolds-Warnhoff, P., 280, *315*
Rice, H. E., 270, *341*
Richards, J. H., 21, *325*
Richey, H. G., 17, 19, 25, 26, 28, 83, 113, 114, 115, 116, 257, 259, 270, 278, *313*, *322*, *339*, *340*
Richey, J. M., 115, 270, *339*
Rickter, D. O., 266, *331*
Ridd, J. H., 167, 168, 310, *339*
Riddle, F. L., 249, *342*
Riesz, P., 146, *343*
Riley, T., 181, 183, *315*, *326*
Ritchie, C. D., 96, 97, 98, 100, 309, *339*
Ritter, J. J., 193, *314*, *339*
Roberts, D. D., 267, 268, 269, *339*, *345*
Roberts, I., 227, *339*
Roberts, J. D., 115, 135, 167, 229, 230, 235, 246, 250, 251, 252, 257, 259, 265, 266, 269, 270, 272, 274, 275, *319*, *320*, *329*, *334*, *338*, *339*, *340*, *341*, *344*, *347*,
Roberts, R. M., 183, 220, *339*
Robertson, R. E., 109, 147, *327*, *333*, *334*, *335*, *339*
Robins, J., 285, *340*
Robinson, E. A., 110, 113, 283, *325*, *326*, *339*
Robinson, G. C., 53, 154, 155, 156, 240, 246, *324*, *346*, *347*
Rogan, J. B., 268, *321*, *339*
Rooney, J. J., 301, *339*
Ropp, G. A., 52, *339*
Rosenbaum, J., 25, *339*

Rosenberg, J. L. von, 116, *339*
Rossetto, O., 158, *330*
Rothberg, I., 233, *318*
Rothstein, E., 10, 51, *330, 339*
Rubinstein, D., 161, 183, *335*
Rüchardt, C., 98, 168, *313, 329, 330*
Rumpf, P., 79, *339*
Rüsberg, E., 283, *330*
Rutherford, P. P., 188, *315*
Rylander, P. N., 281, *339*

S

Sacher, E., 202, *322*
Sadô, A., 15, *345*
Sager, W. F., 50, 96, 97, 98, 100, 309, *339*
Sahyun, M. R. V., 200, *321*
Saines, G. S., 51, 81, 83, 85, 219, 220, 221, *310, 322*
Sambhi, M., 159, *332*
Sampson, R. J., 126, *323*
Sanchez, R. A., 257, *321*
Sandel, V. R., 19, 71, 132, *325, 339, 347*
Sanders, W. W., 7, 49, *336*
Sandri, J. M., 115, 268, 269, *328*
Sano, K., 90, 172, *323*
Šantavý, F., 31, *347*
Santiago, C., 174, *335*
Sargeant, P. B., 277, 299, 300, *339*
Sargent, G. D., 275, 278, 311, *313, 339*
Sasse, H. J., 193, *334*
Satchell, D. P. N., 55, *339, 340*
Satchell, R. S., 53, 94, 292, *326*
Sato, Y., 106, *332*
Sauers, C. K., 249, *320*
Sauers, R. R., 271, *340*
Saunders, M., 18, 56, 114, 116, 210, 213, 260, 275, 276, *323, 340, 342*
Saunders, W. H., 235, 257, 274, 310, *339, 340*
Saville, B., 158, *329*
Saville, R. W., 51, *339*
Sayigh, A., 93, *323*
Scandola, E., 7, 28, *336*
Scatchard, G., 147, *340*
Schaefer, T., 16, 21, *340*
Schaeffer, H. J., 215, 239, *314*
Schaeffer, W. D., 167, 168, 177, *343*
Schaleger, L. L., 39, 146, *340*
Scheibe, G., 21, *341*
Scheppele, S. E., 245, 246, *317*

Schewene, C. B., 273, *326*
Schiavelli, M. D., 97, *336*
Schikora, E., 295, *344*
Schildknecht, C. E., 190, *340*
Schlenk, W., 30, 58, *340*
Schlesinger, A. H., 243, 246, 262, *346, 347*
Schlesinger, H. I., 29, *340*
Schleyer, P. R., 18, 19, 93, 115, 210, 213, 233, 234, 242, 250, 257, 258, 259, 261, 263, 266, 269, 270, 272, 273, 275, 276, 277, 278, 279, 280, *318, 325, 326, 335, 340*
Schmerling, L., 181, 187, *330, 340*
Schmid, G. H., 275, *313*
Schmidlin, J., 6, 13, *340*
Schmidt, H., 283, *330*
Schnack, L. G., 266, *323*
Schneider, A., 48, 220, *313, 319, 327*
Schneider, H. J., 254, *327*
Schneider, W. G., 16, 21, 301, *321, 340*
Schöllkopf, U., 266, *340*
Schrauzer, G. N., 58, *340*
Schreiber, K. C., 152, 154, 242, 243, 246, 257, 272, *346, 347*
Schriesheim, A., 75, 77, 97, 212, 220, *322, 329*
Schrodt, H., 193, *334*
Schubert, W. M., 53, 84, 97, 109, 114, 285, *340*
Schug, J. C., 21, *340*
Schulze, J., 81, 82, 83, 105, *333, 340*
Schuster, I. I., 17, *320, 332*
Schwartz, G. M., 297, *319*
Schwarz, W., 93, *327*
Scott, A. D., 174, *320, 329*
Scott, C. B., 37, 170, 172, *343*
Scott, J. A. N., 301, *325, 340*
Seel, F., 283, *340, 341*
Seidl, G., 249, 250, *329, 330, 341*
Seiffert, W., 21, *341*
Semenow, D. A., 115, 267, *334*
Serini, A., 8, *334*
Serres, C., 220, *341*
Servis, K. L., 251, 252, *341*
Shapiro, U. G., 42, *329*
Sharman, S. H., 41, 178, 183, *341, 347*
Sharp, D. W. A., 14, 54, 72, 129, *341*
Sharpe, T., 17, *341*
Shatavsky, M., 257, 259, *347*
Shatkina, T. N., 265, 266, *339*
Shechter, H., 167, 299, 300, *314, 339*

Sheeto, J. J., 304, *316*
Sheppard, N., 14, 129, *340*
Shields, A. D., 181, *318*
Shiengthong, D., 183, *339*
Shiner, V. J., 110, 197, 198, 264, *329, 341*
Shoemaker, B. H., 54, *333*
Shoosmith, J., 65, *328*
Shoppee, C. W., 230, 262, *341*
Showalter, M., 240, 242, *342*
Shrader, S. R., 271, *321*
Siegel, M., 208, *335*
Siegel, S., 115, 251, 266, *314*
Silver, M. S., 97, 115, 197, 266, 267, 269, 270, *320, 334, 341*
Simmons, H. E., 296, *315, 341*
Simon, W., 30, *339*
Simonetta, M., 111, 121, 125, 129, 134, 230, 250, *328, 341*
Singer, L. A., 232, 250, *321*
Singer, L. S., 301, *341*
Skell, P. S., 52, 200, 266, 297, *341*
Skinner, H. A., 49, *341*
Slansky, C. M., 141, *332, 341*
Slater, G. P., 243, *333*
Sleezer, P. D., 178, *341*
Sloan, M. F., 261, 275, 280, *326*
Small, A., 254, *316*
Small, L. F., 30, *320*
Smid, J., 158, *329*
Smit, P. J., 108, 125, *321, 334*
Smith, B. R., 269, 270, *342*
Smith, G. G., 103, 104, *330, 341, 343*
Smith, H. A., 288, *341*
Smith, J. A., 167, *314*
Smith, J. F., 229, *316*
Smith, J. W., 115, 177, *312, 314*
Smith, P. A. S., 304, 311, *342*
Smith, P. J., 114, *351*
Smith, R. D., 296, *341*
Smith, R. J., 288, *341*
Smith, S. G., 148, 149, 150, 152, 153, 158, 276, *342, 346, 347*
Smith, W. B., 168, 208, 212, 218, 240, 242, *319, 342*
Smoot, C. R., 180, 181, 182, 185, *318, 331, 342*
Sneen, R. A., 38, 172, 174, 177, 193, 249, 269, 270, *342, 345*
Snell, A. H., 47, *342*
Snyder, L. C., 21, 116, 260, *342*
Solladie, G., 193, *319*

Sommer, L. H., 303, 304, 311, *328, 342*
Sonnenberg, J., 270, *347*
Sonoyama, Y., 302, *344*
Sorensen, T. S., 113, 114, 115, 127, 285, *337, 342*
Southam, R. H., 47, 167, *334*
Spangler, M., 51, 220, 221, *322*
Sparks, W. J., 189, *344*
Spietschka, E., 299, *329*
Spille, J., 193, *334*
Spinks, J. W. T., 243, *333*
Spliethoff, W. L., 181, *328*
Sprecher, M., 93, *323*
Spurlock, L. A., 261, *332*
Stafford, E. T., 259, *346, 347*
Stafford, F. E., 146, 280, *333*
Stahly, E. E., 51, *345*
Stang, P. J., 181, *343*
Starer, I., 52, 266, *341*
Stark, F. O., 303, *342*
Staum, M. M., 218, 239, *319*
Steigman, J., 175, *342*
Steiner, B., 65, *324*
Stern, A., 94, *318*
Sternberger, H. R., 215, *313*
Stevens, T. S., 193, *319*
Stevenson, D. P., 220, *337, 342*
Stewart, R., 16, 98, 219, 220, *335, 342*
Stiles, M., 79, 94, 213, 217, 218, *313, 342*
Stock, L. M., 96, 97, 98, 183, 292, 309, *317, 342*
Stork, G., 51, *342*
Story, P. R., 21, 116, 257, 260, *342*
Stothers, J. B., 71, *342*
Strauss, H., 79, 81, *335*
Streitwieser, A., 35, 36, 64, 91, 95, 100, 120, 122, 124, 125, 130, 131, 133, 140, 167, 168, 174, 176, 177, 181, 228, 244, 251, 307, 308, 309, *323, 342, 343*
Struchkov, Y. T., 14, *331*
Sugamori, S., 147, *333, 335*
Sullivan, F. W., 7, *326*
Sullivan, P. D., 301, *325*
Sulzberg, T., 111, *328*
Sundaralingam, M., 14, 128, 129, *343*
Sunko, D. E., 269, 274, *316, 330*
Susz, B.-P., 181, 285, 286, 292, *319, 320, 337, 343*
Sutcliffe, L. H., 301, *313*
Swain, C. G., 37, 39, 158, 170, 172, *343*

Swartz, T. D., 274, *335*
Swinbourne, E. S., 102, 281, *334*
Swindell, R. T., 252, *315*
Symons, M. C. R., 25, 26, 158, 301, 302, 311, *315, 318, 325, 327, 330, 339, 343*
Szabo, A. L., 10, *314*
Szkrybalo, W., 255, *343*
Szwarc, M., 151, 309, *343*

T

Tadanier, J., 264, *320*
Taft, R. W., 22, 30, 31, 53, 81, 87, 90, 99, 100, 101, 103, 109, 113, 142, 146, 150, 172, 176, 208, 309, *316, 318, 319, 323 330, 338, 343*
Taha, I. A. I., 269, 270, *342*
Taher, N. A., 38, 149, 169, 171, *313*
Takahashi, J., 264, *347*
Takeuchi, K., 277, *318*
Tamm, K., 152, *324*
Tanida, H., 261, *343*
Tanner, D., 192, *337*
Tanner, D. D., 250, *321*
Taylor, B. S., 30, *320*
Taylor, J. J., 192, *337*
Taylor, R., 103, 104, 107, 143, 183, 310, *323, 335, 341, 343*
ter Borg, A. P., 112, 220, *343, 344*
Thomas, H., 305, *323*
Thomas, J. H., 71, 72, *324*
Thomas, P. J., 101, 104, *334*
Thomas, R. J., 105, 106, *343*
Thomas, R. M., 189, 190, *331, 344*
Thomson, D., 31, *345*
Thornton, E. R., 109, 307, *325, 344*
Tiffeneau, M., 206, *344*
Tkachuk, R., 243, *333*
Tobey, S. W., 15, 112, *344, 345*
Tobias, M. A., 266, *332*
Tobolsky, A. V., 191, *344*
Tokura, N., 302, *344*
Tolgyesi, W. S., 16, 22, 23, 24, 25, 26, 49, 115, 286, 287, *336, 337*
Towns, D. L., 261, *326*
Trahanovsky, W. S., 135, 230, 275, *313, 344*
Traynham, J. G., 205, 256, *338*
Treffers, H. P., 283, 288, *344*
Treloar, F. E., 189, *330*
Trent, E. S., 278, *331*

Trifan, D., 154, 244, 272, 273, 275, *346, 347*
Tritle, G. L., 250, *318*
Tsuchihashi, G.-I., 158, *343*
Tsuji, T., 261, *343*
Tuck, J. L., 10, *344*
Turner, D. W., 64, 308, *344*
Turner, J. O., 83, 114, 115, 116, *322*
Turner, R. B., 200, 208, *344*
Tweit, R. C., 256, *321*
Tye, F. L., 26, 28, 53, 85, 111, 123, 124, *326*

U

Uda, H., 271, *320*
Umbach, W., 305, *323*
Untch, K. G., 270, *344*

V

Valkanas, G., 202, *344*
van Bekkum, H., 97, *344*
Vandenheuvel, W. J. A., 262, *344*
van der Veen, J. M., 298, *329*
van der Waals, J. H., 16, 55, 68, 85, 86, 87, 108, 124, 125, 126, 129, *334*
Van Dine, G. W., 266, 269, 270, *340*
van Emster, K., 8, 49, *334*
van Helden, R., 112, 220, *343, 344*
van Tamelen, E. E., 258, *344*
Vane, F. M., 212, *331*
Vatakencherry, P. A., 276, *320*
Vaughan, W. R., 16, 132, *314, 321*
Vedeneyev, V. I., 309, *344*
Verbanic, C. J., 110, *341*
Verkade, P. E., 97, *344*
Vernon, C. A., 143, 208, *333, 344*
Verrijn Stuart, A. A., 108, 125, *321*
Veselý, K., 188, *344*
Villiger, V., 3, *313*
Voge, H. H., 283, *327*
Vogel, M., 270, *344*
Vogelfanger, E., 47, 272, 273, *346, 347*
Voithenleitner, F., 112, *331*
Volkmann, D., 275, *329*
Vol'pin, M. E., 14, 31, 112, *331, 344*
Volz, H., 111, *344*
Volz de Lecea, M. J., 111, *344*
Vorster, J., 8, *334*
Voss, D., 180, 183, *313*

W

Waack, R., 21, 25, 27, 189, *337*
Waddington, T. C., 54, *337*
Wadley, E. F., 56, 114, *323*
Wagner, C. D., 220, *337, 342*
Wagner, C. R., 252, *320, 328*
Walborsky, H. M., 257, 280, *344, 347*
Walden, P., 6, *344*
Wallace, W. J., 86, 180, *318*
Wallis, E. S., 208, 262, 301, *330, 332, 344*
Walsh, A. D., 230, 263, *344*
Walsh, T. D., 176, 177, *343*
Wang, C.-S., 77, *325*
Wang, S. S., 159, *320*
Wanless, G. G., 190, *344*
Wanzlick, H. W., 295, *344*
Ward, A. M., 10, *344*
Wardill, J. E., 291, *329*
Wasif, S., 29, *326*
Wasserman, E., 113, *316*
Wassermann, A., 113, 115, *314, 333, 344*
Waterman, D. C. A., 109, *326*
Watson, H. B., 263, *345*
Watson, W. F., 191, *335*
Watts, W. E., 93, 115, 275, 278, *340*
Wawzonek, S., 31, *345*
Weaver, W. M., 171, *345*
Weber, S., 29, 85, *338*
Webster, B., 113, *324*
Webster, E. R., 278, *313*
Wege, D., 275, *327*
Weickel, T., 30, *340*
Weijland, W. P., 301, *312*
Weiner, H., 177, 193, *345*
Weissman, S. I., 25, 129, 301, *319, 345*
Wentzel, F., 7, *331*
Wenzinger, G. R., 271, *345*
Wepster, B. M., 97, *344*
Werner, T. H., 47, 75, *320*
Werstiuk, N. H., 274, *335*
Werth, R., 278, *319*
West, J. P., 187, *340*
West, R., 15, 112, 113, *344, 345*
Westheimer, F. H., 50, 75, *345*
Weston, R. E., 71, *332*
Wetzel, W. H., 103, 104, *343*
Whalen, D. M., 296, *335*
Whalley, E., 39, *345*
Whelan, W. P., 93, *323*

Wheland, G. W., 123, 206, 310, *345*
Whetsel, K. B., 285, *345*
White, W. N., 98, 115, 267, *334, 345*
Whitham, G. H., 258, 262, 263, *331, 333, 345*
Whiting, M. C., 47, 167, *334, 345*
Whitlock, H. W., 194, *345*
Whitmore, F. C., 8, 51, 56, 304, 310, *342, 345*
Whittaker, D., 196, 278, 295, 298, *314, 315*
Wiberg, K. B., 51, 271, 280, *345*
Wickramasinghe, J. A. F., 263, *345*
Widiger, A. H., 55, *318*
Wiedemann, W., 266, *323*
Wieland, H., 193, *345*
Wilcox, C. F., 252, 268, *345*
Wilder, P., 209, 239, *314*
Williams, D. F., 262, *341*
Williams, F., 57, *315*
Williams, G., 75, *333, 335*
Willner, D., 280, *315*
Wills, R., 143, 147, *330*
Wilson, C. L., 8, 229, *335*
Wilt, J. W., 112, 220, 268, 269, *345*
Wimmer, I., 249, *329, 330*
Winberg, H. E., 295, *345*
Winstein, S., 19, 21, 36, 41, 47, 92, 114, 116, 134, 135, 145, 146, 147, 148, 149, 150, 152, 153, 154, 155, 156, 158, 159, 174, 178, 193, 195, 200, 211, 217, 226, 227, 228, 229, 230, 231, 240, 242, 243, 244, 246, 248, 249, 250, 254, 257, 258, 259, 260, 262, 263, 264, 265, 268, 270, 272, 273, 275, 276, 277, 280, 309, *312, 313, 315, 316, 319, 320, 323, 324, 325, 327, 328, 330, 332, 338, 341, 342, 345, 346, 347*
Winter, E. R. S., 283, 290, *334*
Winter, R., 276, *320*
Wisotsky, M. J., 17, 25, 26, 28, 113, 287, *322*
Witschonke, C. R., 49, *347*
Wolf, A. P., 53, 109, 176, *316*
Wollschitt, H., 29, 69, 70, *347*
Wong, E. W. C., 266, 273, *332, 333*
Wonkka, R. E., 147, *330*
Wood, J. L., 48, *318*
Woods, W. G., 135, 230, 250, 259, *347*
Woodward, R. B., 259, 280, *325, 347*

13*

Worsfold, D. J., 57, 189, *318*
Wright, B., 72, *324*
Wu, C. Y., 85, 252, *313*, *328*
Wuhrmann, J.-J., 285, 286, *343*
Wunderlich, K., 3, 48, 50, 219, 220, *334*

Y

Yager, W. A., 113, *316*
Yancey, J. A., 265, *339*
Yates, B. L., 273, *333*
Yates, K., 98, *342*
Yats, L. D., 182, *312*
Young, A. E., 19, 71, 113, *325*, *347*
Young, D. P., 208, *331*
Young, H. H., 291, *336*
Young, H. L., 292, *318*

Young, W. G., 41, 152, 165, 178, 309, 310, *323*, *341*, *347*
Youssef, A. A., 280, *344*

Z

Zahler, R. E., 285, *340*
Zahradnik, R., 125, *347*
Zalar, F. V., 271, *325*
Zeiss, H. H., 140, *323*
Zhdanov, S. I., 31, *344*, *347*
Ziegler, K., 29, 69, 70, *347*
Zimmerman, H. E., 217, *347*
Zimmermann, H., 21, *341*
Zollinger, H., 310, *347*
Zoss, A. O., 190, *340*
Zuman, P., 31, *347*
Zweig, A., 217, *347*

SUBJECT INDEX

A

α-Effect of nucleophiles, 170
$A_{Ac}1$ mechanism, 288
$A_{Ac}2$ mechanism, 290
$A_{Al}1$ mechanism, 48
Acenaphthylene, stereochemistry of addition of DBr in pentane, 102
Acetic acid, protonation, 287
Acetic acid–phosphoric oxide, carbonium ion production by, 51
Acetic anhydride, solvent effect on rates of solvolysis of organic esters, 158
  self-ionization, 283
Acetolysis, observed and calculated relative rates, 234
cis-2-Acetoxycyclohexyl toluene-p-sulphonate, catalysis, 226
trans-2-Acetoxycyclohexyl toluene-p-sulphonate acetolysis, 227
  orthoesters from, 235
Acetyl cations
  from acetic acid, 287
  ultraviolet spectrum, 285
Acetylenic radicals, ionization potentials (table), 65
Acetyl hexafluoroantimonate, X-ray crystallography of, 285
Acetylium ion, 6
Acetylonium ion, 6
Acidity function C_0, definition, 75
Acidity function H_{R^+}, definition, 75
Acidity function H_R' and protonation of olefins, 84
Acidity function J_0, definition, 75
Acrylonitrile, acid-catalysed reaction of t-butyl alcohol and, 194

Activation parameters, mechanistic information from, 39
"Active methylene" compounds, reactions of carbonium ions with, 186
Activity coefficients, 75–76, 81, 84
Acylation of aromatic compounds, 290–293
  isomer proportions (table), 293
  kinetics of, 292
Acyl cations, carbonium ions from, 51–52
Acyl fluorides, ^{1}H- and ^{19}F-spectra of complexes with SbF_5 and BF_3, 287
  complexes with Lewis acids, 285
  solvolysis, 288, 290
Acylium ions, 283–294
  as reaction intermediates, 287–294
  equilibrium with protonated carboxylic acids, 284–285
  nomenclature, 6, 283
  physical evidence, 283–287
  rate and equilibrium constants for formation, 287
  rearrangement of, 294
  spectroscopic studies of, 285–287
1-Adamantyl cations
  stability and rate of formation, 93
  stable solution of, 115
Addition of cations to neutral molecules, 53–57
cis-Addition to olefins, 200
Aliphatic alcohols, cryoscopic behaviour in H_2SO_4, 28
Aliphatic carbonium ions, theoretical treatments of stability, 133–136
Alkanes, mass spectra, 282

Alkenyl groups, bridging by in open-chain systems, 250–263

Alkylation of aromatic compounds, 56, 179–186
  isomer proportions and partial rate factors (table), 184–185
  kinetics of, 180–182
  nature of the reaction, 179–182
  reactivity of aromatic compounds, 182
  rearrangement, fragmentation and racemization of alkyl groups, 181
  S_N2 mechanism for, 182

N-Alkylation of nitriles, 193–194

Alkyl bromides, relative rates of solvolysis in formic acid and aqueous ethanol (table), 91

Alkyl cations
  infrared spectra in solution, 24
  NMR spectra of counter-ions, 23

Alkyl chlorides, relative solvolysis rates, 95

t-Alkyl chlorides, olefin yields in solvolysis (table), 197

Alkyl esters
  gas-phase pyrolysis of, 103
  transition state in gas-phase pyrolysis of, 104

Alkyl groups, migratory aptitudes, 218

Alkyl halides
  duality of mechanism in substitution reactions, 9, 32
  gas-phase elimination of, 280
  pyrolysis in the gas phase, 101–102
  transition state in gas-phase pyrolysis of, 104

Alkyl radicals, ionization potentials (table), 65

Allyl aryl ethers, Claisen rearrangement, 98

Allyl cations
  charge densities (table), 133
  charge distribution according to HMO theory, 127
  energy levels according to HMO theory, 122
  free energy of solvation, 143
  geometrical isomerism in, 177
  stability of, 113–114
  valence-bond representation of, 120

Allyl chloride, rate of unimolecular solvolysis, 143

Allyl radical, energy levels according to HMO method, 122

Allylic cations, products from, 164

Allylic chlorides, solvolysis products (table), 165

Allylic compounds, stereochemistry of substitution at an asymmetric allylic carbon atom, 177

Allylic rearrangement
  ion-pair formation in, 152

Alumina, "non-acidic" rearrangement in eliminations over, 281

Ambident nucleophiles, 276
  tests for ion pairs using, 153

1-Amino-1-phenyl-2-arylpropan-2-ols, steric course of deamination (table), 239

Analogues of carbonium ions, hetero-atom, 302–305

Anchimeric acceleration
  definition, 233
  terminology, 226

Angle strain, 93–94, 234, 274
  in cycloalkylmethyl compounds, 268

Anhydrides, hydrolysis, 290

Aniline, nucleophilic activity of, 169

Anodic oxidation of triarylmethyl radicals, 58

Anthracene
  as electron donor, 159
  electronic spectrum of, 26
  protonation of, 26, 55
  radical cation from, 299, 301

Anthranilic acids, decarboxylation, 98

9-Anthrylethyl cation, ^1H spectrum and structure, 248

9-Anthrylethyltoluene-p-sulphonate, solvolysis, 247–248

9-Anthryl group, bridging by, 19, 247–248

Antimony trifluoride, 301

1-Apocamphanyl chloride, low reactivity in solvolysis, 92

Appearance potentials of carbonium ions, 62–67

Aprotic media, solvation in, 158

Aprotic solvents, modifications to reactivity order of nucleophiles, 171

Aromatic acylation, 290–293

Aromatic hydrocarbons, basicities from rates of aromatic hydrogen exchange, 108

Aromatic hydrogen isotope exchange, relative rates of (table), 107
Aroyl cations, ultraviolet spectra, 285
Arylalkyl chlorides, relative solvolysis rates, 95
Arylalkyl radicals, ionization potentials (table), 65
4-Aryl-1-butyl-*p*-bromobenzene sulphonate, bridged carbonium ions in solvolysis of, 248
Arylethyl acetates, pyrolysis, 98
Aryl groups
  bridging by, 239–250
  bridging by in cyclic systems, 249
  bridging of non-adjacent carbon atoms by, 248
5-Aryl-2-pentyl esters, bridged carbonium ions from, 249
Attack of carbonium centres on C—X multiple bonds, 192–194
Attack of carbonium centres on non-bonded electron pairs, 168–179
Attack of carbonium centres on π-bond electrons, 179–194
Attack of carbonium centres on σ-bond electrons, 194–221
Attack of carbonium ions on carbonyl groups, 193
Autocatalysis of alkylation of phenol by triphenylmethyl chloride, 54
Azide ion
  nucleophilic activity of, 169
  relative reactivity towards carbonium ions (table), 172
  trapping of carbonium ions by, 37–38
Azulene
  calculation of electronic spectrum, 25
  formation in formic acid, 39
  HMO theory and basicity of, 125
  pK-values of, 82
  protonated, 25, 29
  protonation of, 55
1-Azulenium cation, HMO theory and stability of, 111

B

Baeyer-Villiger reaction, 206, 304
Basicity of aromatic compounds from rates of aromatic hydrogen exchange, 106, 108

Basicity of aromatic hydrocarbons, 125, 184
  correlation with cation localization energies (figure), 126
Basicity of nucleophiles, 169
Basicity of olefins, 109
Beckmann rearrangement, 206, 304
Benzamides, acylium-ion formation from, 290
Benzene, hydrogen exchange in, 107
Benzenediazonium ion
  infrared spectrum, 285
  unimolecular decomposition, 171
"Benzenium" ion, 6
"Benzenonium" ion, 6
Benzoic acids
  cryoscopic behaviour in H_2SO_4, 284
  protonation, 98
7-Benzonorbornyl derivatives, bridging in, 260
exo-2-Benzonorbornyl sulphonate esters, acetolysis, 250
Benzo[*a*]pyrene, HMO theory and basicity of, 124
Benzoyl cation, trapping with aniline, 290
Benzoyl chlorides, rates of solvolysis (table), 291
Benzyl alcohols, pK_{R^+}-values of polymethyl-, 77
Benzyl cations
  charge densities in (table), 131
  oxygen analogue, 305
  problems in identifying electronic spectrum, 26
  stability of, 110
Benzyl radicals, ionization potentials (table), 65
Benzylic cations in styrene polymerization, 192
Bicyclic toluene-*p*-sulphonates, rate of solvolysis (table), 280
"Bicyclobutonium" ions, 252, 267–268
Bicyclo[2,2,1]heptyl and related systems, bridging in, 271
2-Bicyclo[2,1,1]hexyl derivatives, solvolysis, 279–280
3-Bicyclo[3,1,0]hexyl derivatives, solvolysis, 270
5-Bicyclo[2,1,1]hexyl derivatives, solvolysis, 279–280

9-Bicyclo[3,3,1]nonyl, solvolysis, 279–280

Bicyclo[2,2,2]octenyl systems, bridging in, 261

Bicyclo[3,2,1]octenyl systems, bridging in, 261

endo-2-Bicyclo[2,2,2]oct-5-enyl toluene-p-sulphonate, solvolysis, 261

anti-8-Bicyclo[3,2,1]oct-2-enyl toluene-p-sulphonate, solvolysis, 261

2-Bicyclo[3,2,1]octyl derivatives, solvolysis, 279–280

2-Bicyclo[2,2,2]octyl derivatives, solvolysis, 279–280

8-Bicyclo[3,2,1]octyl derivatives, solvolysis, 279–280

Biphenyl, hydrogen exchange in, 107

Bond lengths, 14, 120
    HMO prediction of, 128

Bond orders, HMO calculation of, 128

Born equation, 137
    modified, 142–143

Bornyl chloride, rearrangement in gas-phase elimination, 281

Borohydride ion, trapping of carbonium ions by, 219

Boron
    analogy with carbonium carbon, 4–5
    electronic ground state and valency state, 4

Boron hydrides and electron deficient, bridged carbonium ions, 225

Boron (^{11}B) resonance spectra, 23

Boron trihalides, planarity of, 4

Bridged carbonium ions
    alkenyl bridging, 250–263
    alkyl- and hydrogen-bridging in acyclic systems, 263–266
    and rates of reaction, 101
    aryl bridging, 239–250
    conclusion, 282
    electron-deficient, 263–280, 223, 225
    electron-sufficient, terminology, 223–224, 239–263
    energy profiles for formation, 232
    experimental criteria for, 231–239
    formulation of rearrangements, 210–211
    history of, 225–231
    in bicyclo[2,2,1]heptyl compounds, 256–261, 271–278
    in β-phenylethyl systems, 243–246

Bridged carbonium ions—continued
    in rearrangement of camphene hydro-chloride, 41, 229–230
    in studies of ion association, 154
    in the gas phase, 280–282
    kinetic criterion, 231–235
    NMR spectroscopy, of 19–21
    3-phenyl-2-butyl systems, 239–243
    physical methods of study, 231
    product criterion, 235
    quantum-mechanical calculations, 230, 259
    solvation, 234
    stable, 114
    stereochemical criterion, 236–239
    structure of products from (footnote), 211
    terminology, 222–225

Bridgehead carbonium centres, 92, 93

Bromine, carbonium-ion production by, 51

Bromocyclohexa-1,4-dienes, carbonium ions from, 55

Bromohydrins, stereochemistry of bromination, 227–228

"Bromonium" ion, 296

Brönsted acids, enhancement of acidity by metal halides, 53–55

Brönsted-Bjerrum equation, 149

Brönsted catalysis law and aromatic hydrogen-isotope exchange, 105

Brönsted exponent α
    and acid-catalysed hydration of olefins, 109
    for aromatic hydrogen exchange reactions, 108
    significance of, 106

Butadiene, energy levels according to the HMO method, 122

But-3-enyl toluene-p-sulphonate, formolysis, 251

t-Butyl acetate, acid-catalysed hydrolysis, 48

t-Butyl alcohol, ultraviolet spectrum in concentrated sulphuric acid, 25

t-Butylbenzene
    hydrogen exchange in, 107
    mass spectrum, 281

t-Butyl benzoate, acid-catalysed methanolysis, 48

t-Butyl cation
    alternative names, 6

t-Butyl cation—*continued*
derivation from 2-butene, 212
force constants for, 134
formation from esters, 48
from trimethylacetyl chloride, 51
^{1}H-spectrum, 16
hydride abstraction from isopentane, 220
infrared spectrum in solution, 24
reactivity of halide ions with, 170–171
stable solution of, 115
ultraviolet spectrum, 25
t-Butyl chloride
β-hydrogen isotope effect on solvolysis rate, 109
influence of solvent and leaving group on products (table), 196
rate constants and activation parameters for solvolysis (table), 145
rates of solvolysis, 95–97
solvent effects on activation parameters, 146
4-t-Butylcyclohexyl p-bromobenzene-sulphonates, 264
t-Butyl derivatives, solvolysis and elimination, 43
t-Butyl iodide, isotope exchange with iodide, 10
t-Butyl perchlorate as initiator of cationic polymerization, 57
2-Butyl toluene p-sulphonate, stereochemistry of E1-reactions of, 200

C

Camphene hydrochloride
Wagner-Meerwein rearrangement of, 8, 41, 207–208, 229
Carbanions
nomenclature, 5
non-planarity of saturated, 4
Carbenes, 249–300, 304
addition to olefins, 295
formation, 295
hypothetical alkylation of, 57
insertion reaction, 295
rearrangement of, 298
relationship to carbonium ions, 3
relative reactivities with olefins (table), 297
"Carbenium ion", 3
Carbinol convention, 5

Carbon–carbon triple bonds, bridging by, 251
Carbon isotope effect
on ionization of triphenylmethyl chloride, 71
on rates of carbonium-ion formation, 71
Carbon monoxide, infrared spectrum, 285
Carbon (^{13}C)- proton spin coupling constant, relation to s-character, 24
Carbon (^{13}C) resonance spectra, 23
Carbonium centre, definition, 2
"Carbonium valency", 7
Carbonyl addition mechanism, 288
Carbonyl compounds, analogy with carbonium ions, 233, 245
Carboxylic acids, protonation of, 284
"Carbyl salts", 3
β-Carotene, reaction with acid, 114
Cationated cyclopropanes
as π-complexes, 282
in mass spectrometry, 281
Cationic polymerization of tetrahydrofuran, 168
Cationic vinyl polymerization, 56–57, 188–192
activity of metal halides in, 54
olefin structure and reactivity, 190
"pseudocationic" mechanisms, 57
Cation localization energy, 124
Charge distribution in carbonium ions, 121, 164–166
HMO theory, 126–127
molecular orbital treatments, 131–136
Charge transfer, 14, 159
in cycloheptatrienyl iodide, 144
stabilization of halide ions in sulphur dioxide, 50
Chemical methods for the detection of carbonium ions, 39–43
Chloranil reference electrodes, 30
Chloride ion, relative reactivity towards carbonium ions (table), 172
4-Chlorodiphenylmethyl chloride
racemization and radiochlorine exchange of, 193
salt effects on the rate of solvolysis, 149
4-Chlorodiphenylmethyl p-nitrobenzoate, ion-pairs in solvolysis of, 155
Chloroform, hydrolysis, 296

Cholesteryl and related systems, bridging in, 261–263
Cholesteryl chloride, solvolysis of, 230
i-Cholesteryl derivatives, 230, 235, 262
Chromic acid oxidation
  of hydrocarbons, carbonium ions in, 51
  of triphenylmethyl radicals, 58
Cinnamic acids
  cis-trans isomerization, 97
  formation, 97
  hydration, 97
Colligative properties of solutions of carbonium ions, 28
Common-ion effect, 37
  and carbonium-ion selectivity, 169
  as a test for free carbonium ions, 152
  in hydrolysis of chloroform, 296
  on ionization rates, 149, 156
Conductimetric titration of acyl halides, 283
Configuration interaction, 132–133
Conformational effects
  of acyclic carbonium ions, 209–210
  on aryl bridging, 248
  on cyclization of unsaturated esters, 253
  on direction of semipinacolinic de-amination, 214–217
  on olefin formation from carbonium ions, 198–200
  on reactivity in nitrous acid deamina-tion, 167
  on reactivity of cholesteryl compounds, 262
  on S_N1 reactions of α-methylallyl chloride, 178
  on solvolysis rates of alkyl deriva-tives, 265
Co-polymerization, 191
Coulomb integral α, 122
  adjustment of, 129
  use of constant values, 130
  value in MO treatments of hyper-conjugation, 134
"Cracking" of hydrocarbons, 301
cis-Crotyl chloride
  stereochemical course of S_N1 reactions of, 178
Cryoscopy in sulphuric acid, 7, 28, 284, 303, 305

Crystal Violet, alkaline fading, 173
Cyclobutane, protonation and ring-opening, 56
Curtius reaction, 304
Cyclization of allylic cations, 114
Cycloalkenyl systems, bridging in, 255–256
Cycloalkenylmethyl systems, bridging in, 254–255
Cycloalkylmethyl radicals, ionization potentials (table), 65
Cyclobutadienyl dication, HMO theory and stability of, 113
t-Cumyl chlorides, rates of solvolysis, 95–97
Cyclobutenyl cation, chlorotetraphenyl, 113
Cyclobutyl derivatives
  formation from but-3-enyl compounds, 251
  solvolysis, 266–270
3,5-Cyclocholestan-6-yl cation, 262
5-Cyclodecenyl p-nitrobenzoates, solvo-lysis, 256
Cycloheptatrienols, pK_{R^+}-values (table), 79
Cycloheptatrienyl cation
  alternative names, 1
  as electron acceptor, 159
  carbonium centre in, 2
  charge transfer interaction with iodide ion, 14
  formation in fragmentation reactions, 52
  HMO theory and stability of, 111
  hydrogen dichloride salt, 54
  stability of, 59
  by polarography, 31
Cycloheptatrienyl compounds, re-arrangements of, 42
Cycloheptatrienyl halides, oxidation re-actions of, 159
Cycloheptatrienyl iodide, visible spec-trum of, 144
Cycloheptatrienyl radical, ionization potential, 144
Cyclohexadienyl cation, infrared spec-trum, 14
3-Cyclohexyl-2-butyl toluene-p-sulpho-nates
  solvolysis, 264
  steric course of substitution, 265

Cyclo-oct-3-enyl p-bromobenzene-sul-phonate, acetolysis, 255

Cyclo-octyl p-bromobenzenesulphonate, steric acceleration of solvolysis, 255

Cyclopentadienyl cation
HMO theory and stability of, 112
pentachloro, 113

Cyclopentenyl cations, 113

2-Cyclopent-3-enylethyl p-nitrobenzene-sulphonate, solvolysis, 275

Cyclopent-2-enylmethyl naphthalene-2-sulphonate, solvolysis, 254

Cyclopropanes
acid-catalysed ring-opening, 266
by addition of carbenes to olefins, 296
cationated, 281, 282
protonation and ring-opening of, 56

Cyclopropenols, pK_{R^+}-values (table), 79–80

Cyclopropenones, protonated, 112

Cyclopropenyl cations
formation in decarboxylation, 52
HMO theory and stability of, 111
polarographic study, 31
stability of, 59
substituent effects on stability, 112

Cyclopropylmethyl cation, dimethyl, ^{1}H spectrum and "bisected" structure, 16–17

Cyclopropyl groups, stabilizing influ-ence on carbonium ions, 115–116

Cyclopropylmethyl derivatives
formation from but-3-enyl compounds, 251
solvolysis, 266–270

D

Debye-Hückel theory of ions in solution, 138

Decarbonylation reactions, 292

Definitions, 1–3

Delocalization of charge in carbonium ions, chemical consequences, 164–166

Dem'yanov rearrangement, 207

Detection of carbonium ions, 12–43

1,2-Dianisylnorbornyl cation, ^{1}H spec-trum and structure, 19

1,1-Diarylcyclopropenylmethyl toluene-p-sulphonates, solvolysis, 254

Diarylmethanols, pK_{R^+}-values (table), 77

Diarylmethyl cations
reactivity of alcohols towards, 171
stability of, 110

Diarylmethyl halides, relative solvolysis rates and mass law constants, 172

Diazoalkanes, reaction with carbonium ions, 194

Diazoketones, Wolff rearrangement of, 298–299

Diazonium ions
carbonium ions from, 47, 51
special features of, 166–168

Diborane
carbonium analogues of, 4–5
structure, 4

Dicarbonium ions, 113

Dichloromethylene
reactivity towards nucleophiles, 296
relative reactivities of nucleophiles towards (table), 298

Dielectric saturation, 137, 151

Dienes, pK-values of, 83

Dienone-phenol rearrangement, formu-lation, 206

Dihalomethylenes, reactions of, 52, 298

Dihedral angle and magnitude of kinetic hydrogen isotope effects, 264

Dihydrobenzyl toluene-p-sulphonates, solvolysis, 254–255

4,4'-Dimethoxydiphenylmethyl cation, hydride abstraction by, 90

2,6-Dimethylbenzoic esters, hydrolysis, 288

5,5-Dimethyl-2-bicyclo[2,1,1]hexyl tolu-ene-p-sulphonate, solvolysis, 280

3,5-Dimethyloxyphenyl-1-butyl p-bro-mobenzenesulphonate, solvolysis, 249

Diphenyldiazomethane
acid-catalysed decomposition, 98
formation of and reaction with di-phenylmethyl cations, 194
reaction with dimethylformamide, 193
thermal decomposition, 298

1,1-Diphenylethyl cation
from 1,1-diphenylethylene and 1,1-diphenylethanol, 53
^{1}H-spectrum, 16

1,1-Diphenylethylene
electronic spectrum of, 26

1,1-Diphenylethylene—*continued*
    cryoscopic behaviour of H_2SO_4, 28
    pK-value of, 83
    protonated, 26
1,1-Diphenyl-1-hydroxy-2-propylamine,
    semipinacolinic deamination of,
    238–239
Diphenylmethyl cation, hybridization
    of carbonium centre, 24
Diphenylmethyl chlorides
    kinetics of hydrolysis, 10
    trapping of carbonium ions from, 38
Diphenylmethyl p-nitrobenzoates, sol-
    volysis, 97
Diphenylmethyl radical, ionization po-
    tential, 65
Dissociation of ion pairs
    equilibrium constant for, 69
    suppression by common ions, 73
Distribution and vapour pressure mea-
    surements, 85–87

E

E1 elimination
    effect of carbonium-ion structure, 197–
    200
    mechanisms in, 195–196
E1 mechanism and unimolecular sub-
    stitution, 42
Electrical conductivity
    and spectra of carbonium ions, 15
    of acetic anhydride, 283
    of acyl halides with Lewis acids, 283
    of halides of Group IVB elements,
    303
    of solutions of carbonium salts, 28–29,
    68–71
Electrolysis of solutions of carbonium
    salts, 29–30
Electronegativities of elements (table),
    302
Electronic sextet
    in carbonium ions and boranes, 4
    in molecular rearrangements, 9
Electronic spectra of carbonium ions,
    in solution, 25–28
    use of NMR spectrum in assignment,
    26
Electron impact, 62, 299, 303
    carbonium ions by, 13

Electron removal from neutral species,
    57–58
Electron spin resonance spectroscopy,
    12, 302
Electrophilic aromatic substitution and
    σ^+-values, 98–99
Electrophilic nature of carbonium ions,
    160
cis-Elimination from alkyl derivatives in
    solution, 200
Elimination reactions, detection of carb-
    onium ions in, 42–43
EMF-measurements
    and carbonium-ion equilibria, 30, 87
    pK_{R^+}-values from, 78
Encumbered carbonium ions (footnote),
    176
Energetics of carbonium-ion formation,
    59–87
Enthalpy of activation
    in solvolysis of 2-norbornyl deriva-
    tives, 273
    of solvation of alkyl cations, theoreti-
    cal estimates (table), 141
Entropy of activation
    and bridged-ion formation, 232, 248
    and detection of aroyl cations, 290
    and reaction mechanism, 146
    and solvation of carbonium ions, 141,
    143
    in solvolysis of 2-norbornyl deriva-
    tives, 273
    of solvation of alkyl cations, theoreti-
    cal estimates (table), 141
Equilibrium constants, prediction, 120
Ester hydrolysis, 288
    oxonium ions in acid-catalysed, 47–49
Esterification, 288
    complication of pK_{R^+} determination,
    80
E_S-values
    definition, 101
    table of, 100
Ethyl acetates
    1-aryl-
        pyrolysis, 103
    2-aryl-
        pyrolysis, 103
    1-aryl-2-phenyl-
        pyrolysis, 103
Ethyl cation, formation from ethyl
    bromide, 50

E_T-values for cycloheptatrienyl iodide (table), 144
Extended Hückel theory, 135–136, 282
External factors governing the stability of carbonium ions, 136–159

F

Ferricinium ion, 159
Ferrocene as electron donor, 159
Fluorenyl cations, stability of, 111
Fluorescence spectra, polarization measurements on, 25
Fluorine (^{19}F) chemical shifts
  and charge density, 22
  and stability of triarylmethyl cations, 22
Fluorine (^{19}F) NMR spectra, 17, 21–23
Force constants, 134
Formate ion
  as hydride ion donor, 220
  mobility of in formic acid, 29
Formation of carbonium ions, quantitative aspects, 59–116
Formic acid as solvent for S_N1-reactions, 91
Fragmentation of carbonium ions, 51–52, 200, 202–204
Fragmentation reactions, 51–52
Free energies of ionization and dissociation of triarylmethyl chlorides in presence of mercuric chloride (table), 73
Free radicals
  carbonium ions from, 62
  conversion to carbonium ions by electron impact, 57
  in Friedel-Crafts reaction, 301
  oxidation to carbonium ions, 58
Friedel-Crafts alkylation, 179–186
  kinetic and thermodynamic control of products, 161
Friedel-Crafts catalysts
  complexes with benzene derivatives, 14
  in rearrangement of camphene hydrochloride, 8
  promotion of ionization by, 49

G

Galvanic cells
  incorporating carbonium salts, 30

Galvanic cells—*continued*
  reactions involving carbonium ions in, 58
Gas chromatography, 85
Gas phase, carbonium ions in, 13, 47
General acid catalysis of hydrogen exchange, 105
Glass electrode, 30
Glycols, pinacol rearrangements of, 213

H

Halide ions, enthalpies of reaction with boron trifluoride, 49
α-Halocarbanions, 296
Halochromism, 7
Halogen exchange between acyl halides and metal halides, 292
Hammett's acidity function H_0
  and aromatic hydrogen-isotope exchange, 106
  and ester hydrolysis, 288
  application to protonation of hydrocarbons, 81
  definition, 75
Hammett's $\rho\sigma$ rule, 96
Hammond's postulate, 89, 231
Heat capacity of activation, 147
Henry's law constants, 141, 146
Heptalene, pK-value of, 82
Heptalenium cation, HMO theory and stability of, 111
$\alpha,\alpha,2,3,4,5,6$-Heptamethylbenzyl alcohol pK_{R+} 77
Heptamethylcyclohexadienyl cations, stability of, 114
Heptatrienyl cation, charge distribution according to HMO theory, 127
Heterolysis, carbonium-ion formation by, 46–52
Heterolysis of organic molecules, enthalpy cycles for, 66
"Heterolytic bond dissociation energies" and activation energy in gas-phase pyrolysis, 104
  of hydrocarbons (table), 67
  of organic bromides (table), 67
Heterolytic reactions in the gas phase, 101–105
Hexa-arylethanes, formation in electrolysis of triarylmethyl halides, 30

Hexafluoroantimonate ion, stability of, 49

Hexamethylbenzene
 methylation of, 56
 protonation of, 18, 83
 radical cations from, 301, 302

5-Hexenyl *p*-nitrobenzensulphonate, formolysis, 253

Historical introduction to carbonium ions, 6–11

HMO method, modifications of, 129–136

Hofmann degradation of amides, 206

Homoallylic cations, 250–263
 theoretical treatments, 134

Homoallylic systems, carbonium ions from, 224

Homoaromatic compounds, 270

Homocycloheptatrienyl cation, 116

"Hot" carbonium ions, 167

Hückel molecular orbital (HMO) method for conjugated carbonium ions, 121–128

Hückel's $4n+2$ rule, 112, 121

Hybridization at carbonium centres, 24

Hydration of olefins, carbonium ions in, 53

1,3-Hydride shifts in rearrangement of bicyclic monoterpenoids, 205

6,2-Hydride shifts in reactions of 2-norbornyl derivatives, 274–275

Hydride transfer
 intermolecular, 50, 218–221
  in alkylation of paraffins, 187
  mechanism, 219
  to acylium ions, 294
  to arylmethyl cations, 90
 intramolecular, 50
  in medium-sized rings, 205
  in substituted 2-norbornyl derivatives, 278

Hydrogen bonding
 and anomalous behaviour of nitro-substituted triphenylmethyl cations, 142
 and indicator behaviour, 81
 influence on conformations of amino-alcohols, 214

Hydrogen dihalide ions, 72
 and acidity of hydrogen halides, 54

Hydrogen fluoride
 in distribution measurements, 85
 solvent for conductance studies, 68

Hydrogen isotope effects
 α-, 109
 β-, 109
  on rates of bridged-ion formation, 264–265
  on infrared spectra, 14
  on rates of intramolecular hydride shift, 218
  on olefin formation in E1 reactions, 196
  on products from diphenyldiazo-methane, 298
  on rate of hydrogen migration, 18
  on rates of aromatic alkylation, 180, 292
  on rates of β-proton removal from carbonium ions (table), 197
  on rates of intermolecular hydride transfer, 220
  on rates of solvolysis of cyclopropyl-methyl derivatives, 268–269
  on rates of solvolysis of 2-norbornyl esters, 274

Hydrogen-isotope exchange, aromatic, 105–109
 catalysis by stannic chloride and carboxylic acids, 55
 relative rates (table), 107

Hydrogen sulphate ion, mobility in sulphuric acid solution, 29

Hydroxide ion, nucleophilic activity of, 169

β-(4-Hydroxyphenyl)ethyl bromide, methanalysis, 247

Hyperconjugation
 and β-hydrogen isotope effects, 110
 and bridged carbonium ions, 265
 and proton coupling contrasts, 22
 carbon–carbon, 225
 in aliphatic carbonium ions, 133–134
 influence of on E1 reactions, 198
 stabilization of alkyl cations and infrared spectra, 24

I

Indeno[2,1-*a*]phenalene, HMO theory and basicity of, 125

Indicator equilibria involving carbonium ions, 26

Indoles, protonation of, 82

Induced common-ion effect, 156

Inductive effect in carbonium ions, influence on product-determining steps, 166

Infrared spectroscopy
of acylium ions, 285–287 (table), 286
of carbonium ions in solution, 24–25
of protonated naphthalene, 86
of solid carbonium salts, 14–15

Inorganic salts
relaxation studies, 151
solvation energies of, 141

Interaction of carbonium ions with other ions, 148–158

Internal factors stabilizing carbonium ions, 118–136

Internal pressure of the solvent and salt effects, 150

Internal return, 157, 242, 273
and kinetic detection of bridging, 234
in 1,2,2-triphenylethyl derivatives, 236–237

Internal rotation in carbonium ions, 210

Iodine, electron affinity, 144

Ion association, 12, 13, 15, 138, 150–158, *see also* ion pairs
and electrical conductance, 69
and spectrophotometric equilibrium constants, 71
complication of kinetic laws by, 38
effects on spectra of carbonium ions, 15
electrostatic theory, 150–152
of carbonium salts in sulphur dioxide, 29
possible magnetic anisotropy from, 22

Ionic atmosphere, 36

Ionization
and dissociation of organic molecules in solution
energy profile (figure), 151
equilibrium constants for, 69
of alcohols in acidic media, 73–81
of organic halides and alcohols
HMO theory of, 125
of triarylmethyl chlorides
spectrophotometric studies, 72–72

Ionization potentials
adiabatic, 63
and bridged-ion formation, 263
methods of measurement, 62–63
of arylalkyl radicals (table), 65

Ionization potentials—*continued*
of benzyl radicals, 65
correlation with σ^+-values, 98
of cyclalkylmethyl radicals (table), 65
of methyl and t-butyl radicals, 119
of olefinic and acetylenic radicals (table), 65
of radicals, 62–67
of radicals and the stability of gaseous carbonium ions, 118
of radicals by the HMO theory, 130
of simple alkyl radicals (table), 65
relation to appearance potentials, 63
relation to chemical oxidation of free radicals, 64
"vertical", 63

Ion pairs
and stereochemistry of S_N1 reactions, 176
by protonation of aliphatic polyenes, 114
contact (intimate), 152, 240
formation in carbonium-ion reactions, 152–158
formation in gas-phase pyrolysis, 102
in aromatic acylation, 292
in aromatic alkylation, 182
in cationic vinyl polymerization, 191
influence on products of E1 reactions, 195
in gas-phase elimination, 280
of acylium ions
NMR spectra, 287
return, 155–158
solvent-separated, 151, 246

Ion quadruplets, isomerism in, 176

Isobornyl chloride,
pyrolysis of, 102
rearrangement in gas-phase elimination, 281

Isobutene, cationic polymerization of, 188

Isobutyl vinyl ether, stereochemistry in BF_3-catalysed polymerization, 190

Isocyanates, carbonium ions from, 52

Isomerization, complication of pK_{R^+} determination, 81

Isopropylidene group, bridging by, 257–258

Isothiocyanates, carbonium ions from, 52

Isotope effects, 109–110

Isotope exchange between iodide and
    t-butyl iodide, 10
I.U.P.A.C. 1965 rules, nomenclature of
    carbonium ions in, 6

K

Ketene, infrared spectrum, 285
Kinetic methods for detection and study
    of carbonium ions, 31–39
Kolbe reaction, 58

L

Lattice energy of silver halides, 50
LCAO approximation of MO theory, 122
Lead tetra-acetate, reaction with carb-
    onium ions, 58
Leaving groups, effects on product pro-
    portions in E1 reactions, 42
Lewis acidity of metal halides, 49
Life-times of carbonium ions, 136
    and stereochemistry of S_N1 reactions,
    174
"Limiting" solvolysis, 91
Linear free energy relations and detec-
    tion of bridging, 233
Lossen reaction, 304
Lucas's reagent, 267

M

Macroscopic conductors, analogy with
    carbonium ions, 118–119
Malachite Green and derivatives, alka-
    line fading, 173
Mass-law constant
    and selectivity of carbonium ions, 171–
    172
    definition, 35
Mass-law effect and carbonium ion
    stability, 38
Mass spectrometry, 13
    determination of appearance poten-
    tials by, 62
    rearrangement of ions in, 64
Medium-sized rings
    intramolecular hydride shifts in, 205
    transannular reactions in, 256
Mercuric chloride and ionization of
    triarylmethyl chlorides, 72–73
Mesitoyl cation, 290
Mesitoyl chloride, hydrolysis, 290

Mesitylene
    alkylation by diarylmethanols, 185
    protonation, 83
Methanesulphonic acid, cryoscopy in, 28
threo-3-*p*-Methoxyphenyl-2-butyl-*p*-
    bromobenzenesulphonate, solvo-
    lysis of, 157–158
p-Methoxyphenylethyl chloride, ^{1}H
    spectrum of ion from, 20
α-Methylallyl chloride, stereochemical
    course of S_N1 reactions of, 178
9-Methylanthracene
    electronic spectrum of, 26
    protonated, 26
Methylbenzenes
    basicities of (table), 184
    equilibrium constants for protona-
    tion of (table), 68
3-Methyl-2-butyl toluene-*p*-sulphonate,
    solvolysis, 263
9-Methylfluorenol, pK_{R^+} of, 77
Methylhelium cation, methyl cations
    from, 47
Methyl mesitoate, hydrolysis, 288
4-Methylpent-3-enyl chloride, reaction
    with phenol, 252
Migratory aptitudes
    ground state control of, 215
    in carbene rearrangement, 299
    (table), 300
    in carbonium-ion rearrangements,
    212–218
    of aryl groups in pinacol rearrange-
    ments (table), 215
    relative
    from product ratios, 213
Mobility of carbonium ions, 29
Monomer reactivity ratios, 191

N

v-Values for benzoyl derivatives in
    H_2SO_4 (table), 284
Nametkin rearrangement, 207
Naphthalene
    HMO theory and basicity of, 125
    hydrogen exchange in, 107
Neighbouring-group participation, 95,
    225–229
    by acetoxyl groups, 226–227
    by bromine, 227–228
    driving force due to, 229

Neopentyl chloride, pyrolysis of, 102, 281

Neopentyl halides, rearrangement during solvolysis, 11

Neopentyl iodide, rearrangement in presence of silver acetate, 9

Neopentyl toluene-*p*-sulphonate, acetolysis, 263

Nitration, aromatic, 99

Nitrilium salts, 193

Nitrobenzene oxidation of triphenyl methyl radicals, 58

Nitrogen analogues of carbonium ions, 304–305

Nitrosyl cation
    carbonium ion formation from isocyanates, etc. by, 52
    hydride abstraction by, 50

Nitrous acid deamination, 166–168, 299
    of but-3-enylamine, 251
    of *cis*-bicyclo[3,1,0]hexylamine, 270
    of cyclopropylamine and cyclobutylamine, 267
    of 2-norbornylamines, 276
    β-substituted ethylamines, 265
    of 1,2,2-triphenylethylamine, 237

No-bond structures, 223

"Non-classical" carbonium ions, 94
    origin of term, 229
    use of term, 222–223

Nomenclature of carbonium ions, 5–6
    of acylium ions, 283

Norborna-2,5-diene, electrophilic addition to, 257

7-Norbornadienyl cation, 116
    ¹H spectrum and structure, 21, 259–260

7-Norbornadienyl chloride, solvolysis in presence of Na⁺BH₄⁻, 260

7-Norbornenyl cation
    ¹H spectrum, 259
    HMO treatment of, 135

2-Norbornenyl derivatives, solvolysis, 256

7-Norbornenyl derivatives, solvolysis, 258

2-Norbornyl cation
    dianisyl
        ¹H spectrum and structure, 19
    ¹H spectrum, 275, 276
    stable solution of, 115

Norbornyl derivatives
    carbonium ion reactions of, 271–277
    equilibrating unbridged ions from, 275
    substituted
        solvolysis, 277–278

2-Norbornyl derivatives
    bridged carbonium ions from, 273–275
    rates of solvolysis, 271–273
    solvolysis products, 273

2-Norbornyl toluene-*p*-sulphonate, 6,6-dimethyl, solvolysis, 278

7-Norbornyl toluene-*p*-sulphonate, steric effects on solvolysis rate, 258

Nortricyclene from solvolysis of 2-norbornyl derivatives, 273

Nortricyclyl compounds, formation and solvolysis, 257

Nuclear magnetic resonance spectroscopy,
    for studying carbonium ion rearrangements, 17–19
    line broadening and signal collapse, 17–19
    of acylium ions, 287
    of carbonium ions in solution, 16–24
    of protonated aromatic hydrocarbons, 86

Nucleophilic activity, measures of (table) 170

Nucleophilic substitution
    at carbonyl carbon, 287–288
    measurements, 288
    mechanistic criteria, 289
    at silicon, 303

O

ω-Technique, 131

¹⁸O-equilibration in the reactions of esters, 153, 155

¹⁸O-exchange
    in hydrolysis of mesitoyl chloride, 290
    in s-butyl alcohol, 176

2-n-Octyl derivatives, solvolysis and elimination, 43

Olefinic radicals, ionization potentials (table), 65

Olefins
    addition of bromine, 296
    addition of carbenes, 295
    alkylation of by carbonium ions, 186, 187

Olefins—*continued*
  as electron donors, 159
  γ-radiolysis of, 57
  reactions of carbonium ions with,
    186–192
Olefin formation, eclipsing effects on in
  E1 reactions (table), 199
Olefin hydration, 108–109
  and proton removal from carbonium
    ions, 195–196
  mechanism of, 109
Olefin yields in unimolecular solvolysis
  of alkyl derivatives (table), 43
Onium ions
  carbonium ions from, 46
  distinction from carbonium ions, 3
  proton removal from, 46
Optical activity and ion pairs in solvolysis, 153
Organomercuric cations, carbonium ions
  from, 47
Orientation in E1 eliminations, 198
Oxidation reactions
  complicating effects on carbonium
    ion formation, 44
  complication of pK_{R^+} determination,
    80
Oxidizing agents, carbonium ion formation by, 50–51
Oxocarbonium ion, 6
Oxonium complexes
  in aromatic acylation, 292
  of acyl halides with Lewis acid, 285
Oxonium ions
  formation from carbonium ions, 168
  from protonation of alcohols and
    esters, 47
  spectroscopic distinction from carb-
    onium ions, 15–16
  trialkyl
    reaction with carbonyl compounds,
      193

P

π-Complexes
  bridged carbonium ions as, 222
  in electrophilic aromatic substitution,
    183
  of benzene and $AlCl_3$, 301
  representation of cationated cyclo-
    propanes, 282

π-Route to bridged bicyclic cations,
  275
Paraffins, alkylation of by carbonium
  ions, 187
Partial rate factor, definition, 182
Pentachloroallyl cation, solid salts of, 113
Pentadienyl cation, 113
$\alpha,\alpha,2,4,6$-Pentamethylbenzyl alcohol,
  pK_{R^+}, 77
Pentamethylbenzyl radical, 302
t-Pentyl cation
  infrared spectrum in solution, 24
  rearrangement of, 18
t-Pentyl derivatives, solvolysis and elimination, 43
Perchlorate esters in cationic polymerization, 189
Peresters and peroxides, decomposition
  in presence of cupric ions, 58
Perylene, radical cation from, 301
Phenalenyl cation, HMO theory and
  stability of, 111
Phenol, alkylation of by triphenylmethyl chloride, 54
"Phenonium" ions, 6, 223
β-Phenylallyl cation, charge densities in
  (table), 131
3-Phenyl-2-butanol, ^1H spectrum of ion
  from, 21
2-Phenyl-2-butyl cation from 3-phenyl-
  2-butyl compounds, 243
3-Phenyl-2-butyl systems, bridging in
  solvolysis of, 239–243
3-Phenyl-2-butyl toluene-*p*-sulphonates
  acetolysis, 153, 230, 240
  formolysis, 240
  ^1H spectrum of carbonium ions from,
    243
  stereochemistry of rearrangement
    during solvolysis, 210
Phenyl cation, 113
  low selectivity of, 171
p-Phenylene groups, bridging by, 250
α-Phenylethyl chloride
  kinetics of hydrolysis, 10
  metal halides and rate of racemization,
    49
9-Phenylfluorenol, pK_{R^+}, 80
threo-4-Phenyl-3-hexyl toluene-*p*-sul-
  phonate, solvolysis, 246
Photoionization, 63
Photosensitization, 295

Pinacol and related rearrangements
formulation, 206
stereochemical course of, 208–210
β-Pinene, fragmentation of, 200
pK-values
of azulenes, 82
of dienes, 83
of 1,1-diphenylethylene, 83
of heptalene, 82
of methylbenzenes, 83
of polycyclic aromatic hydrocarbons, 86
of 1,3,5-trimethoxybenzene, 82
pK_{R^+}-values
and rates of intermolecular hydride transfer, 221
of cycloheptatrienyl derivatives (table), 79–80
of cyclopropenyl derivatives (table), 79
of diarylmethanols (table), 77
of triarylmethanols (table), 76
Planarity of carbonium ions, 4, 10
and proton coupling constants, 22
and rates of solvolyis, 92–93
and stereochemistry of S_N1 reactions, 174
and steric course of nucleophilic substitution, 40
effect on vibrational frequencies, 24
Planarity of conjugated carbonium ions, 128–129
Polarimetric rate constants for solvolysis, 153
Polarity of solvents, measures of, 147–148
Polarizability of nucleophiles, 169
Polarography of carbonium ions, 30–31
ionization potentials and, 66
charge distribution and chemical shifts, 127
Polycyclic aromatic hydrocarbons, pK-values (table), 86
Polyenyl cations, 114
Polyisoprenoids, biological cyclization, 253
Polymerization, 56, see also Cationic vinyl polymerization
complication of pK_{R^+} determination, 80
degree of, 187
of olefins, 186
charge transfer interaction in, 159

Polymerization—continued
of olefins initiated by radical cations, 302
Polymers from cationic polymerization, structure of, 189–190
Potentiometric redox titrations of carbonium ions, 30
Potentiometric titration, pK_{R^+}-values by, 78
Product-determining steps of carbonium-ion reactions, kinetic treatment, 161
"Product spread" in reactions of allylic cations, 164–166
Propionyl cations, ultraviolet spectrum, 285
i-Propyl alcohol as hydride ion donor, 220
n-Propylamine, nitrous acid deamination, 265–266
i-Propyl cation
by protonation of propene and cyclopropane, 56
^{1}H-spectrum, 16
hybridization of carbonium centre, 24
infrared spectrum in solution, 24
stable solution of, 115
n-Propyl chloride, alkylation of benzene with, 181
n-Propyl system, rearrangement in, 94
Proton addition to unsaturated systems, 81–84
Protonated alkanes, 55–56
Protonated cyclopropanes
in deamination of alkylamines, 266
in reaction of dihalocarbenes with alkoxide ions, 266
in ring-opening of cyclopropanes, 266
predicted structure, 282
Protonation
NMR study of, 16
of arylolefins
HMO theory, 124
of carboxylic acids, 284
of cyclo-octatetraene, 116
of phenols and aromatic ethers, 114
of unsaturated systems
HMO theory, 123–126
Protonation of aromatic hydrocarbons, 14–15, 26, 28, 55, 68, 301
HMO theory, 124
intramolecular hydrogen migration in, 18

Protonation of olefins, 26
  acidic solvents for, 53
  in aprotic media, 158
Proton chemical shift
  and charge density, 21
  and structure of arylmethyl cations, 21
  in spectra of carbonium ions (table), 23
Proton magnetic resonance spectra, 16–23
Proton screening constants and electron density in carbonium ions, 119

Q

Quantum-mechanical calculations on carbonium ions, general aims, 119–121
Quinones, Thiele acetylation, 290

R

Racemization
  as a criterion of carbonium-ion formation, 40
  of silyl halides, 303
Radical cations, 299–302
  as by-products in carbonium ion-forming reactions, 44
  detection of, 12
  formation by charge transfer, 159
  formation by chemical oxidation, 57
  formation in radiolytic experiments, 57
  status as carbonium ions, 1
Radio-chlorine exchange in silyl halides, 303
γ-Radiolysis, cationic vinyl polymerization by, 57
Rare-gas hydride cations, 55
Rate laws for reactions involving carbonium ions, 32–36
Rates of carbonium-ion formation, 88–110
  relation to carbonium-ion stability, 88–90
Reactions of carbonium ions, 160–221
  table of reaction types, 162–163
Reactivity of carbonium ions with nonbonded electron pairs, effect of carbonium-ion structure, 171–174
Rearrangement
  as a criterion of carbonium-ion formation, 40–42

Rearrangement— *continued*
  during cationic vinyl polymerization, 190
  during solvolysis of 1,2,2-triphenylethyl derivatives, 237
  in pyrolysis of neopentyl chloride, 281
  in reactions of cyclopropenylmethyl derivatives, 268
  of acylium ions, 294
  of carbenes. 298–299
  of cyclic allylic cations, 114
  of n-propyl compounds, 94
Rearrangement of carbonium ions, 204–218
  by hydride shift, 41
  direction of, and stability of ions, 41, 59–60, 211–212
  mechanism and stereochemistry of, 207–211
  migratory aptitudes, 212–218
  prior to fragmentation, 204
Resonance integral β, 122
  adjustment of, 129
  use of constant values, 130
  value, 126
  value in HMO treatment of homoallylic cations, 134
Restricted rotation in carbonium ions, 174
Retarding potential difference (RPD) method, 63
Ritter reaction, 193–194
Rydberg series, 63

S

σ-Complexes
  detection, isolation and characterization, 180
  in aromatic alkylation, 179
σ-Route to bridged bicyclic cations, 275
σ-Values and substituent effects on phenyl-bridging, 247
σ^*-Values, 99–101
  definition, 99
  table of, 100
σ^+-Values, 95–99
  and ester hydrolysis, 290
  and rates of aromatic acylation, 292
  and rates of gas-phase pyrolysis of arylethyl acetates, 103
  and substituent effects on phenyl-bridging, 247

σ^+-Values—*continued*
correlation of reactivity of styrenes in cationic polymerization, 192
correlation with migratory aptitudes, 217
correlation with rates of olefin hydration, 109
correlation with rates of aromatic alkylation, 183
organic reactions correlated by, 97–98
table of, 96
σ^0-Values and rates of gas-phase pyrolysis of alkyl benzoates, 103
S_N1 mechanism, early examples of, 10
S_N1 reactions, 90–95
S_N2C^+ mechanism, 34
Salt effects
on ionization rates (table), 150
on kinetics of carbonium-ion reactions, 36–37
on rates of carbonium-ion formation, electrostatic theory, 148–150
on rates of solvolysis, 155–158
on the structure of liquids, 36
Salting out, in mixed solvents, 37
SCF-modification of molecular orbital calculations, 125
Schmidt reaction, 304
Secondary bases, alcohols as, 74
Selectivity of carbonium ions, 90
definition, 33
Selectivity relation,
in electrophilic aromatic substitution, 183, 292
Self-consistent field calculations, 130–131
Semihydrobenzoinic change, 206
Semipinacolinic change, 206
Semipinacolinic deamination of 1,1-diphenyl-1-hydroxy-2-propylamine, 238–239
Shielding of carbonium ions, 40, 43
1,2-Shifts, general formulation, 205
Silica-alumina catalysts
carbonium-ion production by, 51
radical cation formation on, 301
Siliconium ions, 303–304
Silver hexafluoroantimonate, 55
Silver tetrafluoroborate, carbonium-ion formation from organic bromides and, 50
Singlet carbenes, 294–300

Sodium borohydride
ketone reduction and solvolysis rates, 245
trapping of carbonium ions by, 260
Solvation numbers of carbonium ions, 176
Solvation of carbonium ions, 15, 136–148
effect of carbonium-ion structure, 142–144
effect of the solvent, 144–147
effect on product-determining steps, 166
energetics, 140–142
in aprotic media, 158
nature of the interaction, 139–140
Solvent deuterium isotope effects on rates of ionization, 147
Solvent effects
on ground and transition state solvation energies, 146
on rate of rearrangement of camphene hydrochloride, 8
on rates of carbonium-ion formation, 145
on rates of hydrolysis of benzoyl chlorides (table), 291
Solvent polarity, measures of (table), 148
Solvent structure
and activation parameters in solvolysis, 146
and solvation, 137
Solvents, suitability for preparation of carbonium ions, 44–45
Solvolysis, ambiguities in rate laws for, 35
Solvolysis of t-alkyl halides, correlation of rates with σ^*-values, 100
Source of carbonium ions, 44–58
influence on reactions, 166–168
Special salt effect, 155, 157, 240, 246, 270
mechanism of, 156
parameters of (table), 156
Spectrophotometry
and carbonium ion equilibria, 71–84
for studying ionization equilibria, 69
Spectroscopy of carbonium ions in solution, 15–28
Sphere in continuum model of carbonium ions in solution, 137–138
Stability of carbonium ions
and direction of rearrangement, 211

Stability of carbonium ions—*continued*
and fragmentation, 202
factors governing, 117–159
quantitative definition, 60–62
reference systems (table), 61
relation to reactivity, 171
Stable carbonium ions, survey of, 110–116
Steady-state hypothesis, application in carbonium ion reactions, 33
Stereochemical course of unimolecular substitution, 154
Stereochemistry of carbonium ion reactions, 174–179
β-proton removal, 198
the S_N1 rule, 174
Stereochemistry of E1 reactions, 199–200
of the 3-deuterio-2-butyl toluene-*p*-sulphonates, 201
Stereochemistry of gas-phase eliminations, 102, 104
Stereochemistry of reactions at an asymmetric carbon atom, 174–177
Stereochemistry of S_N1 substitution at an asymmetric carbon atom (table), 175
Stereochemistry of unimolecular substitution in organic halides, 139
Stereoregularity of polymers, 190
Steric acceleration of ionization, 45, 93–95, 233, 234, 242, 245, 255, 263, 264, 277, 278
examples, 94
Steric course
of nucleophilic substitution, 10
of semipinacolinic deamination, 239
of solvolysis of 3-phenyl-2-butyl toluene-*p*-sulphonates, 241
of substitution in saturated bicyclic systems, 280
of substitution of β-phenylethyl derivatives, 245
Steric effects
on acid-catalysed ester hydrolysis, 101
on carbonium-ion equilibria, 60
on carbonium-ion formation, 45
on competition between substitution and elimination in S_N1 reactions, 198
on intermolecular hydride transfer, 90

Steric effects—*continued*
on migratory aptitudes, 215, 217
on nucleophilic activity, 170–171
on rate of solvolysis of 7-norbornyl esters, 258
on rates of intermolecular hydride transfer, 221
Steric hindrance
of ionization, 94 (footnote), 233, 275, 278
of solvolysis, 143, 242, 263, 275
Steric substituent constants E_S, 101
"Structural hypothesis" for solvated carbonium ions, 176–177
and stereochemistry of S_N1 reactions, 177
Styrenes
hydration, 97
polymerization of, 192
Substituent effects
of non-migratory groups on migratory aptitude of methyl, 217
on acylium-ion formation from benzoic acids, 284
on aromatic alkylation, 183
on carbonium-ion fragmentation (table), 203
on carbonium ion stability
HMO method for, 129–130
electrostatic theory, 118
on enthalpies of gaseous ionization, 67
on equilibrium constants for ionization of triphenylmethyl chloride, 70
on free energy of ionization of triphenylmethanol, 87
on migratory aptitudes of aryl groups, 215
on phenyl bridging, 246–248
on pK_{R^+} of diphenylmethanol (table), 77
on pK_{R^+} of triphenylmethanol (table), 76
on rate of solvolysis of 2-norbornyl derivatives, 277
on rates of acyl halide solvolysis, 290
on rates of alkaline fading of triphenylmethane dyes, 172–173
table, 173
on rates of aromatic acylation, 290
on rates of formolysis of but-3-enyl-toluene-*p*-sulphonate (table), 252
on rates of gas-phase pyrolysis, 102

Substituent effects—*continued*
of esters, 103–104
on rates of solvolysis of β-phenylethyl compounds, 243–245
on rates of solvolysis of benzoyl chloride (table), 291
on reactivity of olefins towards carbenes, 296
on solvolysis of cholesteryl compounds, 262
on solvolysis of cyclopropylmethyl derivatives, 268–270
on stability of arylmethyl cations, 110
σ^{+}- and σ^{*}-values, 95–101
Sulphenium ions, 305
Sulphenylamines, carbonium ions from, 52
Sulphenyl halides, cryoscopic behaviour in H_2SO_4, 305
Sulphonation
complication of cryoscopy in H_2SO_4, 28
complication of pK_{R^+} determination, 80
Sulphur dioxide, solvent for conductivity measurements on carbonium salts, 29
Symmetrical glycols, pinacol rearrangement of, 214
Symmetry numbers, 124
Synartesis, terminology, 229

T

Tacticity of polymers, 190
Taft-Ingold equation, 100, 264
and detection of bridging, 233
deviations from in solvolysis, 228
Terpene rearrangements, carbonium ions in, 8
Tertiary alkyl halides, ionization in solvolysis of, 48
Tetrahydrofuran, polymerization of, 168
Tetraiodoborate salts of carbonium ions, 23
Thermodynamic control of reaction products, 161
Thermodynamic quantities for formation of carbonium ions from arylmethanols (table), 78

Thiele acetylation of quinones, 290
Threo and *erythro* terminology (footnote), 153
Titrimetric rate constants for solvolysis, 153
Toluene
hydrogen exchange in, 107
relative rates and isomer properties in alkylation, 181–182
4-Toluene-*p*-sulphonyloxymethylquinuclidine, fragmentation during solvolysis, 204
Torsional effects on carbonium-ion reactions, 275
Transport numbers of carbonium ions, 29
Trapping of intermediate carbonium ions, 37–39
Tri(*p*-aminophenyl)methyl perchlorate, bond lengths in, 14
2,2,2-Triaryldiazoethanes, thermal decomposition, 299
Triarylmethane dyes, reactions of, 169
Triarylmethanols
as indicators, 74
cryoscopic behaviour in H_2SO_4, 28
pK_{R^+}-values (table), 76
thermodynamic quantities for ionization of, 78
Triarylmethyl cations
electrostatic treatment of solvation, 142
free energy of formation from EMF measurements, 87
hydride abstraction by, 90
stability of, 110
Triarylmethyl chlorides
effect of hydrogen chloride on ionization, 72
Triarylmethyl halides
electrolysis of solutions of, 29–30
ionization by metal halides, 49
relative equilibrium constants for ionization (table), 70
Triarylmethyl perchlorates, electrical conductance of, 70
Triarylmethyl radicals in electrolysis of carbonium salts, 30
Tri-carbonium ions, 111
Tricyclopropylmethanol
cryoscopic behaviour in H_2SO_4, 28
^{1}H-spectrum, 17
pK_{R^+}, 80

Tricyclopropylmethyl cation, ^{1}H-spectrum and structure of, 17

Trihalocyclopropenyl salts, infrared spectra, 15

1,3,5-Trimethoxybenzene, pK-value of, 82

hydrogen exchange in, 106

Trimethylacetyl cation, 294

Trimethylacetyl chloride, fragmentation, 51

Trimethylboron, planarity of, 4

Trimethylsilyl cations from trimethylsilyl halides, 303

Triphenylacetic acid, decomposition of, in H_2SO_4, 52

Triphenylcyclopropenyl cation
    bond lengths compared with prediction from HMO method, 128
    planarity of, 129

Triphenylcyclopropenyl perchlorate, structure by X-ray crystallography, 14

1,2,2-Triphenylethanol, ^{1}H-spectrum and structure of carbonium ions from, 237

1,2,2-Triphenylethyl cation, 245

1,2,2-Triphenylethyl derivatives, solvolysis, 236–238

Triphenylethyl toluene-p-sulphonate, solvolysis rate, 245

1,2,3-Triphenylindenol, pK_{R^+}, 80

Triphenylmethane dyes, substituent effects on rate of fading, 172–173

Triphenylmethanol, polarographic reduction of, 31

Triphenylmethyl cation
    as electron acceptor, 159
    bond lengths compared with predictions from HMO method, 128
    charge densities in (table), 131
    chlorine exchange with triarylmethyl chloride, 19
    colour of, 7
    D_3 symmetry of, 129
    formation from esters, 48
    formation in H_2SO_4, 7
    from triphenylmethanol and acid, 48
    from triphenylmethyl ethyl ether and BF_3, 48
^{1}H-spectrum, 16

^{1}H-spectrum—continued
    hydride abstraction from formate ion, 219
    hydride abstraction from i-propyl alcohol, 219
    hydride abstraction from tribenzylamine, 220
    hydrogen dichloride salt, 54
    interpretations of NMR spectrum, 132
    NMR spectra of counter-ions, 23
    propeller structure of fluorine-substituted, 17
    reaction with diazomethane, 194
    relative reactivity of nucleophiles towards, 169–170
    structure of, 71
    symmetry of from fluorescence spectrum, 25
    valence-bond theory and stability of, 120–121

Triphenylmethyl chloride, common-ion effect in hydrolysis, 37

Triphenylmethyl halides
    electrical conductivity in solution, 6–7
    in sulphur dioxide, 69–71

Triphenylmethyl perchlorate
    electrical conductivity of, 7
    lattice energy of, 50

Triphenylmethyl radical, formation by electron transfer, 159

Triphenylmethyl salts
    planarity of carbonium centre in, 14
    propeller shape, 14

Triplet state of carbenes, 294

Triplet states of carbonium ions, 112

Trishomocylopropenyl cation, 270

Trixenylmethyl cation, symmetry of from fluorescence spectrum, 25

Tropenium ion, 1

Tropyl ion, 1

Tropylium ion, 1

U

Ultraviolet absorption maxima of carbonium ions (table), 27

Ultraviolet spectra of acylium ions, 285

"Unsolvated" carbonium ions, 167

V

Valency bond formulae for carbonium ions, 2

Vapour pressure measurements in the system HF–BF$_3$-base, 87

Volume of activation in solvolysis of 2-norbornyl derivatives, 273

W

Wagner-Meerwein (retropinacol) rearrangement
formulation, 206–207
in gas-phase pyrolysis of organic halides, 102
in tests for ion-pair formation, 152
stereochemical course of, 208
Walden inversion, 226
Whelan-Mann method, 131
Whitmore theory of rearrangements, 8–9, 205
"Windshield wiper effect", 275
Wolff rearrangement, of diazoketones, 206, 298

X

Xanthene as hydride ion donor, 220–221
Xanthone, Lewis acidity of boron halides towards, 49
Xanthydrol
pK_{R^+} of, 77
thermodynamic quantities for ionization of, 78
Xanthydryl (xanthenyl) cation, stability of, 111
X-ray crystallography, 13–14
of acyl halide-Lewis acid complexes, 285

Y

Y-values, 148

Z

Z-values and solvent polarity, 145